D1097811

# THE "PARTICLES" OF MODERN PHYSICS

# THE "PARTICLES" OF MODERN PHYSICS

By J. D. STRANATHAN, Ph.D.

Professor of Physics and Chairman of
the Department, University of Kansas

THE BLAKISTON COMPANY, INC.

New York · Toronto

Reprinted November, 1952



PRINTED IN THE UNITED STATES OF AMERICA

# DEDICATION

**Dedicated to my former teachers—particularly Professors A. H. Compton, A. J. Dempster, and the late A. A. Michelson, all of the University of Chicago, Professor K. T. Compton of the Massachusetts Institute of Technology, and Professor F. E. Kester of the University of Kansas—who have instilled in me the curiosity to learn.**

A Statement by the Publisher

# Nuclear Energy

The present widespread interest in the release of nuclear energy, as illustrated so dramatically by the atomic bomb, leads us to call attention to certain sections of this book in which the author has discussed in detail the principles underlying the release of nuclear energy, often, though somewhat improperly, called atomic energy. Although large-scale release of nuclear energy, as in the bomb, is relatively recent, information concerning the conversion of mass into other more commonly recognized forms of energy, the splitting of uranium 235, the tremendous energy released by this splitting, and the production of the new elements 93 and 94 (named neptunium and plutonium) by neutron bombardment of uranium 238, is contained herein. The author is to be congratulated upon having incorporated so much of the information pertinent to the atomic bomb in a book published in 1942.

The basis of releasing nuclear energy, and specifically of the atomic bomb, is the conversion of mass into other forms of energy. Energy is released or absorbed in all nuclear (often called atomic) disintegrations. When uranium, thorium, protoactinium, and the new element plutonium are disintegrated by neutron bombardment, the nucleus of the atom is split into two roughly equal fragments. This splitting process is called fission. Large amounts of energy are released. Uranium 235 and plutonium are of unusual importance because they can be split by slow neutrons. Development of the atomic bomb itself was largely a matter of accumulating enough uranium 235 or plutonium to release the required energy, and of controlling the splitting of these atoms so that they will not be split until desired but so that many can be split in a short interval of time when it is desired. Complete details of separating uranium 235 from the more abundant but still rare uranium 238, and of making plutonium from uranium 238 on a sufficiently large scale, have not yet been released. The underlying principles, however, were known prior to World War II, and are discussed herein.

For the convenience of the reader who is interested in developments leading to the atomic bomb, we call attention to the following specific discussions in this book:

Interchangeability of Mass and Energy, pp. 185, 374, 387, 396, 445, 449.
Energies Associated with Nuclear Disintegrations, pp. 445–447.
Splitting of Uranium, pp. 447–449.
Energy Released in Splitting Uranium 235, pp. 449–450.
The New Elements, Neptunium and Plutonium, pp. 448, 451–452.

*December, 1947*

# PREFACE

The study of the fundamental particles of physics is unusually interesting to most students. At the same time it constitutes one of the most basic fields of preparation for understanding the modern concepts of atomic structure. It is essential to an appreciation of research being carried on in many fields. Out of these studies have come many important discoveries. There are, for example, the atomic character of electricity, the existence of isotopes, the photon character of radiant energy, the positron, the neutron, the mesotron, the artificial disintegration of the elements, the nature of radioactive processes in both natural and artificial radioactivity, the nature of cosmic rays, and the all-important discovery of the conversion of mass into energy, and vice-versa.

For the past fifteen years it has been the author's pleasant duty to give annually to a class of juniors, seniors and beginning graduate students at the University of Kansas, a survey course in the field of modern physics. This course has been built around the "particles" of modern physics, the electron, positive rays, photons, positrons, neutrons, mesotrons, X-rays, $\alpha$, $\beta$, and $\gamma$-rays, and cosmic rays. It is essential that one proposing to study in the field of physics becomes familiar early in his program with the experimental evidence for the existence of these "particles," and with the many physical concepts to which studies of this character have led. A great many of these concepts are equally important in chemistry, and in certain fields of biology, and of electrical engineering. Through the years the author has attempted to present these concepts and the evidence which serves as their foundation, in a relatively simple yet thorough manner which can be followed by any good student who has had the usual courses in general physics. The enthusiastic response of students, as evidenced by eager interest in the classroom and by numerous statements made by former students, has convinced the author that he has been successful in this attempt.

The present book covers essentially the same material as has been presented to these classes, and the order of presentation is much the same. Naturally, more detailed discussions have been incorporated in the book than have been possible in class lectures. Many parts of the book have been mimeographed in abbreviated form in past years and used by students. The author hopes the book will serve two purposes. First, it is intended to convey to the student early in his career many of the essential fundamental concepts of modern physics. The experimental foundation for these concepts has been stressed throughout. Second, it is intended to serve as a valuable reference book for the more advanced student. Many specific references have been incorporated for this purpose. It has of course been impossible to make these references all-inclusive in any given field. Specific references have generally been given to the early works in a particular field, to a number of the more important intervening ones, to numerous of the recent researches, and to published summaries. From the last two of these, the student can obtain an excellent start on the literature in a given field.

In writing this book, the author makes no claim to originality of material. The author's contribution has been only to keep himself well read in this periodical literature, and to arrange in a logical and teachable form what are generally regarded as the most significant concepts which have sprung from these researches. In this undertaking the author is greatly indebted to authors of books in specialized fields. The material contained therein, and often referred to specifically, has been valuable in helping the author decide just what to include in a general survey of this character. The writer is also indebted to those authors and publishers who have so kindly allowed the reproduction of numerous photographs, and he takes pleasure in expressing his appreciation at this time. He is grateful also to his colleagues who have offered criticisms of this work. Particularly does he wish to express his appreciation to Dr. Richard M. Sutton of Haverford College in this connection. The author wishes to express his appreciation also for considerable stenographic work and for some drafting work furnished by the N.Y.A.

J. D. STRANATHAN.

UNIVERSITY OF KANSAS
(*March*, 1942)

# ACKNOWLEDGMENTS

The author and the publisher take pleasure in expressing their appreciation to several publishers who have so courteously given permission to reproduce in this book certain illustrations from copyrighted works. Particularly do we wish to express appreciation to the following publishers for the right to reproduce the figures of this book, which are listed below:

Edward Arnold & Co., Publishers of Mass Spectra and Isotopes, by F. W. Aston: Fig. 2, p. 151; Fig. 7, p. 161; Fig. 12, p. 175; Fig. 22, p. 200.

Prentice-Hall, Inc., Publishers of Atomic Spectra and Atomic Structure, by G. Herzberg: Fig. 1, p. 214.

D. Van Nostrand Co., Inc., Publishers of X-Rays in Theory and Experiment, by A. H. Compton & S. K. Allison: Fig. 14, p. 258; Fig. 1, p. 264, Fig. 2, p. 264; Fig. 11, p. 271; Fig. 12, p. 272; Fig. 16, p. 275.

McGraw-Hill Book Co., Publishers of Applied X-Rays, by G L. Clark: Fig. 5, p. 266.

Julius Springer, Publisher of Spektroskopie der Röntgenstrahlen, by M. Siegbahn: Fig. 27, p. 298.

Farrar & Rinehart, Publishers of Introduction to Atomic Physics, by H. Semat: Fig. 36, p. 313.

Macmillan Company, Publishers of Radiations from Radioactive Substances, by E. Rutherford, J. Chadwick, & C. D. Ellis: Fig. 5, p. 331.

Cornell University Press, Publishers of Wave Mechanics and Free Electrons, by G. P. Thomson: Fig. 6, p. 546.

University of Chicago Press, Publishers of Electrons (+ and −), Protons, Photons, Neutrons, and Cosmic Rays, by R. A. Millikan: Fig. 7, p. 546

# CONTENTS


PAGE

PREFACE ........ vii

ACKNOWLEDGMENTS ........ ix

*Chapter* 1

GASEOUS IONS AND THEIR BEHAVIOR ........ 1

1. General Concepts of Ionization ........ 1
   - SOME ELEMENTARY OBSERVATIONS ........ 1
   - METHODS OF MEASURING SMALL CURRENTS ........ 5
   - THE IONIZATION THEORY OF CONDUCTION ........ 7
     - *Interpretation of General Phenomena* ........ 7
     - *Townsend's Theory of Ionization by Collision* ........ 11
     - *Sparking Potentials* ........ 23
2. The Recombination of Ions ........ 27
3. The Mobilities of Ions ........ 31
   - EXPERIMENTAL METHODS ........ 31
   - RESULTS AND THEIR INTERPRETATION ........ 34
4. The Manner of Formation of Ions ........ 39
   - THE GENERAL STRUCTURE OF ATOMS ........ 40
   - THE WILSON CLOUD EXPANSION PHENOMENON ........ 41
   - PHOTOGRAPHIC STUDIES OF THE MANNER OF ION FORMATION ........ 43

*Chapter* 2

THE ELECTRON ........ 46

1. The Atomic Character of Electricity—The Electronic Charge e ........ 46
   - EARLY INDICATIONS OF THE EXISTENCE OF THE ELECTRON ........ 46
   - MILLIKAN'S OIL DROP EXPERIMENT ........ 49
     - *Conclusive Proof of the Atomic Character of Electricity* ........ 49
     - *Typical Student Data on the Oil Drop Experiment* ........ 52
     - *Evaluation of Avogadro's Number from Millikan's Work* ........ 54
     - *Other Interesting Observations* ........ 55
2. Recent Refinements in the Numerical Value of e ........ 56
   - OTHER METHODS OF DETERMINING e ........ 56
   - RECENT ELIMINATION OF A SMALL ERROR IN THE MILLIKAN VALUE 60

*Chapter* 3

THE ELECTRICAL DISCHARGE ........ 65

1. The Various Types of Discharge ........ 65
2. The Glow Discharge Through Gases at Reduced Pressure 66
   - APPEARANCE OF THE DISCHARGE ........ 66
     - *General Features* ........ 66
     - *The Cathode Dark Space* ........ 67
     - *The Positive Column* ........ 68
     - *The Normal Versus the Abnormal Discharge* ........ 71

PAGE

NATURE OF THE PARTICLES RESPONSIBLE FOR THE CURRENT.... 71
POTENTIAL REQUIRED TO MAINTAIN THE DISCHARGE............ 73
ELECTRIC FIELD DISTRIBUTION IN THE DISCHARGE............. 74
*Methods of Investigating*........................................ 74
*Experimental Results—Field Distribution*.................... 79
*Experimental Results—Potential Distribution*............. 82
DISTRIBUTION OF IONS IN THE DISCHARGE...................... 86
ELEMENTARY THEORY OF THE DISCHARGE........................ 89
*The Cathode Dark Space*........................................ 89
*The Negative Glow and the Faraday Dark Space*............. 97
*The Striated Positive Column*.................................. 98
*The Light from the Discharge*................................... 100

*Chapter* 4

CATHODE RAYS—THE RATIO e/m FOR ELECTRONS......... 101
1. WHAT ARE CATHODE RAYS?........................................ 101
2. DIRECT MEASUREMENTS OF THE VELOCITY OF CATHODE RAYS.... 102
3. THE DEFLECTION OF MOVING CHARGED PARTICLES IN ELECTRIC AND MAGNETIC FIELDS.............................................. 104
DEFLECTIONS IN ELECTRIC FIELDS................................ 104
DEFLECTIONS IN MAGNETIC FIELDS................................ 106
4. THE RATIO e/m FOR ELECTRONS.................................. 108
DEFLECTION METHODS............................................... 108
*Thomson's Method*................................................. 108
*Kaufmann's Method*............................................... 110
*Classen's Method*................................................. 112
*Bucherer's Method*............................................... 113
*Busch's Method*................................................... 116
SPECTROSCOPIC METHODS.......................................... 119
COMPARISON OF RESULTS BY THE TWO METHODS UP TO 1929.... 120
5. RECENT REFINEMENTS IN THE RATIO $e/m_0$........................ 121
IMPROVEMENTS IN FREE ELECTRON METHODS...................... 121
*Kirchner's Method*................................................ 121
*Dunnington's Method*............................................. 124
*Kretschmar's Method*............................................. 126
*Shaw's Method*.................................................... 126
IMPROVEMENTS IN SPECTROSCOPIC METHODS..................... 127
SUMMARY OF EXISTING DETERMINATIONS OF $e/m_0$............. 128
6. THE VARIATION OF MASS WITH VELOCITY....................... 129
WHY MASS MUST BE ATTRIBUTED TO THE ELECTRON............. 129
THE THEORETICAL VARIATION OF MASS WITH VELOCITY......... 134
EXPERIMENTAL EVIDENCE OF THE CHANGE OF MASS WITH VELOCITY.......................................................... 138
*Bucherer's Method*............................................... 138
*Hupka's Method*................................................... 140
*Guye and Lavanchy's Method*.................................... 140
*Tricker's Method*.................................................. 142
*Zahn and Spees' Method*.......................................... 144
MORE EXACT EXPRESSION FOR KINETIC ENERGY.................. 145

PAGE

*Chapter 5*

POSITIVE RAYS—ISOTOPES ........ 147
1. WHAT ARE POSITIVE RAYS? ........ 147
2. METHODS OF STUDYING THE RATIO e/m FOR POSITIVE RAYS ........ 148
THOMSON'S PARABOLA METHOD ........ 148
DEMPSTER'S DIRECTION FOCUSING METHOD ........ 154
ASTON'S VELOCITY FOCUSING METHOD ........ 156
3. THE GENERAL EXISTENCE OF ISOTOPES ........ 162
4. ACCURATE DETERMINATION OF ATOMIC WEIGHTS OF INDIVIDUAL ISOTOPES ........ 167
ARE ATOMIC WEIGHTS OF ISOTOPES EXACTLY WHOLE NUMBERS? ........ 167
ATOMIC WEIGHTS FROM POSITIVE RAY STUDIES ........ 168
*Aston's Accurate Atomic Weights of 1927* ........ 168
*Aston's Original Packing Fraction Curve* ........ 170
*Recent Refinements in Mass Spectrographs* ........ 172
*Numerical Values of Atomic Weights* ........ 178
ATOMIC WEIGHTS FROM NUCLEAR DISINTEGRATION STUDIES ........ 183
*Basis of the Method* ........ 183
*Numerical Results and Comparison of Atomic Weights by the Two Methods* ........ 186
PACKING FRACTION CURVE FOR THE ELEMENTS ........ 196
5. OTHER METHODS OF DETECTING ISOTOPES ........ 198
6. THE SEPARATION OF ISOTOPES ........ 203

*Chapter 6*

PHOTONS—THE PHOTOELECTRIC EFFECT—RADIATION AND ABSORPTION ........ 212
1. THE EMISSION AND ABSORPTION OF RADIANT ENERGY ........ 213
GENERAL INFORMATION REGARDING EMISSION FROM GASES ........ 213
THE CLASSICAL CONCEPT OF RADIATION ........ 215
BOHR'S THEORY OF RADIATION ........ 216
SOMMERFELD'S THEORY OF FINE STRUCTURE ........ 224
MORE RECENT THEORIES OF THE ATOM ........ 227
2. IONIZATION AND RESONANCE POTENTIALS ........ 229
GENERAL INFORMATION ........ 229
METHODS OF MEASURING CRITICAL POTENTIALS ........ 231
EXPERIMENTAL RESULTS ........ 233
3. THE PHOTOELECTRIC EFFECT ........ 236
METALS ILLUMINATED WITH VISIBLE OR ULTRAVIOLET LIGHT ........ 236
*Early History* ........ 236
*Einstein's Interpretation of the Effect* ........ 240
*Millikan's Verification of the Einstein Equation* ........ 241
*Other Interesting Aspects of the Effect* ........ 245
MATERIALS ILLUMINATED WITH X-RAYS OR $\gamma$-RAYS ........ 249
*Solids* ........ 249
*Gases* ........ 252
4. THE SCATTERING OF X-RAYS ........ 254

PAGE

*Chapter 7*

X-RAYS . . . . . 260

1. GENERAL PROPERTIES OF X-RAYS . . . . . 261
   - THEIR PRODUCTION . . . . . 261
   - VELOCITY . . . . . 262
   - DIFFRACTION AND INTERFERENCE . . . . . 262
     - *Diffraction by Slits* . . . . . 262
     - *Diffraction by Crystals* . . . . . 265
     - *Diffraction by Ruled Gratings* . . . . . 271
   - REFRACTION . . . . . 272
   - REFLECTION . . . . . 277
   - POLARIZATION . . . . . 278
   - SCATTERING . . . . . 280
   - ABSORPTION . . . . . 286
2. X-RAY SPECTRA . . . . . 290
   - CONTINUOUS RADIATION . . . . . 291
   - CHARACTERISTIC RADIATION . . . . . 295
3. DIFFRACTION BY CRYSTALS AND CRYSTAL STRUCTURE . . . . . 303
   - THE LAUE METHOD . . . . . 303
   - THE BRAGG METHOD . . . . . 305
   - THE POWDER CRYSTAL METHOD . . . . . 312

*Chapter 8*

$\alpha$, $\beta$ AND $\gamma$-RAYS—NATURAL RADIOACTIVITY . . . . . 315

1. GENERAL PHENOMENA OF RADIOACTIVITY . . . . . 315
   - THE DISCOVERY . . . . . 315
   - THE HALF LIFE PERIOD . . . . . 316
   - NATURE OF THE EMISSIONS . . . . . 317
   - THE TRANSFORMATION SERIES . . . . . 317
2. THE THEORY OF RADIOACTIVE TRANSFORMATIONS . . . . . 324
   - GENERAL CONSIDERATIONS . . . . . 324
   - RELATIONSHIPS AMONG THE SEVERAL RADIOACTIVE CONSTANTS . . 325
   - THE MANNER IN WHICH A NEW SUBSTANCE BUILDS UP . . . . . 326
3. ALPHA PARTICLES, THEIR ORIGIN AND PROPERTIES . . . . . 329
   - THE NATURE OF THE PARTICLES . . . . . 329
   - VELOCITY AND RANGE . . . . . 330
   - PRODUCTION OF IONIZATION . . . . . 336
   - LONG RANGE PARTICLES AND FINE STRUCTURE . . . . . 339
     - *Long Range Particles* . . . . . 339
     - *Fine Structure of Alpha Rays* . . . . . 344
     - *The Origin of Long Range and Fine Structure Particles* . . . . . 346
4. $\beta$ AND $\gamma$ RAYS, THEIR ORIGIN AND PROPERTIES . . . . . 349
   - NATURE OF THE RADIATIONS . . . . . 349
   - BETA AND GAMMA RAY SPECTRA . . . . . 352
     - *The Continuous Beta Ray Spectrum* . . . . . 352
     - *Beta Ray Line Spectra* . . . . . 354
     - *Gamma Ray Line Spectra* . . . . . 355
     - *The Origin of Beta and Gamma Rays* . . . . . 355

PAGE

*Chapter* 9

THE POSITRON ........ 362
1. Discovery of the Positron ........ 362
2. Are Positrons Abundant in Nature? ........ 371
3. Creation and Annihilation of Electron-positron Pairs .... 374

*Chapter* 10

THE NEUTRON ........ 386
1. Discovery of the Neutron ........ 386
2. Sources of Neutrons ........ 393
3. The Mass of the Neutron ........ 395
4. The Magnetic Moment of the Neutron ........ 400

*Chapter* 11

ATOMIC NUCLEI—ARTIFICIAL DISINTEGRATION ........ 403
1. Early Experiments on the Structure of the Nucleus ...... 403
   - rutherford's work on the scattering of alpha particles by thin films ........ 403
   - failure of the inverse square law of repulsion between nuclei ........ 410
   - the first successful experiments on artificial disintegration ........ 412
   - the present concept of atomic structure ........ 417
2. Recent Production of Extremely High Energy Particles .. 420
   - early types of apparatus ........ 420
   - the cyclotron ........ 422
   - the van de graaff machine ........ 427
   - accelerating tubes ........ 431
3. Artficial Disintegration ........ 433
   - disintegration by proton bombardment ........ 433
   - disintegration by deuteron bombardment ........ 436
   - disintegration by alpha particle bombardment ........ 438
   - disintegration by neutron bombardment ........ 441
   - disintegration by photon bombardment ........ 443
   - different ways of producing the same material ........ 444
   - the mass changes and energies associated with disintegration ........ 445
   - fission ........ 447
4. Artificial Radioactivity ........ 452
   - the discovery and extent of ........ 452
   - types of radioactive decay ........ 453
   - the possible significance of these materials ........ 456

*Chapter* 12

COSMIC RAYS ........ 460
1. The Early History of Cosmic Rays ........ 460
2. Evidence Bearing on the Nature of Cosmic Rays ........ 463
   - the variation of intensity with altitude ........ 463

PAGE
THE ABSORPTION IN MATTER .......... 468
THE LATITUDE EFFECT .......... 475
SEASONAL, DIURNAL AND OTHER CHANGES IN INTENSITY .......... 489
THE EAST-WEST DIRECTIONAL EFFECT .......... 494
COINCIDENCE AND CLOUD CHAMBER STUDIES .......... 497
SHOWERS AND BURSTS .......... 509

*Chapter* 13

THE MESOTRON .......... 520
1. DISCOVERY OF THE MESOTRON .......... 520
EARLY HISTORY .......... 520
EVIDENCE FROM COSMIC RAY STUDIES .......... 521
EVIDENCE FROM CLOUD CHAMBER PHOTOGRAPHS .......... 523
2. THE MASS OF THE MESOTRON .......... 529
3. RADIOACTIVE DECAY OF THE MESOTRON .......... 534

*Chapter* 14

PARTICLES?—OR WAVES? .......... 538
1. DE BROGLIE'S THEORETICAL CONSIDERATIONS .......... 538
2. EXPERIMENTAL OBSERVATIONS OF THE DIFFRACTION OF ELECTRONS .......... 541
REFLECTION FROM CRYSTALS .......... 541
TRANSMISSION THROUGH CRYSTALS .......... 545
DIFFRACTION BY GASES .......... 547
3. CRYSTAL STRUCTURE BY ELECTRON DIFFRACTION .......... 549
4. DIFFRACTION OF ATOMS AND MOLECULES .......... 550

PROBLEMS .......... 557

AUTHOR INDEX .......... 569

SUBJECT INDEX .......... 579

Chapter 1

# GASEOUS IONS AND THEIR BEHAVIOR

## I. GENERAL CONCEPTS OF IONIZATION

### Some Elementary Observations

Under normal conditions gases are among the best insulators of electricity known. They are such good insulators that, in the early days of science, argument arose as to whether they conduct electricity at all. It is now known that all gases under all practical conditions do conduct somewhat. But under normal conditions the conductivity is so small that careful observations are necessary to prove that it exists. From the first studies of electricity it was known that a gold leaf electroscope or other charged body gradually loses its charge regardless of precautions taken to insure good insulation. But it was not known whether the conduction of electricity from the charged body took place entirely through or over the surface of the solid insulators used, or whether the surrounding air or other gas was also conducting.

Coulomb[1] was the first to conclude that, after allowing for the charge lost by a body due to conductivity of the solid insulator used, there remained an additional loss of charge which must be attributed to leakage through the surrounding air. This conclusion was repeatedly verified as other observers added further information.[2] Perhaps the most direct proof that a normal gas does conduct somewhat was furnished by a simple experiment performed almost simultaneously by C. T. R. Wilson[3] and by Geitel.[4] Wilson used an electroscope such as shown in Fig. 1. It differed from the usual type only in the addition of a second insulator $B$ and a switch $D$. The electroscope was connected to a source of fixed potential difference, and the leaf system $E$ charged by tipping the instrument until switch $D$ made contact. The switch was then allowed to open, but $C$ was left connected to the source of potential. It was observed that the leaf system gradually lost its charge. This could not be due to leakage across the

[1] C. A. Coulomb, *Memoires de l'Academie des Sciences*, 612 (1785).

[2] J. J. Thomson and G. P. Thomson, *Conduction of Electricity Through Gases*, (3rd ed.; London: Cambridge University Press, 1928), Vol. I, pp. 1–12, have traced these developments in detail.

[3] C. T. R. Wilson, *Proc. Camb. Phil. Soc.*, **11**, 32 (1900); *Proc. Roy. Soc.*, A, **68**, 151 (1901).

[4] H. Geitel, *Phys. Zeits.*, **2**, 116 (1900).

insulator *B*, for since *C* is maintained at its original potential, any leakage across the insulator would tend to keep the leaf charged. The air itself must conduct electricity from the leaf, and in this experiment the leakage through the air was more than could be compensated by that across the sulphur insulator *B*.

Numerous other workers contributed further information.[2] Leakage through a gas depends upon the difference in potential between the charged body and its surroundings. Or, more properly, it depends upon the electrical field strength in the gas. The leakage current grows larger with increases in field strength, gradually arriving at a maximum value which remains constant for any further reasonable increase in field. The leakage is less the lower the pressure of the gas. Crookes[5] showed very early that a pair of gold leaves placed in a good vacuum retained a charge for several months. The maximum value of the leakage increases with the volume of the vessel inclosing the charged body. The maximum leakage is proportional both to the volume of the vessel and to the pressure of the gas. It is thus proportional to the total number of molecules nearby, just as if a given fraction of these contribute to the conduction. Peculiarly, the leakage depends upon the thickness of the walls of the vessel containing the gas, and even upon the thickness of some material such as lead which may be placed around the outside of the vessel. The leakage decreases rather rapidly at first as the surrounding lead is made thicker, due, as was found later, to the absorption of stray radioactive radiation which renders a gas conducting. After the thickness of the lead reaches an inch or two, the further reduction with subsequent increases in lead thickness is very slow indeed. Regardless of any practical thickness of lead used, some leakage is still apparent. This is due to the very penetrating cosmic rays discovered not so many years ago. These render a gas conducting, and their effect has been observed[6] even after they have penetrated some 1,600 feet through the earth. It was found[7] that the leakage through air in caves and cellars where the air is stagnant is much greater than in the open air. This is due

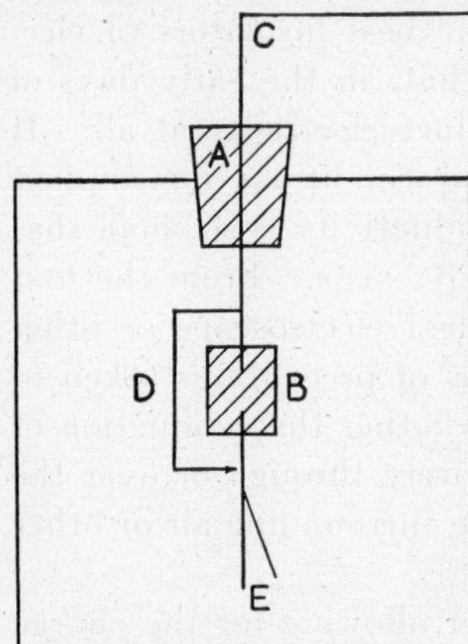


FIG. 1.—Illustrating the electroscope used by Wilson to show directly that a gas conducts electricity. *A* and *B* are sulphur insulators. *D* is a switch that can be closed or opened by tipping the electroscope.

[5] W. Crookes, *Proc. Roy. Soc.*, A, **28**, 347 (1879).
[6] V. C. Wilson, *Phys. Rev.*, **53**, 204, 337 (1938).
[7] J. Elster and H. Geitel, *Phys. Zeits.*, **2**, 560 (1901).

to minute quantities of radioactive substances in the earth; these give rise to radioactive gases which diffuse slowly through porous walls into the stagnant air, rendering it conducting by their subsequent radiations. While it is evident that the normal leakage through air depends greatly upon a number of variable quantities, it is always very small, something of the order of $10^{-18}$ amperes per cubic centimeter of air contained in a small vessel at atmospheric pressure.

There are, however, many ways in which the conductivity of a gas can be increased tremendously. For example, the current carried by the gas in the usual neon sign, or in certain types of "vacuum" tubes, is millions of millions times the normal leakage current. The conductivity of a gas can be increased greatly by bombarding the gas with high speed particles, such as electrons. Or it is increased if any radioactive material is placed nearby; and this is the case regardless of whether the radioactive substance emits alpha, beta, or gamma radiation. Or if X-rays are allowed

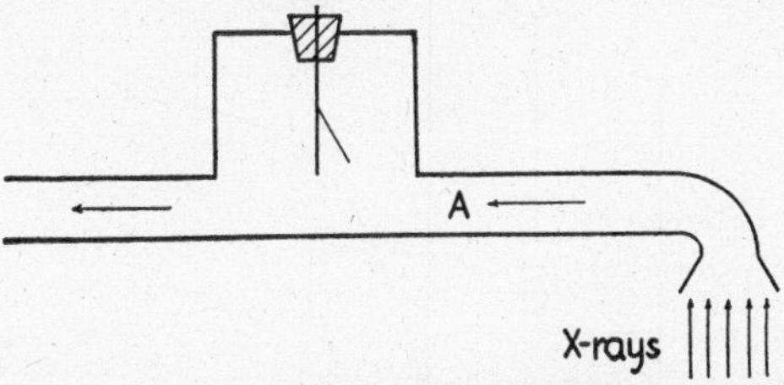


Fig. 2.—Illustrating that a gas retains the property of conducting electricity for a short time after the exciting agent is removed.

to pass through the gas the conductivity is greatly increased. Ultraviolet light produces a similar effect, though visible light, infrared heat radiation, and radio waves have no effect. Or the gas can be made conducting by heating it to a high temperature, as with a Bunsen flame. In each of these cases, the conductivity (the reciprocal of the resistance) varies with the potential difference established across the gas. Unlike the case of a metallic conductor, no fixed resistance can be assigned to a sample of gas. When sufficiently large potential differences are applied across a gas, the conductivity is found to increase rapidly with further increases in potential; finally the gas becomes so conducting that a spark discharge occurs between electrodes. These observations must all be considered in any theory of the manner in which a gas conducts electricity.

Another significant fact is that if a gas be subjected to radioactive radiations, X-rays, ultraviolet light, or a flame, and be drawn immediately through a charged electroscope, Fig. 2, the leaf system discharges rapidly; if the gas be allowed to stand for a few minutes after exposure and then be drawn through the electroscope, the conductivity is no greater than if the gas had never been excited by one of the agencies mentioned. The gas does retain the ability to conduct, however, for a good number of seconds after the exciting agent is withdrawn; the conductivity gradually diminishes with time, finally approaching the value prevailing before the excitation. There are several ways, however, in which the ability to conduct can be destroyed even though the gas is drawn through the electroscope immediately after excitation. If the gas is made to pass through a glass wool plug placed in the tube at $A$, or made to bubble through water, or made to pass between two small metal plates between which a strong electric field exists, the gas is no more conducting than if it had not been subjected to the exciting agent.

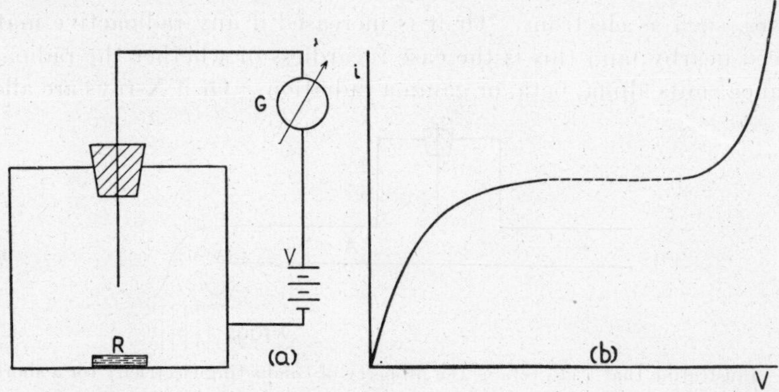


FIG. 3.—(*a*) An ionization chamber with radioactive material $R$ to render the gas conducting. (*b*) A typical current versus potential curve.

The manner in which the current carried by a gas varies with the potential difference applied between the electrodes is also significant in forming any concept of the conduction process. Let us consider a gas, say air at atmospheric pressure, within a so-called ionization chamber as shown in Fig. 3(*a*). Let some radioactive material $R$ be placed within the chamber so as to render the gas appreciably conducting during the experiment. If various potential differences $V$ are now applied across the gas and the resulting currents $i$ measured by some sensitive instrument $G$, the current is found to vary in the manner shown in Fig. 3(*b*). For very low applied potentials the curve starts off essentially as a straight line; that is, the gas approximately obeys Ohm's law. At slightly higher potentials the current increases less rapidly than necessary to conform to Ohm's law; the "resistance" of the gas has increased. At still higher potentials the current approaches an essentially constant value known as the saturation current; further increases in applied potential (within limits) fail to increase the current. At very much higher potentials the current again begins to mount, slowly at first, and then more and more rapidly, until finally a spark discharge occurs. The actual magnitude of the current at any particular applied potential, as well as the actual potential difference corresponding to any characteristic part of the curve, depends upon the strength of the radioactive material, the volume of the ionization chamber, and the position of the electrode within the chamber. Larger saturation currents result from stronger exciting agents, but a larger potential is required to produce saturation current. This saturation current is a measure of the strength of the exciting agent, provided other things remain the same. The final spark discharge occurs, in air at atmospheric pressure, when the potential is sufficient to produce a field strength of the order of 30,000 volts per cm. in the gas.

**Methods of Measuring Small Currents**

Currents of the size indicated in Fig. 3(*b*) cannot be measured with the ordinary portable ammeter, or even with the most sensitive D'Arsonval galvanometer. The limit of the former is around $10^{-6}$ amperes, while that of the latter is around $10^{-10}$. There are other methods, however, which allow the measurement of currents far smaller than this, currents as small as $10^{-17}$ amperes; and often it is desirable to measure these minute currents. The oldest and most widely used method consists of observing the rate at which some form of electroscope or electrometer loses or gains charge as the desired current is allowed to flow to it. Fig. 4 shows several forms of such instruments, the details and use of which are described elsewhere.[8] The position of the gold leaf in the electroscope, the angular position of the movable vane in the quadrant electrometer, or the position of the "string" in the string electrometer depends upon the potential to which the movable element is charged.

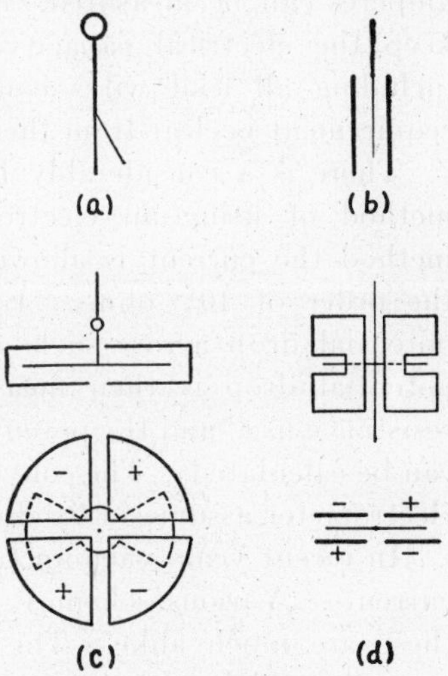

(a) (b) (c) (d)

Fig. 4.—Types of current measuring instruments. (*a*) Gold leaf electroscope. (*b*) Single fiber string electrometer. (*c*) Dolezalek quadrant electrometer. (*d*) Lindemann electrometer.

Let $V_1$ and $V_2$ be the potentials corresponding to two positions of the movable element. And let $t$ be the time required for this element to move from the first to the second position as the desired current $i$ is allowed to

[8] J. B. Hoag, *Electron and Nuclear Physics* (2nd ed.; New York: D. Van Nostrand, 1938), pp. 396–408.

charge or discharge it. If $Q$ be the quantity of electricity which must be delivered to or taken from the insulated element to change its potential from $V_1$ to $V_2$, and if $C$ be the electrical capacity of this element and all wires connected to it, then

$$Q = C(V_2 - V_1).$$

But the current flowing to or from the instrument is given by

$$i = \frac{Q}{t}.$$

Hence

$$i = C\frac{V_2 - V_1}{t}.$$

Knowing the potentials $V_1$ and $V_2$ corresponding to the two positions between which the movable element was timed, and knowing the capacity $C$, the current can be evaluated. In this way currents as small as $10^{-16}$ amperes can be measured. For high current sensitivity it is essential to keep the electrical capacity of the insulated part of the electrometer, including all lead wires connected thereto, as small as possible. This requirement is clear from the equation above.

There is a considerably more convenient but somewhat less sensitive method of using an electrometer to measure small currents. In this method the current is allowed to flow through a very high resistance, of the order of $10^{10}$ ohms. Even though the current be very small, the potential drop across such a high resistance is appreciable. This small potential drop is then measured with the electrometer. Knowing the resistance used and the potential sensitivity of the electrometer, the current can be calculated. The convenience of this method lies in the fact that the electrometer assumes a fixed deflection corresponding to a given current.

In recent years vacuum tubes have often been used in measuring small currents. Various schemes[9] have been employed. In principle, most of these are much alike. The current to be measured is allowed to flow through a high resistance, say $10^{10}$ ohms. One or more vacuum tubes, comprising a direct current amplifier, are then used to amplify this potential drop. The amplified output, which is sufficiently large to measure with a sensitive D'Arsonval galvanometer, or in many cases with a portable instrument, gives a measure of the desired current. Currents as low as $10^{-17}$ amperes can be measured in this way.

Regardless of what method is used to measure these small currents, many precautions are necessary if large errors are to be avoided. Leakage currents across dirty insulators may be larger than the current one is attempting

[9] K. Henney, *Electron Tubes in Industry* (2nd ed.; New York: McGraw-Hill, 1937), pp. 73–91.

to measure. Leakage through the surrounding atmosphere will often entirely mask the small current being measured. In order to avoid this, it is necessary to inclose all parts of the insulated system, including connecting wires, within a grounded metal shield. This reduces the leakage by limiting the volume of air contributing to the leakage; it also insures a much more nearly constant leakage. At the same time such shielding insures a constant capacity for the system. This is important in methods where this capacity is involved.

**The Ionization Theory of Conduction**

*Interpretation of General Phenomena.*—Let us now consider the actual conduction of electricity through a gas, particularly the manner in which this conduction takes place. In view of the various observations already mentioned, it appears that conduction can be interpreted best by supposing that the passage of radioactive radiations, X-rays, or cosmic rays through the gas, or the heating of the gas, produces charged systems within the gas. These charged systems are molecules which have either lost or gained an electron, thus making them positive or negative. They are called ions. The agencies that render a gas conducting are said to ionize the gas. Actual conduction takes place by movement of the gaseous ions along the direction of the applied field, the positive ions drifting in the direction of the field and the negative ions in the opposite direction. Ionization of the gas surrounding a charged electroscope would account for the fact that the leaf gradually loses its charge; the leaf attracts ions of sign opposite to its own, thus neutralizing the charge thereon. The fact that an electroscope or other charged body always discharges to some extent, indicates that the air is always slightly ionized. This condition is due to slight radioactive contamination in the earth and in walls of buildings, and to the ever present penetrating cosmic rays. With this concept of conduction in mind a great majority of the facts previously mentioned become obvious. For example, the leakage through a gas increases with the volume of the vessel containing the gas simply because the charged electrode can draw ions from a greater region. Likewise, the gradual decrease in conductivity of a gas after the ionizing agent has been removed means that positive and negative ions gradually recombine. During the many collisions of the ions with other molecules, ions of opposite sign often come sufficiently close together that they unite, forming neutral molecules; they do not contribute further to the transfer of electricity. Removal of the ability to conduct by filtering an ionized gas through glass wool or water means merely that the ions have been removed by the filtering.

The ionization theory, with certain logical additions, will also explain the general features of the current-potential curve shown in Fig. 3(*b*).

Let us say that there are $q$ pairs of ions per cc. produced per second throughout a gas by the action of an ionizing agent. In general these ions disappear by three distinct processes. Some of them are urged to the electrodes of the ionization chamber by the applied electric field; these contribute the current observed. Other ions recombine before reaching the electrodes. Still other ions are lost by slow diffusion to the walls of the containing vessel and to the electrodes. In many cases the effect of diffusion is negligible; in other cases it cannot be ignored. Let us suppose that there are $n$ pairs of ions present per cc. at any time, $n$ positive ions and $n$ negative ions. The probability that one particular positive ion will collide with some negative ion and thus recombine, is proportional to the number of negative ions present per cc., that is, to $n$. Since there are $n$ positive ions present per cc., the chance of a collision between some positive ion and some negative ion is, therefore, proportional to $n^2$. The number of recombinations $R$ per cc. per second is then given by

$$R = \alpha n^2 \tag{1}$$

where $\alpha$ is a constant called the coefficient of recombination, a constant which can be measured experimentally.[10] If one allows an ionizing agent to act upon a gas continuously, there are $q$ new pairs of ions appearing per cc. per second. If no electric field is applied the ion concentration increases for a time, but as more and more ions are furnished to the space, the chance of recombination grows larger. The actual ion concentration $n$ continues to build up until the number of ions recombining per second is just equal to the number of new ions furnished per second. When equilibrium conditions are reached

$$\alpha n^2 = q.$$

Thus the number of pairs of ions actually present per cc. at any time is

$$n = \sqrt{\frac{q}{\alpha}} = \text{a constant.} \tag{2}$$

In case an electric field is applied across the gas the situation is in general quite complex. Let an electric field $E$ be applied. The positive and negative ions will be set into motion by this field. The force acting upon any one ion with charge $e$ and mass $m$ is $Ee$. The acceleration of the ion is $Ee/m$. The ion will increase in speed until it collides with a molecule. It is assumed that on the average the ion loses all of the energy imparted to it by the field and that it again starts out after each collision with zero

[10] J. J. Thomson and G. P. Thomson, *Conduction of Electricity Through Gases* (3rd ed.; London: Cambridge University Press, 1928), Vol. I, pp. 20–40, discuss a number of methods of measuring this coefficient.

velocity of drift. If $\tau$ be the mean time between collisions of the ion with molecules, the final velocity the ion will acquire, on an average, between consecutive collisions is $(Ee/m)\tau$. The average velocity $U$ is then

$$U = \frac{e\tau}{2m} E = uE$$

where $u$ is a constant. That is, the average velocity with which an ion drifts through a gas is proportional to the field strength urging the ion. The factor of proportionality $u$ is called the mobility of the ion; it is numerically equal to the velocity imparted by unit field. This drift velocity imparted by the electric field is, of course, superimposed upon the velocity of thermal agitation which is shared by the ions as well as the molecules. It can be shown that the average kinetic energy of thermal agitation of a particle of mass $m$ flying around with an average velocity $v$ is given by

$$\tfrac{1}{2}mv^2 = \tfrac{3}{2}kT$$

where $k$ is the Boltzmann gas constant per molecule appearing in the gas law, and where $T$ is the absolute temperature. If one calculates the average velocity of an oxygen molecule at about room temperature, he finds a value approximately $5 \times 10^4$ cm/sec. This is roughly the velocity of a rifle bullet. It will be shown later that the average drift velocity imparted to an ion by an electric field of a few volts per cm. is only a few cm/sec. Thus, for reasonable fields, the drift velocity is very small as compared to the thermal velocity. But on the average the ion gets nowhere due to its thermal motion; it drifts gradually toward the electrode due to the small drift velocity.

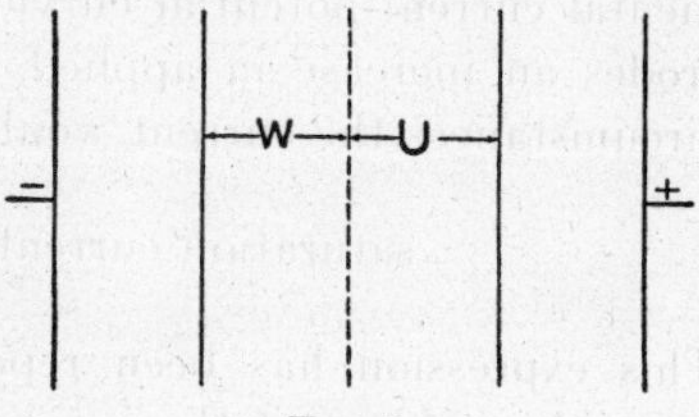

Fig. 5.

Let us proceed now to calculate the current through an ionized gas when a field $E$ is applied. The mobilities of positive and negative ions may well be different; let them be represented by $u$ and $w$ respectively. Consider any section through a gas taken perpendicular to the electric field. The current density through the gas is the charge passing through unit area of this section per second. The velocities of positive and negative ions are respectively

$$U = uE \qquad \text{and} \qquad W = wE$$

Then in one second all positive ions within a distance $U$, Fig. 5, on one side of the section and all negative ions within a distance $W$ on the other side of the section will pass through the section. If there be $n$ ions of each kind per cc., if each ion carry a charge $e$, and if $A$ be the area of the section, the resulting current is

$$i = n(uE + wE)Ae = nAe(u + w)E \tag{3}$$

This is in general quite complex, for $n$ is a function of the current $i$. There are, however, two limiting cases which are simple. First, if the field applied across the gas is so small that the number of ions drawn to the electrodes is negligible as compared to the number recombining, then the number of ions present per cc. is essentially constant and equal to the equilibrium value given by Eq. (2). Under such conditions the current given by (3) becomes

$$i = \sqrt{\frac{q}{\alpha}}\, Ae(u + w)E = (\text{a constant})\; E$$

Thus, for very small fields the current is proportional to the field applied; that is, the gas obeys Ohm's law. This explains the initial nearly straight line section of the current-potential curve observed experimentally and illustrated in Fig. 3($b$). Secondly, if the applied field is so large that practically all of the ions are drawn to the electrodes before recombination takes place, the phenomenon represented by the horizontal section of the experimental current-potential curve results. If all ions are drawn to the electrodes an increase in applied potential can draw no more. Under such circumstances the current would be

$$\text{saturation current} = qe\ (\text{volume of gas ionized}).$$

This expression has been repeatedly verified as regards its dependence upon the volume of the ionized gas. The fact that the field required to produce saturation current depends upon the intensity of ionization in the gas and upon the shape of the vessel and the position of electrodes therein, is to be expected. The more intense the ionization the greater is the field necessary to produce saturation. Likewise, in a vessel of such shape that some of the ionized gas is far from the electrodes, the field necessary to produce saturation current would be large.

Quantitative interpretation of that section of the current-potential curve lying intermediate to the part conforming approximately to Ohm's law and the part representing saturation, is far more involved. Over this range the number of ions recombining is of the same order as the number reaching the electrodes; hence, neither of the above special treatments apply. Qualitatively at least, this section of the experimental curve runs as one would expect from the ionization theory. Also, the rapid increase in current for very large applied potentials is consistent with the ionization theory, provided one assumes that gaseous molecules can be ionized when struck by ions of sufficiently high velocity. Let us therefore investigate the possibility of ionization by collision.

*Townsend's Theory of Ionization by Collision.*—Each atom that goes into the formation of a molecule is itself composed of a small, positively charged central nucleus surrounded by planetary electrons arranged in definite shells. It takes a definite amount of energy to detach one of these electrons from any particular kind of atom or molecule. Even before this detailed knowledge was available, it seemed logical that it might require a definite amount of energy to ionize a molecule of a certain gas, an amount of energy independent of the nature of the ionizing agent. One would expect that any agent capable of transferring this amount of energy to a molecule would be capable of ionizing the gas. An electron or a gaseous ion with sufficient velocity to possess the required amount of energy might ionize a molecule with which it collides. It is found experimentally that it often does.

From extensive studies[11] of the rapid increase in current at potentials nearing that necessary for the spark discharge to occur, Townsend concluded that the rapid increase in current accompanying an increase in applied field is due mainly to the production of new ions by collision. The ions initially present, those formed by the source of ionization, are given relatively high velocities by the applied field before they undergo a collision with a molecule. If the applied field is sufficiently high that the amount of energy required for ionization is imparted to the ion during its description of one free path, it may, upon collision at the end of this path, ionize the molecule which it strikes; thus additional ions are formed. In the same way these additional ions are given high velocities and they in turn ionize other molecules with which they collide. The process is cumulative until in the end the spark discharge occurs through the gas. Except at pressures so low that the mean free path of the molecule is comparable with the dimensions of the vessel containing the gas, one would expect the field strength necessary to cause extensive ionization by collision and the consequent spark discharge, to be proportional to the gas pressure; for the mean free path is inversely proportional to pressure, and the energy imparted to an ion between collisions is proportional to the product of field strength and mean free path. It is found experimentally that the field necessary to cause the discharge is closely proportional to pressure, down to pressures of the order of a cm. of mercury. From data on gases in non-uniform fields, say in a cylinder with a coaxial wire, Townsend concluded that the negative ion is more effective than the positive ion in producing ionization by collision.

In studying quantitatively the theory of ionization by collision, let us consider first only the ionization produced by negative ions.[12] Consider

[11] J. S. Townsend, *Electricity in Gases* (Oxford: Clarendon Press, 1915), pp. 260–336.
[12] J. S. Townsend, *Phil. Mag.*, 1, 198 (1901).

one particular negative ion a distance $a$ from the positive electrode, Fig. 6. In its passage to the positive electrode many additional ions will be formed. Let $\alpha$ be the number of new pairs of ions formed by collision per cm. length of path of an ion. And let $n$ be the number of ions existing due to the one original ion, after the original ion has travelled a distance $x$ on its journey to the plate; $n$ includes the one original ion and all others formed either directly or indirectly by it. Within the small additional distance $dx$ there will be more new ions formed. Let $dn$ represent the number of new pairs formed in the additional distance $dx$. Then from the definition of $\alpha$

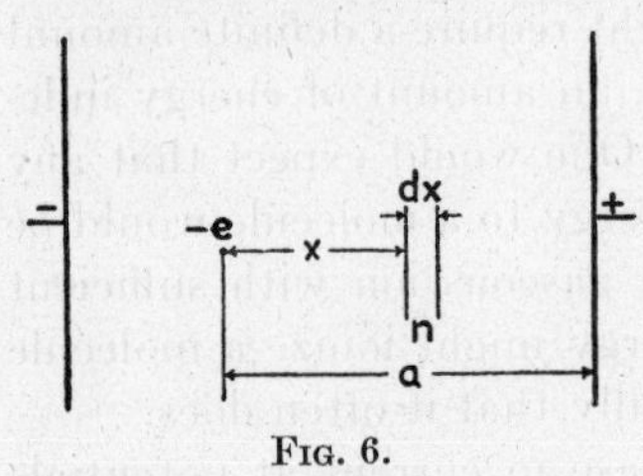

FIG. 6.

$$dn = n\alpha\, dx$$

In order to find the total number of negative ions $n_a$ that finally reach the positive plate due to the one original ion that started a distance $a$ from the plate, one needs only sum all of the small quantities $dn$ corresponding to all possible elements $dx$ between the values $x = 0$ and $x = a$. Over this range of $x$ the quantity $n$ varies from the original 1 ion when $x = 0$ to the final value $n_a$ when $x = a$. Thus

$$\int_1^{n_a} \frac{dn}{n} = \int_0^a \alpha\, dx$$

Integrating each side of this equation,

$$[\log n]_1^{n_a} = [\alpha x]_0^a \qquad \text{or} \qquad n_a = \epsilon^{\alpha a}$$

That is, for every one ion starting a distance $a$ from the plate, $\epsilon^{\alpha a}$ ions finally reach the plate.

Now in any actual case the original negative ions may all start at the same distance from the positive plate; or they may start at various places within the gas, and hence at all possible distances from the plate. A practical way of causing all the original negative ions to start at the same distance from the positive plate is to use a photoelectrically active plate as the negative electrode and to shine ultraviolet light upon this. Electrons freed from the negative electrode provide the original ionizing particles. Whether these electrons are themselves the ionizing particles, or whether they attach themselves almost immediately to neutral molecules and thus form negative ions, is a question of importance, but one which will be deferred for the present. If the distance between the plates be $d$, and if there be $N_0$ electrons freed per second per unit area of the negative electrode, then the total number $N$ of ions arriving per second per unit area of the positive plate is

$$N = N_0 \epsilon^{\alpha d}$$

Since the current density $i$ is given by $Ne$, where $e$ is the charge carried by each ion,

$$i = Ne = N_0 e \epsilon^{\alpha d} = i_0 \epsilon^{\alpha d}$$

where $i_0$ is the photoelectric current density furnished by the negative plate. The current $i_0$ is that corresponding to the horizontal section of the current versus potential curve; it is the saturation current density.

If, however, the original ions are formed not photoelectrically at one plate, but by ionizing the gas between the plates uniformly by shining X-rays upon it, the expression for the current takes on a different form. In this case the original ions start at various distances from the positive plate. For one ion starting a distance $a$ from the positive plate there are $\epsilon^{\alpha a}$ ions reach the plate. Let $N_0$ be the number of original negative ions formed per second per unit volume by the ionizing agent. Then the number of original ions starting between the distances $a$ and $(a + da)$ from the positive plate in Fig. 7 will be $N_0 da$ per unit area of the plate. Due to ionization by collision there will be a larger number reach the plate, $N_0\, da\, \epsilon^{\alpha a}$ per second per unit area. This number is due just to those negative ions which start between $a$ and $(a + da)$. Actually, original ions start at all distances between $a = 0$ and $a = d$. The total number of ions $N$ reaching unit area of the plate per second, due to original ions starting at all possible places, must then be obtained by another summation. Thus,

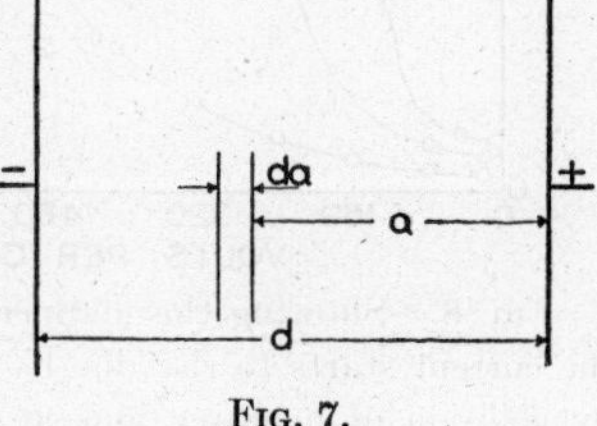

Fig. 7.

$$N = \int_0^d N_0 \epsilon^{\alpha a}\, da = N_0 \left[ \frac{\epsilon^{\alpha a}}{\alpha} \right]_0^d = N_0 \frac{\epsilon^{\alpha d} - 1}{\alpha}$$

The current density is then given by

$$i = Ne = N_0 e \frac{\epsilon^{\alpha d} - 1}{\alpha} = i_0 \frac{\epsilon^{\alpha d} - 1}{\alpha d}$$

where $i_0$ is the saturation current $N_0 ed$, the current provided by drawing all of the original ions out before they recombine, but drawing them out with an electric field sufficiently low that there are no new ions produced by collision. This expression takes into account the ionization produced by collision of negative ions only; nothing has been said regarding possible ionization due to positive ions. Also, it has been assumed in both deductions, the one for which the negative ions were all formed at the negative electrode and the one for which they were formed uniformly throughout the gas, that there are no ions lost through recombination. As soon as ionization by collision sets in, the ion concentration is increased greatly by the new ions formed; even though the field strength necessary to produce such ionization is more than sufficient to draw normal saturation current, it is not certain that it will be sufficient to draw out the now more closely spaced ions before recombination sets in. Even so, recombination is fairly negligible in most cases.

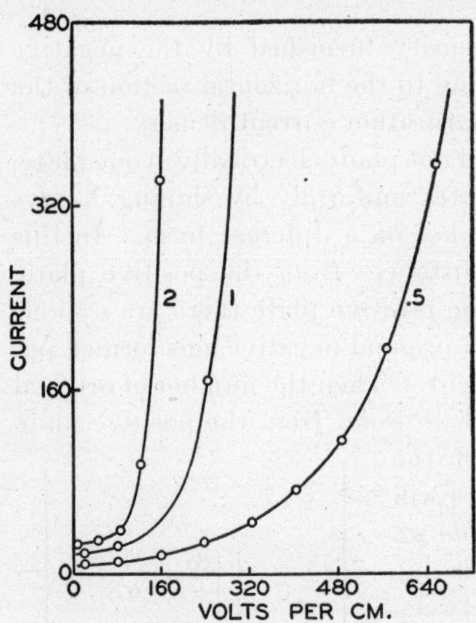


Fig. 8.—Showing the manner in which the current starts to rise due to ionization by collision of negative ions at high field strengths. Curves are shown for three different plate spacings, 2, 1, and 0.5 cm. Note that for a given field the ionization current is larger for a large separation of the plates than for small separation. Data are for air at a pressure of 1.10 mm. of Hg.

Although the contribution due to positive ion collisions has not yet been considered, it is nevertheless interesting to see how the concept so far developed fits experimental data. It is found experimentally that for electric fields at which this phenomenon first sets in, that is, for fields just above those corresponding to the horizontal section of the current versus potential curve shown in Fig. 3($b$), the negative particle is far more effective in producing ionization by collision than is the positive ion. Hence, the concept of ionization by collision of negative ions can be tested by confining measurements to fields which are relatively low, yet large enough to produce some ionization by collision. Using a pair of parallel plates adjustable as to distance of separation, and using X-rays as a source of uniform ionization, Townsend[12] secured sufficient data to plot numerous curves similar to those reproduced in Fig. 8. Curves were obtained not only for various distances between plates, but also for various gas pressures and various degrees of original ionization. The theory was then tested by using experimental values of $i/i_0$ and $d$ in the equation

$$i = i_0 \frac{\epsilon^{\alpha d} - 1}{\alpha d}$$

and calculating the value of $\alpha$. The fact that $\alpha$ is found to be constant for any one gas under a particular pressure and field strength, regardless of the degree of ionization and of the distance between plates, shows that the theoretical equation fits the experimental curves. As one would suspect, $\alpha$ does depend upon the pressure of the gas and upon the electric field strength.

Another method of testing the collision theory and of determining the value of $\alpha$, a method more convenient and more accurate than that utilizing uniform volume ionization, is one in which all of the original negative ions are formed photoelectrically at the negative electrode. It has been shown that under this condition

$$i = i_0 \epsilon^{\alpha d}$$

If measurements are made for two different plate spacings $d_1$ and $d_2$, using the same electric field strength and the same original ionization in each case, the two corresponding currents are given by

$$i_1 = i_0 \epsilon^{\alpha d_1} \qquad \text{and} \qquad i_2 = i_0 \epsilon^{\alpha d_2}$$

Dividing one of these equations by the other,

$$\frac{i_1}{i_2} = \epsilon^{\alpha(d_1 - d_2)}$$

Using the observed ratio of currents and the difference of the observed distances between plates in the two cases, one can calculate the constant $\alpha$. For any given gas at a given pressure and field strength, the value found by this method agrees with that found by the uniform ionization method.

Experiment shows that the quantity $\alpha$ varies with pressure and field strength in such a manner that the ratio $\alpha/p$ is some function of the ratio $E/p$, where $p$ is the pressure of the gas and $E$ is the electric field strength applied across the gas. That is, specification of the ratio $E/p$ determines completely the ratio $\alpha/p$. The data[11] in Table I are taken at several different pressures and field strengths so chosen as to bring out this functional relationship. Many data[11] of this character led Townsend to write the functional relationship

$$\frac{\alpha}{p} = f\left(\frac{E}{p}\right)$$

TABLE I

Experimental values of $\alpha$ for various pressures of hydrogen subjected to various field strengths. Pressures are in mm. of Hg; field strengths are in volts/cm.

| $p$ | $E$ | $\alpha$ |
|---|---|---|
| 8 | 1050 | 14.8 |
| 4 | 525 | 7.4 |
| 2 | 262 | 3.7 |

where the form of the function $f$ is undetermined. One can best test this general relationship by plotting values of $\alpha/p$ against corresponding values of $E/p$ for any given gas. If the functional relationship holds, then the individual data should fall on a smooth curve regardless of the values of pressure and field strength at which they are taken. Townsend's[12] test of this relationship is reproduced in Fig. 9. This curve was actually continued up to field strengths some six times the largest shown here, and the additional points were found to fall equally well on a smooth curve. More recently Sanders[13] has made a far more accurate and extensive test of this relationship, and found it to hold quite accurately. Whereas Townsend's measurements were all made at or near atmospheric pressure, Sanders' observations were made at pressures of 1 mm. of Hg and 380 mm. of Hg.

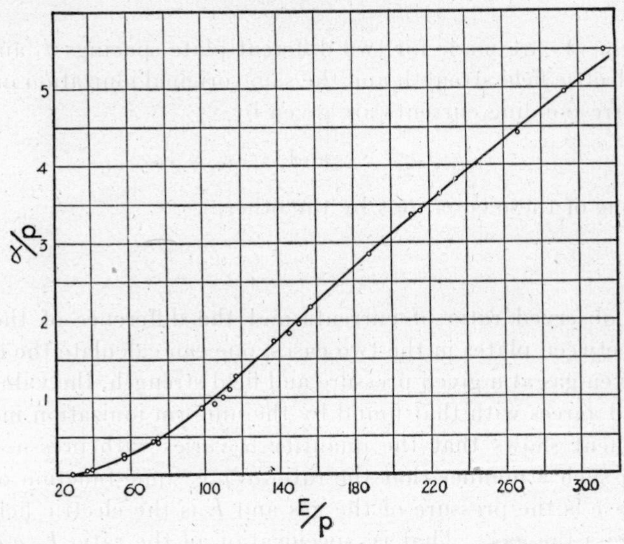


FIG. 9.—Test for a functional relationship between the quantities $\alpha/p$ and $E/p$.

The existence of this functional relationship was regarded as strong evidence in favor of the concept of ionization by collision, for it can be argued on quite general grounds that one would expect such a relationship. The argument can be made as follows: When a negative ion moves through a gas under the action of an electric field, it collides with a number of neutral molecules, some of which become ionized as a result of the collision. One would expect the fraction of collisions resulting in ionization to depend upon the energy of the ion at impact. At any rate, as long as the gas pressure and the field are so related that the energy of impact is a certain definite

[13] F. H. Sanders, *Phys. Rev.*, **41**, 667 (1932); **44**, 1020 (1933).

value, one would certainly expect the fraction of collisions resulting in ionization to be constant, independent of the individual values of pressure and field. Now the energy of impact is determined by the field strength and the mean free path of the ion; it is proportional to the product of these. Since on the kinetic theory of gases the mean free path of a molecule or of an ion is inversely proportional to the pressure, that is, inversely proportional to the number of molecules per unit volume, it follows that the energy acquired by an ion between impacts is directly proportional to the field strength and inversely proportional to the pressure. That is, the energy of impact is proportional to $E/p$. Then since the fraction of collisions resulting in ionization is a function of the energy of impact, it follows that this fraction is a function of the ratio $E/p$. But the quantity $\alpha$, the number of collisions resulting in ionization per centimeter length of path, is proportional both to the fraction of collisions resulting in ionization and to the total number of collisions made per centimeter of path. The number of collisions per centimeter of path is proportional to the pressure. It therefore follows that $\alpha$ is proportional to $p$ and also to some function of $E/p$. That is,

$$\alpha = pf\left(\frac{E}{p}\right) \quad \text{or} \quad \frac{\alpha}{p} = f\left(\frac{E}{p}\right)$$

wherein the factor of proportionality is absorbed in the function $f$. This is precisely the relationship found to exist.

Nothing has been said as yet concerning the form of the function $f$; as far as the above argument goes, it is unrestricted. It would be possible to determine the form empirically from an experimental curve such as that shown in Fig. 9, except that the curve should of course extend over a wider range of field strength. Sanders[13] obtained empirically a simple exponential function which fitted well over a restricted range, but it failed to fit when the range of $E/p$ was extended. Several theoretical developments[14] have been made. Townsend[11] deduced a simple exponential relationship, but it does not hold over an extensive range. Townsend had supposed that the negative particle responsible for ionization by collision was a negative ion, not a free electron. It has since been found that the ionizing particle is the electron, entirely unattached to any atom or molecule. With this in mind, and assuming a Maxwellian distribution of electron energies, and taking into account the energy loss of the electron per collision as well as the probability that a collision will result in ionization, it is possible to deduce[14] theoretically the form of this function on modern concepts. The result is a relatively complex expression which, at high values of $E/p$, reduces to the

[14] L. B. Loeb, *Fundamental Processes of Electrical Discharge in Gases* (New York: John Wiley & Sons, 1939), pp. 336–407.

original Townsend exponential form as an approximation. It is known that even the more general form does not hold accurately under all conditions.

Let us now consider, with Townsend, the possibility of ionization by collision of positive ions with neutral molecules. Although it seemed certain that the initial rise in the current versus potential curve of Fig. 3(*b*) in that region just above the long horizontal section was brought about mainly through ionization by collision of negative particles, it was equally apparent that this same phenomenon could not account for the very rapid rise in current at still higher fields. It was assumed by Townsend[15,11] that in this region the positive ions in the gas become effective in producing new ions by collision. Consider a gas between two parallel plates, Fig. 10, one of which is illuminated by ultraviolet light capable of ejecting $n_0$ photo-

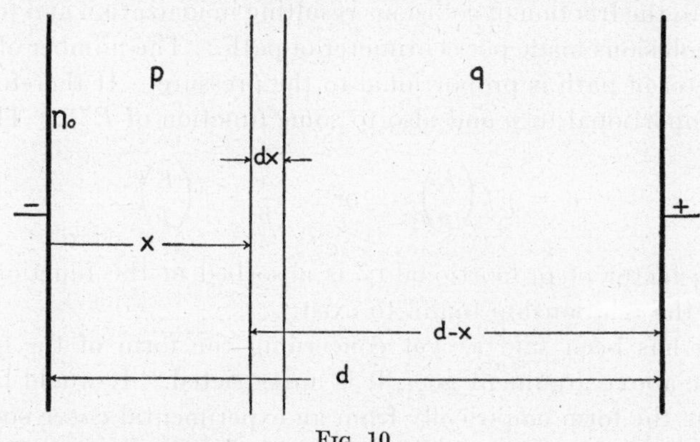


Fig. 10.

electrons per unit area per second from the plate. Let the quantity $\alpha$ have the same significance as it had in the discussion of ionization by collision of negative ions only. Let $\beta$ represent the number of new pairs of ions formed by collision per centimeter travel of a positive ion through the gas. As the original negative ions given off at the negative plate proceed toward the positive plate, they produce $\alpha$ new negative and $\alpha$ new positive ions per centimeter of travel. The newly formed negative ions, as well as the original, proceed toward the positive plate, producing more new ions on their journey. The newly formed positive ions proceed toward the negative plate, producing $\beta$ new negative and $\beta$ new positive ions per centimeter of their travel. One desires to find how many negative ions, due to all kinds of ionization, reach the positive plate per second. Or one might equally well find the total number of positive ions reaching the negative plate per second.

[15] J. S. Townsend, *Electrician*, **50,** 971 (1903); Phil. Mag. **6,** 598 (1903).

Referring to Fig. 10, let there be $p$ pairs of ions formed per second per unit area of plate by collisions of both negative and positive ions between the negative plate and a plane $x$ distant from this plate. And let there be $q$ pairs of ions formed per second per unit area of plate by both processes within the region $(d - x)$. The total number of negative ions $n$ reaching unit area of the positive plate per second is then

$$n = n_0 + p + q$$

The number of negative ions passing through unit area of the element $dx$ per second is $(n_0 + p)$, while the number of positive ions passing through this element per second is $q$. Recalling the physical significance of the quantities $\alpha$ and $\beta$, it is clear that these ions produce by collisions within the element $dx$ a number of new ions each second given by

$$dp = (n_0 + p)\alpha\, dx + q\beta\, dx$$

Solving the previous equation for $q$ and substituting the value in this equation,

$$dp = (n_0 + p)(\alpha - \beta)dx + n\beta\, dx$$

This can be written

$$\frac{dp}{(n_0 + p)(\alpha - \beta) + n\beta} = dx$$

Integrating each side of this equation,

$$\frac{1}{\alpha - \beta} \log\,[(n_0 + p)(\alpha - \beta) + n\beta] = x + \log A$$

where log $A$ is a constant of integration. Taking the antilog of each side,

$$(n_0 + p)(\alpha - \beta) + n\beta = A^{(\alpha-\beta)}\epsilon^{(\alpha-\beta)x}$$

or

$$n_0 + p = \frac{A^{(\alpha-\beta)}}{\alpha - \beta}\,\epsilon^{(\alpha-\beta)x} - \frac{n\beta}{\alpha - \beta}$$

Now it is obvious that when $x = 0$, $p = 0$. Therefore

$$n_0 = \frac{A^{(\alpha-\beta)}}{\alpha - \beta} - \frac{n\beta}{\alpha - \beta} \qquad \text{or} \qquad \frac{A^{(\alpha-\beta)}}{\alpha - \beta} = n_0 + \frac{n\beta}{\alpha - \beta}$$

Substituting this in the equation above,

$$n_0 + p = \left(n_0 + \frac{n\beta}{\alpha - \beta}\right)\epsilon^{(\alpha-\beta)x} - \frac{n\beta}{\alpha - \beta}$$

Again it is obvious that when $x = d$, $(n_0 + p) = n$, for under this condition $q = 0$. Therefore

$$n = \left(n_0 + \frac{n\beta}{\alpha - \beta}\right)\epsilon^{(\alpha-\beta)d} - \frac{n\beta}{\alpha - \beta}$$

Solving this explicitly for the quantity $n$,

$$n = n_0 \frac{(\alpha - \beta)\epsilon^{(\alpha-\beta)d}}{\alpha - \beta\epsilon^{(\alpha-\beta)d}}$$

Since the actual current density $i$ and the saturation current density $i_0$ are proportional to $n$ and $n_0$, respectively, this may be written

$$i = i_0 \frac{(\alpha - \beta)\epsilon^{(\alpha-\beta)d}}{\alpha - \beta\epsilon^{(\alpha-\beta)d}}$$

This is the complete Townsend equation, deduced nearly 40 years ago.[15]

This expression can be checked against experimental data by observing the currents produced under various degrees of original ionization at the negative plate, and under various distances $d$ between plates. Since $\alpha$ and $\beta$ are functions of the field strength and the gas pressure, both of these quantities must be kept constant while securing the data. The effect of the intensity of original ionization can be tested by observing values of the ratio $i/i_0$ for various intensities of ultraviolet light falling on the negative plate. The current $i$ is measured while there is applied a high field, the field chosen for making the test. Current $i_0$ is measured while a much smaller field is applied, a field sufficient to draw saturation current and yet not sufficient to cause any ionization by collision. It is found that the ratio $i/i_0$ is independent of the intensity of original ionization, as is predicted by the Townsend equation. That the variation of current with the distance between plates is also in accord with this equation is evident from the data reproduced[16,11] in Table II.

TABLE II

Comparison of the calculated and observed variation of current with changes of distance between plates. The data are for air at a pressure of 4 mm. of Hg, subjected to a field of 700 volts/cm. The values of the ionization coefficients used are $\alpha = 8.16$ and $\beta = 0.0067$

| $d$ in mm. | 2 | 3 | 4 | 5 | 6 | 7 | 8 |
|---|---|---|---|---|---|---|---|
| $i$ observed | 5.12 | 11.4 | 26.7 | 61 | 148 | 401 | 1500 |
| $i$ calculated from $i = i_0\epsilon^{\alpha d}$ | 5.11 | 11.6 | 26.1 | 59 | 133 | 301 | 680 |
| $i$ calculated from $i = i_0 \frac{(\alpha - \beta)\epsilon^{(\alpha-\beta)d}}{\alpha - \beta\epsilon^{(\alpha-\beta)d}}$ | 5.11 | 11.6 | 26.5 | 62 | 149 | 399 | 1544 |

[16] J. S. Townsend and H. E. Hurst, *Phil. Mag.*, **8**, 738 (1904).

Included in this table are the currents calculated on the supposition that the entire effect is due to ionization by collision of negative ions only. For this case $i = i_0\epsilon^{\alpha d}$. Although currents calculated from this expression agree with those observed for the smaller spacings between plates, there are large discrepancies at the higher plate spacings. On the other hand, when the currents are calculated from the complete Townsend expression, that taking account of ionization by positive as well as negative ions, the values agree well with those observed. Townsend[11] presented many other data of this character in support of this equation and the concept on which it is founded. The constant $\beta$ varies with both field and pressure, as does $\alpha$. The ratio $\beta/p$ turns out to be a function of $E/p$ only, just as did the ratio $\alpha/p$. In more recent years an abundance of more precise data has been obtained. These data have been well summarized by Loeb.[14] The equation certainly leads to ionization currents in essential agreement with experiment.

In spite of the apparent agreement between theory and experimental data, physicists have come to doubt seriously the entire correctness of the Townsend concept of ionization by collision. The doubt is cast upon the role played by the positive ions, not upon that played by the negative. It is certain that ionization by collision of negative particles, as conceived by Townsend, is the primary process in such phenomena, although it has turned out to be the electron rather than the negative ion that is the active particle. The role played by the positive ions is questioned, not because it fails to lead to the correct manner of increase of current with field, but because the physical process itself seems quite improbable at the lower fields for which it is necessary to suppose it exists. In many cases it appears[14,17] that this secondary phenomenon becomes effective at values of $E/p$ so low that the potential drop per mean free path in the gas is only a fraction of a volt. Under such conditions the fraction of positive ions which would have actual free paths long enough to permit these ions to gain an energy equal to the ionization potential is exceedingly small, so small that the probability of the process occurring is negligible. Furthermore, there are[18] recent experiments which show that positive ions do not ionize perceptibly until they attain energies many times the ionization potential of the gas. Whereas the ionization potential of a gas is of the order of 15 electron volts, a positive ion is found not to ionize most gases appreciably until it attains an energy of the order of 300 volts. The required positive ion energy is somewhat lower, about 60 volts, for ionization of some of the inert gases. Since there is such a small chance of a positive ion acquiring in one free

[17] J. J. Thomson and G. P. Thomson, *Conduction of Electricity Through Gases* (3rd ed.; London: Cambridge University Press, 1933), Vol. II, p. 516.

[18] L. B. Loeb, *Rev. Mod. Phys.*, **8**, 267 (1936).

path even the energy equivalent to the ionization potential, and since in order to produce appreciable ionization it must actually acquire an energy far larger than this, it appears impossible to regard ionization by positive ions as an important process in ordinary discharge phenomena. These same objections cannot be raised against the concept of ionization by collision of negative particles, even though this phenomenon sets in at still lower values of $E/p$. Under normal circumstances it is the free electron that produces ionization by collision, and the electron has a mean free path enough longer than that of a molecular ion to allow it to gain the energy required to ionize. Furthermore, experiment shows that electrons with energies only slightly greater than the ionization potential of a gas are capable of producing ionization, whereas positive ions must have much greater energies.

There have been suggested several alternate concepts[14,18] to displace that of ionization by positive ion collision. It is possible that by a photoelectric effect the radiation from the gas may produce additional electrons either at the cathode or in the gas itself. It is possible that additional electrons may be freed at the cathode surface or in the gas by the action of metastable atoms. Or it is possible that positive ions formed in the gas by electron collision may free additional electrons from the cathode when they impinge upon this electrode. In fact this latter concept was suggested early by Townsend[11] himself, but discarded in favor of that of ionization by collision. It has since been urged, however, by Thomson[17] and many others[14,18] as the more probable of the two. Again following Townsend, let $\gamma$ represent the number of electrons freed at the cathode per positive ion bombarding this electrode, and let $\alpha$ have the same significance as it has had heretofore. It has already been shown that if there are $n_0$ electrons liberated per unit area per second at the negative electrode, $n_0\epsilon^{\alpha d}$ electrons will reach the positive plate. It is clear that $n_0(\epsilon^{\alpha d} - 1)$ of these were formed by collision in the gas. Then this also represents the number of positive ions formed in the gas. When these strike the cathode there will be liberated $\gamma n_0(\epsilon^{\alpha d} - 1)$ additional electrons. These, multiplying through ionization by collision, will account for an additional number $\gamma n_0(\epsilon^{\alpha d} - 1)\epsilon^{\alpha d}$ reaching the positive plate. Since $\gamma n_0(\epsilon^{\alpha d} - 1)(\epsilon^{\alpha d} - 1)$ of these were formed by collision, there will be this many new positive ions to bombard the cathode. Thus the process continues. If $n$ be the total number of electrons arriving per second per unit area of the positive plate, one can write

$$\begin{aligned} n &= n_0\epsilon^{\alpha d} + \gamma n_0(\epsilon^{\alpha d} - 1)\epsilon^{\alpha d} + \gamma^2 n_0(\epsilon^{\alpha d} - 1)^2\epsilon^{\alpha d} + \cdots \\ &= n_0\epsilon^{\alpha d}[1 + \gamma(\epsilon^{\alpha d} - 1) + \gamma^2(\epsilon^{\alpha d} - 1)^2 + \cdots] \\ &= n_0 \frac{\epsilon^{\alpha d}}{1 - \gamma(\epsilon^{\alpha d} - 1)} \end{aligned}$$

or in terms of current density,

$$i = i_0 \frac{\epsilon^{\alpha d}}{1 - \gamma(\epsilon^{\alpha d} - 1)}$$

This expression is quite similar in form to that resulting from the concept of ionization by positive ion collision. The constant $\alpha$ is called the first Townsend coefficient; $\gamma$ is known as the second Townsend coefficient. By proper choice of these constants this equation can be made to fit experimental data fully as well as did the original Townsend expression; but it fits no better. The two equations are so nearly alike in form that it is impossible to distinguish between them on the basis of present experimental data on the manner of variation of current. But nearly all auxiliary data seem to support the second concept, that of electron emission at the cathode due to positive ion bombardment rather than that of ionization by positive ion collision. This concept has been strengthened greatly in recent years by the direct observation that electrons are freed from metal surfaces by bombardment of positive ions.[19,20] The weight of evidence is heavily in favor of this concept. Still another concept leads to an expression of essentially the same form as those deduced on the suppositions of ionization by positive ion collision and of positive ion bombardment of the cathode. This other concept is that the additional electrons are freed from the cathode by the photoelectric effect of radiation excited in the ionized gas. The similarity of form resulting from the various concepts of what contributes to the second Townsend coefficient has made it impossible to distinguish with certainty among the concepts. The original Townsend concept of ionization by positive ion collision is ruled out on other grounds. It is probable that several of the other phenomena contribute in varying degrees, with the likelihood that the release of electrons by positive ion bombardment of the cathode may be the predominating factor.

*Sparking Potentials.*—Townsend[15] pointed out many years ago that his theory of ionization by collision of both negative and positive ions led immediately to a theory of sparking potentials at least closely in agreement with fact. It has been shown that for plane parallel electrodes sufficiently close together that the electric field between them is essentially uniform, the theory of ionization by collision of both negative and positive ions leads to the expression

$$i = i_0 \frac{(\alpha - \beta)\epsilon^{(\alpha-\beta)d}}{\alpha - \beta\epsilon^{(\alpha-\beta)d}}$$

[19] M. L. E. Oliphant, *Proc. Roy. Soc.*, A, **127**, 373 (1930); **132**, 631 (1931).

[20] J. J. Thomson and G. P. Thomson, *Conduction of Electricity Through Gases* (3rd ed.; London: Cambridge University Press, 1933), Vol. II, pp. 206–218.

where $\alpha$ and $\beta$ are the first and second Townsend coefficients and where $d$ is the distance between electrodes. For a given field strength and a fixed pressure, this current increases as the distance between electrodes is increased. The data in Table II show this expected increase. As the distance between plates is increased the denominator of the above expression becomes smaller; it approaches zero for some particular value of $d$. Thus the current continues to grow, more and more rapidly as $d$ increases, finally approaching infinity for some particular value of plate separation. Because of resistance in the circuit the observed current never becomes truly infinite, but it does increase to a value many millions of times $i_0$. The plate spacing for which the current approaches this large value was interpreted by Townsend as the sparking distance corresponding to that potential applied between electrodes. Theoretically, sparking will occur when the demoninator of the expression for the current becomes zero, that is, when

$$\alpha = \beta\epsilon^{(\alpha-\beta)d_s}$$

where $d_s$ is now written for $d$ because this particular value of plate spacing represents the theoretical sparking distance. Taking the logarithm of each side of this equation and solving for $d_s$,

$$d_s = \frac{1}{\alpha - \beta} \log \frac{\alpha}{\beta}$$

If $E$ be the field strength maintained between plates, and if $V_s$ be the sparking potential, then

$$V_s = d_s E = \frac{E}{\alpha - \beta} \log \frac{\alpha}{\beta}$$

Having already determined experimentally the values of $\alpha$ and $\beta$ pertaining to the gas pressure and field strength used, the numerical value of the sparking potential can be calculated. This can be compared with the directly measured sparking potential. The close agreement between calculated and observed sparking potentials is illustrated by the data[11] in Table III. Equally good agreement has been found[11] for the sparking potentials in hydrogen, nitrogen, carbon dioxide, and argon.

Such striking agreement between calculated and observed sparking potentials would seem at first to confirm convincingly the Townsend theory of ionization by collision of both negative and positive ions. Such is not necessarily the case, however. The mere fact that a theory leads to essentially correct numerical results does not necessarily prove the correctness of the underlying physical concept. It has already been shown that

TABLE III

A comparison of calculated and observed sparking potentials for air at various pressures. Field strengths are given in volts/cm., pressures in mm. of Hg, and sparking potentials in volts

| $E$ | $p$ | $V_s$ calculated | $V_s$ observed |
|---|---|---|---|
| 1050 | 8 | 803 | 803 |
| 1400 | 8 | 601 | 603 |
| 1050 | 6 | 601 | 604 |
| 700 | 4 | 610 | 615 |
| 1050 | 4 | 477 | 480 |
| 525 | 2 | 481 | 488 |
| 700 | 2 | 403 | 407 |
| 350 | 1 | 395 | 398 |
| 437 | 1 | 364 | 365 |
| 350 | .66 | 338 | 340 |
| 437 | .66 | 335 | 336 |

it is unnecessary to postulate ionization by positive ion collisions to interpret quantitatively the rapid rise in current at high field strengths. This phenomenon was interpreted equally well by supposing the existence of ionization by collision of negative electrons only, and by supposing that additional electrons were freed from the cathode by positive ion bombardment of this electrode. This concept led to the expression

$$i = i_0 \frac{\epsilon^{\alpha d}}{1 - \gamma(\epsilon^{\alpha d} - 1)}$$

where $\gamma$ represents the number of electrons freed per positive ion striking the cathode. This concept also leads to a theory of sparking potentials. Arguing as before, a spark should take place when the denominator becomes zero, that is, when

$$1 = \gamma(\epsilon^{\alpha d_s} - 1)$$

Here again $d_s$ has been written for $d$, for this particular plate spacing represents the theoretical sparking distance. Since the quantity $\epsilon^{\alpha d_s}$ is usually quite large as compared to unity, this condition is frequently written in the approximate form $1 = \gamma\epsilon^{\alpha d_s}$. If one solves the exact expression for $\epsilon^{\alpha d_s}$, takes the logarithm of each side, and then solves for the sparking distance, he obtains

$$d_s = \frac{1}{\alpha} \log \frac{1 + \gamma}{\gamma}$$

The sparking potential $V_s$ is then given by

$$V_s = \frac{E}{\alpha} \log \frac{1 + \gamma}{\gamma}.$$

When experimentally determined values of $\alpha$ and $\gamma$ are used to calculate sparking potentials, the numerical agreement is fully as good as that resulting from calculations based upon Townsend's original concept. The theory just discussed is much preferred, however, because of auxiliary data bearing on the fundamental concepts involved.

In quite recent years it has been shown that the spark discharge between parallel electrodes is by no means as simple as it here appears, and that neither of the simple theories of sparking potentials leads to a truly definite value for the sparking potential. It has been argued[21,22] convincingly that the condition we have set for the theoretical sparking potential represents in reality only the onset of a condition of instability, a condition which ultimately leads to a spark. It represents only a threshold below which a spark cannot pass. Beyond this condition a spark may pass immediately, or one may pass after considerable lapse of time, depending largely upon the probability of certain unusually large pulses of ionization taking place in the gas. In fact, it appears physically that the sparking potential is not a well-defined quantity; if one is willing to wait longer for the spark it may be produced by a lower potential. If this general interpretation be correct, then it is remarkable that values calculated in the usual way agree so closely with observed sparking potentials. This agreement certainly means that the spark actually takes place at a potential but little different from that representing the onset of the condition of instability; the breakdown always occurs within a very narrow range of potentials, a region bounded on the lower side by that value calculated theoretically. The spark discharge, even for the simple case of parallel plate electrodes, is a very complex phenomenon. The many details bearing on the phenomenon have been discussed admirably by Loeb.[22] This author has also given an excellent bibliography of recent work in the field.

Only the most basic features of the simplest type of spark discharge, that between parallel plate electrodes sufficiently close together that the intervening electric field can be considered uniform, have been discussed here. The problem of the spark discharge between points, or between a point and a plane, or between two spheres, is greatly complicated by the nonuniformity of the electric field. The basic features of such discharges[18,21–23] are the same as those which we have already discussed, but their application is much more difficult. There are available tables[24]

[21] L. B. Loeb and A. F. Kip, *Jour. App. Phys.*, **10**, 142 (1939).

[22] L. B. Loeb, *Fundamental Processes of Electrical Discharge in Gases* (New York: John Wiley & Sons, 1939), pp. 408–559.

[23] J. J. Thomson and G. P. Thomson, *Conduction of Electricity Through Gases* (3rd ed.; London: Cambridge University Press, 1933), Vol. II, pp. 470–573.

[24] *International Critical Tables* (New York: McGraw-Hill, 1929), Vol. VI, pp. 79–80.

giving the potential differences required to cause a spark between spherical electrodes placed various distances apart. These values are known to within a few percent, and they are frequently used in the actual measurement of high potentials. But these tabular values have been observed directly, not calculated from any theory. Such data show that it requires a potential difference of approximately 30,000 volts to produce a spark across a gap one centimeter long between smooth spheres in air at atmospheric pressure. The exact value of the potential required depends upon the temperature, upon the diameter of the spheres, and upon whether one of the two spheres is grounded.

## 2. THE RECOMBINATION OF IONS

It has already been pointed out that ions formed in a gas have a tendency to recombine. The ions no doubt share in the thermal agitation of the molecules, and in their repeated thermal excursions oppositely charged ions frequently come sufficiently close to one another that their electrical attraction causes them to reunite. It has already been argued that the number of recombinations $R$ which take place per second per unit volume of gas should be given by

$$R = \alpha n^2$$

where $n$ represents the number of pairs of ions per unit volume and where $\alpha$ is a constant called the coefficient of recombination. This constant has no relation to the Townsend coefficient of ionization which was represented by the same symbol.

The fact that recombination starts just as soon as there are ions present in a gas means that when an ionizing agent is turned on a gas the ion concentration will not continue to grow indefinitely, but will gradually build up to such a value that the rate of recombination is just equal to the rate at which new ions are being formed by the ionizing agent. If $dn$ represents the increase in ion concentration which occurs in time $dt$, and if $q$ represents the number of new pairs of ions formed per second per unit volume by the activating agent, then

$$dn = (q - \alpha n^2)dt$$

or

$$\frac{dn}{q - \alpha n^2} = dt$$

If this be integrated over the time interval $t$, during which interval the ion concentration builds up from its original value zero to some value $n$, one obtains

$$n = \sqrt{\frac{q}{\alpha}} \frac{\epsilon^{2\sqrt{q\alpha}\,t} - 1}{\epsilon^{2\sqrt{q\alpha}\,t} + 1}$$

This expression gives the ion concentration existing at any time $t$ after the ionizing agent has been turned on. The concentration starts at zero and gradually builds up at a continually decreasing rate, finally approaching a fixed value $\sqrt{q/\alpha}$ after a sufficient length of time. This represents an equilibrium condition; the rate of recombination of ions is just equal to the rate at which new ions are being formed. This theoretical relationship can be tested experimentally by making measurements of $n$ simultaneously with the shutting off of the ionizing agent at the end of various times $t$. The quantity $q$ is measured by drawing saturation current from the gas. Experiment shows that the theoretial relationship describes rather accurately the growth of the ion concentration. The time required for the ion concentration to approach fairly closely its equilibrium value is normally of the order of a few seconds.

It also requires an appreciable length of time for the ions to disappear by recombination after the ionizing agent is turned off. If $dn$ again represents the increase in ion concentration in time $dt$ after the ionizing agent has ceased to act, then one can write

$$dn = -\alpha n^2 dt$$

the negative sign appearing because the remainder of the right hand side of the equation represents a decrease rather than an increase of ions. If this be written

$$\frac{dn}{n^2} = -\alpha\, dt$$

and integrated over the time interval $t$ after the ionizing agent ceases, one obtains

$$\frac{1}{n} - \frac{1}{n_0} = \alpha t$$

where $n_0$ represents the ion concentration at the instant the ionizing agent was turned off, and where $n$ represents the concentration still remaining $t$ seconds later. If this is written

$$n = \frac{n_0}{1 + n_0 \alpha t}$$

it is apparent that the ion concentration gradually approaches zero after a sufficient length of time. This expression can be tested experimentally by measuring $n$ at various times $t$ after the ionizing agent has been turned off. That the form of the expression is correct has been proved by many such experiments. It may take a few seconds or a few minutes for a majority of the ions to disappear, depending upon whether the original ionization $n_0$ was large or small.

Many methods have been devised for measuring the coefficient of recombination $\alpha$. These have been discussed in detail elsewhere.[10] One of the earliest methods,[25] and one of the simplest, though certainly not one of the most accurate, is illustrated in Fig. 11. Gas passing continuously through the system is ionized in the region $A$ by X-rays. This ionized gas then passes with a uniform velocity through a tube having a series of

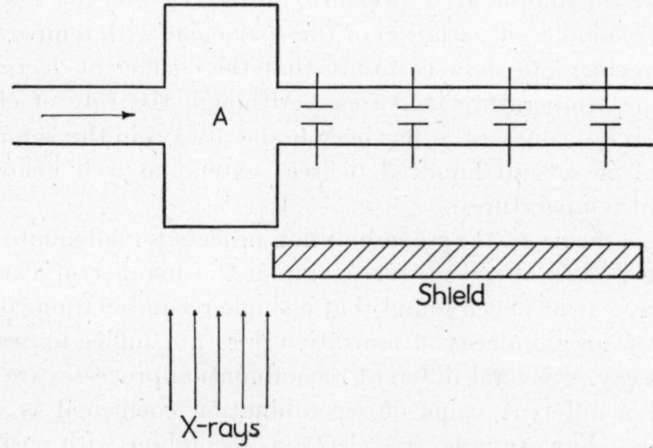


FIG. 11.—Illustrating the Townsend method of determining the rate of recombination of ions.

electrodes placed along its length. If saturation current is drawn from first one pair of electrodes and then another, the respective currents will be proportional to the ion concentrations still existing at the times the gas reaches the various pairs of electrodes. These times can be calculated from the measured velocity of the gas. Using these data in the expression

$$n = \frac{n_0}{1 + n_0 \alpha t}$$

the coefficient of recombination $\alpha$ can be calculated. The correctness of the analytical expression describing the decay of ionization is judged from the constancy of values obtained at different times. Early data[26] indicated that the theoretical expression did describe the decay properly and that the value of $\alpha$ was approximately $1.6 \times 10^{-6}$ for gases at near atmospheric

[25] E. Rutherford, *Phil. Mag.*, **44**, 422 (1897); **47**, 109 (1899).
[26] J. S. Townsend, *Phil. Trans. Roy. Soc.*, **193**, 157 (1900).

pressure. More recent data[27] have yielded values agreeing essentially with this. Different gases have somewhat different coefficients, the values usually falling within a range of a factor of 2.

More recent experimental methods of studying recombination have been summarized by Loeb,[27] and the general findings have been discussed by Thomson[10] and by Loeb.[27] The coefficient is affected greatly by the presence of dust particles or minute quantities of impurities in the gas. Although various experimental findings are far from consistent, it is certain that the coefficient decreases rather rapidly with decreases in pressure below atmospheric. As the pressure is increased above approximately 1 atmosphere the coefficient also decreases. Thus the coefficient of recombination is a maximum at a pressure in the vicinity of 1 atmosphere. Studies of the manner of variation of the coefficient with temperature are in sufficient agreement to show certainly that the coefficient decreases rather rapidly as the temperature increases. Although the rate of change with temperature is not constant, it has been found always in the same direction over a range of several hundred degrees extending well below and well above normal temperatures.

The simple theory of the recombination process is inadequate to explain many of the details observed, for example, the manner of variation of $\alpha$ with pressure. It has been found that a single recombination constant $\alpha$ in the expression for the decay of ionization does not suffice to describe accurately the decay. Several different recombination processes are now recognized,[27] and a different value of recombination coefficient is required to describe each. For example, free electrons recombine with positive ions at a different rate than do negative ions. Furthermore, the electron recombination depends appreciably upon the energies given the electrons when they are formed by the ionizing agent. Also, different methods of ionization produce different relative concentrations of positive and negative particles at different places in the gas, and the recombination is affected by this distribution. The several recombination processes, together with modifications of the simple theory necessary to interpret them, have been discussed in detail by Loeb.[27] In many cases several of these processes go on simultaneously. One process may predominate near the beginning of the decay of ionization by recombination, while another may be the more important near the end. It is, therefore, not surprising that one often finds a significant variation of the constant $\alpha$ during the time of decay. In view of the variety of recombination processes active, it is almost meaningless to state a value for the coefficient of recombination unless one states carefully all of the conditions under which it is observed.

[27] L. B. Loeb, *Fundamental Processes of Electrical Discharge in Gases* (New York: John Wiley & Sons, 1939), pp. 86–160.

## 3. THE MOBILITIES OF IONS

It has already been argued that an ion in an electric field should acquire a certain velocity of drift. The force exerted by the field causes the ion to be accelerated during its travel of one free path. This motion imparted by the field, and superimposed upon the much larger thermal motion, is interrupted when the ion next makes a collision. It is assumed that on the average the ion loses all of the energy imparted by the field and must start anew after each collision. There will then exist an average velocity with which the ion drifts through the gas due to the presence of the electric field. It has already been shown that this drift velocity should be proportional to the electric field applied. The average velocity of drift per unit of applied field is called the mobility of the ion.

### Experimental Methods

Numerous workers have devised a large number of methods of measuring the mobilities of ions in various gases. The early methods and results have been well summarized by Thomson,[28] while the more recent works have been covered admirably by Loeb.[29] Although many of the methods are quite interesting and ingenious, attention will be called here to but one or two which are rather typical. A majority of methods fall into one of three general classes. In one group are those which utilize a stream of gas to carry the ions in one direction while an electric field urges them in a transverse direction. These are called flow, or blast, methods. In another group are those which employ an alternating or an interrupted electric field; the distance the ions move between the known times of reversal of the field is measured. In a third group fall a number of so-called electrical shutter methods, wherein the times at which bursts of ions can enter and leave a given region are controlled electrically. Many methods might properly be placed in either of the last two groups.

Fig. 12 illustrates the essentials of a simple flow method developed and used extensively by Erikson.[30] A uniform stream of gas is caused to flow between the two parallel metal plates $A$ and $B$. A small amount of radioactive material $C$ ionizes the gas passing through an auxiliary chamber. Due to the velocity of the gas, these ions formed move out of the auxiliary chamber and into the region between $A$ and $B$. An electric field applied between these plates causes either the positive or the negative ion to move

[28] J. J. Thomson and G. P. Thomson, *Conduction of Electricity Through Gases* (3rd ed. London: Cambridge University Press, 1928), Vol. I, pp. 85–192.

[29] L. B. Loeb, *Fundamental Processes of Electrical Discharge in Gases* (New York: John Wiley & Sons, 1939), pp. 1–85.

[30] H. A. Erikson, *Phys. Rev.*, **17**, 400 (1921); **18**, 100 (1921); **20**, 117 (1922); **24**, 502 (1924); **26**, 465 (1925); **28**, 372 (1926); **29**, 215 (1927); **33**, 403 (1929); **34**, 635 (1929).

toward $B$. This ion is carried forward at the same time, due to the velocity of the gas. The combination of the two velocities causes the ions to move in the direction indicated. The plate $B$ is constructed with a narrow insulated electrode $D$ running crosswise of the plate. This electrode is connected to an electrometer and held at the same potential as the remainder

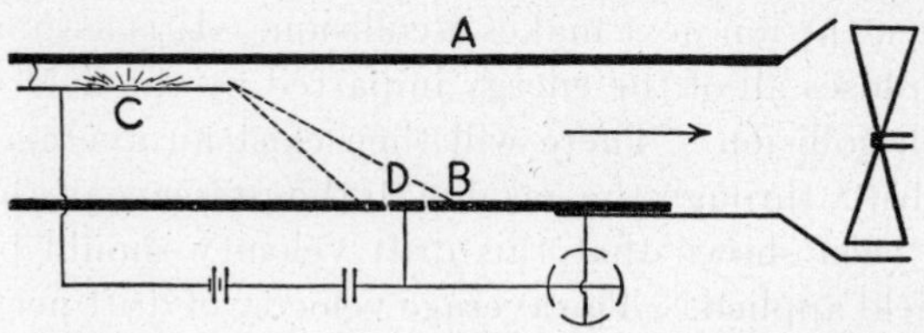


FIG. 12.—Illustrating Erikson's apparatus for determining ion mobilities.

of the plate. The position at which the ions reach the lower plate is determined by moving the entire plate longitudinally until a maximum number of ions fall upon the insulated electrode. Having located the position at which these ions fall, and knowing the velocity with which the gas is moving along the apparatus, the transverse velocity imparted to the ion by the known electric field can be calculated. Thence, the mobility of the ions

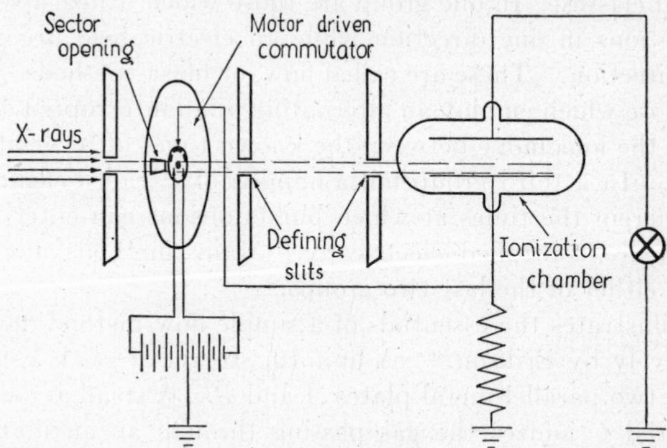


FIG. 13.—Illustrating one of the electrical shutter methods of determining ion mobilities.

is obtained by dividing this velocity by the field strength. The method is clearly applicable to the measurement of the mobility of either the positive or the negative ion; one needs only apply the electric field in the proper direction. Unfortunately, air flow methods are in general inaccurate and unreliable. Troublesome eddy currents can scarcely be avoided in such methods.

In one satisfactory alternating field method, Bradbury[31,32] utilized a narrow beam of X-rays to produce a very thin sheath of ionization within a region between two large, parallel plates. The essentials of this method are shown in Fig. 13. X-ray pulses coming through an opening in a rotating disk produce in an ionization chamber a thin sheath of ions at regular time intervals. These ions are drawn to the plates by an electric field applied intermittently by a commutator arrangement mounted on the rotating disk. After a certain interval of time the commutator reverses this electric field; the reverse field is not necessarily of the same strength as that previously applied. This all takes place during one revolution of the commutator, before the succeeding pulse of X-rays forms a new sheath of ions. It is clear that the ions will move in one direction during application of the first field. If this field is not maintained sufficiently long for all ions to reach the plate, the remaining ions are reversed in direction with reversal of the electric field. In general, therefore, the electrometer receives some negative and some positive ions. The fraction of these which are of one sign depends upon the frequency with which the disk, and hence the commutator, is rotated. For some particular frequency of rotation the current received by the electrometer is a maximum. Knowing the frequency leading to this maximum, the fraction of a period for which ions were drawn to the electrometer, the electric field applied during this interval, and the distance the ion moved during this time, it is possible to calculate the mobility of the ion. The maximum in the current versus the frequency curve is quite sharp; this leads to a well defined value for the mobility. The method has produced trustworthy results.

A number of other workers[33–38] have used some form of electrical shutter method. The basis of this method is illustrated by the method of Tyndall and Powell.[33] In Fig. 14 $A$, $B$, $C$ and $D$ represent gauze wire electrodes, and $E$ represents the final collecting electrode. Ions are brought up to $A$ by a small auxiliary field. An alternating potential applied between $A$ and $B$ allows a pulse of these ions to pass once each cycle from $A$ to $B$, and thence enter the region $BC$. At some later time, depending on the mobility of the ion and on the fixed electric field applied between $B$ and $C$, these ions arrive at $C$. The same alternating potential is applied between $C$

[31] A. M. Tyndall and G. C. Grindley, *Proc. Roy. Soc.*, A, **110**, 341 (1926).

[32] N. E. Bradbury, *Phys. Rev.*, **37**, 1311 (1931); **40**, 508, 524 (1932).

[33] A. M. Tyndall and C. F. Powell, *Proc. Roy. Soc.*, A, **129**, 162 (1929); **134**, 125 (1932); **136**, 145 (1932).

[34] C. F. Powell and L. Brata, *Proc. Roy. Soc.*, A, **138**, 117 (1932).

[35] R. J. Van de Graaff, *Phil. Mag.*, **6**, 210 (1929).

[36] N. E. Bradbury and R. A. Nielsen, *Phys. Rev.*, **49**, 388 (1936); **51**, 69 (1937).

[37] R. A. Nielsen, *Phys. Rev.*, **50**, 950 (1936).

[38] R. N. Varney, *Phys. Rev.*, **42**, 547 (1932).

and $D$ as is applied between $A$ and $B$. The pulse of ions arriving at $C$ will proceed to $D$ and thence to the collecting electrode $E$, only if the phase of the potential is the same as that at the time they passed from $A$ to $B$. Thus, ions will be collected only if they require some whole number of periods to travel between the two electrical shutters $AB$ and $CD$. One therefore measures the current to electrode $E$ for various frequencies of alternating potential applied to $AB$ and $CD$. If these currents be plotted against corresponding values of frequency, sharp maxima in current occur at those frequencies for which the ion required some whole number of periods to travel from $AB$ to $CD$. Knowing the period of the alternating potential, the distance between the electrical shutters $AB$ and $CD$, and the electric field applied between $B$ and $C$, the mobility of the ion can be calculated. Modifications of this original electrical shutter method have been used by other workers.[36,37] The method leads to well defined values for ion mobilities.

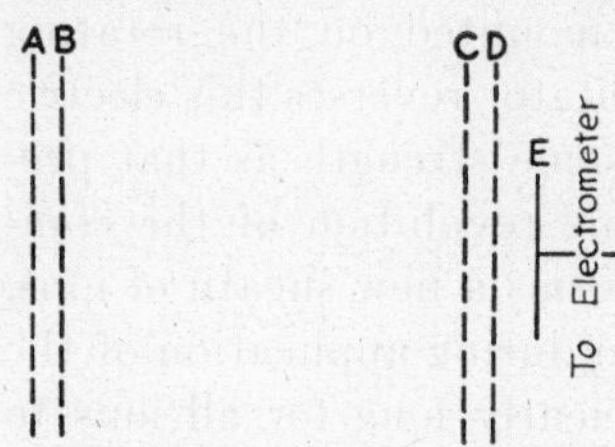


Fig. 14.—Illustrating the electrical shutter method used by Tyndall and Powell in measuring ion mobilities.

## Results and Their Interpretation

Results obtained by various methods of mobility study previous to 1930 were in general inaccurate and unreliable. Air flow methods suffered both from the effect of nonuniform flow and from the lack of a well-defined group of ions with which to work. While early alternating electric field methods were free from the first of these defects, they were subject to the latter. Most early works suffered also from failure to realize the marked changes in ion mobility produced by the presence of water vapor or other impurities in the gas being studied. Even minute traces of some impurities, traces so small that they are difficult or impossible to eliminate, affect the mobility seriously.[39,29] It was recognized rather early that the positive ion showed an aging affect; the mobility of the ion changed considerably with increases in the interval of time between formation of the ion and measurement of its mobility. As a consequence of these difficulties early values for the mobilities of ions are not at all trustworthy. Since 1930 the mobilities of a few ions in a few different gases have been obtained accurately under conditions which indicate that the values are reliable.

The magnitude of the mobility is of the order of a few centimeters per second per volt per centimeter. Erikson,[30] whose work was the most extensive and perhaps the most reliable of the earlier studies, obtained mobilities of 1.87 cm/sec/volt/cm. for both freshly formed positive and

[39] L. B. Loeb, *Phys. Rev.*, **32**, 81 (1928).

negative ions in air at atmospheric pressure and room temperature. While the negative ion retained this mobility, the positive ion had a mobility of only 1.36 after it attained an age of a few hundredths of a second. A more recent and more reliable determination[32] of the mobilities in air of ions formed in air yielded a mobility of 2.21 for the negative ion and 1.60 for the aged positive ion.

The mobility of an ion depends both upon the ion and upon the gas through which the ion moves. Hydrogen and helium ions in their respective gases have high mobilities, Bradbury[32] finding 8.2 and 17.0 cm/sec/volt/cm., respectively. Tyndall and Powell[33] found a mobility of 21.4 for helium at 76 cm. of mercury and 20° C, and this is perhaps the more reliable value. It has been shown that ion mobilities are independent of the applied electric field over a wide range of field strength. In the case of air at atmospheric pressure this range extends from less than 1 volt per cm. to 16,000 volts per cm. For hydrogen no change in mobility is observed up to 20,000 volts per cm. Some ions in certain gases do show changes of mobility at fields considerably less than these upper limits. Theoretically the mobility should change with field strength only for fields sufficiently high to give the ion, during one free path, a velocity comparable with that of thermal agitation. Theoretically the ion mobility should be inversely proportional to the concentration of gas molecules. At constant temperature it should be inversely proportional to pressure. This has been found true over a pressure range from less than 1 mm. of mercury up to 60 atmospheres. Mobility has been found to change somewhat with temperature but the change is small, even over considerable ranges of temperature, when the gaseous density is kept constant. It has been stated that the mobility of an ion depends both upon the mass of the ion and upon the gas through which the ion moves. This is shown clearly by the measurements of Tyndall and Powell[33] which are reproduced in Table IV.

TABLE IV

The mobilities of different ions in argon, neon, and helium

| Gas | Mobility of ion (cm/sec/volt/cm.) | | | |
|---|---|---|---|---|
| | Sodium | Potassium | Rubidium | Caesium |
| Argon | 3.21 | 2.77 | 2.37 | 2.23 |
| Neon | 8.87 | 7.88 | 7.08 | 6.49 |
| Helium | 23.1 | 22.3 | 20.9 | 19.2 |

In considering theoretically the motion of an ion of charge $e$ and mass $m$ in an electric field $E$, it has already been shown that on the simplest picture possible the average velocity of drift $U$ acquired by the ion is

$$U = \frac{e\tau}{2m} E = uE$$

where $u$ is by definition the mobility of the ion and where $\tau$ is the average time between collisions of the ion with gaseous molecules. If $l$ be the mean free path of the ion and $v$ the average velocity with which the ion is flying around, then the time between collisions is given by $\tau = l/v$. Since the drift velocity imparted by the electric field is small, the average velocity $v$ is essentially that of thermal agitation. Ignoring the difference between the average velocity and the root mean square velocity, $\frac{1}{2}mv^2 = \frac{3}{2}kT$. Making these substitutions for $\tau$ one finds for the ion mobility

$$u = \frac{e\tau}{2m} = \frac{e}{2m}\frac{l}{v} = \frac{el}{2\sqrt{3kTm}}$$

This simple theory could not give more than a rough approximation to the truth for several reasons. It ignores the fact that ions have a wide distribution of actual free paths and uses only the average of these. It neglects the wide distribution of velocities about the mean, and even uses the root mean square velocity in place of a mean. More serious by far, it assumes that on the average each ion loses all of its drift velocity at each collision, whereas one should consider the interchange of momentum between the ion of mass $m$ and a gaseous molecule of mass $M$. Furthermore, it ignores any electrical force between the charged ion and the neutral but polarizable molecule with which the ion collides. Taking a number of these factors into account, Langevin[40] showed in 1905 that the ion mobility should be given by

$$u = \frac{0.235\sqrt{\dfrac{M+m}{m}}}{\dfrac{\rho}{\rho_0}\sqrt{(K_0 - 1)M_0}}$$

where $\rho$ is the density of the gas, $\rho_0$ the density at 76 cm. of mercury and 0° C, $K_0$ the dielectric constant of the gas under these standard conditions, and $M_0$ the molecular weight of the gas. Loeb[41] has arrived at the same type of theoretical expression, except that the constant factor is smaller.

This theoretical expression, while by no means always accurate, has been found to work surprisingly well. For alkali ions in the pure gases A, Kr and Xe, for which the details of the theoretical development indicate that it should hold rather well, Powell and Brata[34] found that it holds well indeed. The values of the theoretical constant 0.235 they found necessary

[40] P. Langevin, *Ann. Chim. et Phys.*, **8,** 238 (1905).
[41] L. B. Loeb, *Phil. Mag.*, **48,** 446 (1924); **49,** 517 (1925).

to give the observed mobilities were 0.23, 0.24 and 0.245, respectively, for A, Kr and Xe. On the other hand, it does not hold well for Ne and He. Judging from the theoretical expression, different ions in the same gas should have mobilities proportional to $\sqrt{(M+m)/m}$; the mobility should decrease as the mass of the ion increases. Table IV shows this variation. The table shows also that the mobility of a given ion in the similar gases He, Ne and A decreases as the mass of the gaseous molecule increases. While the mobility of the ion should be affected by both the mass of the ion and that of the gaseous molecule when these masses are comparable, it is interesting to look into two limiting cases. Recalling that $M_0$ in the theoretical expression is proportional to $M$, it is clear that for very light ions in a gas composed of very heavy molecules the ion mobility should be independent of the mass of the gaseous molecule; and it should be inversely proportional to the square root of the mass of the ion. At the other extreme, all heavy ions in a very light gas should have the same mobility; the mobility is theoretically independent of the mass of the ion.

Since it has been assumed throughout that the velocity of drift acquired by the ion in an electric field of the strength commonly used is small as compared to the velocity of thermal agitation, it is interesting to compare these velocities now that measured mobilities are at hand. Taking the mobility of newly formed ions in air as 2.2 cm/sec/volt/cm., the drift velocity acquired by an ion in a field of 100 volts/cm. is 220 cm/sec. On the other hand, the root mean square velocity of thermal agitation of an oxygen molecule, or ion, at room temperature, as calculated from the relationship $\frac{1}{2}mv^2 = \frac{3}{2}kT$, is approximately $5 \times 10^4$ cm/sec. This is more than 200 times the drift velocity of an ion in a field of 100 volts/cm. The drift velocity imparted by the field constitutes, therefore, but a small directed motion superimposed upon the much larger but random motion of thermal agitation.

It has been remarked that, according to Erickson,[30] whereas the negative and positive ions newly formed in air have equal mobilities, the mobilities of the two are quite different after the ions become a few hundredths of a second old. This aging effect has been found to occur quite generally, and has been the cause of many inconsistent results reported in the literature. Not more than a decade ago there was considerable doubt among workers whether a given ion actually possessed a definite mobility. Perhaps ions of one type exhibited mobilities distributed over a considerable range.[42] The poor resolving power of early instruments made it difficult to tell whether the apparent distribution of mobilities was real or caused by the instrument. Today it seems certain[42,29] that a given ion does have a unique mobility, one that does not change with time. It has been found

[42] L. B. Loeb, *Phys. Rev.*, **38**, 1716 (1931).

that the aging of an ion takes place abruptly, not continuously. For the first few ten-thousandths of a second, depending upon the purity of the gas, all ions, both positive and negative, are found to have the same mobility. Shortly after the aging process starts one finds a few ions of a different mobility, though most of the ions still have the initial mobility. A little later a still larger fraction of the ions are found to have the new mobility. That is, the ions gradually change from one mobility to the other, but each ion makes the change abruptly. There are no intervening mobilities. The aged mobility and the time required for complete aging, that is, the time required for all ions to take on the new mobility, depend upon the nature of and the amount of impurity present in a gas.

Since simple theory indicated that the mobility of an ion should be inversely proportional to the square root of the mass of the ion, and since the ratio of mobilities for the newly formed and the aged positive ions in air was found to be $1.87/1.36 = 1.375$, Erickson[30] was led to believe that the original positive ion soon changed into a two-molecule ion. The closeness of the ratio 1.375, or 1.38 from later work,[32] to the square root of 2 indicated this doubling of the ion mass. Erickson supposed that the negative ion remained a single-molecule ion. Actually the aging process has proved far more complex than this. The difference between the mobilities of aged positive and negative ions, as well as the aging process itself, is now attributed to the presence of impurities. Since an ion in a gas at atmospheric pressure makes $10^9$ collisions per second with gas molecules, it is clear that if an impurity is present to 1 part in $10^6$ the ion will encounter this impurity on the average in $\frac{1}{1000}$ second. Either of two things may happen. First, the original ion may transfer its charge to the impurity molecule, thus forming an ion of an entirely different character. Second, the original ion may attach itself to the impurity molecule, thus forming a complex ion, again quite different from the original. It is known that transfer of charge does take place, and also that complex ions are often formed. Both processes are conditioned upon the characteristics of the impurity molecule. Some molecules are known to associate themselves readily with positive ions, some with negative, and some with neither.

A great deal of experimental data since 1930 has supported this general view. Much of this evidence has been summarized by Loeb.[29] The sign preferences shown by gaseous molecules are essentially the same as those shown by the same molecules in solution. The addition of a relatively heavy molecule which likes to associate itself with a positive ion reduces materially the mobility of the positive ion. The further addition of some lighter molecule with a stronger tendency to associate with positive ions increases the positive ion mobility. The lighter molecule has now displaced the heavier in the complex ion. The negative ion has also been found to suffer changes in mobility. For example, molecules of water or of the alcohols readily become attached to negative ions. This general view accounts readily for the difference between the aged negative and positive ion mobilities and for the change of mobility upon aging. It also accounts for the different mobilities observed by different workers for what was thought to be the same ion. There is every reason to believe that if one could obtain an absolutely pure gas an ion in this gas would have an unique mobility. Once the free electron originally formed in the ionization process combined with a molecule to form a negative ion, there would be no further change in either the positive or the negative ion mobility. In order to observe these unique mobilities one would have to work with the purest gases available, and should measure the mobility within say $10^{-4}$ seconds after ion formation in order to avoid the effect of those impurities necessarily present.

Nothing has been said yet regarding the mobility of free electrons. The free electron originally formed when a gas is ionized usually attaches itself to a neutral molecule almost immediately, thus forming a negative ion. The average time for which the electron remains free depends upon the nature of the gas and upon the pressure of the gas. At low pressures, as one might expect, it remains free longer than at high pressures. In electronegative gases such as oxygen and water vapor, this attachment takes place very soon. In certain other pure gases such as nitrogen, hydrogen, and helium,[32] the electron never does attach itself to a molecule. In these gases there is no negative ion; the negative particle remains a free electron. The mobility of free electrons is relatively great; it is thousands of times the mobility of an ion. Many early measurements of negative ion mobility gave far too high values because they failed to take into account the fact that the negative particle was a free electron during a part of the time over which its velocity was being measured. Clear-cut measurements of ion mobility must eliminate in some way the effect of the presence of these free electrons. This is often done by applying momentarily an electric field which sweeps the free electrons from the chamber. This procedure is made possible by the very high mobility of these electrons.

## 4. THE MANNER OF FORMATION OF IONS

Although some of the more general properties of ions have been discussed at some length, little has been said concerning the actual physical process by which ions are formed in a gas. Mainly for the purpose of a better understanding of phenomena to be discussed in succeeding chapters, it would be well to look briefly into the general structure of atoms and molecules, and into the physical processes by which various ionizing agents produce ions from these.

**The General Structure of Atoms**

The present purpose will be served sufficiently well by a few bare statements of present day concepts regarding atomic structure. Evidence from which these concepts came will be presented from time to time in succeeding chapters. One of the most fundamental facts of observation is that electrons, very light particles bearing a negative electrical charge, can be forced out of every known substance—out of elements and compounds, of metals and non-metals, of liquids, solids and gases. Moreover, an electron obtained from any one material by any process whatever is found to be identical with electrons obtained from any other material. It is therefore natural to assume that the atoms of every material contain one or more electrons apiece. That is, the electron is one of the building stones of which all atoms are constructed. But the atoms of matter are electrically neutral; they possess no net charge. It therefore follows that atoms must contain positive charges in addition to electrons; and these positive charges must just balance the negative charge due to the electrons.

Evidence to be presented later shows definitely that all of the positive charge associated with an atom is concentrated in a very small region called the nucleus. The diameter of this nucleus is less than 1/10,000 that of the atom itself. In spite of this, the nucleus accounts for almost the entire mass of the atom. Surrounding this nucleus are electrons, the actual number depending upon the atom being considered. The number varies from 1 for hydrogen to 92 for uranium. These are called planetary electrons, for it is conceived that these execute orbits about the central nucleus. These planetary electrons are arranged at various well-defined effective distances from the nucleus; they are arranged in so-called shells. The outermost ones are easily removed from the atom; the inner ones require a great deal more energy for their removal. Evidence will be cited later to show how many electrons are associated with a given atom, and just how many of these normally reside in each of the various shells. The energy required to dislodge any particular electron from its shell and take it sufficiently far away that it is no longer under the influence of this particular atom is known for a great majority of atoms. Such details, however, are not necessary for the present purpose; they can be deferred for the time being.

Molecules in general are made up of one, two, three or more atoms. These atoms are held together by forces which arise between the component parts of the atoms, forces which are probably of electrical or magnetic origin. In any case the molecule consists of one, two, three or more atomic nuclei fairly well bound together, these nuclei being held characteristic distances apart, and the entire configuration being surrounded by all of those planetary electrons which were previously a part of the component atoms. The outermost electrons are rather easily taken from a molecule, just as they are from an atom.

A molecule or an atom can be ionized by any process which is capable of taking away one of the planetary electrons. This is usually, though by no means always, the outermost one. This ionization results in two particles, a free negative electron and a positively charged atomic or molecular ion. There are numerous ways by which this ionization can be accomplished. Heating a gas to a high temperature produces thermal agitation sufficiently energetic to cause ionization by collision of molecules. High speed charged particles produce ionization, the charged particles knocking off electrons through the electrical forces they exert at close distances. Ultraviolet light, X-rays and gamma rays from radioactive materials likewise produce ionization, but the physical process by which this is accomplished is not obvious without further study. And lastly, the exceedingly penetrating cosmic radiation produces ionization.

**The Wilson Cloud Expansion Phenomenon**

Just before the beginning of the present century C. T. R. Wilson[43] made an interesting discovery, the importance of which to modern physics can scarcely be overestimated. It has made it possible to observe the paths of single charged particles, and has thus become indispensable in the study of many important phenomena. Among many other contributions, it has led to a clearer insight into the details of the ionization processes. It had long been known that the degree to which a region could be supersaturated with water vapor depended greatly upon the care exercised in freeing the region from such foreign bodies as dust particles. It was known that when condensation took place from a supersaturated vapor, dust particles served admirably as nuclei about which the droplets might start to form. In the absence of such particles a much greater degree of supersaturation could be attained before the onset of condensation.

Wilson made a careful study of this phenomenon, using apparatus the principle of which is illustrated in Fig. 15. A small amount of water in the space $R$ kept this region saturated with water vapor at room temperature. Any desired degree of supersaturation could be produced by abruptly moving the piston $P$ downward, thus expanding adiabatically the gas in region $R$. The abrupt lowering of temperature produced by this expansion results in a new saturated vapor pressure, one much lower than that existing just before the expansion. As a result the region $R$ becomes supersaturated unless some of the water vapor originally present condenses. Any desired

[43] C. T. R. Wilson, *Phil. Trans. Roy. Soc.*, A, **189**, 265 (1897); **192**, 403 (1899).

degree of supersaturation could be produced by increasing the volume of the region $R$ in the proper ratio. It was found that if the region were carefully freed from all foreign bodies this ratio could be made as great as 1.375 without causing condensation to set in. Under these conditions the vapor pressure after the expansion is eight times that required to saturate at the new temperature. At this degree of supersaturation a fine mist develops, regardless of how carefully the region may have been freed from dust particles. It is presumed that the small droplets constituting this mist utilize as nuclei of condensation the molecules of gas present. Some particle of finite size is necessary to serve as a nucleus. It can be shown that the vapor pressure above a convex surface of liquid is greater than that above a flat surface. The excess vapor pressure above the convex surface is, theoretically, inversely proportional to the radius of curvature of this surface. Since the vapor pressure is smaller for a large drop, a large drop might continue to grow whereas a small one would evaporate. In order to grow, a drop must start with some finite size; it therefore requires some nucleus of condensation.

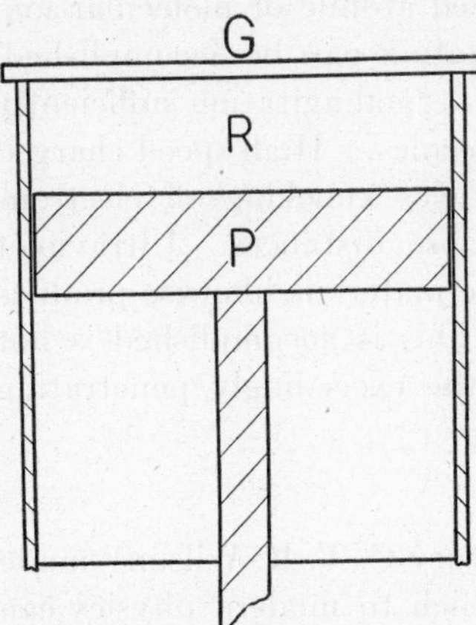


FIG. 15.—Illustrating the principle of the Wilson cloud expansion chamber.

Wilson found, however, that when ions were present condensation set in at a much lower degree of supersaturation. An expansion ratio of 1.26, for which the final vapor pressure is some four times that required to saturate, was sufficient to cause condensation on negative ions. When the vapor pressure exceeded six times the saturated value, resulting from an expansion ratio of 1.30, condensation was found to take place on positive ions also. It might be anticipated that the presence of ions would favor condensation. The potential energy of an electrically charged sphere becomes less for a given charge as the size of the sphere increases. Since any system tends toward a minimum of potential energy, the presence of the charge would favor growth of the droplets. One may also view the problem in a slightly different way. The surface tension of a liquid causes a drop to contract. Charges present on the surface of this drop repel one another, thus tending to make it expand. It is clear, therefore, that a charged droplet might grow whereas an uncharged one might not. The fact that negative ions serve more effectively than positive for the condensation of water droplets is probably due to the known affinity of negative ions and water molecules.

Some years after its original discovery, Wilson[44] utilized this condensation phenomenon to make visible the actual paths traversed by high speed charged particles in passing through a gas. As an ionizing particle moves through a gas it leaves along its path many positive and negative ions. If an expansion be produced immediately after passage of the particle, water droplets condense upon these ions. Thus one sees water droplets distributed along the path of the ionizing particle. This path can be seen visually, or it can be photographed. The Wilson cloud chamber has undergone many modifications[45–50] in design and control, although the underlying principle has remained the same. Until 1934 a piston was used almost universally for producing the expansion. Since then nearly all chambers use a flexible rubber diaphragm to produce the change in volume. Most chambers today use alcohol vapor rather than water vapor. This vapor requires a smaller expansion ratio to produce the desired results, and has several other advantages. Many chambers today are from 15 to 30 cm. in diameter. Many use gases other than air, and some operate at pressures of 20 or more atmospheres. Today there are means of causing an ionizing particle entering the chamber to trip[47] relays which in turn produce the expansion and expose the photographic film at the proper instant. A particle can thus be made to take a photograph of its own track. Photographs are ordinarily taken from more than one direction. These stereoscopic views allow one to calculate the actual path, while a single photograph gives only the projection of this path in one plane.

### Photographic Studies of the Manner of Ion Formation

Attention should be called at this time to the noticeably different tracks left by different ionizing particles. Some information regarding the manner of ionization can be gathered from even casual inspection. Figures 16, 17 and 18 reproduce some of the earliest photographs obtained by Wilson.[44] Fig. 16 shows the tracks of two alpha particles given off by radium. These appear very intense. The alpha particle must form many ions per cm. of travel, ions on which the innumerable water droplets have condensed. The ions formed directly by the alpha particle must all have been of very low speed; otherwise the track would not be as narrow and sharply defined. Alpha particle tracks are relatively straight, although there are occasional

[44] C. T. R. Wilson, *Proc. Roy. Soc.*, A, **85**, 285 (1911); **87**, 277 (1912).

[45] P. M. S. Blackett, *Jour. Sci. Instr.*, **6**, 184 (1929).

[46] C. D. Anderson, *Phys. Rev.*, **44**, 406 (1933).

[47] P. M. S. Blackett and G. P. S. Occhialini, *Nature*, **130**, 363 (1932); *Proc. Roy. Soc.*, A, **139**, 699 (1933).

[48] W. M. Brubaker and T. W. Bonner, *Rev. Sci. Instr.*, **6**, 143 (1935).

[49] J. C. Street and E. C. Stevenson, *Rev. Sci. Instr.*, **7**, 347 (1936).

[50] G. L. Locher, *Rev. Sci. Instr.*, **7**, 471 (1936).

abrupt bends as illustrated in the photograph. These abrupt deflections usually, though not always, occur near the ends of the tracks. They are often accompanied by a short spur, as is the one in the photograph. Occasionally one finds a single track splitting into two, the new tracks proceeding for a considerable distance in quite different directions. These observations must bear directly upon important physical phenomena. We shall attempt

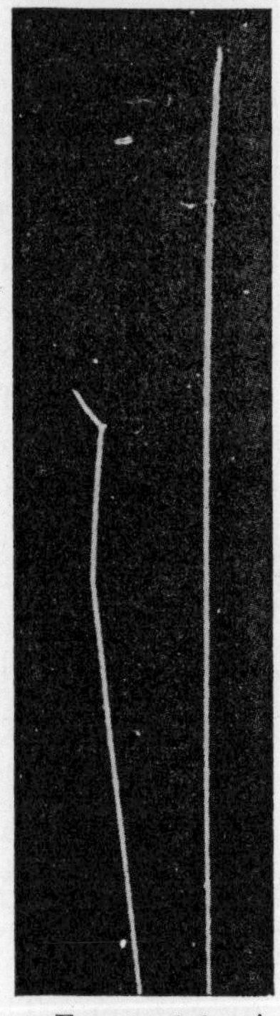

FIG. 16.—A cloud chamber photograph of the tracks left by two alpha particles.

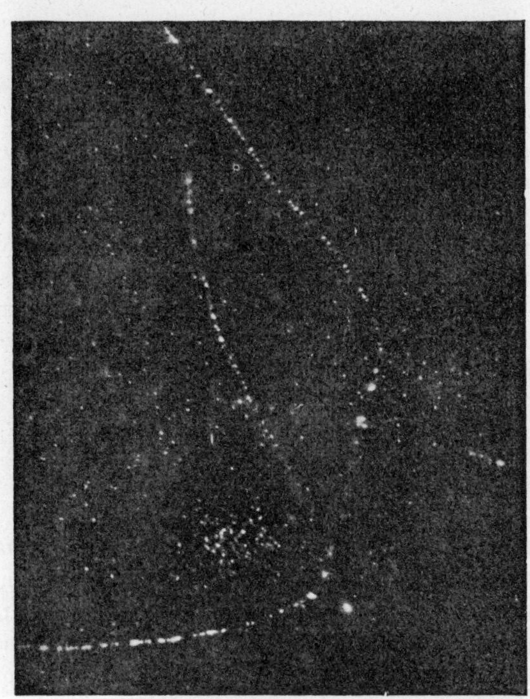

FIG. 17.—A cloud chamber photograph of the track left by a beta ray.

later to learn just what these may be. Fig. 17 shows the track of a beta ray, a high speed electron. This particle does not produce nearly as many ions per cm. as does the alpha particle. Furthermore, its path shows many gradual bends.

Fig. 18 represents the ionization produced by a narrow beam of X-rays. The width of the X-ray beam used was much less than the width over which the ionization extends. The individual tracks are those of high speed electrons. If one examines carefully photographs of this character, he finds that all electron tracks start within the narrow beam of X-rays passing through the gas. They proceed outward in all directions. One concludes, therefore, that X-rays produce most of the ionization indirectly; they produce a few very high speed electrons, and these in turn produce many low energy ions. Thus the process by which X-rays produce ionization is quite different from that by which high speed charged particles produce ions. Charged particles are capable of producing directly many low speed ions by virtue of the fact that they exert electrical forces on planetary electrons near which they pass. X-rays do not exert such forces; they are uncharged.

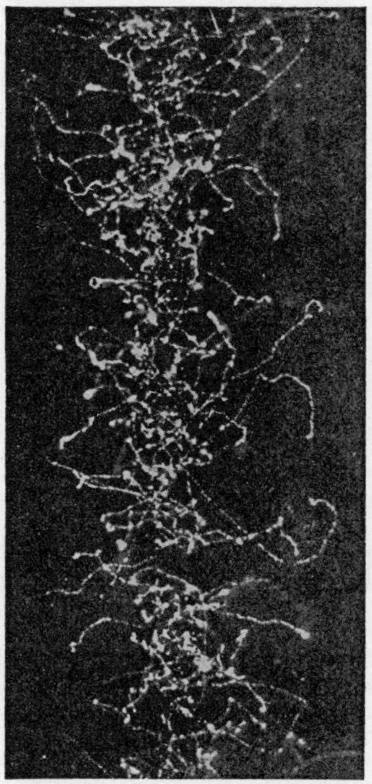

FIG. 18.—A cloud chamber photograph of the ionization produced by a narrow beam of X-rays.

Nevertheless, they do appear to cause the ejection of an occasional high speed electron. These are photoelectrons ejected by the X-rays from the gas on which the radiation falls. This process of photoelectric ejection by X-rays is entirely similar to that by which electrons are ejected from metals such as sodium when illuminated with light.

The reader may grasp from these remarks some idea of the importance of the Wilson condensation phenomenon to studies of modern physics. Very few single tools have been as helpful to the experimenter. Without the aid of this particular tool the present state of knowledge would be far less advanced and far less definite. The many applications of the cloud chamber will be emphasized by repeated reference to it in the succeeding chapters.

## Chapter 2

# THE ELECTRON

### 1. THE ATOMIC CHARACTER OF ELECTRICITY—THE ELECTRONIC CHARGE e

**Early Indications of the Existence of the Electron**

From the time of the discovery of electrification by rubbing there were many speculations as to the nature of electricity. Benjamin Franklin in 1750 was apparently one of the first to conceive of it definitely as having an atomic structure.[1] He pictured the flow of electricity not as a continuous process, but rather as the flow of a large number of discrete charges. This was pure speculation, for the first bit of experimental evidence in its favor appeared nearly a century later. In 1833 Faraday announced his so-called laws of electrolysis. He had found that exactly the same quantity of electricity must be passed through a solution to transport one gram mole of any monovalent material from one electrode to the other; twice as much electricity was required to transport one gram mole of a divalent material. Since a gram mole of any substance contains a definite number of molecules, quite independent of the nature of the material, the logical though not entirely necessary conclusion was that each molecule of a monovalent material carried the same discrete charge through the solution; each molecule of a divalent material carried twice as great a charge. Faraday's experiments suggested strongly that electricity exists only in multiples of some fundamental unit of charge. They did not allow the calculation of the size of this fundamental unit, for the number of molecules per gram mole was not known at that time.

Faraday's results did not show conclusively that electricity is atomic in character. Faraday actually measured the total charge carried by a very large but unknown number of molecules. He did not prove definitely that each molecule carried the same fundamental unit of charge or a multiple thereof. Perhaps some molecules carried one charge and others quite different charges; the average charge per molecule would come out always the same because of the multitude of molecules transported in such studies.

[1] R. A. Millikan, *Electrons (+ and −), Protons, Photons, Neutrons, and Cosmic Rays* (Chicago: University of Chicago Press, 1935), pp. 6–44, has summarized at length the early history of electrical theory and experiment.

Findings on electrolysis did point strongly toward an atomic nature of electricity, but they were far from conclusive.

In 1874 Stoney, using a crude value for Avogadro's number obtained from kinetic theory of gas studies, calculated from Faraday's work the average charge carried by an ion in solution; and he supposed that all monovalent ions carried this same charge. He later called this charge the "electron." The numerical value of the supposed unit of charge represented by the electron was greatly in error, being only $\frac{1}{16}$ the now accepted value. But evidence continued to accumulate. In 1870 Sir William Crookes discovered the cathode rays in a partially evacuated discharge tube. In 1897 Sir J. J. Thomson found that these cathode rays were negatively charged electrons traveling along the tube at very high speed. Numerous studies of this character seemed to indicate the atomic character of electricity, but the proof was by no means direct or conclusive.

About 1900 there were several partially successful attempts to determine the charge of the electron. Wilson's discovery of the cloud expansion phenomenon had been reported in 1897. Most early efforts to determine the electronic charge $e$ were based upon this. Efforts were made to measure the small charges on the droplets of water which had condensed on ions in the expansion chamber. Thomson[2] arranged the expansion ratio of a Wilson apparatus so that condensation took place only on negative ions. The air and saturated water vapor in the chamber were ionized by X-rays. Droplets were then condensed on the negative ions by expansion. From the calculated masses of water vapor necessary to saturate the space at the temperatures before and after expansion, he obtained the mass of water vapor actually condensed. He then observed through a microscope the rate of fall of the cloud of condensed water droplets. It had long been known that a small spherical body falling through a viscous medium soon attains a limiting velocity of fall. As the falling body increases its velocity the frictional retarding force due to the viscous medium increases rapidly. When this retarding force becomes equal to the force urging the body downward, no further acceleration results; the body has acquired a limiting velocity of free fall, and it continues to fall thereafter with this constant velocity. Stokes had shown mathematically that for a body of spherical shape, and of dimensions large as compared to the distance between atoms of the medium, the limiting velocity of free fall is given by

$$v = \frac{2}{9}\frac{gr^2(\rho - \rho_m)}{\eta} \qquad (1)$$

where $g$ is the acceleration of gravity, $r$ the radius of the falling sphere,

[2] J. J. Thomson, *Phil. Mag.*, **46**, 528 (1898); **48**, 547 (1899); **5**, 346 (1903).

$\rho$ the density of the spherical body, $\rho_m$ the density of the medium, and $\eta$ the viscosity of the medium.

While in general the time required for a body to attain this limiting velocity depends upon several factors in the above expression, a small water droplet of the size with which Thomson worked attains this velocity through air in a very short interval of time; it falls an inappreciable distance before attaining the limiting velocity. By observing the velocity of fall of the cloud of condensed water droplets, Thomson calculated the radius of the droplets, assuming them all of equal size. From the total mass of water condensed, together with the size of each droplet, he calculated the number of droplets formed. From this and the measured total charge carried down by the entire cloud, he calculated the average charge on each droplet. Assuming that each droplet condensed on a single ion, this represents the charge on the electron. The 1898 work led to a value some 35 percent higher than that now accepted; the 1903 work yielded a value 30 percent low. Considering the two very questionable assumptions—the equality of droplet radii and the existence of but a single charge on each droplet—and the difficulties introduced by reevaporation of the droplets during the gradual warming of the cooled gas after expansion, it is surprising that Thomson's early work gave the correct magnitude of this charge.

Other workers continued along somewhat the same lines. H. A. Wilson[3] used a method in which an electric field was applied to suspend the cloud of charged droplets. The cloud was formed and the radii of the droplets determined as in Thomson's method. Knowing the radius of the droplet, the mass $m$ was calculated. An electric field was then applied vertically to suspend the charged cloud. It was adjusted to some value $E$ just sufficient to balance the downward pull of gravity. Under these circumstances $Ee = mg$, if it is assumed again that each droplet carries a single charge. Since $E$, $m$, and $g$ were known, $e$ could be calculated. Wilson reported a value some 25 percent less than that now accepted. Wilson noticed that when the electric field was applied the cloud of droplets was gradually divided into layers. This stratification supposedly indicated that each droplet did not carry a single charge; some carried two or three. Under the action of an electric field this would lead to stratification. Millikan and Begeman,[4] realizing the meaning of such stratification, followed a procedure similar to that of Wilson except that they observed the behavior of a single stratum of droplets in the electric field. The value of $e$ reported was $4.03 \times 10^{-10}$ e.s.u., a value 16 percent less than the present accepted value. Begeman[5] made an independent determination by the same method, obtain-

[3] H. A. Wilson, *Phil. Mag.*, **5**, 429 (1903).

[4] R. A. Millikan and L. Begeman, *Phys. Rev.*, **26**, 197 (1908).

[5] L. Begeman, *Phys. Rev.*, **31**, 41 (1910).

ing a value $4.67 \times 10^{-10}$ e.s.u., a value only 3 percent less than that now accepted.

In the meantime two values had been reported for the electronic charge determined from studies of the charge carried by the alpha particles given off spontaneously from many radioactive materials. Rutherford and Geiger[6] measured the rate of accumulation of charge on an electrometer connected to a screen which was being struck by alpha particles from a source giving off a known number of particles per second. The positive charge carried by each alpha particle was reported as $9.3 \times 10^{-10}$ e.s.u. Assuming, for it amounted to little more than an assumption at the time, that this represented two electronic charges, the electron charge was $4.65 \times 10^{-10}$ e.s.u. Regener,[7] using much the same method, reported the value $4.79 \times 10^{-10}$ e.s.u. for the electronic charge. As it has turned out this last value was very close to the truth, though this did not appear at all certain at the time. Such was the state of affairs in 1909. Most physicists were convinced that electricity existed only in multiples of the electronic charge, though the evidence was far from direct and none too conclusive. A rough value for the electronic charge was known.

## Millikan's Oil Drop Experiment

*Conclusive Proof of the Atomic Character of Electricity.*—In 1909 Millikan[8–11] undertook an investigation the results of which were destined to represent one of the outstanding achievements of physics, and to win for the investigator the Nobel Prize. Millikan conceived the idea of obtaining charged droplets by spraying from an atomizer some relatively nonvolatile liquid such as oil, glycerin, or mercury into the space above a small hole in the upper of two parallel metal plates $B$ and $C$ of Fig. 1. Many droplets fell through the opening $A$. These could be viewed individually with a telescope of high magnification. By applying an electric field between plates $B$ and $C$ it was found that many of the droplets were charged, some positively and some negatively. The droplets no doubt acquired frictional charges in the spraying, and often changed their charges thereafter by collisions with stray ions in the air. When the air was ionized by X-rays the droplets were found to change their charges more frequently. The main advantages of this arrangement are obvious. Error due to evaporation was minimized by using a relatively nonvolatile liquid. The spray eliminated the necessity of an expansion followed by the gradual rise in temperature

[6] E. Rutherford and H. Geiger, *Proc. Roy. Soc.*, A, **81,** 162 (1908).
[7] E. Regener, *Ber. Preuss. Akad. Wiss.*, **37,** 948 (1909).
[8] R. A. Millikan, *Phil. Mag.*, **19,** 209 (1910).
[9] R. A. Millikan, *Phys. Rev.*, **32,** 349 (1911).
[10] R. A. Millikan, *Phys. Rev.*, **2,** 109 (1913).
[11] R. A. Millikan, *Phil. Mag.*, **34,** 1 (1917).

of the cooled gas. Since a particular drop was observed, it was no longer necessary to assume equality of drop sizes; nor was it necessary to assume equal charges on all droplets. The actual charge on a particular droplet could be determined. It should be emphasized that no assumption is made regarding the discrete character of charge; the measured charge may or may not turn out to be some whole multiple of a smallest possible charge, depending upon whether electrical charge is or is not of atomic character. Millikan's actual apparatus was of course more extensive than that indicated in Fig. 1. Mechanisms were provided for maintaining constant temperature, measuring pressure and temperature, and ionizing the air within the apparatus.

Millikan's procedure was in principle as follows: A particular drop in the region between plates was chosen. The fall of this drop under gravity was

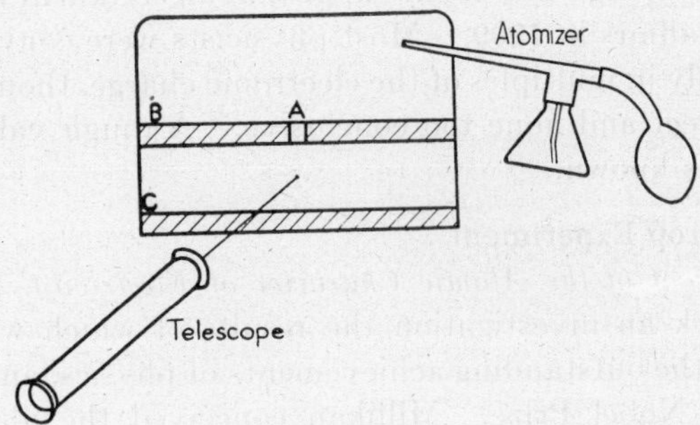


Fig. 1.—Schematic sketch of the Millikan apparatus for determining the electronic charge.

observed, and its velocity of free fall deduced. By Stokes' law this should be given by Eq. (1). Millikan found in the end that the value of the electronic charge calculated, using this law, varied slightly with the radius of the droplet and with the pressure of the gas through which the droplet fell. He could explain this only as indicating a discrepancy in Stokes' law; the errors were greater for small droplets and for low pressures. Now this law in its original form (Eq. 1) was deduced on the assumption that the spherical droplet is of dimensions so large as compared to the distance between molecules that the medium through which it falls can be considered continuous. For very small drops and low pressures the medium can no longer be thought of as continuous; the drop is no longer large as compared to the distance between molecules of the gas through which it is falling. Millikan found experimentally that the actual velocity of fall is given accurately by

$$v = \frac{2}{9}\frac{gr^2(\rho - \rho_m)}{\eta}\left(1 + \frac{b}{pr}\right) \tag{2}$$

where the last parenthesis is a correction term, but slightly larger than unity, taking account of the discontinuous character of the medium. The constant $b$ has the value 0.000617 provided $p$ is measured in cm. of Hg and $r$ in cm.

Using this corrected form of Stokes' law, along with the observed value of $v$, Millikan calculated the radius of the droplet. He then established an electric field between plates and urged the droplet upward against the force of gravity. When there is no electric field applied, the force pulling the droplet downward is given by

$$\text{Force downward} = \tfrac{4}{3}\pi r^3 g(\rho - \rho_m)$$

When the electric field is applied the net force urging the droplet upward is given by

$$\text{Net force upward} = Eq - \tfrac{4}{3}\pi r^3 g(\rho - \rho_m)$$

where $q$ is the charge on the drop and where $E$ is the electric field established between plates. Let it be emphasized again that $q$ is simply the charge on the drop; it is not assumed that the drop possesses a single electronic charge, or even that the charge $q$ is a multiple of some fundamental unit. Millikan assumed that the velocity with which the drop drifts through the gaseous medium is proportional to the net force urging it. This assumption was verified experimentally by observing the behavior of a charged drop in fields of different strengths. If $v$ and $v_1$ represent the drop velocities downward and upward, respectively, then

$$\frac{v}{v_1} = \frac{\tfrac{4}{3}\pi r^3 g(\rho - \rho_m)}{Eq - \tfrac{4}{3}\pi r^3 g(\rho - \rho_m)} \tag{3}$$

or

$$q = \frac{4\pi r^3 g(\rho - \rho_m)}{3E}\,\frac{(v + v_1)}{v} \tag{4}$$

Using the radius $r$ calculated from Eq. (2), and the observed velocities $v$ and $v_1$, $q$ can be calculated.

When Millikan calculated the values of $q$ from different observations he obtained a great number of different values. That is, the charges on different drops, or even on the same drop at different times, were often different. However, the striking thing is this: Millikan never observed a charge smaller than $4.774 \times 10^{-10}$ e.s.u., and all other charges observed were whole multiples of this smallest value. Sometimes 1, 2, 3, 4, 5, and even as high as 150 of these elementary charges were found on a droplet. What more direct or conclusive evidence of the atomic character of electricity could be desired? Results were of course much more certain when dealing with drops on which but a few elementary charges resided, and it is data on such drops that show conclusively the atomic nature of electricity and yield an accurate value for $e$. Millikan reported the values

1911 value[8] .......................... $e = 4.891 \times 10^{-10}$ e.s.u.
1913 value[10] .......................... $e = (4.774 \pm 0.009) \times 10^{-10}$
1917 value[11] .......................... $e = (4.774 \pm 0.005) \times 10^{-10}$

Numerous improvements in details of the method, together with a supposedly more refined value for the viscosity of air, were responsible for the difference between the 1911 and the 1913 values. The 1917 value represents still greater effort toward precision, together with what Millikan considered an improvement in the viscosity of air by Harrington.[12] The resultant value of $e$ was identical with the 1913 value, except for a decrease in the probable error. The 1917 work was undertaken largely because Ehrenhaft[13] and his coworkers Konstantinowsky[14] and Zerner[15] reported seriously inconsistent results. These works seemed to question the existence of any fixed fundamental unit of charge, or at least to indicate that it was a much smaller unit than the Millikan value. These workers used very small globules of solid material or of mercury. Millikan[16] criticized these works on several scores. There seems serious question as to the spherical shape and as to the density of such particles. Such extremely small charged particles are not known to fall in accord with Stokes' law. The large Brownian motions of such small particles certainly introduce irregularities. Today there is no substantial evidence whatever for a charge smaller than the fundamental unit found by Millikan. His 1917 value, when corrected for better values of the velocity of light and the absolute ohm by Birge[17] and by Millikan,[18] represented by far the most reliable value of $e$ available until recent years. This value was

$$e = (4.770 \pm 0.005) \times 10^{-10} \text{ e.s.u.}$$

*Typical Student Data on the Oil Drop Experiment.*—Before proceeding to other interesting consequences of Millikan's work, and to the more recent researches on the electronic charge, the author can not refrain from indicating how easy it is today for an undergraduate student to find for himself by an afternoon's work that electrical charge is atomic in character, and to obtain a fairly good value for the electronic charge. Table I is a summary

[12] E. L. Harrington, *Phys. Rev.*, **8** 738 (1916).
[13] F. Ehrenhaft, *Ann. d. Physik*, **44**, 657 (1914).
[14] D. Konstantinowsky, *Ann. d. Physik*, **46**, 261 (1915).
[15] F. Zerner, *Phys. Zeits.*, **16**, 10 (1915).
[16] R. A. Millikan, *Phys. Rev.*, **8**, 595 (1916).
[17] R. T. Birge, *Rev. Mod. Phys.*, **1**, 1 (1929).
[18] R. A. Millikan, *Phys. Rev.*, **35**, 1231 (1930).

of typical results found by two students in one of the author's laboratory classes in 1932.

TABLE I

Typical student observations on a charged oil drop. The oil used was watch oil. The air viscosity is that used by Millikan

Distance between plates = 0.7135 cm.
Potential between plates = 735 volts
Distance through which drop drifted = 0.145 cm.
Barometric pressure = 74.26 cm. Hg.

Temperature = 21.5° C
Density of oil = 0.893 gr/cc.
Viscosity of air = 0.0001817

| Time of free fall | Time of rise with field | | Average of times of rise | Calculated charge on drop, e.s.u. | Number of elementary charges on drop | $e \times 10^{10}$ |
|---|---|---|---|---|---|---|
| | (*Con't.*) | | | | | |
| 34.4 sec. | 10.1 | 28.7 | 22 observations | $4.79 \times 10^{-10}$ | 1 | 4.79 |
| 33.9 | 10.2 | 28.3 | averaging 28.77 | | | |
| 34.5 | 10.5 | 4.5 | | | | |
| 34.3 | 10.3 | 4.6 | | | | |
| 34.0 | 10.2 | 4.4 | | | | |
| 34.4 | 10.2 | 4.4 | | | | |
| 34.2 | 28.6 | 4.3 | 11 observations | 9.45 | 2 | 4.725 |
| 34.3 | 28.5 | 4.5 | averaging 10.31 | | | |
| 33.9 | 28.6 | 4.5 | | | | |
| 33.8 | 28.7 | 4.6 | | | | |
| 34.2 | 29.0 | 4.4 | | | | |
| | 29.1 | 6.1 | | | | |
| | 29.1 | 6.0 | 7 observations | 14.43 | 3 | 4.81 |
| Average = 34.17 | 28.4 | 6.2 | averaging 6.11 | | | |
| | 28.9 | 6.1 | | | | |
| | 29.0 | 6.2 | | | | |
| | 10.6 | 6.1 | 9 observations | 18.93 | 4 | 4.73 |
| | 10.2 | 6.1 | averaging 4.47 | | | |
| | 10.5 | 28.6 | | | | |
| | 10.4 | 28.7 | | | | |
| | 10.2 | 29.1 | | | | |
| | 29.1 | 28.9 | | | | |
| | 28.6 | 29.0 | Radius of drop calculated to be $5.90 \times 10^{-5}$ cm. | | | |
| | | 28.6 | | | | |
| | | 28.8 | | | | |

The quite small drop which these students chose to watch had different charges on it at different times. But the charge was always some multiple of the smallest value observed. Even these relatively meager data indicate strongly that electrical charge exists only in multiples of a fundamental unit; and they yield a rather good value for $e$. If the several values for $e$

be weighted proportional to the number of observations associated with each, the mean value obtained is $4.77 \times 10^{-10}$. The exact agreement with the Millikan value is of course somewhat accidental. It is truly remarkable that such evidence can be obtained by the undergraduate student today, when the first conclusive evidence for the existence of a fundamental unit of charge was obtained only 30 years ago.

*Evaluation of Avogadro's Number from Millikan's Work.*—Another very important constant of nature could be evaluated once Millikan's reliable value of $e$ was available. This constant is the number of molecules per gram mole, known as Avogadro's number. Electrolytic studies had shown that 96494 absolute coulombs of electricity are required to transport one gram mole of any monovalent material through solution. This was the best value available in 1917, and was used by Millikan.[11] The later value ($96489 \pm 7$) accepted by Birge,[17] and still used today, is but slightly different. If one supposes that the fundamental unit of charge carried by monovalent ions in solution is the same as that elementary unit encountered in gas ion studies and measured by Millikan, the number of molecules $N$ in a gram mole of any material is given by

$$N = \frac{96494 \times 2.9990 \times 10^{9}}{4.774 \times 10^{-10}} = (6.062 \pm 0.006) \times 10^{23}$$

This was the value given by Millikan[11] in 1917; except for the probable error it is identical with that given[10] in 1913. It was the first accurate value of this important constant. Except for the value obtained through Millikan's earlier work, it was the first value which could be considered reliable in the least. Corrected by Birge[17] for better values of the Faraday, the velocity of light, and the absolute ohm, this became

$$N = \frac{(96489 \pm 7) \times (2.99796 \pm 0.00004) \times 10^{9}}{(4.770 \pm 0.005) \times 10^{-10}}$$
$$= (6.064 \pm 0.006) \times 10^{23}$$

Until recently this remained the most reliable value available. While other values have been obtained from studies[19] of the Brownian movements of colloidal particles in suspension, from measurements of the rate of diffusion of colloidal particles, from studies of the thickness of mono-molecular films similar to the early works of Devaux and Langmuir[20] and of du Noüy,[21] and from observations on the scattering of light, none of these are comparable in accuracy or reliability with that calculated above.

[19] L. B. Loeb, *Kinetic Theory of Gases* (New York: McGraw-Hill, 1927), pp. 338–357.
[20] I. Langmuir, *Jour. Amer. Chem. Soc.*, **39**, 1860 (1917).
[21] P. L. du Noüy, *Phil. Mag.*, **48**, 264, 664 (1924).

In the above calculation of Avogadro's number, it was supposed that the elementary charge encountered in electrolytic studies is the same as that found in gas ion studies. Actually this had already been shown by a beautiful experiment carried out by Fletcher[22] on the Brownian movement of a single charged oil droplet. A small charged droplet was suspended by an electric field opposed to gravity, and the Brownian displacements observed over a long period of time. These displacements were made large by using a gaseous medium at low pressure. The theory underlying the work involves considerable statistical treatment which need not be discussed here. Probability considerations of the random displacements suffered by a particle undergoing Brownian movement lead to an expression for the product $Ne$ in terms of the temperature, the mean square of the Brownian displacements suffered over a given interval of time, and the drift velocity acquired by the charged Brownian particle when placed in a known electric field. As a result of 1735 observed displacements suffered by a charged particle, Fletcher found the product $Ne$ to be 96100 coulombs, where $N$ is the number of molecules per gram mole, and where $e$ is the elementary charge encountered in gas ion studies. This differs from the product $Ne$ found in electrolysis by less than one-half percent. Certainly then the elementary charges encountered in the two studies are identical.

*Other Interesting Observations.*—Another interesting observation made in the course of Millikan's work had to do with the probability of a change occurring in the charge on a particular drop, and with the greatest charge commonly found on a drop of given size. One finds a variety of charges, sometimes negative and sometimes positive, on a particular drop. Changes of charge often result from collision of the drop with stray ions in the gaseous medium. These changes can be made to occur almost at will by ionizing the medium more intensely. If one is observing a fairly large drop, it is relatively easy to cause the drop to assume a charge, either positive or negative, of several hundred electrons. It is difficult, however, to obtain a charge of more than a few electrons on a very small drop. As a drop becomes more highly charged it becomes less probable that it will pick up an additional charge of the same sign. As Millikan[9] pointed out, these changes of charge are no doubt due to thermal collisions of ions with the drop. As a drop becomes more highly charged, an ion of like sign must possess more kinetic energy of thermal agitation to overcome the repulsive force and attach itself to the drop. Since the mean kinetic energy of thermal agitation is fixed by the temperature, one would expect a rough upper limit to the charge that might reasonably be expected on a drop of given size. As an example substantiating this concept, Millikan[9] found that a drop of 0.000658 cm. radius and possessing a charge of 150 electrons had practically no tend-

[22] H. Fletcher, *Phys. Rev.*, **33**, 81 (1911).

ency to pick up an additional charge of like sign. Assuming a spherical distribution of charge on the surface of the drop, the electrical potential of this drop would be

$$\text{Potential} = \frac{q}{C} = \frac{150e}{r} = \frac{150 \times 4.77 \times 10^{-10}}{0.000658} = 1.09 \times 10^{-4} \text{ e.s.u.}$$

where $C$ is the capacity of the spherical drop and where $r$ is the radius. The energy required to drive another electronic charge of like sign onto this drop would be

$$\begin{aligned} \text{Energy} = \text{potential} \times \text{charge} &= 1.09 \times 10^{-4} \times 4.77 \times 10^{-10} \\ &= 5.2 \times 10^{-14} \text{ ergs.} \end{aligned}$$

It is instructive to compare this with the average kinetic energy of thermal agitation. This is given by

$$\text{K.E.} = \tfrac{3}{2}kT = \tfrac{3}{2} \times 1.38 \times 10^{-16} \times 293 = 6.1 \times 10^{-14} \text{ ergs}$$

where $k$ is the Boltzmann gas constant per molecule, and where $T$ is the absolute temperature. This is clearly of the same order as the energy an ion must have to drive itself onto the already highly charged drop. Such calculations constitute excellent evidence as to the correctness of the concept that changes of charge are brought about by thermal collisions.

## 2. RECENT REFINEMENTS IN THE NUMERICAL VALUE OF e

### Other Methods of Determining e

As other methods are developed and as technique is improved, there usually follow successive refinements in the values of important physical constants. A notable improvement in the value of the electronic charge has been accomplished in recent years. Not until 1928 did there appear any evidence whatever to indicate any need for a slight revision of the Millikan value. Not until 1935 was the necessity of a revision accepted fully.

Two intervening determinations by Mattauch[23] and by Hull and Williams[24] gave $4.758 \times 10^{-10}$ and $4.76 \times 10^{-10}$ e.s.u., respectively. While both of these were slightly lower than the Millikan value, neither compared with it in accuracy. Mattauch's determination was by the Millikan method. Hull and Williams used an entirely different attack. If the emission of electrons from a heated filament in a vacuum tube is random in character, one would expect high frequency oscillations to be set up in a plate circuit composed of an inductance, a capacity, and a resistance. These oscillations are due to the electrical impulses communicated to the plate

[23] J. Mattauch, *Zeits. f. Physik*, **32**, 439 (1925).
[24] A. W. Hull and N. H. Williams, *Phys. Rev.*, **25**, 147 (1925).

by the individual electrons. These oscillatory currents have been found and measured. The phenomenon is known as the shot effect. It turns out theoretically that the mean square of the oscillatory current can be expressed in terms of the saturation current to the plate, the electronic charge, and the resistance and capacity of the circuit. Since all quantities other than the electronic charge can be observed experimentally, $e$ can be calculated. Hull and Williams found the value $4.76 \times 10^{-10}$ e.s.u., representing the average of a number of determinations. The individual determinations varied among themselves by as much as 2%. This value, obtained by an entirely different method, compared favorably with that found by Millikan. Though this result has a larger probable error than that associated with the Millikan value, Hull and Williams believed that with proper refinements the method might yield a result of comparable accuracy. No further success has yet been accomplished in this direction.

In 1928 there appeared a determination[25] by still another method, one which proved to be the forerunner of a long series of researches. The details of this method cannot be appreciated unless one is familiar with the methods of measuring X-ray wave lengths. The general procedure can be made clear, however, if the reader will accept for the present a few statements which will be substantiated in detail in a later chapter. There are two main methods of measuring X-ray wave lengths. The first method used was that of reflection from the faces of natural crystals such as calcite. Marked reflection occurs only at certain angles, and these angles are functions of the wave length and the distance between atoms in the crystal. Knowing the general arrangement of atoms in the crystal, and taking Avogadro's number obtained through use of the Millikan value for $e$, it is possible to calculate the distance between atoms in the crystal. From this, together with the observed angles at which a given X-ray is reflected, the wave length of the X-ray can be obtained. The second method, developed somewhat later, depends upon the reflection of X-rays from a ruled grating. In general the method is analogous to the determination of optical wave lengths through use of ruled reflection gratings. Knowing the distance between lines ruled on the grating, together with the angular positions at which the maximum intensities of reflected X-ray energy occur, the wave length of the X-ray can be calculated.

Long before 1928 it was recognized that X-ray wave length measurements by the crystal method were quite precise. Measurements made by the ruled grating method should be equally precise. Bäcklin[25] found, however, that the two methods gave slightly different values for the wave length of a given X-ray. The discrepancy was more than should be expected from the probable errors involved. One possible interpretation of this dis-

[25] E. Bäcklin, *Diss., Uppsala* (1928).

crepancy was that the results of crystal measurements might be in error, due to the use of a slightly incorrect calculated spacing between atoms resulting from an incorrect value of Avogadro's number. If the previously accepted value of Avogadro's number was in error, then it follows that a similar error existed in the Millikan value for the electronic charge, for it is exceedingly unlikely that an error of this size could possibly exist in the experimental determination of the Faraday. Bäcklin therefore proposed to reverse the procedure. Taking the X-ray wave length obtained from ruled gratings as correct, he calculated the spacing between atoms in the crystal necessary to account for the observed reflection therefrom. From this spacing, together with the density and the general arrangement of atoms in the crystal, he obtained a value for Avogadro's number. Combining this with the Faraday led to a value for the electronic charge. Bäcklin's original observations yielded values

$$N = (6.037 \pm 0.008) \times 10^{23}$$
$$e = (4.794 \pm 0.006) \times 10^{-10}$$

These results are respectively ½ percent lower and ½ percent higher than the Millikan values,[17,18] and they have associated with them but slightly larger probable errors. The discrepancy is approximately twice the sum of the probable errors. While this in itself proves nothing, it is indeed suggestive. This was the first indication that the Millikan values might need slight revision, and it was followed by a long series of researches and discussions.

Peculiarly, the early work of Wadlund[26] by the same method gave results contrary to those of Bäcklin; the results duplicated almost exactly those of Millikan. But this is the only work by this method that has not led to a slightly higher value of $e$. Almost immediately Bearden[27] undertook a series of investigations which has proved outstanding in settling the issue. Bearden's early work by the X-ray method gave values

$$N = 6.022 \times 10^{23}$$
$$e = 4.804 \times 10^{-10}$$

and these are very close to the more accurate later works which have now been accepted. The work of Millikan was so firmly entrenched, however, and the suspicion of error in the ruled grating wave length measurements so widespread, that Millikan's values were still accepted by nearly all physicists. Birge,[17] in a survey of the most probable values of physical constants, and Millikan,[18] in a survey limited largely to the value of the electronic charge,

[26] A. P. R. Wadlund, *Proc. Nat. Acad. Sci.*, **14**, 588 (1928); *Phys. Rev.*, **32**, 841 (1928).
[27] J. A. Bearden, *Proc. Nat. Acad. Sci.*, **15**, 527 (1929).

still accepted the Millikan value. The general attitude remained unchanged after the further works of Cork[28] and Bearden,[29] probably largely because Bearden[30] had obtained by calculation of wave lengths from index of refraction measurements, some evidence that the ruled grating measurements were in error. Bearden himself still felt, as did Birge,[31] that the Millikan value would prove correct. Shiba,[32] however, in a critical summarization of the most probable values of several important physical constants, expressed definitely a conviction to the contrary. While he admitted the forcefulness of arguments in favor of the Millikan value, he felt that the discrepancy was in this value, and that it was due to an incorrect value for the viscosity of air. To substantiate this argument he pointed out that if weights obtained from probable error considerations were assigned to existing viscosity determinations, the most probable value for the viscosity was somewhat higher than that used by Millikan. This higher viscosity combined with Millikan's oil drop data gave

$$e = (4.803 \pm 0.010) \times 10^{-10}$$

a value almost identical with those obtained from X-ray measurements. Shiba's suggestion has proved correct, and it was probably quite instrumental in bringing about final agreement between results by the two methods.

Almost immediately further work by Bearden and Shaw,[33] Bäcklin,[34] Söderman[35] and Bearden[36,37] made it appear almost certain that ruled grating wave lengths, and thence the higher value of $e$, were correct. Bearden and Shaw had calculated wave lengths from refractive data. Söderman had compared X-ray wave lengths directly with that of a well-known line in the visible spectrum. In each case results agreed with those obtained from ruled grating measurements. In an excellent summary of results by the X-ray method, Bearden[37] gave as most probable values

$$N = (6.0221 \pm 0.0005) \times 10^{23}$$
$$e = (4.8036 \pm 0.0005) \times 10^{-10}$$

[28] J. M. Cork, *Phys. Rev.*, **35**, 1456 (1930).
[29] J. A. Bearden, *Phys. Rev.*, **37**, 1210 (1931).
[30] J. A. Bearden, *Phys. Rev.*, **39**, 1 (1932).
[31] R. T. Birge, *Phys. Rev.*, **40**, 228 (1932).
[32] K. Shiba, *Inst. Phys.* and *Chem. Res.*, Tokyo, *Sci. Papers*, **19**, 97 (1932).
[33] J. A. Bearden and C. H. Shaw, *Phys. Rev.*, **46**, 759 (1934).
[34] E. Bäcklin, *Zeits. f. Physik*, **93**, 450 (1935).
[35] M. Söderman, *Nature*, **135**, 67 (1935).
[36] J. A. Bearden, *Phys. Rev.*, **47**, 811 (1935).
[37] J. A. Bearden, *Phys. Rev.*, **48**, 385 (1935).

While Schopper[38] had in the meantime obtained essentially the Millikan value from a determination of the charge carried by the alpha particle, the results were not considered seriously. They were criticized on several scores,[39] and Schopper[40] himself later reported irregularities present in his measurements. The 1935 Bearden values were accepted by nearly all workers, and they still are accepted. They have since been substantiated by the work of DuMond and Bollman[41] and by that of Miller and DuMond.[42] The latter observers obtained X-ray data from seven different kinds of crystals, and their average value was not essentially different from that by Bearden.

**Recent Elimination of a Small Error in the Millikan Value**

At about this time (1935) it was shown that the main error in the Millikan value was definitely due to the use of an incorrect value for the viscosity of air, as had been suggested by Shiba.[32] Kellström[43] made a very careful determination of the viscosity of air, obtaining a value appreciably higher than the Harrington[12] value which had been used by Millikan. Bond[44] obtained independently a value almost exactly equal to Kellström's. Combining the orignal Millikan oil drop data with his own viscosity determination, Kellström reported a value

$$e = (4.818 \pm 0.011) \times 10^{-10}$$

Thus the oil drop data lead to a value fully as high as the X-ray value. This one result is even higher, though the difference is not unreasonable as judged from the probable errors involved. Still more recent viscosity measurements[45—49] make it appear certain that the viscosity of air is higher than was supposed previous to Kellström's work, though perhaps not quite as high as found by Kellström. Recent viscosity determinations are shown in Table II.

[38] E. Schopper, *Zeits. f. Pkysik*, **93**, 1 (1934).

[39] R. T. Birge and E. McMillan, *Phys. Rev.*, **47**, 320 (1935).

[40] E. Schopper, *Zeits. f. Physik*, **94**, 649 (1935).

[41] J. W. M. DuMond and V. L. Bollman, *Phys. Rev.*, **50**, 524 (1936).

[42] P. H. Miller and J. W. M. DuMond, *Phys. Rev.*, **57**, 198 (1940).

[43] G. Kellström, *Nature*, **136**, 682 (1935); *Phys. Rev.*, **50**, 190 (1936); *Phil. Mag.*, **23**, 313 (1937).

[44] W. N. Bond, *Phil. Mag.*, **22**, 624 (1936); *Proc. Phys. Soc.*, London, **49**, 205 (1937).

[45] W. V. Houston, *Phys. Rev.*, **52**, 751 (1937).

[46] P. J. Rigden *Nature*, **141**, 82 (1938); *Phil. Mag.*, **25**, 961 (1938).

[47] G. B. Banerjea and B. Plattanaik, *Nature*, **141**, 1016 (1938); *Zeits. f. Physik*, **110**, 676 (1938).

[48] V. D. Majumdar and M. B. Vajifdar, *Proc. Indian Acad. Sci.*, **8A**, 171 (1938).

[49] J. A. Bearden, *Phys. Rev.*, **56**, 1023 (1939).

TABLE II

Experimental determinations of the viscosity of air at 23° C. Values are in c.g.s. units

| Observer | Viscosity × 10⁷ |
|---|---|
| Harrington[17] | 1822.6 ± 0.7 |
| Kellström[43] | 1834.9 ± 2.7 |
| Bond[44] | 1834.7 ± 0.8 |
| Houston[45] | 1829.2 ± 4.5 |
| Rigden[46] | 1830.3 ± 0.7 |
| Banerjea & Plattanaik[47] | 1833.3 ± 2.1 |
| Majumdar & Vajifdar[48] | 1834.4 ± 0.35 |
| Bearden[49] | 1834.12 ± 0.06 |

If the average of the seven recent values is combined with the Millikan oil drop data, one finds

$$e = 4.811 \times 10^{-10}$$

This is slightly higher than the X-ray value, whereas early viscosity data led to a value considerably lower.

It has been suggested by Bäcklin and Flemberg[50] that a small additional error exists in the Millikan oil drop data proper. Recent oil drop observations by these workers, when combined with the Kellström value for the viscosity of air, yield for the electronic charge

$$e = (4.800 \pm 0.008) \times 10^{-10}$$

This is appreciably lower than that reported by Kellström who used the Millikan data; it is almost exactly the X-ray value. This agreement gave some weight to the suggestion of a possible small additional error in the Millikan data.

Ishida, Fukushima and Suetsugu[51] have also repeated the oil drop experiment. The apparatus and method were essentially the same as used by Millikan. The authors claim improvement in the elimination of several possible small errors, those introduced by slight changes in oil density, by the use of non-spherical drops, and by the influence of convection currents upon the drop's motion. Using the old Harrington[12] value for the viscosity of air, they obtained

$$e = (4.806 \pm 0.003) \times 10^{-10} \text{ e.s.u.}$$

where the probable error does not include that associated with the viscosity determination. This is quite close to the X-ray value. If, however, any

[50] E. Bäcklin and H. Flemberg, *Nature*, **137**, 655 (1936).

[51] Y. Ishida, I. Fukushima and T. Suetsugu, *Nature*, **140**, 29 (1937); *Inst. Phys. and Chem. Res.*, Tokyo, *Sci. Papers*, **32**, 57 (1937).

of the more recent viscosity determinations are used, a value much higher than this is obtained. These workers remark that, "If Kellström's determination of the viscosity of air is correct, then we come to the unavoidable conclusion that the electronic charge must be greater than the value determined by the X-ray method."

Laby and Hopper[52] have recently obtained oil drop data by a somewhat different method. These observers used vertical rather than horizontal plates. Instead of viewing the drop directly they took a series of short exposure pictures of it, one picture each $1/25$ of a second. With the plates shorted the drop is shown in one after another position as it falls vertically between the plates. With the field applied it is shown in one after another position as it moves in a straight line under the combined velocities of free fall and drift in the electric field. From these data, together with the viscosity of air, the charge on the drop can be calculated. Arbitrarily accepting the value $1830 \times 10^{-7}$ for the viscosity of air at 23° C, they found for the electronic charge

$$e = (4.8020 \pm 0.0013) \times 10^{-10}$$

For the sake of comparison of oil drop data it is well to calculate from each series of data the value of the electron charge, using in each calculation the same value for the viscosity of air. Although Table II indicates that the value $1830 \times 10^{-7}$ arbitrarily chosen by Laby and Hopper may be slightly low, this value cannot be far from correct, and it will serve as well as any for comparative purposes. On this basis one finds that the several sets of oil drop data lead to the values given in Table III.

TABLE III

Comparison of oil drop data, assuming the value $1830 \times 10^{-7}$ for the viscosity of air at 23° C. The probable errors of the first and last values are those associated with the oil drop data only

| Data | $e \times 10^{10}$ |
|---|---|
| Millikan | 4.799 ± 0.0037 |
| Bäcklin and Flemberg | 4.781 |
| Ishida, Fukushima and Suetsugu | 4.835 |
| Laby and Hopper | 4.8020 ± 0.0013 |

It is obvious that the oil drop data do not agree among themselves. The recent data by Laby and Hopper by the photographic method yield a result agreeing closely with that of Millikan. One other set of data yields a value considerably lower, while still another leads to a value much higher. While all of these values may have to be raised slightly if the viscosity proves to be greater than $1830 \times 10^{-7}$, as appears likely, the Millikan and the Laby

[52] T. H. Laby and V. D. Hopper, *Nature*, **143**, 157 (1939); **145**, 932 (1940).

and Hopper values will still be close to the X-ray value. Ishida, Fukushima and Suetsugu's contention of the alarmingly higher oil drop value ignores all data except their own. As Robinson[53] points out, by choosing proper oil drop data and combining it with proper viscosity data one can obtain a value for the electronic charge ranging from well below to well above the X-ray value. There is no reason to believe today that any real discrepancy exists between the oil drop and the X-ray values. The X-ray value is and will no doubt continue to be by far the more precise, but its substantiation by oil drop data was an important contribution.

Birge,[54] considering all except recent works, suggested the most probable values

$$N = (6.0230 \pm 0.0005) \times 10^{23}$$
$$e = (4.8029 \pm 0.0005) \times 10^{-10}$$

These are almost identical with the Bearden[37] values, and with these constitute the accepted values today. They likewise agree closely with values given in a still more recent summary by Millikan.[55] Table IV summarizes values of $e$ and $N$ obtained by various workers and by various methods.

[53] H. R. Robinson, *Nature*, **142**, 160 (1938).
[54] R. T. Birge, *Nature*, **137**, 187 (1936).
[55] R. A. Millikan, *Ann. d. Physik*, **32**, 34 (1938).

TABLE IV

Experimental values of the electronic charge $e$ and Avogadro's number $N$. Under method, the words drop, X-ray, alpha, and shot refer respectively to the oil drop, the X-ray wave length, the alpha particle, and the shot effect methods

| Author | Date | Method | $e \times 10^{10}$ e.s.u. | | $N \times 10^{-23}$ | |
|---|---|---|---|---|---|---|
| Rutherford & Geiger[6] | 1908 | Alpha | 4.65 | | | |
| Regener[7] | 1909 | Alpha | 4.79 | | | |
| Millikan[10] | 1913 | Drop | 4.774 | ± 0.009 | 6.062 | ± 0.012 |
| Millikan[11] | 1917 | Drop | 4.774 | ± 0.005 | 6.062 | ± 0.006 |
| Mattauch[23] | 1925 | Drop | 4.758 | | 6.080 | |
| Hull & Williams[24] | 1925 | Shot | 4.76 | | | |
| Bäcklin[25] | 1928 | X-ray | 4.794 | ± 0.006 | 6.037 | ± 0.008 |
| Wadlund[26] | 1928 | X-ray | 4.774 | ± 0.007 | 6.061 | ± 0.009 |
| Bearden[27] | 1929 | X-ray | 4.804 | | 6.022 | |
| Birge[17] | 1929 | Summary | 4.770 | ± 0.005 | 6.064 | ± 0.006 |
| Millikan[18] | 1930 | Drop | 4.770 | ± 0.005 | 6.064 | ± 0.006 |
| Cork[28] | 1930 | X-ray | 4.816 | | 6.006 | |
| Bearden[29] | 1931 | X-ray | 4.806 | ± 0.003 | 6.019 | ± 0.003 |
| Birge[31] | 1932 | Summary | 4.769 | ± 0.004 | 6.065 | ± 0.005 |
| Shiba[32] | 1932 | Summary | 4.806 | ± 0.0014 | 6.019 | ± 0.002 |
| Schopper[33] | 1934 | Alpha | 4.768 | ± 0.005 | | |
| Bäcklin[34] | 1935 | X-ray | 4.805 | ± 0.004 | 6.020 | ± 0.005 |
| Söderman[35] | 1935 | X-ray | 4.806 | ± 0.003 | 6.019 | ± 0.003 |
| Robinson[56] | 1935 | Summary | | | | |
| Bearden[37] | 1935 | X-ray | 4.8036 | ± 0.0005 | 6.0221 | ± 0.0005 |
| Kellström[43] | 1935 | Drop | 4.818 | ± 0.012 | 6.004 | |
| DuMond & Bollman[41] | 1936 | X-ray | 4.799 | ± 0.007 | 6.028 | |
| Birge[54] | 1936 | Summary | 4.8029 | ± 0.0005 | 6.0230 | ± 0.0005 |
| Bond[44] | 1936 | Drop | 4.814 | | 6.009 | |
| Bäcklin & Flemberg[50] | 1936 | Drop | 4.800 | ± 0.008 | 6.027 | |
| Friesen[57] | 1937 | Summary | 4.800 | | 6.027 | |
| Houston[45] | 1937 | Drop | 4.796 | | 6.032 | |
| Ishida, Fukushima, & Suetsugu[51] | 1937 | Drop | 4.806 | | 6.019 | |
| Rigden[46] | 1938 | Drop | 4.800 | ± 0.004 | 6.027 | |
| Banerjea & Plattanaik[47] | 1938 | Drop | 4.811 | ± 0.009 | 6.013 | |
| Robinson[53] | 1938 | Summary | 4.803 | | 6.023 | |
| Millikan[55] | 1938 | Summary | 4.796 | ± 0.005 | 6.032 | |
| Dunnington[58] | 1939 | Summary | 4.8025 | ± 0.0007 | 6.0235 | |
| Laby & Hopper[52] | 1940 | Drop | 4.802 | | 6.024 | |
| Miller & DuMond[42] | 1940 | X-ray | 4.801 | ± 0.002 | 6.026 | ± 0.002 |

[56] H. R. Robinson, *Rep. on Prog. in Phys.*, **2,** 247 (1935).

[57] S. von Friesen, *Proc. Roy. Soc.*, A, **160,** 424 (1937).

[58] F. G. Dunnington, *Phys. Rev.*, **55,** 683 (1939); *Rev. Mod. Phys.*, **11,** 65 (1939).

Chapter 3

# THE ELECTRICAL DISCHARGE

## 1. THE VARIOUS TYPES OF DISCHARGE

The study of the discharge of electricity through gases at reduced pressures has led to the discovery of cathode rays, positive rays, X-rays, and numerous other phenomena. Detailed studies of each of these have led in turn to further important findings, some of which will be discussed in succeeding chapters. For the present, however, our attention will be confined to the more general features of the discharge. The general appearance and other characteristics of the electrical discharge through a gas depend upon many factors, the nature and pressure of the gas, the size and shape of the vessel containing the gas, the nature, shape, and separation of the electrodes, and the current density in the gas. Discharges are often classified as the dark discharge, the glow discharge, the brush discharge, the spark discharge, and the arc discharge, although there do not exist sharp lines of demarcation among these.

When the potential difference applied between two electrodes is gradually increased, a measurable flow of electricity starts before any visible signs of a discharge appear. The discharge is called a dark discharge. If the potential difference is further increased, sharp luminous streamers appear on either electrode. These are not continuous from one electrode to the other; they extend out a short way from the electrode and then disappear. The phenomenon is termed a brush discharge. Under other conditions the discharge appears as a series of intermittent sharp sparks extending from one electrode to the other, and is accompanied by explosive-like sounds. This is called a spark discharge. Under other conditions, when the discharge appears as a more or less continuous glow filling a large part of the space between electrodes, it is referred to as a glow discharge. Under still other conditions, usually associated with large current densities, a continuous arc appears between electrodes, and the phenomenon is called the arc discharge. Various aspects of discharge phenomena have been treated by numerous authors. Langmuir and K. T. Compton[1,2] have discussed elaborately the underlying behavior of ions responsible for such phenomena. J. J. and

[1] K. T. Compton and I. Langmuir, *Rev. Mod. Phys.*, **2**, 123 (1930).

[2] I. Langmuir and K. T. Compton, *Rev. Mod. Phys.*, **3**, 191 (1931).

G. P. Thomson[3] have treated at length the observations and concepts associated with various types of discharges. Loeb[4] and Loeb and Meek[5] have discussed the spark discharge in detail. Loeb[6] has summarized the essential features of both the glow and the arc discharge. Any critical study of the subject shows immediately that the discharge is in general a quite complex phenomenon; it is a complicated mixture of a large number of contributing effects. Under some conditions certain of these contributions stand out; under but slightly different conditions other contributions predominate. The type of discharge is determined by the nature of the effect or effects largely responsible for the maintenance of the discharge. For example, the essential difference between a glow and an arc discharge is a difference in the mechanism by which electrons are supplied at the cathode. Our present interest is in the more fundamental concepts associated with discharge phenomena, rather than in detailed interpretations of the various types of discharge. Let us therefore direct our attention to some of the more general features associated with the discharge of electricity through gases at low pressure.

## 2. THE GLOW DISCHARGE THROUGH GASES AT REDUCED PRESSURE

### Appearance of the Discharge

*General Features.*—If one applies sufficient potential between the electrodes of a tube to cause a visible discharge, the appearance of the discharge changes with changes of gas pressure. At atmospheric pressure the discharge appears as a series of discontinuous sharp sparks. As the pressure is reduced to 5 or 10 cm. of Hg the discharge takes on a continuous thread-like appearance. The color of the discharge depends upon the gas within the tube; for air it is lavender-like at this stage of exhaustion. It is at this pressure that the two electrodes begin to take on different appearances. As one proceeds to lower pressures the thread-like discharge spreads laterally until at 1 cm. of Hg it fills the entire cross section of the tube. At this stage the strong violet glow on the cathode, the negative electrode, stands out distinctly. As the pressure is further reduced the lavender glow begins to recede from the cathode, forming the positive column and the Faraday dark space.

At a few mm. of Hg pressure the positive column may be a uniform glow, or it may consist of alternate light and dark sections known as striations.

[3] J. J. Thomson and G. P. Thomson, *Conduction of Electricity Through Gases* (3rd ed.; London: Cambridge University Press, 1933), Vol. II, pp. 292–598.

[4] L. B. Loeb, *Rev. Mod. Phys.*, **8**, 267 (1936).

[5] L. B. Loeb and J. M. Meek, *Jour. App. Phys.*, **11**, 438, 459 (1940).

[6] L. B. Loeb, *Fundamental Processes of Electrical Discharge in Gases* (New York: John Wiley & Sons, 1939), pp. 560–641.

If striations are present the luminous layers are very close together at first, and gradually separate as the pressure is further reduced. At this stage of exhaustion the apparent features are the striated positive column, the Faraday dark space, and the violet negative glow near the cathode. As the pressure is further reduced to about 1 mm. of Hg the negative glow separates into two parts, leaving a sharply defined dark space between. This dark space is known as the Crookes dark space, or as the cathode dark space, and constitutes the most sharply defined feature of the discharge. Fig. 1, taken from a recent survey by Compton and Langmuir,[2] represents a typical glow discharge at about this pressure. The thin glow between the

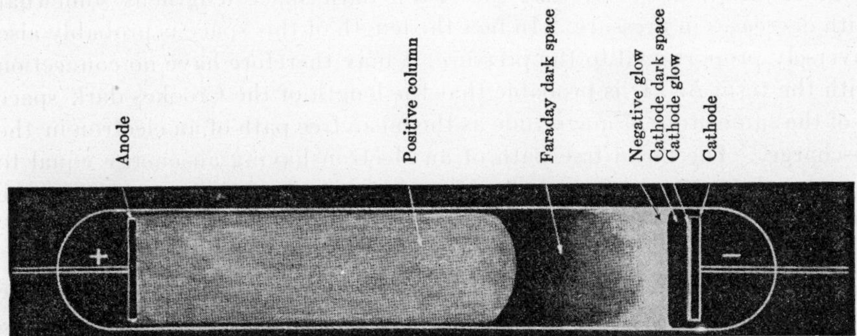


FIG. 1.—A typical glow discharge in a gas at approximately 1 mm. of Hg pressure.

Crookes dark space and the cathode is known as the cathode glow. As the pressure is still further reduced the positive column continues to recede from the cathode, the striations become more coarse and indistinct, and the Crookes dark space lengthens. If the pressure is reduced sufficiently the positive column disappears entirely and the Crookes dark space, its boundaries becoming more and more indistinct, gradually fills the entire tube. At a pressure of a few microns (a micron is $\frac{1}{1000}$ of a mm. of Hg) the walls of the glass tube begin to fluoresce. The color of the fluorescent light depends upon the kind of glass; it is a yellowish green for commonly used glass. Pressures still lower than this are found in X-ray tubes and in most vacuum tubes used in radio.

*The Cathode Dark Space.*—The length of the Crookes dark space, from cathode surface to negative glow, is roughly inversely proportional to the pressure;[7] it may be given more closely by the expression

$$d = \frac{A}{p} + B$$

[7] A. Güntherschulze, *Zeits. f. Physik*, **20**, 1 (1923); **30**, 175 (1925); **34**, 549 (1925).

where $A$ and $B$ are constants. The numerical value of $B$ is small, 1 mm. or less. It seemed at one time that the term $B$ represented the length of still another dark space which has not yet been mentioned. In a number of pure gases a very thin region known as the Aston dark space appears between the cathode surface and the cathode glow. Aston[8] found this to be approximately 1 mm. thick; and there appeared no appreciable change with pressure. It therefore seemed that the entire cathode dark space $d$ was made up of two parts, the thin Aston dark space which was essentially independent of pressure, and the remaining distance out to the negative glow, this latter being inversely proportional to the pressure. Güntherschulze[9] has observed more recently, however, that the Aston dark space lengthens somewhat with decreases in pressure. In fact the length of this space is probably also inversely proportional to the pressure; it may therefore have no connection with the term $B$. It is probable that the length of the Crookes dark space is of the same order of magnitude as the mean free path of an electron in the discharge. The mean free path of an electron having an energy equal to that acquired in traversing the Crookes dark space is much greater than the mean free path of a molecule of the gas at a pressure encountered in the discharge tube; the ratio[10] of these may be of the order of 50.

The sharpness of contrast in the luminous glow at the boundary of the Crookes dark space varies greatly with the gas. The line of demarcation is particularly sharp in oxygen; in helium and hydrogen the change in luminosity is so slight that the boundary cannot be located at all accurately by visual observation. Certain electrical methods[11] to be mentioned shortly can be used to locate this boundary, and these serve even when the visual line of demarcation is indistinct. The extent of the discharge tube occupied by the cathode glow, the Crookes dark space, the negative glow, and the Faraday dark space is determined by the material of the cathode, the nature of the gas, and the pressure of the gas; it is essentially independent of the distance between electrodes. On the other hand, the positive column conveniently adjusts its length to fill the remainder of the tube regardless of how long the tube may be. It is this positive column that is seen in the ordinary neon sign.

*The Positive Column.*—The positive column itself is an interesting and varied phenomenon. It is sometimes uniform and sometimes striated. Holm[12] has shown that striations exist only within certain interdependent

[8] F. W. Aston, *Proc. Roy. Soc.*, A, **80**, 45 (1908).

[9] A. Güntherschulze and F. Keller, *Zeits. f. Physik*, **71**, 238 (1931).

[10] J. J. Thomson and G. P. Thomson, *Conduction of Electricity Through Gases* (3rd ed.; London: Cambridge University Press, 1933), Vol. II, p. 302.

[11] A. Güntherschulze, *Zeits. f. Physik*, **40**, 414 (1926).

[12] R. Holm, *Phys. Zeits.*, **25**, 497 (1924).

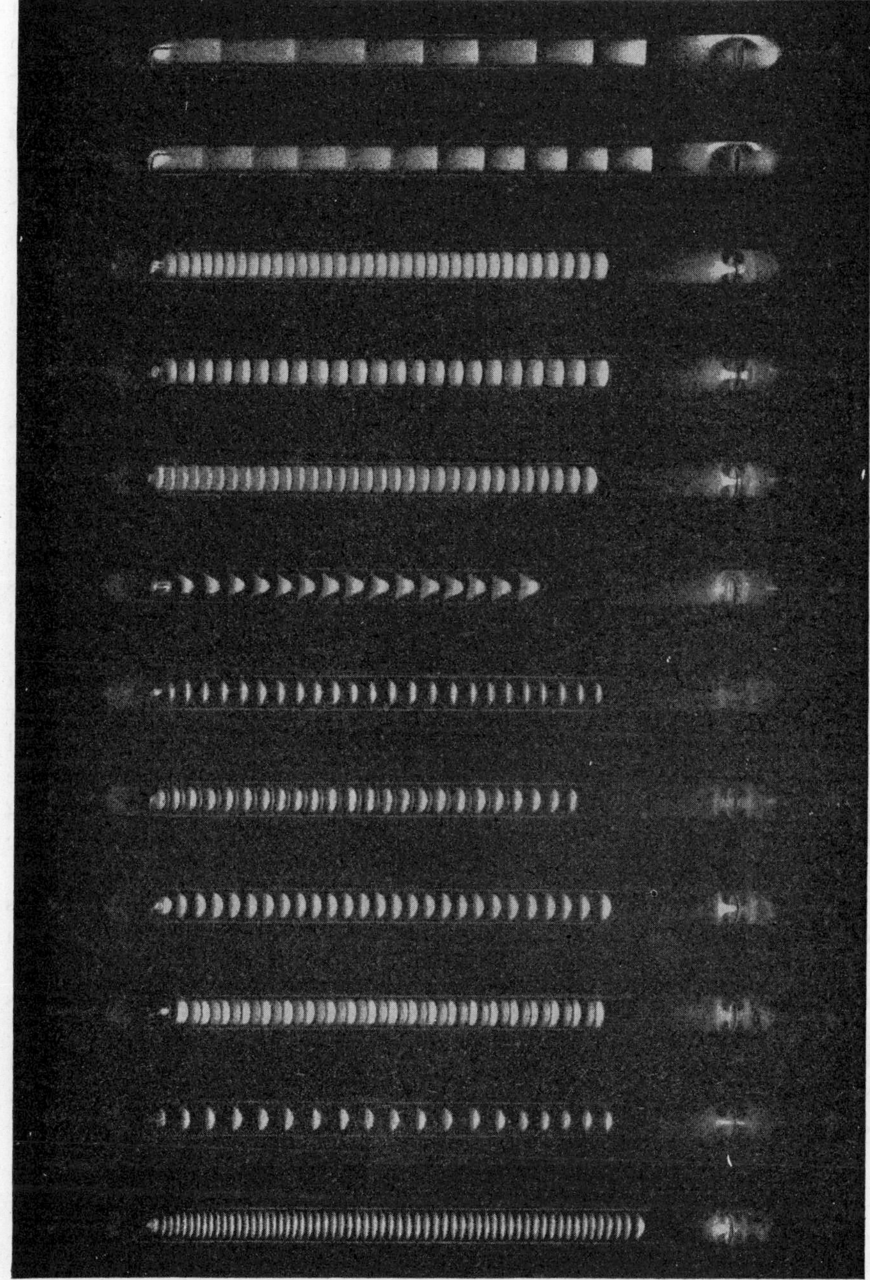

FIG. 2.—Photographs of typical glow discharges in several gases under various conditions

ranges of pressure and current density. If either the pressure or the current density falls outside these boundaries, the positive column is a uniform glow. Even under conditions such that striations are present, the appearance of the striations is quite varied. This is indicated by Fig. 2, a reproduction of some very early photographs taken by De La Rue and Müller.[13] The distance between striations depends upon the nature and pressure of the gas, the current density, and the diameter of the discharge tube. Occasionally only that part of the positive column nearest the cathode is striated, while the remainder is a uniform glow.

Under certain conditions an apparently uniform positive column when viewed in a rotating mirror is found[14] to be striated; the striations can be seen moving rapidly along the tube toward the cathode. An extended study of these moving striations was made many years ago by Spottiswoode.[15] More recently Aston and Kikuchi[16] have measured the speeds with which these striations move in several gases. They found speeds of the same order as the velocities of sound in the respective gases, but the speed increases with decreases in gas pressure. J. J. Thomson[17] has called attention to the fact that the range of pressure over which moving striations are observed is that in which the intermittent character of the discharge is quite pronounced. He therefore suggests that the motion may result from puffs produced by the successive explosions of the intermittent discharge. These moving striations are probably associated with the so-called plasma oscillations in an ionized gas. Since electrons have a very much lower inertia than positive ions, parts of an ionized region must be able to respond very quickly to any change in electric field. Hence the ionized gas in the positive column, called plasma by Langmuir, is capable of propagating electrical waves. Very high frequency oscillations of this plasma have actually been observed.

Under other conditions striations remain quite stationary. This is evident from the photographs of Fig. 2 by De La Rue and Müller,[13] for which the exposure times were of the order of 15 seconds. The photographs indicate that a variety of forms is possible. Sometimes the luminous sections are thin and sharply defined; sometimes they are quite thick and diffuse. Often the striations occur in close pairs, the two components giving different spectra.[18] Even with single striations the color is sometimes different at different parts of a striation. Zeleny[19] has reported that in a discharge

[13] W. De La Rue and H. W. Müller, *Phil. Trans. Roy. Soc.*, **169**, 155 (1878).

[14] A. Wüllner, *Pogg. Ann. Jubelband*, p. 32 (1874).

[15] W. Spottiswoode, *Proc. Roy. Soc.*, A, **25**, 73 (1876).

[16] F. W. Aston and T. Kikuchi, *Proc. Roy. Soc.*, A, **98**, 50 (1920).

[17] J. J. Thomson, *Phil. Mag.*, **11**, 724 (1931).

[18] W. Crookes, *Proc. Roy. Soc.*, A, **69**, 399 (1902).

[19] J. Zeleny, *Jour. Frank. Inst.*, **209**, 625 (1930).

through hydrogen he obtained red striations in one part of the tube and blue in another part. The shape of the striations is variable; it is ordinarily convex toward the cathode, and this side is more sharply defined than the other. Small amounts of impurity in the gas affect the striated positive column greatly. In fact it seems doubtful[20,21] whether stationary striations ever occur in highly purified gases. On the other hand, moving striations, which constitute an entirely different phenomenon, occur in both pure and impure gases.

*The Normal Versus the Abnormal Discharge.*—One other interesting visible feature of the discharge will be mentioned. This has to do with the area of the cathode covered by the cathode glow. It was discovered early by three different observers[22–24] working independently, that the electrical discharge from a cathode is confined to that area covered by the luminous cathode glow, and that an increase in current through the tube increases this area proportionally. The current density at the cathode remains fixed as long as the entire cathode is not covered by the glow. The discharge is referred to as normal as long as the cathode glow does not cover the entire cathode surface. Currents higher than that for which the glow first covers the entire cathode lead to the so-called abnormal discharge. The normal current density depends[25] upon the nature and pressure of the gas, and upon the metal used as cathode.

Many features of the discharge change as the discharge passes from the normal to the abnormal state. Whereas the length of the Crookes dark space $d$ is independent of the current through the tube for the normal discharge, it diminishes with increasing current in the abnormal discharge. It depends upon the current density, which is constant for the normal discharge but which increases as the discharge passes to the abnormal state. For very high current densities in the abnormal discharge the dark space again becomes essentially independent of the current. For this limiting case Güntherschulze[26] has found that the product $pd$ for at least a number of gases becomes approximately one-fifth the corresponding value for the normal discharge.

## Nature of the Particles Responsible for the Current

Evidence is clear that the transfer of electricity through the discharge must be attributed to the movement of both negative particles and positive

[20] J. J. Thomson and G. P. Thomson, *Conduction of Electricity Through Gases* (3rd ed.; London: Cambridge University Press, 1933), Vol. II, p. 381.

[21] W. H. McCurdy, *Phil. Mag.*, **48**, 898 (1924).

[22] A. Wehnelt, *Ann. d. Physik*, **7**, 237 (1902).

[23] H. A. Wilson, *Phil. Mag.*, **4**, 608 (1903).

[24] N. Hehl, *Phys. Zeits.*, **3**, 547 (1902).

[25] A. Güntherschulze, *Zeits. f. Physik*, **20**, 14 (1923).

[26] A. Güntherschulze, *Zeits. f. Physik*, **59**, 433 (1930).

particles. It was about 1870 when Crookes discovered the phenomenon of "cathode rays," particles leaving the cathode. He referred to these cathode rays as a "fourth state of matter." Nearly 30 years later Thomson[27] found that these cathode ray particles could be deflected by electric and by magnetic fields, and he measured their velocity and their ratio of charge to mass. The particles travel in straight lines, as shown by the shadows cast by objects placed in their paths; they are ejected normally from the cathode; they penetrate thin pieces of matter; they heat any object upon which they impinge; they are deflected by an electric field in the direction negative charges would be urged; they are deflected in a magnetic field as would be a current flowing in the direction opposite that taken by the cathode rays; they charge bodies upon which they strike negatively; they produce fluorescence. The evidence shows clearly that the cathode rays are streams of electrons ejected from the region of the cathode. These electrons travel at very high speeds, thousands of miles per second. The exact velocity with which the fastest travel is determined by the potential difference across the discharge.

Not all electrons arise in the region of the cathode. The discharge is maintained only by virtue of ionization by collision. Additional electrons, together with positive ions, are produced at various points along the discharge. Those produced at some distance from the cathode of course fall through a smaller potential difference and consequently attain a smaller velocity. Also, certain of those produced at the cathode give up energy by collision in their passage through the gas. Experiments indicate, however, that a great majority of the cathode rays observed after passing through the Crookes dark space have velocities comparable with the maximum. By deflecting these moving electrons in electric and magnetic fields, Thomson determined the ratio charge/mass for the particle. While the electronic charge was very poorly known at that time, it was nevertheless obvious that the mass of the electron was very small. Thomson[27] found that the ratio $e/m$, and hence the mass of the electron, was always the same regardless of what gas was in the tube and of what metal was used as cathode; and he could find no change of mass with velocity. Except for a now well-established slight change of mass with velocity, more recent experiments have substantiated Thomson's early findings. It is now known that for low velocity electrons the mass is accurately $1/1837$ that of the hydrogen atom.

Observations show also that positive particles move toward the cathode. An opaque screen placed within the Crookes dark space casts a shadow on the cathode; the cathode glow disappears within the shadow. Those particles which normally arise beyond the point where the screen is placed,

[27] J. J. Thomson, *Phil. Mag.*, **44**, 293 (1897).

and which proceed toward the cathode, must be positively charged. This has been shown directly by allowing the particles to fall on some insulated conductor and observing the sign of the charge accumulated. The particles travel in straight lines, heat objects on which they impinge, and cause fluorescence of glass or properly prepared screens. They were first observed by Goldstein who, upon allowing some of them to pass through small holes in the cathode, noticed streams of luminous gas behind the cathode. Goldstein called the phenomenon "Kanalstrahlen." The particles are now known as positive rays. While Goldstein did not succeed in deflecting these particles by electric and magnetic fields, Wien[28] showed that they could be so deflected; larger fields than those suitable for deflecting equivalent electrons were necessary, however. From the direction of the deflection the particles were found to be positively charged; from the magnitude of the deflection they were found to be much more massive than the electron. It is now known that these positive rays are molecules which have lost one or more electrons; they are positive ions of the gas in the discharge tube, formed no doubt by electron collisions with molecules. These positive particles travel at high speeds, but not as fast as do the cathode rays. Experiments show that the maximum energy acquired by a singly charged positive ion in the discharge is the same as that acquired by an electron. This maximum energy is that attained by the ion in falling freely through the entire potential difference across the discharge tube. Many positive ions have energies much less than this. These positive particles will be discussed in detail later; a great deal has been learned from them.

### Potential Required to Maintain the Discharge

It has been found that for a fixed distance between electrodes the potential necessary to maintain a discharge decreases rapidly as the pressure is decreased from atmospheric. The decrease continues until a pressure of the order of 1 mm. of Hg is reached. With further decreases in pressure the potential necessary to maintain the discharge increases rapidly. The general shape of the curve is indicated in Fig. 3. The minimum of the curve may be only a few hundred volts, even though tens of thousands of volts may have been required to maintain the discharge at pressures near atmospheric. At pressures higher than that leading to a minimum potential it is supposed that the presence of so many molecules hinders the process of ionization by collision by decreasing materially the mean free path of the ion. This would necessitate a greater potential across the tube to provide the stronger field necessary to give to the ion, during its relatively short free path, sufficient energy to ionize. At lower pressures it is supposed that there are no longer sufficient molecules present in the gas to render

[28] W. Wien, *Ann. d. Physik*, **65**, 440 (1898).

most efficient the ionization process. An ion capable of ionizing has too small a chance of striking a molecule. This would lead again to a greater potential necessary to maintain the discharge.

Another interesting phenomenon is that for a given gas at a fixed pressure there exists a critical distance between electrodes for which the potential necessary to maintain the discharge is a minimum. If the distance between electrodes is either increased or decreased from this critical value the potential necessary to maintain the discharge is increased. This is easily demonstrated by use of a tube similar to that illustrated in Fig. 4. At proper gas pressures the discharge will pass between electrodes over the long path rather than over the short one. The long path in this case is near that critical distance between electrodes for which the potential necessary to maintain the discharge is a minimum. This phenomenon was

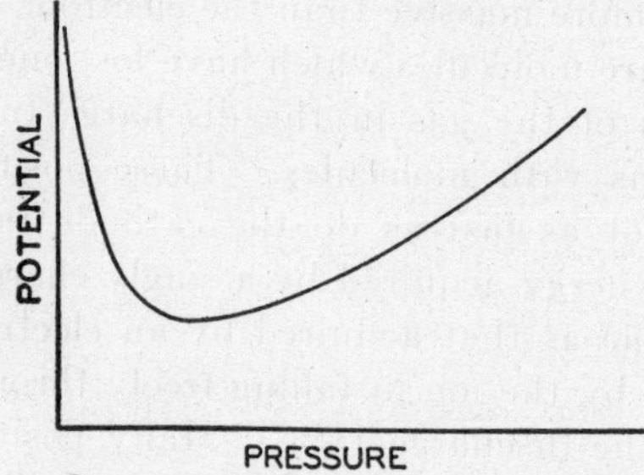


FIG. 3.—Showing the manner in which the potential required to maintain a gaseous discharge varies with the pressure of the gas.

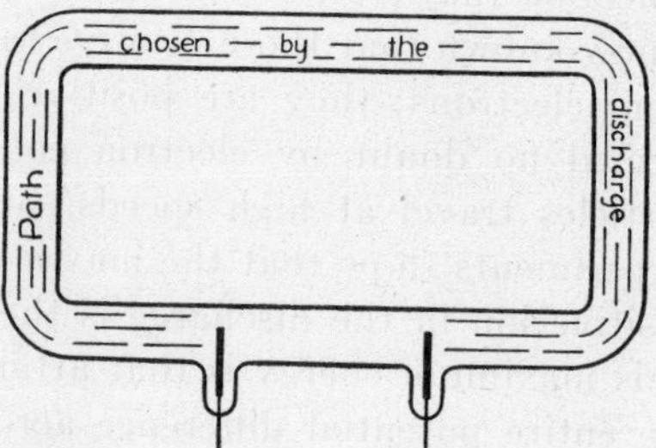


FIG. 4.—Indicating that under certain conditions it is easier to maintain a discharge over a long path than over a short one.

employed in an early form of neon glow tube used in television, where it was desired to have the cathode glow on the outer surface of the cathode so that it could be seen readily.

It is also of interest that a considerably greater potential difference is required to start a discharge through a tube than to maintain this discharge when once started. A potential difference of a few hundred volts can maintain a discharge which requires several thousand volts to start. The reason for this has to do with the change in potential distribution along the tube when the discharge starts.

## Electric Field Distribution in the Discharge

*Methods of Investigating.*—There are several ways in which the potential distribution, and hence the electric field distribution, within the discharge can be studied. Early observers used a single probe method in which a fine platinum wire probe connected to an electrometer is placed at various points along the discharge. The electrometer measures the potential of the probe relative to some fixed point, usually the anode. It is hoped that the probe will take up the potential of that point of the discharge where it is placed. It probably does so if there is a generous supply of both positive and negative ions in that part of the discharge being studied. If the ions are mainly of one kind, however, as is the case in certain parts of the discharge, these moving ions will continue to drive themselves onto the probe until the probe assumes a potential sufficient to prevent by electrical repulsion any more ions of this sign reaching it. The potential assumed by the probe will also depend upon the relative energies of the positive and negative ions in the immediate vicinity. Langmuir[29] has pointed out that such an isolated probe often takes up a potential from 5 to 15 volts below the actual potential of the space immediately surrounding it. Results are therefore trustworthy only at certain parts of the discharge.

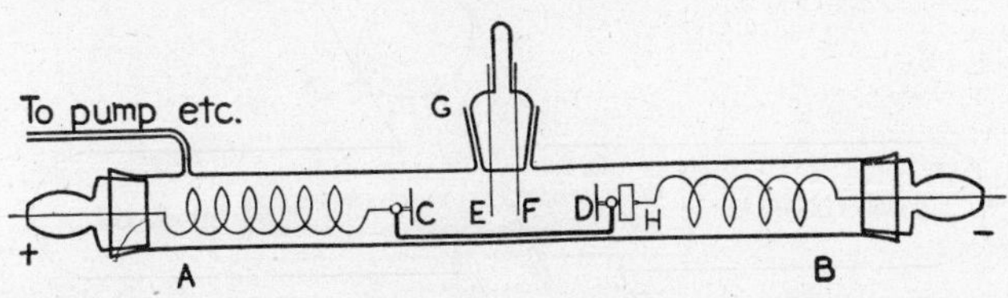


Fig. 5.—Wilson's apparatus for measuring the potential distribution along the discharge. The discharge takes place between electrodes *C* and *D*, which are held a fixed distance apart by a glass rod. *E* and *F* are two small wires, very close together, between which the potential difference is measured.

The work of H. A. Wilson,[30] apparatus for which is shown in Fig. 5, is typical. The difference in potential between two fixed probes a millimeter or so apart was measured by an electrometer. Measurements at different parts of the discharge were made by moving the entire discharge with respect to the fixed probes. This method is much less susceptible to error than is the single probe method; while the potential assumed by either electrode may be in error, these errors are largely eliminated by measuring directly the difference of potential. The difference of potential between probes in the two probe method is a direct measure of the electric field at a particular part of the discharge, while in the single probe method the electric field must be deduced from the rate of change of probe potential with displacement along the discharge. Holm[31] has subjected the two probe method to certain tests as to accuracy, and concluded that it is reliable within 2 percent, at least in hydrogen and air at pressures above 2 mm. of Hg. The error becomes appreciable only when the potential or the ion concentration in the vicinity of the probe changes so rapidly that

[29] I. Langmuir, *Jour. Frank. Inst.*, **196**, 751 (1923).
[30] H. A. Wilson, *Phil. Mag.*, **49**, 505 (1900).
[31] J. M. Holm, *Phil. Mag.*, **11**, 194 (1931).

the two probes, even though close together, find themselves in quite different surroundings. Under such conditions the potentials assumed by the two probes will not be in error by the same amount. Holm has analyzed the error which results.

Thomson[32] devised an ingenious method employing an auxiliary beam of electrons moving perpendicular to the discharge under investigation. The general method is illustrated in Fig. 6. The electric field at any point along the main discharge is measured by observing the deflection suffered by the auxiliary electron beam as it is passed through this point. With proper design of apparatus, and with the use of a very fine pencil of rather

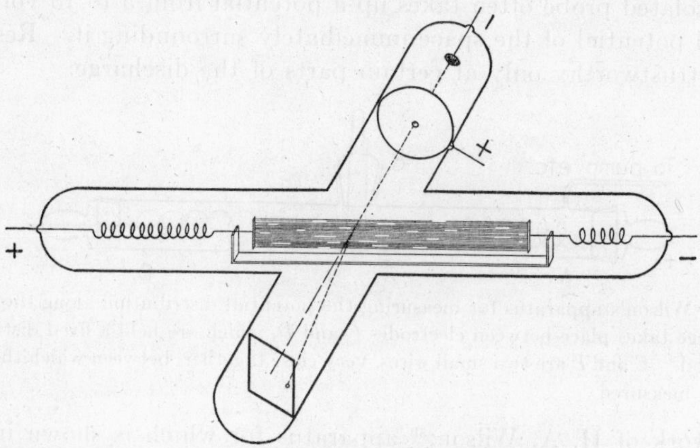


FIG. 6.—Sketch of Thomson's crossed electron beam method of measuring electric field distribution in discharge.

high speed electrons, the effect of the auxiliary discharge upon the one under study is negligible. Results obtained by the method seem entirely trustworthy. Unfortunately, the method is not particularly sensitive, and it is therefore most applicable to those parts of the discharge where the field is relatively high.

Brose[33] developed still another method. When an atom emits light while it is in a strong electric field the characteristic spectral lines are split into multiplets. This is known as the Stark effect. The separation of component lines of the multiplet depends upon the strength of the electric field. Brose determined the electric field distribution in the discharge by observing the magnitude of the Stark effect in light coming from different parts of the tube. Sufficient light for such studies comes even from the dark spaces of the discharge. Brose's method certainly produces no interference with the discharge. It has the serious limitation, however, that

[32] J. J. Thomson, *Phil. Mag.*, **18**, 441 (1909).
[33] E. Brose, *Ann. d. Physik*, **58**, 731 (1919).

large electric fields are required, fields larger than are found at most places in the normal discharge.

Langmuir has investigated the errors associated with the early single probe studies, and has suggested two modifications free from the uncertainties associated with the older method. One of these[29] employs a heated filament as probe. This filament is placed in series with a battery and with sufficient resistance that the temperature of the filament is just below that at which it begins to emit electrons. A shorting switch is placed across a part of this resistance. This part is so chosen that when it is shorted by closing the switch the filament is heated to a temperature sufficiently high to emit electrons. If the space surrounding the probe is at a potential higher than that of the probe, electrons leave the hot filament. If the space potential is the lower, electrons cannot leave the emitting surface. One therefore varies the potential at which the probe is held, usually relative to the anode, until the current to it does not change upon heating the probe. Except for two small corrections, the potential of the space is given by the most negative probe potential for which the current remains unchanged upon heating the probe; electrons are then just on the verge of being able to escape. Small corrections must be made for the potential drop along the hot filament and for the thermal velocities with which the electrons are emitted. The method is quite reliable. McCurdy[21] remarks that reliable results are obtained even in electric fields where no appreciable discharge is present.

The second method suggested by Langmuir[29,34] is a modification of the single cold probe procedure. The modification required to give trustworthy results has been investigated thoroughly,[34] both theoretically and experimentally. If a single probe placed at some point in the discharge is held at a potential negative with respect to the surrounding space, positive ions are drawn to it and electrons are driven away. An accumulation of positive ions forms a so-called positive ion sheath about the probe. The thickness of this sheath can be calculated in terms of the probe potential and the ion concentration. The sheath can actually be observed[35] as a very thin dark region of the order of 0.1 mm. thick surrounding the probe. Observed thicknesses agree with those calculated. The presence of this sheath nullifies the field due to the negative probe at all points outside the sheath, and thus seriously limits the current to the probe. In fact the positive ion current to the probe is nearly independent of the probe potential as long as this potential is well below that of the surrounding space. As the potential of the probe is increased to near that of the space, some of the more energetic electrons are able to drive themselves onto the probe in spite

[34] I. Langmuir and H. Mott-Smith, *Gen. Elec. Rev.*, **27**, 449, 539, 616, 762, 810 (1924).

[35] I. Langmuir and H. Mott-Smith, *Gen. Elec. Rev.*, **27**, 539 (1924).

of its still slightly negative potential. The net positive ion current to the probe is thus decreased. The current to the probe becomes zero at that potential for which a sufficient number of electrons drive themselves onto the probe to compensate for the positive ions drawn thereto. This is the potential assigned to the space in the early single probe studies. Actually the positive ion sheath is still present, though now very thin, and the probe is still at a potential lower than that of the space. As the probe potential is further increased, the number of electrons able to drive themselves onto the still negative probe increases; the probe current has now reversed. When the probe potential reaches the potential of the space, the positive ion sheath disappears and a negative electron sheath begins to form. With further increases in probe potential electrons are actually attracted to the

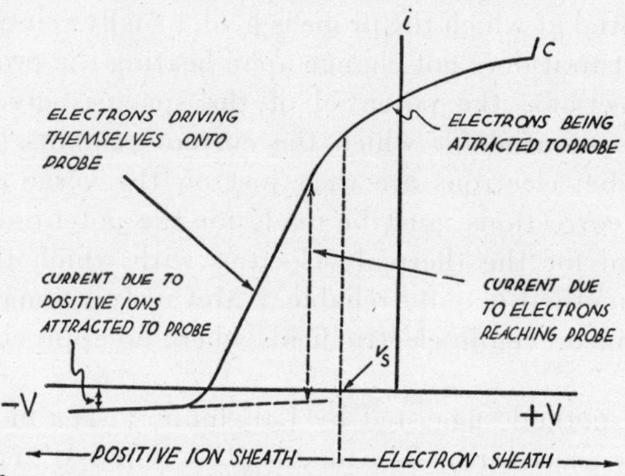


FIG. 7.—Showing the manner in which the current to a Langmuir probe varies with the potential of the probe.

probe, and the negative sheath becomes increasingly thicker. As the probe potential is carried higher than the space potential by appreciably more than the ionization potential of the gas, the probe current increases rapidly due to ionization by collision. These successive changes in probe current are illustrated in Fig. 7.

Mathematical treatment of the manner of variation of the current to the probe with changes of probe potential shows that if the electrons have a Maxwellian distribution of velocities, then for potentials below that of the surrounding space the logarithm of the electronic current to the probe should vary linearly with potential. For potentials above that of the space the current should be proportional to the square root of the excess potential. While near the space potential the probe current is a combination of effects, and therefore does not follow either simple law, extrapolation of the theoretical curves does allow accurate location of the space potential. Details[34] of the procedure have been summarized elsewhere.[36] While actual curves sometimes have the shape theoretically expected, they are frequently distorted seriously, due probably to a non-Maxwellian distribution of velocities. Typical semilogarithmic curves are shown in Fig. 8, reproduced from the work of Compton, Turner, and McCurdy[37] on the hot cathode mercury vapor discharge. These workers take as the true potential of the space that potential for which an abrupt change of slope occurs in the semilogarithmic plot. These points are indicated by arrows on the four experi-

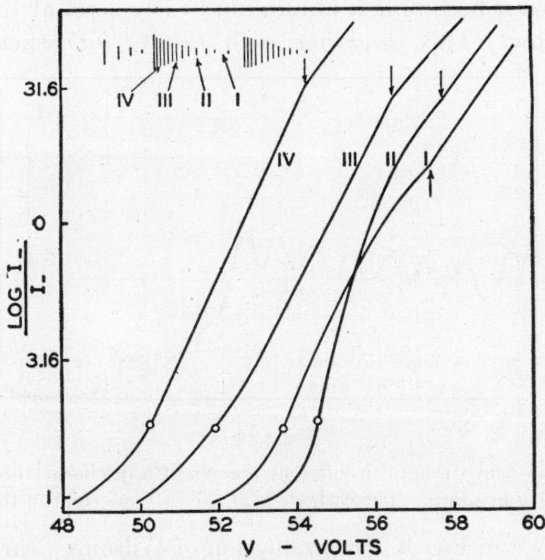


Fig. 8.—Curves I, II, III, and IV show the electron current to an exploring electrode placed in the parts of a striation indicated in the upper left corner of the diagram. The arrows, marking the positions of abrupt changes of slope, indicate the potentials of the several regions with respect to the cathode. The circles represent the potentials which would have been assigned to the several regions on the basis of the old single exploring electrode method.

mental curves. The circles indicate the incorrect potentials which would have been assigned using the old single probe method. The authors also used a hot probe to determine the potentials of numerous points in the discharge. Results obtained by the two methods were identical. The modified cold probe method gives entirely reliable results. It is widely used today.

*Experimental Results—Field Distribution.*—Numerous workers have used each of the available methods in determining the potential distribution, and thence the electric field distribution, throughout the discharge. In

[36] J. B. Hoag, *Electron and Nuclear Physics* (2nd ed.; New York: D. Van Nostrand, 1938), pp. 166–172.

[37] K. T. Compton, L. A. Turner and W. H. McCurdy, *Phys. Rev.*, **24**, 597 (1924).

addition to the early work of Wilson[30] covering the entire length of the discharge, the extensive work of Aston[38] within the cathode dark space, and the findings of Thomson[32] within the straited positive column, significant contributions have been made by many others.[21,31,37,39] As might be expected, results depend somewhat upon the character of the discharge, and they have not always been entirely consistent as regards details. Nevertheless, certain salient features stand out. There is a very strong field near the cathode. This decreases as one proceeds outward across the Crookes dark space, becoming a minimum, nearly zero, at the near edge of the negative glow. This, together with results for other parts of the

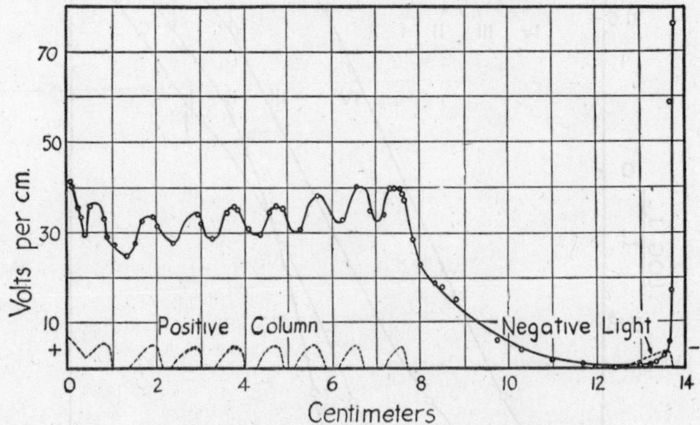


Fig. 9.—Showing the field strength in different regions of a discharge through hydrogen at 2.25 mm. of Hg pressure. The cathode is at the extreme right of the diagram.

discharge, is shown in Fig. 9, a reproduction of Wilson's[30] early work. The actual manner in which the field decreases as one leaves the cathode is shown more clearly by Fig. 10, a reproduction of Aston's[38] findings. Similar results were obtained for various gases. It is clear that the field strength within the cathode dark space increases linearly with the distance from the edge of the negative glow, becoming very large as the cathode is approached.

As one proceeds beyond the cathode dark space the electric field remains nearly zero throughout the negative glow and the first part of the Faraday dark space. Wilson[30], Fig. 9, found it to increase considerably in the latter half of the Faraday space. Fig. 11, reproduced from the more recent work of Holm,[31] shows a similar increase. In Fig. 12, however, also from the work of Holm, the field remains nearly zero right up to the start of the striated positive column. In fact the field appears to be slightly but definitely negative over this region. Obviously, details vary, depending upon the gas and conditions of the discharge. In any case the field here is very small as compared to that near the cathode.

[38] F. W. Aston, *Proc. Roy. Soc.*, A, **84**, 526 (1911).

[39] A. Wehnelt and G. Schmerwitz, *Ann. d. Physik*, **86**, 864 (1928).

If the positive column be uniform the electric field remains practically constant throughout. This is evident from Fig. 11. The magnitude of this field depends upon the character of the discharge and upon the gas. There is practically no field[40] within the positive column for argon and neon,

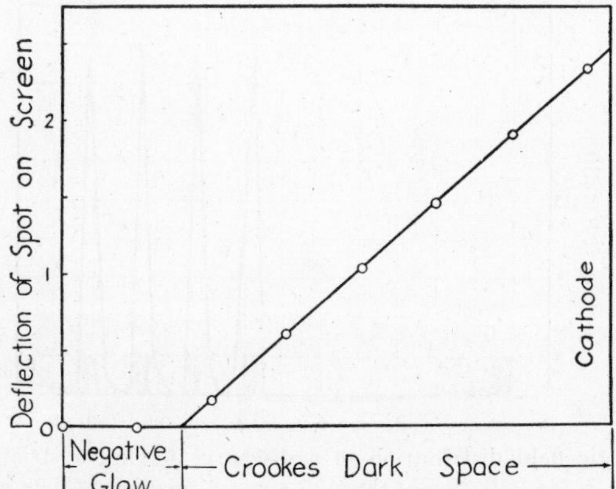


Fig. 10.—Aston's curve showing the manner in which the field strength decreases from the cathode out to the negative glow. The field strength is closely proportional to the deflection of the spot on the screen.

and only a small one for helium. This seems to be true over a considerable range of pressure. On the other hand, the normal field[40] in hydrogen is quite appreciable, and it is proportional to the gas pressure over a considerable range. It is 2.40 volts per cm. per mm. of Hg pressure. Zimmerman[41] has attempted to link the magnitude of the electric field in the positive

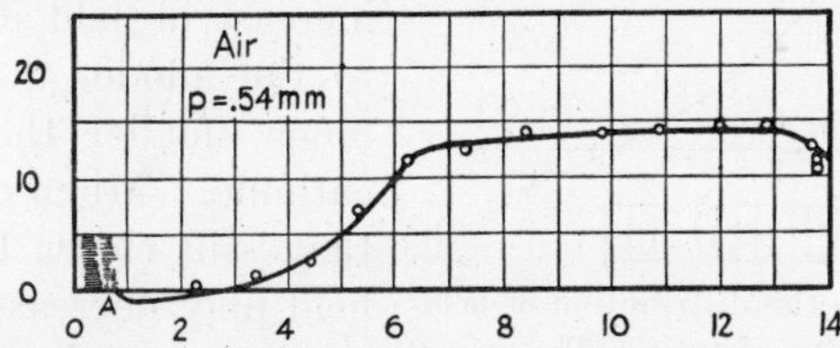


Fig. 11.—The electric field distribution in a discharge having a uniform positive column. This curve is for a discharge through air at a pressure of 0.54 mm. of Hg.

column with the rate of diffusion of electrons along the discharge. If the positive column is striated the average field throughout its length is approximately the same as that in the uniform column, but distinct maxima and minima of field strength are found. The maxima occur just inside the front edges of the luminous sections; the minima occur in the intervening dark

[40] A. Güntherschulze and F. Keller, *Zeits. f. Physik*, **77**, 703 (1932).

[41] G. Zimmermann, *Zeits. f. Physik*, **91**, 767 (1934).

sections. These maxima and minima are shown strikingly by the work of Holm,[31] Fig. 12. The minima appear here to be zero. Thomson[32] has shown, however, that the field may even be negative within the dark sections of the striated column; and he has fixed accurately the positions of the

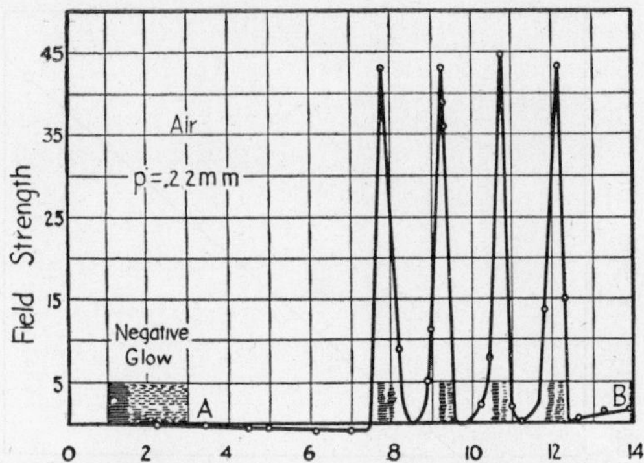


FIG. 12.—The electric field distribution in a discharge having a striated positive column. This curve is for a discharge through air at a pressure of 0.22 mm. of Hg.

maxima and minima. Fig. 13 is Thomson's[42] representation of his findings. The existence of these negative fields at certain points in the discharge is well established. They have been found by both the two probe method and the auxiliary electron beam method; they have been found in discharges utilizing either a cold or a hot cathode.

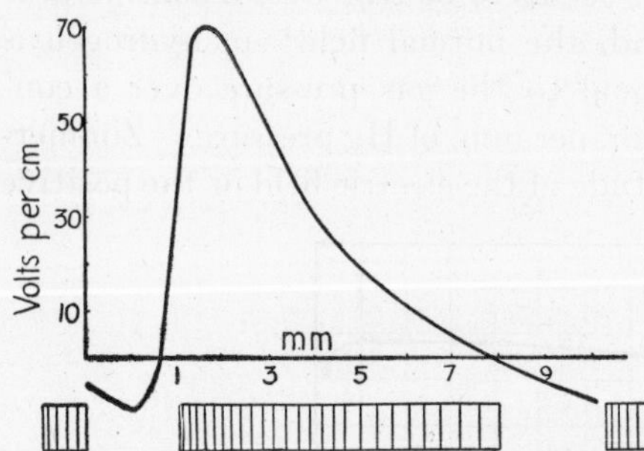


FIG. 13.—Showing the distribution of field intensity in the vicinity of stria. The curve extends over just one of numerous luminous sections. The cathode is far to the left.

There appears to be a rapid increase in field strength very close to the anode, though this field is much smaller than that near the cathode. Much evidence indicates that still closer to the anode the field may decrease again, even becoming negative. These changes occur so close to the anode surface that it is difficult to make accurate measurements, and the experimental probe cannot be gotten close enough to the anode to trace out the changes in their entirety.

*Experimental Results—Potential Distribution.*—The potential distribution along the discharge can of course be obtained immediately from the curve

[42] J. J. Thomson and G. P. Thomson, *Conduction of Electricity Through Gases* (3rd ed.; London: Cambridge University Press, 1933), Vol. II, p. 385.

showing the field distribution. From the definitions of potential difference and field strength it follows that the potential drop across any section of the discharge is represented by the area under the field distribution curve between two lines bounding this section. It is therefore obvious that there is a large potential drop across that section of the discharge extending from the cathode out to the near edge of the negative glow. In fact this drop constitutes a major part of the potential difference across the entire tube. For example, Aston[38] concluded that, under the conditions prevailing in the discharges he studied, this potential drop was equal, within the limits of experimental error, to the entire potential applied to the discharge tube. This means that there was practically no potential drop from the cathode edge of the negative glow over to the anode. Possible error of measurement might allow a drop of 10 to 15 volts, but even this is certainly small as compared to the drop of from 200 to 600 volts which existed near the cathode. It is therefore obvious that an electron leaving the cathode attains nearly its maximum velocity within the Crookes dark space. And the direction of its flight is determined largely within this space, even though the anode may be placed off to one side in an arm of the main discharge tube.

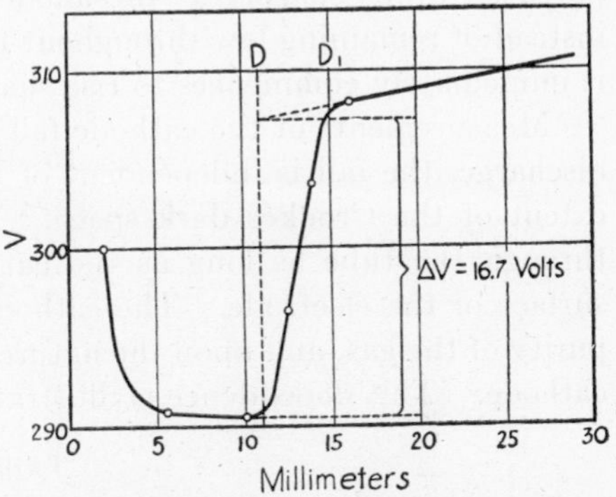

FIG. 14.—Showing the variation of potential required to maintain a discharge as the distance between electrodes is varied. The fixed cathode is at the left, the movable anode at the various positions indicated by the abscissae.

The drop in potential across that region extending from the cathode to the near edge of the negative glow is known as the cathode fall of potential. In many gases it is difficult to determine visually the length of the dark space and the extent of the region over which to measure the cathode fall of potential. In these cases, however, the boundary can be located by an electrical method.[11,43] If in a normal discharge the anode is moved gradually toward the cathode, the potential difference required to sustain the discharge falls but slightly until the Faraday dark space is reached. As the anode enters this dark space, however, the potential drops rapidly, due probably to the fact that some primary electrons are now able to reach the anode. This drop is shown in Fig. 14, modeled after the findings of Güntherschulze.[11] As the distance between electrodes is further diminished,

[43] J. J. Thomson and G. P. Thomson, *Conduction of Electricity Through Gases* (3rd ed.; London: Cambridge University Press, 1933), Vol. II, pp. 293, 403.

the potential remains nearly constant until the anode reaches the boundary between the negative glow and the Crookes dark space. As the anode enters this dark space the potential required to maintain the discharge rises sharply. Thus the position of the outer boundary of the cathode dark space can be located. This method of location agrees with the visual method in those cases where the boundary is distinctly visible. It can therefore be used with confidence in those cases where no sharp boundary is visible. Güntherschulze[11] finds that in the abnormal discharge the potential drops sharply as the anode enters the Faraday dark space; but instead of remaining low throughout this dark space and the negative glow, it immediately commences to rise sharply again.

Measurements of the cathode fall of potential show that, in the normal discharge, the fall is independent of the pressure; it is independent of the extent of the Crookes dark space. It is also independent of the current through the tube as long as the cathode glow does not cover the entire surface of the electrode. The cathode drop depends upon the nature and purity of the gas, and upon the nature and condition of the material used as cathode. This dependence is illustrated by the brief data of Table I.

TABLE I

Cathode falls of potential for various gases when used with various metals as cathode

| Cathode | | Gas | | | | | | |
|---|---|---|---|---|---|---|---|---|
| Metal | $\phi$ | Air | $H_2$ | $N_2$ | $O_2$ | He | Ne | A |
| K | 2.2 | ... | 172 | 170 | ... | 69 | 68 | 64 |
| Na | 2.4 | ... | 185 | 178 | ... | 80 | 74 | ... |
| Al | 3.0 | 229 | 168 | 179 | 310 | 141 | 120 | 100 |
| Mo | 4.15 | ... | ... | ... | ... | 171 | 160 | 145 |
| W | 4.54 | ... | ... | ... | ... | 155 | 153 | 143 |
| Ni | 4.9 | 226 | 211 | 197 | ... | 181 | 172 | 160 |
| Pt | 6.0 | 277 | 276 | 230 | 370 | 194 | 178 | 192 |

Values of $\phi$ represent the work, expressed in equivalent volts, required to free an electron from the metal. Values listed under the various gases represent the respective cathode drops of potential in volts.

Although most of the data of Table I have been taken from the fairly recent work of Pike[44] and other workers,[45] they should be regarded as approximate only. The presence of very small cathode surface impurities, or the adsorption of a gaseous layer on the cathode, is known to affect the

[44] E. W. Pike, *Zeits. f. Physik*, **90**, 319 (1934).

[45] J. J. Thomson and G. P. Thomson, *Conduction of Electricity Through Gases* (3rd ed.; London; Cambridge University Press, 1933), Vol. II, pp. 331, 332.

work function greatly; it also affects the cathode fall of potential. Small impurities[46] in the gas lead to large changes in cathode potential drops. Güntherschulze[47] has found that as little as 1/1000 percent of alkali or alkaline earth in mercury vapor lowers the normal cathode fall appreciably. In a study of the discharge through nitrogen when different metals are used as cathode and anode, Kasiwagi[48] found that in many cases a thin layer of the anode metal is deposited on the cathode, thus changing the cathode fall. Pike[44] emphasizes the approximate character of results even when every effort is made to purify the gas and to outgas the electrodes. It is nevertheless apparent that the cathode drop is appreciably smaller for the electropositive metals K and Na than for the more electronegative metals Ni and Pt. This is no doubt due to the greater ease with which

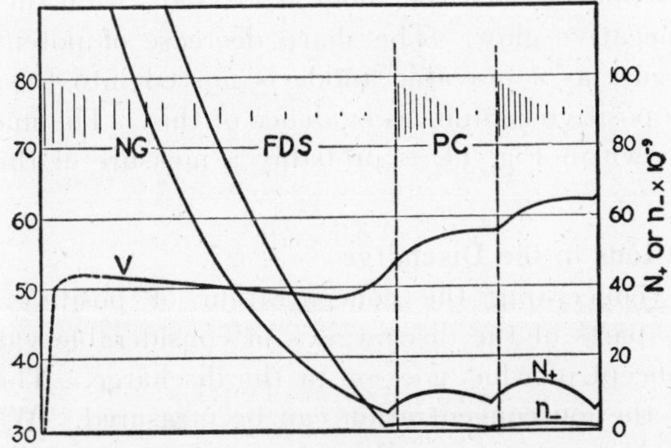


FIG. 15.—Showing the distribution of potential $V$ throughout a discharge through mercury vapor. Variations of positive and negative ion concentrations are shown by curves $N_+$ and $n_-$.

electrons can be freed from the electropositive metals, those metals having low work functions. It is apparent also that the cathode drop is relatively small for the inert gases He, Ne and A, and this despite the fact that these gases have high ionization potentials. Although the data are not included in the table, the cathode drops in Hg vapor are approximately twice those in He, even though the ionization potential of Hg is less than half that of He. This is probably due to the fact that the light He positive ion is somehow more effective than the Hg ion in freeing electrons from the cathode by bombardment.

As one proceeds from the cathode edge of the negative glow through this glow, the Faraday dark space, and the positive column, the potential drop is sometimes positive and sometimes negative. Rises and falls of

[46] A. Güntherschulze, *Zeits. f. Physik*, **21**, 50 (1924).
[47] A. Güntherschulze, *Zeits. f. Physik*, **39**, 491 (1926).
[48] Y. Kasiwagi, *Inst. Phys.* and *Chem. Res.*, Tokyo, *Sci. Papers*, **34**, 461 (1938).

potential of course correspond to the positive and negative electrical fields. The total potential drop across this entire region is quite small as compared to the cathode fall of potential. Changes in potential throughout a portion of the negative glow, the Faraday dark space, and the striated positive column are shown in Fig. 15.

Observations show also an appreciable drop in potential near the anode. The fairly strong field near the anode, as shown in Fig. 9, indicates the existence of this. The drop occurs very close to the anode surface, still inside any investigating probe placed as close as practical. The anode drop in potential is much smaller than the cathode drop; it is of the order of 10 to 20 volts. The actual value depends upon the anode metal[48,49] and upon the gas,[49] and is quite sensitive to impurities. The anode drop of potential disappears when the anode is located within the Faraday dark space or the negative glow. The sharp decrease of potential across the tube which occurs as a movable anode is moved into the Faraday dark space from the positive column, is evidence of this. The magnitude of the decrease, as shown in Fig. 14, is probably a measure of the anode fall of potential.

## Distribution of Ions in the Discharge

Knowledge concerning the concentration of positive and negative ions in various parts of the discharge is of considerable value in arriving at a proper concept of what goes on in the discharge. There are several ways in which the ion concentration can be measured. Wilson[30] was the first to make such observations. He arranged two very small (1.5 × 5 mm.) platinum plates, parallel and 1.5 mm. apart, near the central axis of the discharge, and applied to them a small fixed potential. These plates, together with the single cell supplying their potential, were insulated so that they might take up the potential of the point in the discharge where they were placed. This minimized any effect the auxiliary plates might have on the main discharge. Currents to the auxiliary plates, resulting from ions drawn thereto, were then measured for various positions of the plates along the discharge. Since these currents were always very small it was assumed that they were proportional to the ion concentrations existing at the respective points. While results depend somewhat upon the nature of the discharge, the more important findings are as shown in Fig. 16, a reproduction of Wilson's results. Although both electrons and positive ions contribute to the observed currents, these currents are taken as a measure of the electron concentrations. Although positive ions are no doubt numerous they contribute only a small fraction to the current

[49] J. J. Thomson and G. P. Thomson, *Conduction of Electricity Through Gases* (3rd ed.; London: Cambridge University Press, 1933), Vol. II, p. 401.

because of their much lower mobility. This fraction probably becomes appreciable in regions where the positive ions are far more numerous than electrons. The mere presence of the auxiliary plates in the discharge may also introduce some error. Wilson recognized that, although the entire plate system was insulated, the presence of the plates did disturb the discharge at certain points along the tube.

Van der Pol[50] developed a method which did not necessitate the placing of auxiliary plates in the discharge. It is well known that the conductivity of a material placed in the electric field about a high frequency oscillator affects both the frequency and the amplitude of oscillation; the material behaves as a dielectric and thus influences the capacity of and the energy

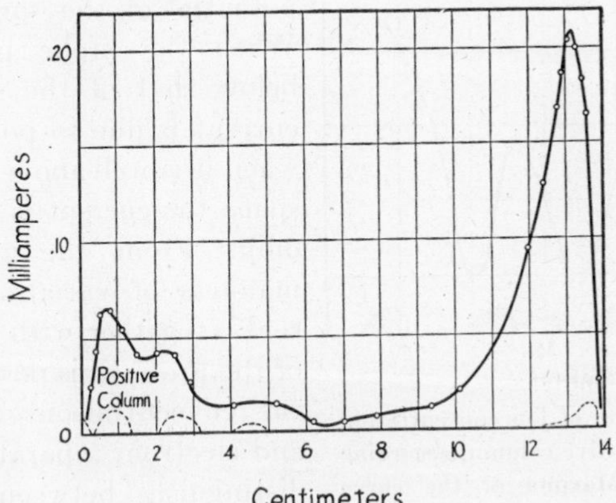


Fig. 16.—Showing the ion concentrations (proportional to the ordinates) along a discharge through air at 0.3 mm. of Hg pressure.

loss in the oscillatory circuit. Van der Pol observed the magnitudes of these effects when different parts of the discharge were placed between two wires forming a part of an oscillatory circuit. From these observations he evaluated the conductivity, and thence the ion concentration, at various points along the discharge. Results obtained by this method were similar to those of Wilson. An exception occurs, however, in the positions of maximum and minimum electron concentrations along the striated positive column. Wilson's work indicated that the concentration minima occurred in the dark sections of the column; maxima occurred in the light sections, though perhaps somewhat nearer the anode edges. Fig. 17 shows how well defined were the maxima and minima observed by Van der Pol. The maxima of this curve represent minimum electron concentrations; the minima of the curve represent maximum concentrations. Minimum electron concentrations occur at the front (cathode) edges of the luminous

[50] B. van der Pol, *Phil. Mag.*, **38**, 352 (1919).

striations, closely in those regions for which maxima of electric field strength are found.[31,32] If the ion velocity is proportional to the field strength at any point, these high field strengths would move the ions out of these regions rapidly, thus leading to a small ion concentration. Again judging from Van der Pol's results, maximum ion concentrations fall near the anode edges of the striations, where the fields are relatively weak.

A third method of measuring ion concentrations utilizes the Langmuir[34] modified probe procedure. The observations are much the same as those made in determining the potential distribution throughout the discharge. The current to the probe is measured for various probe potentials ranging from well below to well above the potential of the surrounding space. When the probe potential is well below that of the space the probe current is due to positive ions only; when it is well above the surrounding space the current is due to electrons only. From the magnitudes and manners of variation of these currents, together with the surface area of the probe, it is possible to evaluate the concentrations of positive ions and electrons separately. Ability to distinguish between positive and negative ions is a distinct advantage of the method. Fig. 15 represents the findings of Compton, Turner and McCurdy[37] for a mercury vapor discharge. Minima of both electron and positive ion concentrations fall just in front of the cathode edges of the striations. The net charge concentration in the positive column appears slightly positive, although this may be due to the fact that positive ion concentrations are only roughly determined. The net charge in the Faraday dark space and into the negative glow is definitely negative. Although these authors did not determine the ion concentrations in the Crookes dark space, other works show that the electron concentration is much less than in the negative glow; but the positive ion concentration is much greater. The Crookes dark space is a region in which a large net positive ion concentration exists. This is consistent with the existence of a very strong electric field near the cathode, between the cathode and this nearby positive space charge. It is consistent also with the relatively small fields beyond the edge of the negative glow; the effect of the negative cathode is largely balanced by the intervening positive space charge.

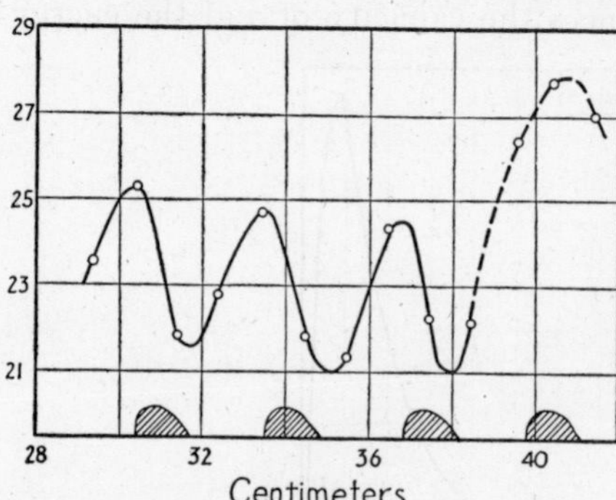


Fig. 17.—Variation of ion concentration along the striated positive column, according to Van der Pol. Maxima of the curve represent minimum electron concentrations; minima represent maximum concentrations. The cathode is far to the left, at the origin.

## Elementary Theory of the Discharge

Although a great deal has been learned about the glow discharge in the past half century, and although the general process that goes on is understood, a definite and unquestioned concept into which all of the many detailed observations fit has not been formulated. This is due in part to the way in which experimental results vary with conditions existing in the discharge, and in part to the number of phenomena contributing simultaneously to the maintenance of the discharge. Only a few of the many ramifications which any critical survey of the literature will show to exist have been discussed here.

The general process by which the discharge is maintained is fairly clear, however. The start of the discharge must come by virtue of stray ions in the gas. After the start has been made the discharge itself furnishes the ions required to maintain it. Conclusive evidence that electrons move from cathode to anode within the discharge, and that positive ions move toward the cathode, has already been pointed out. Let us now inquire where and how these ions are formed. Consider an electron starting out from the surface of the cathode, refraining for the moment to ask what gives rise to it. This electron gains energy rapidly as it moves through the strong electric field near the cathode. After traveling only a short distance, perhaps $\frac{1}{20}$ of the way across the cathode dark space, it has sufficient energy to ionize. Just how much it does ionize in the cathode dark space is debatable. It is true that the mean free path of a molecule of gas at a pressure of the order of that found in the discharge tube is such that the molecule would make some 50 collisions[10] in traversing the cathode dark space. But the mean free path of an electron is much longer than that of a molecule. Some evidence which allows a comparison of this free path with the length of the cathode dark space will be quoted shortly.

*The Cathode Dark Space.*—Several theories[51–55] of the cathode dark space have been advanced. Some of these[51,55] assume extensive ionization by collision in the dark space; others[52,54] start with the assumption that neither the electrons nor the positive ions traveling through the dark space make any ionizing collisions therein. One[53] attempts to account for ion production as an indirect result of collisions. On this theory the collisions serve mainly to excite the atoms struck; the subsequent radiation from these atoms is then supposed to ionize other atoms on which it falls. The most elaborated and most widely accepted theory is that advanced by

[51] H. A. Wilson, *Phys. Rev.*, **8**, 227 (1916).
[52] J. W. Ryde, *Phil. Mag.*, **45**, 1149 (1923).
[53] J. J. Thomson, *Phil. Mag.*. **48**, 4 (1924).
[54] A. Güntherschulze, *Zeits. f. Physik*, **33**, 810 (1925).
[55] K. T. Compton and P. M. Morse, *Phys. Rev.*, **30**, 305 (1927).

Wilson.[51] On this concept it is supposed that the electrons leaving the cathode, together with other electrons and positive ions produced by collision, produce cumulative ionization by collision throughout the dark space. The resulting positive ions move toward the cathode, and it is assumed that their bombardment of the cathode surface frees electrons. This is the supposed source of the primary electrons starting from the cathode.

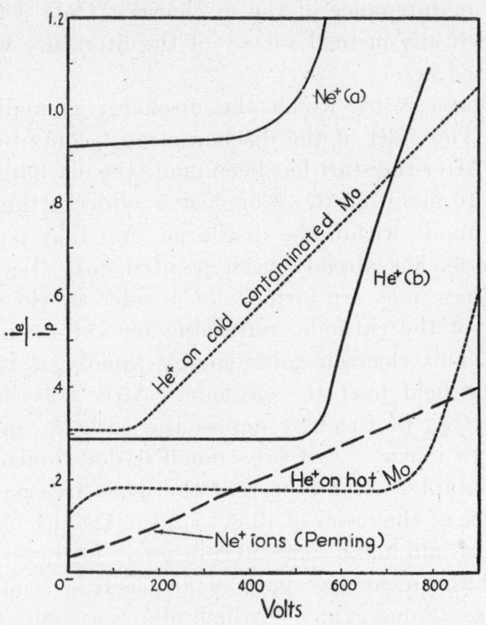


FIG. 18.—Showing the emission of electrons from a tungsten cathode caused by bombarding it with positive ions of various energies. Ordinates represent the number of electrons ejected per positive ion striking the cathode. Abscissae represent the energies of the incident positive ions.

It has long been known that bombardment of a metal surface with energetic ions will free electrons from the surface. It has more recently been learned that positive ions with energies even as small as those acquired in the cathode dark space are capable of ejecting electrons. Horton and Davies[56] found that the positive ions of helium with only 10 equivalent volts energy would cause ejection. Oliphant[57] has made more extensive investigations of the numbers of electrons ejected by positive ions of several gases when these ions are allowed to bombard a metal target with various energies. Fig. 18 shows some of his results. Ions with energies less than

[56] F. Horton and A. C. Davies, *Proc. Roy. Soc.*, A, **95**, 333 (1919).

[57] M. L. E. Oliphant, *Proc. Roy. Soc.*, A, **127**, 373 (1930); **132**, 631 (1931).

around 500 equivalent volts eject electrons to about the same extent regardless of their energy; ions with energies above this become much more efficient ejectors. It may be that low energy ions cause ejection not directly by bombardment, but rather because they may exist as an absorbed layer on the cathode for an appreciable time. This causes a lowering of the effective work function of the cathode; and the lowering may be sufficient to cause the existing electric field itself to liberate the electrons.[58] In any case it is certain that electrons are liberated at the cathode by impinging positive ions; and these electrons in turn produce more positive ions. Each is dependent upon the other for production.

There are several lines of evidence which bear directly on how extensive the ionization by collision in the Crookes dark space really is. The first of these is a calculation of the number of ions produced by collision, using the appropriate Townsend coefficients. Compton and Morse,[55] in extending quantitatively the Wilson theory of the cathode dark space, made calculations of this character. Their calculations indicate that some 50 positive ions should arrive at the cathode for every 1 electron leaving this surface; furthermore, the number of positive ions entering the cathode dark space from the negative glow is negligibly small as compared to the number of electrons proceeding in the opposite direction. It would therefore appear that each electron leaving the cathode surface must be responsible, either directly or indirectly, for the formation of some 50 new pairs of ions within the Crookes dark space. Others[59] have arrived at similar conclusions. This extensive ion formation in the dark space would no doubt mean that a large fraction of the total energy furnished the discharge tube is dissipated within the cathode dark space. Güntherschulze[60] has concluded from calorimetric experiments that some 80 percent of the total energy goes to heating the cathode. Other workers,[61,62] by extending the theory to certain chemical changes[63] produced within the discharge, conclude that from 80 to 85 percent of the total energy is dissipated within the cathode dark space, and most of the remainder in the negative glow. While such conclusions, drawn from both experiment and calculation, have some little to recommend them, they are not altogether in agreement with other experimental findings. In fact some observations to be mentioned shortly are quite contradictory to them.

[58] A. K. Brewer and J. W. Westhaver, *Jour. App. Phys.*, **8**, 779 (1937).

[59] E. G. Linder and A. P. Davis, *Jour. Phys. Chem.*, **35**, 3649 (1931).

[60] A. Güntherschulze, *Zeits. f. Physik*, **15**, 8 (1923); **19**, 313 (1923); **23**, 334 (1924).

[61] E. G. Linder, *Phys. Rev.*, **38**, 679 (1931).

[62] K. G. Emeleus and D. Kennedy, *Phil. Mag.*, **18**, 874 (1934).

[63] A. K. Brewer and Others, a series of articles, *Jour. Phys. Chem.*, **33**, 883 (1929) to **36**, 2133 (1932).

Perhaps a more reliable type of calculation of the extent of ionization in the dark space is that carried out by Thomson.[64] In calculating the number of ions produced by the passage of an electron through the dark space, it is necessary to take into account the fact that the velocity of the ionizing electron is constantly changing, and that the ionizing power of the electron depends upon the velocity with which it is moving. From many early experiments, together with several more recent and reliable works,[65–70] the number of ions produced by an electron per centimeter of

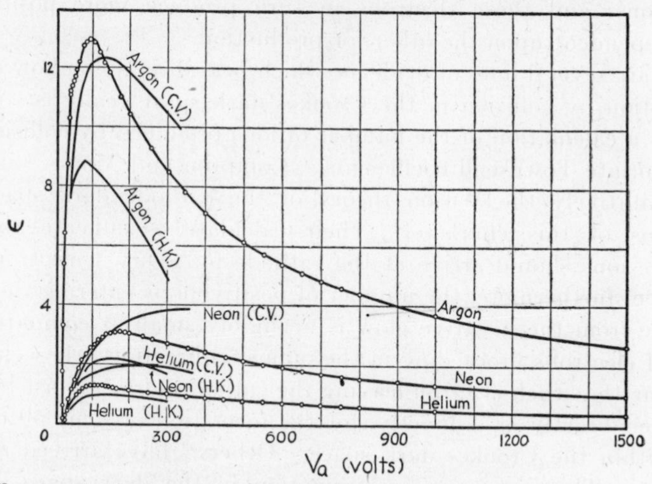


Fig. 19.—Showing the efficiency of ionization by electrons of various energies $V_a$ when passing through He, Ne, and A at 1 mm. of Hg pressure.

travel through a gas is known. Fig. 19, reproduced from the work of Smith,[69] and including results of Hughes and Klein[65] and of Compton and Van Voorhis[66] as well, makes clear the general findings. The electron starts to ionize as soon as its energy, expressed in equivalent volts, becomes greater than the ionization potential of the gas through which it is passing. The ionizing efficiency increases with increases in energy of the electron, the number of ions formed per centimeter being closely proportional to the amount by which the electron energy exceeds the ionization potential. This proportionality soon breaks down, however, and a maximum ionizing

[64] J. J. Thomson and G. P. Thomson, *Conduction of Electricity Through Gases* (3rd ed.; London: Cambridge University Press, 1933), Vol. II, pp. 311–316.

[65] A. L. Hughes and E. Klein, *Phys. Rev.*, **23**, 450 (1924).

[66] K. T. Compton and C. C. Van Voorhis, *Phys. Rev.*, **26**, 436 (1925); **27**, 724 (1926).

[67] T. J. Jones, *Phys. Rev.*, **29**, 822 (1927).

[68] W. Bleakney, *Phys. Rev.*, **35**, 139 (1930); **36**, 1303 (1930).

[69] P. T. Smith, *Phys. Rev.*, **38**, 1293 (1930).

[70] J. T. Tate and P. T. Smith, *Phys. Rev.*, **39**, 270 (1932).

efficiency occurs at an electron energy of from 100 to 300 volts. The position of the maximum depends upon the gas. Higher energy electrons ionize less and less efficiently, the ionizing power of high speed electrons being inversely proportional[69] to the electron energy. Further results of this character, together with the underlying theory which is in the main supported, are discussed elsewhere.[71] Our present interest is to utilize these data to calculate the number of positive ions formed as the electron travels across the cathode dark space.

Calculations of this character have been carried out by Thomson[64] for a normal discharge through helium at 1 mm. Hg pressure, for which discharge the dark space extends 1.3 cm. from the cathode. When secondary ionization by newly formed electrons is taken into account, but no allowance made for the probably negligible ionization due to positive ions, it appears that 1 electron in traveling through the Crookes dark space would produce on the average about 3 positive ions. This is subject to some variation, depending upon whose data are used for the ionizing power of the electron. Now as shown in Fig. 18, Oliphant[57] found about 0.3 of an electron ejected per positive ion bombarding the cathode. The 3 positive ions formed above would then just account for the 1 primary electron leaving the cathode. This substantiates the view that ionization by collision of electrons, together with the ejection of electrons from the cathode due to the bombardment by the positive ions so formed, are the most important contributing factors in sustaining the discharge.

There are no doubt other agents which contribute somewhat. For example, there is emitted from certain parts of the discharge, particularly the negative glow, radiation,[72,73] which is capable of ionizing the gas and also of causing photoelectric ejection of electrons from the cathode surface. Calculations such as the above indicate, however, that these contributions are not large; the factors considered in Thomson's calculation seem to be the important ones. On the other hand, some rather recent experiments of Uyterhoeven and Harrington[74] have indicated strongly that electron emission from the cathode is only in part due directly to positive ion bombardment. An appreciable part of the emission may be due to the presence of metastable atoms in the discharge. These atoms, temporarily in an excited state, may eject photoelectrons by their subsequent radiation. Or they may free electrons in some more obscure manner as they strike the cathode

[71] J. J. Thomson and G. P. Thomson, *Conduction of Electricity Through Gases* (3rd ed.; London: Cambridge University Press, 1933), Vol. II, pp. 91–102.

[72] J. J. Thomson, *Proc. Camb. Phil. Soc.*, **10,** 74 (1899); **14,** 417 (1907); **15,** 482 (1908); *Phil. Mag.*, **48,** 1 (1924); **49,** 761 (1925).

[73] A. Dauvillier, *Phil. Mag.*, **2,** 1046 (1926).

[74] W. Uyterhoeven and M. C. Harrington, *Phys. Rev.*, **36,** 709 (1930).

surface. They have sufficient excess energy to do this. In any case this recent work has seemed to show that positive ion bombardment is by no means the only method by which electrons are freed from the cathode. If Thomson's calculations are accepted, then in the discharge just considered, for which the dark space is 1.3 cm. long, each electron on the average moves[64] nearly 1 cm. from the cathode before producing its first new pair of ions. Thus the calculations lead to the conclusion that the mean free path of the electron is quite comparable with the length of the cathode dark space. In the abnormal discharge, for which the dark space is much shorter for a given pressure, the mean free path of the electron no doubt exceeds the length of the cathode dark space.

A second line of evidence bearing on the number of ions produced in the cathode dark space comes from measurements of the positive ion current at the surface of the cathode. The ratio of this current to the electron current leaving the surface has been measured by several workers. Aston[75] measured the positive ion current received by a collector placed immediately behind a perforated cathode. His observations showed that approximately half the current was carried by positive ions; that is, the number of positive ions arriving at the cathode was approximately equal to the number of electrons leaving the cathode. On the other hand, Güntherschulze[76] has concluded from the heating of the cathode that the positive ion current may become ten times as large as the electron current. It seems probable that early results may have been influenced through neglect of the possible electron emission due to metastable atoms.[74] Brewer and Miller[77] have attempted to make measurements free from this error. They find that at pressures above 0.5 mm. of Hg the positive ion current is but a small fraction of the total. At lower pressures this fraction increases, reaching approximately one half at pressures of the order of 0.01 mm. of Hg. While it is clear that experimental findings vary greatly among themselves, measurements of this character make it seem probable that the ionization within the dark space is by no means as extensive as is sometimes supposed.

A third line of evidence bearing on the extent of ionization in the dark space is furnished by actual measurement of the energies still retained by electrons after they reach the near edge of the negative glow. If the electron has produced no new ions by collision during its passage through the cathode dark space, its energy expressed in equivalent volts should be equal to the cathode fall of potential. If it has produced new ions by collision then its energy should be less than this. If some of the electrons make ionizing collisions while others do not, one should find electrons arriving at the near

[75] F. W. Aston, *Proc. Roy. Soc.*, A, **96**, 200 (1919).
[76] A. Güntherschulze, *Zeits. f. Physik*, **37**, 828 (1926).
[77] A. K. Brewer and R. R. Miller, *Phys. Rev.*, **42**, 786 (1932).

edge of the negative glow with various energies. Some of the newly formed electrons would arrive with quite low energies; they would certainly be formed at various parts of the dark space, and some would fall through only a small potential difference. Measurements of the energies retained by the electrons after passing through the dark space are therefore significant.

Thomson[78] was the first to make measurements of this character. Electrons leaving the dark space were allowed to enter a metal tube which served as anode. After passing through the small opening running the length of this tube, they were allowed to fall on a fluorescent screen. A small circular luminous spot was visible on the screen. Now an electron stream can be bent by either an electric or a magnetic field whose direction is perpendicular to the motion of the electron. Observations of the amount of bending allow calculation of the electron's velocity and hence its energy. Thomson observed the deflections produced by a known magnetic field and found, surprisingly, that all electrons appeared to have the same velocity. The deflected spot was still small and circular; it was not elongated as it would be if a variety of velocities were present. Furthermore, the observed velocity corresponded to that which an electron would attain in falling freely through the entire cathode fall of potential. These findings have been verified more recently by Brewer and Westhaver.[58] These authors feel that their measurements are sufficiently precise to detect the loss of energy of electrons making more than two ionizing collisions within the dark space. Experiments of this type show also the absence of any appreciable number of new electrons formed by cumulative ionization. Some of these would be formed near the end of the dark space, and consequently would have low velocities. Since both observers used a fluorescent screen for detecting the position of the deflected electron stream, however, it is possible that electrons of quite low velocity might be missed; these are by no means as effective as high speed particles in producing luminosity of the screen. But even if the low speed particles were missed, the fact remains that no electrons are found with energies measurably less than that corresponding to free fall through the entire dark space.

This evidence thus indicates strongly that ionization by collision in the cathode dark space is not extensive. The primary electron leaving the cathode can form directly not more than one or two new pairs of ions before reaching the negative glow; and cumulative ionization resulting from these must be small. Brewer and Westhaver[58] point out that this small ionization can account for an energy dissipation in the dark space of only some 10 percent of the total energy supplied to the discharge. This energy expendi-

[78] J. J. Thomson, *Phil. Mag.*, **48**, 1 (1924); J. J. Thomson and G. P. Thomson, *Conduction of Electricity Through Gases* (3rd ed.; London: Cambridge University Press, 1933), Vol. II, p. 322.

ture is quite inconsistent with the previously mentioned estimates[60–62] of around 80 percent. As substantiating evidence Brewer and Westhaver compare the observed length of the cathode dark space with the mean free path of the electron as obtained from previous data.[69,70] Their results for three gases are shown in Fig. 20. The mean free path between ionizing collisions is of the same order as, or actually somewhat greater than, the length of the dark space. This indicates clearly that somewhat less than one pair of ions is formed directly by each primary electron in traversing

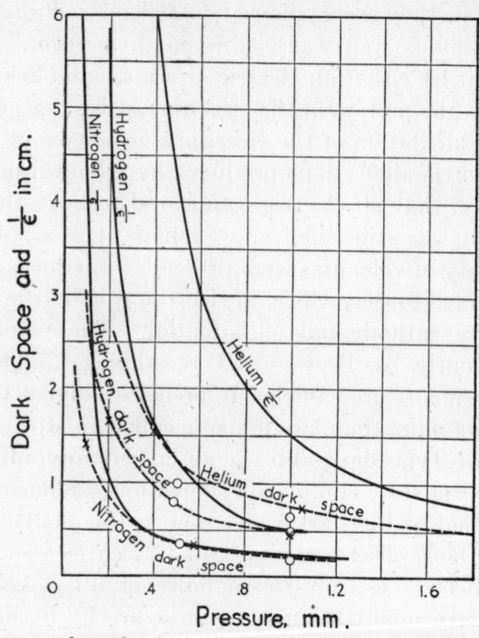


Fig. 20.—The crosses, through which the dashed curves are drawn, represent measured lengths of the cathode dark space for various gas pressures; the circles represent lengths calculated from Aston's equation. The full lines represent the mean free path of the electron at any pressure; values of the mean free path were obtained from the measurements of Smith[69] and Tate.[70]

the dark space. Allowance for additional ionization by these newly formed ions leads to a total of only approximately one or less positive ions formed for each electron leaving the cathode. While actual results depend somewhat upon the gas and the pressure of this gas, this number is quite different from the previous calculated values[55,59,62] of 50 to 100 positive ions per electron. And the present energy loss in the dark space corresponding to this lower ionization is of the order of 10 percent. While this also depends considerably upon the gas and the pressure of the gas, this figure is decidedly smaller than previous estimates. On the other hand, the present conclusions regarding the extent of ionization and the energy loss in the dark space are entirely consistent with the failure to detect any appreciable loss of energy of the primary electrons in their passage through the dark space. They are also consistent with the more recent measurements of the ratio of positive to negative ion currents at the surface of the cathode.

*The Negative Glow and the Faraday Dark Space.*—Certain concepts regarding the negative glow seem fairly well established. It appears that an electron entering this glow with an energy corresponding closely to the cathode fall of potential gives up most of this energy in traveling the length of the luminous region. Brewer and Westhaver[58] have found that although the electron arrives at the edge of the negative glow with an energy corresponding closely to the entire drop of potential across the dark space, it begins to decrease in velocity almost immediately upon entering the glow. These same wokers have compared the length of the negative glow with the known range[79] of the electrons entering it. Their results are reproduced in Fig. 21. It is clear that the length of the glow is closely equal to the range of the electrons entering the glow. The primary electron apparently gives up practically its entire energy by making collisions resulting in ionization or excitation of atoms within the negative glow.

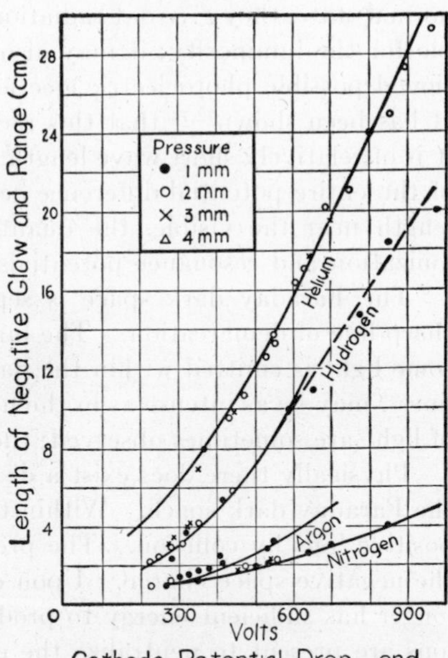


FIG. 21.—The points represent measured lengths of the negative glow corresponding to various cathode potential drops. The full lines are drawn not through the observed points but rather to represent the range of electrons as given by Lehmann.[79]

It has often been supposed that the main supply of positive ions in the discharge comes from the negative glow. Certainly many are produced there. But the evidence indicates that very few of these ever get over to the cathode. It has been shown that the calculated number of positive ions formed in the dark space per electron traveling through it is approximately sufficient to eject one electron from the cathode. There seems to be no room for many additional positive ions coming from the negative glow. The current is carried through the boundary between the dark space and the negative glow almost entirely by electrons. The failure of positive ions

[79] J. F. Lehmann, *Proc. Roy. Soc.*, A, **115**, 624 (1927).

formed in the glow to cross this boundary is not surprising in view of the very weak electric field in the region where they are formed. Most of them probably recombine before they are moved out by the field.

When the excited and ionized atoms in the negative glow return to their normal state, they give out radiation. It is this radiation which is responsible for the luminosity; it may also be responsible for the previously mentioned possible photoelectric ejection of electrons from the cathode surface. It has been shown[72,73] that this radiation is of two types. A small part of it is of relatively short wave length, the quanta having energies of the order of the entire potential difference between electrodes. More of it is of wave length near the visible, the quanta having energies of the order of the ionization and resonance potentials of the gas in the discharge tube.

The Faraday dark space is separated from the negative glow by no sharp line of demarcation. The luminosity gradually fades out. Actually some light is emitted within the dark space; certain characteristic spectral lines[80] may be as intense as in the negative glow. Curious visible patches[81] of light are sometimes observed; the cause of these is not known.

Physically there does exist a distinction between the negative glow and the Faraday dark space. Within the glow, the primary electrons produce positive ions by collision. The presence of these positive ions neutralizes the negative space charge. Upon entering the dark space the electron no longer has sufficient energy to produce ionization. Since but few positive ions are present to neutralize the electron concentration, a large negative space charge is built up in the Faraday space. As the electron drifts slowly through this space, there finally comes a time when it has again acquired sufficient energy to produce ionization, or at least excitation. This is the start of the visible positive column.

*The Striated Positive Column.*—The position of the beginning of the positive column is practically independent of the length of the tube. The first luminous section occurs whenever the electrons coming through the Faraday dark space have again acquired sufficient energy to excite atoms. The energy for excitation of course comes from the kinetic energy of the electron. The speed of the particle is decreased abruptly. As the electron proceeds toward the anode it gradually acquires sufficient energy to repeat the process. The second luminous striation is the result. This goes on, resulting in alternate light and dark sections, until the electron finally reaches the anode.

If this view of the striated column is correct there must exist some tendency to form alternate regions of positive and negative electrification throughout the positive column. Otherwise the positions of striae could

[80] R. Seeliger, *Ann. d. Physik*, **67**, 352 (1922).

[81] J. Zeleny, *Nature*, **125**, 562 (1930); J. M. Holm, *Phil. Mag.*, **11**, 194 (1931).

scarcely be so well fixed. Compton, Turner and McCurdy[37] have argued that this tendency would exist by virtue of the effect of inelastic collisions, resulting in the excitation of atoms, upon the mobility of the electron and thence upon the potential distribution. Fig. 22 shows the variations of electrification and potential they deduced on theoretical grounds. An accumulation of positive ions is pictured near the front of a luminous section, and an accumulation of negative charge in the intervening dark space. These alternate regions of positive and negative electrification appear reasonable when it is recalled that the space charge contributed by the movement of a given number of particles per second through a region depends upon the velocity with which the charged particles move. A greater space charge is set up where the particles move slowly. The type of

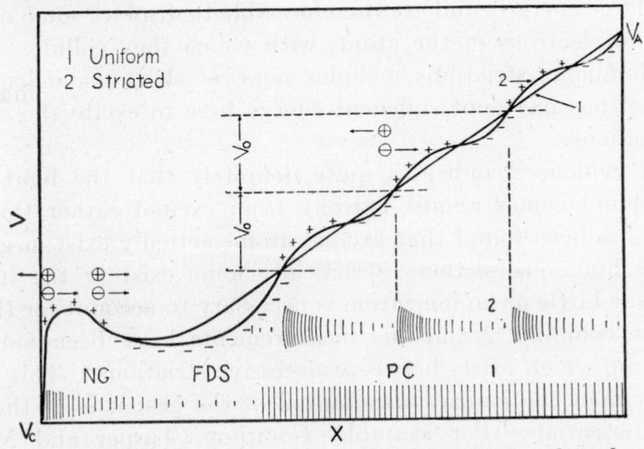


**Fig. 22.**—Showing the theoretical charge and potential distribution throughout a glow discharge having either a uniform or a straited positive column.

charge distribution pictured is consistent with Thomson's observation that the electric field may be negative just in front of a luminous striation. The adjacent positive and negative space charges produce a field opposite to that set up by the potential difference applied to the electrodes; and it is apparently sufficiently strong to determine the direction of the resultant field within the region between.

One might inquire how the electrons ever proceed through those regions in which the electric field is negative. In some cases the electron no doubt comes into such a region with sufficient energy to carry it across in spite of the fact that it is somewhat retarded. In other cases the charge is transported across such regions largely by diffusion. If at any one place the electron concentration is much higher than in adjacent regions, these electrons will gradually diffuse into the adjacent space. Diffusion of charges no doubt plays a rather important part in the discharge tube.

*The Light from the Discharge.*—The origin of light given out from various luminous sections of the discharge is interesting. It was once supposed that most of the light is given out during the process of recombination of positive and negative ions. Evidence does not support this view. The intensity of light from a luminous striation is as great or greater than that from the negative glow, yet the number of ions recombining per second is far less in the striation than in the glow. As has been remarked, most of the radiation from the negative glow is of wave lengths corresponding to energies of the order of the ionization and excitation potentials of the gas.[72,73] Some of it is of much shorter wave length, the energy often corresponding to the entire drop of potential across the discharge tube. This energetic radiation is not unexpected; electrons coming into the negative glow have large energies and are therefore able to displace some of the more firmly bound electrons of the atoms with which they collide. Radiation from the luminous striations includes none of short wave length. The moving electrons have not sufficient energy here to excite the short wave length radiations.

Certain evidence[37] indicates quite definitely that the light from the positive column comes almost entirely from excited rather than ionized atoms. It has been found that excited atoms actually exist in great numbers in the luminous sections; practically none exist in the intervening dark spaces. Little or no ionization is necessary to account for the light in the positive column. Numerous measurements have been made of the potential drop which exists between successive striations. This drop is in general less than the ionization potential of the gas; it is of the order of excitation potentials. For example, Compton, Turner and McCurdy[37] found the measured potential drop between mercury striations to be approximately 4 volts, whereas the ionization potential of this gas is between 10 and 11 volts. This is excellent confirmation of the view that the radiation is largely from excited rather than ionized atoms.

## Chapter 4

# CATHODE RAYS—THE RATIO e/m FOR ELECTRONS

## 1. WHAT ARE CATHODE RAYS?

The phenomenon of cathode rays was discovered by Plücker in 1862. Crookes[1] was the first to recognize the rays as negatively charged particles leaving the cathode of the glow discharge. He referred to these as a "fourth state of matter." Some years later it was shown by Perrin, and somewhat more convincingly by Thomson,[2] that these rays charged bodies on which they impinged negatively. It was also shown[2] that, although the particles normally travel in straight lines, they can be deflected by electric and magnetic fields. They are deflected by either of these fields in a direction which shows them to be negatively charged. From the amount of bending in known fields it is possible to find both the velocity and the ratio of charge to mass of the particle. These cathode ray particles are electrons, discrete negative charges of electricity, completely detached from any atom of matter. Their charge is the Millikan value; they have a characteristic mass. The velocity of these electrons is high, thousands of miles per second. Its exact value depends upon the potential drop across the tube in which the cathode ray is produced. In a highly exhausted tube across which a potential difference $V$ exists, the velocity acquired by these electrons can be obtained from the relationship

$$Ve = \tfrac{1}{2}mv^2$$

provided one does not deal with electrons whose velocity is comparable with that of light. For very high speed particles a modification of the above expression becomes necessary. Considerable knowledge has been gained from studies of the ratio $e/m$ for electrons and the possible variation of this ratio for very high speed particles. It will be the purpose of this section to present some of the methods of measuring the velocity and the ratio $e/m$ for these cathode rays, and to call attention to significant findings coming from such studies.

[1] W. Crookes, *Phil. Trans. Roy. Soc.*, **170,** 135, 641 (1879).

[2] J. J. Thomson, *Phil. Mag.*, **44,** 293 (1897).

## 2. DIRECT MEASUREMENTS OF THE VELOCITY OF CATHODE RAYS

Most of the methods for determining the ratio $e/m$ yield also a value for the velocity of the cathode ray particle. There have been developed, however, a number of methods of measuring this velocity directly. Several of these will be mentioned briefly. The principle underlying them is of considerable importance, for it has been used frequently in recent precise determinations of the ratio $e/m$. Essentially the same principle has been used in recent years in obtaining, with a cyclotron, charged particles with energies of several million electron volts.

Wiechert,[3] following some earlier work by Des Coudres, devised a method of measuring the velocity by comparing the time the electrons take to travel a known distance with the known period of an oscillating current. The method is illustrated in Fig. 1. Cathode rays emitted from the concave cathode $C$ would normally pass through the hole $A$ in a metal shield. Some

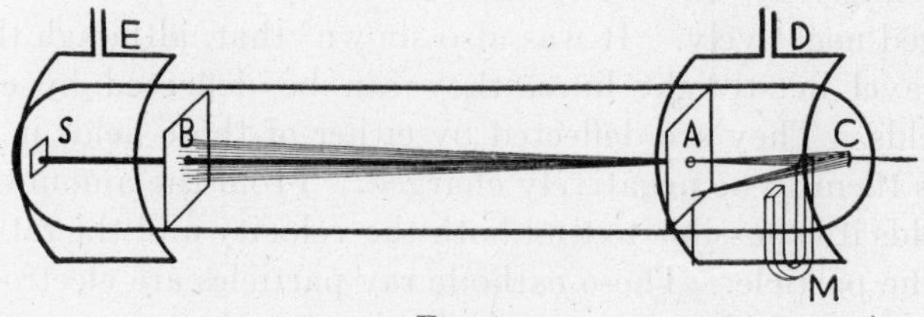


FIG. 1.

of these would pass on through hole $B$ and fall upon the small fluorescent screen $S$. However, a permanent magnet $M$ is so placed that the particles strike the shield considerably to one side of the opening $A$. Coils $D$ and $E$, connected in series, are placed so as to produce a magnetic field perpendicular to the cathode ray stream. An alternating current of known high frequency is passed through these coils. The varying magnetic field due to coil $D$ bends the electron stream first up and then down. The current through the coil and the position of the magnet $M$ are adjusted so that the electron stream passes through hole $A$ only when this current has its maximum value in one direction. At this time the current is changing very slowly and a maximum number of electrons is therefore allowed to pass through the opening. Some of the electrons getting through $A$ pass on through opening $B$. Were it not for the magnetic field due to coil $E$ they would strike the screen $S$. Those electrons which arrive at that instant for which the current, and thence the magnetic field, is zero, will strike the screen. Those coming at any other time will be deflected to one side. When the frequency of the alternating current is adjusted so that electrons strike the

[3] E. Wiechert, *Ann. d. Physik*, **69**, 739 (1899).

screen, one knows that these particles have required a time equal to one-fourth, three-fourths, five-fourths, etc., of a period of the alternating current to travel from one coil to the other. Knowing the length of the electron path and the frequency of the alternating current, the velocity of the electron can be calculated.

A somewhat similar method, utilizing deflections suffered in electric fields, has also been used. An electron stream is directed between two pairs of parallel plates as shown in Fig. 2. The same high frequency potential is applied to each pair of plates. The electric fields are therefore in phase but perpendicular to each other. The deflections suffered by the electron at the two pairs of plates are therefore perpendicular to each other, and their magnitudes depend upon the phase of the alternating potential at the instant the electron passes. Since electrons pass $A$ at all possible phases,

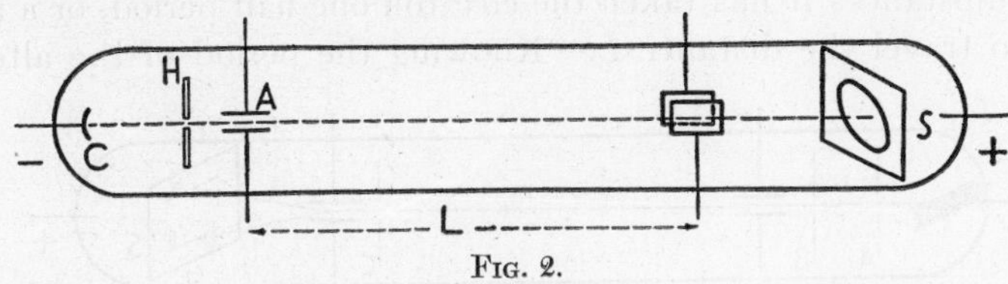


FIG. 2.

the luminous trace where electrons strike the fluorescent screen $S$ will in general be an ellipse. For the special case, however, when the time taken for the electron to travel the distance $L$ is exactly one-half period or any multiple of this, the ellipse degenerates into a straight line. When this condition exists,

$$\frac{L}{v} = \frac{nT}{2}$$

where $v$ is the velocity of the electron, $n$ any whole number and $T$ the known period of the alternating potential. Hence $v$ can be determined. Hammer[4] has used this method to measure the velocity of positive hydrogen ions. Using the velocity so obtained, along with the deflection suffered by these ions in an electric field, Hammer found the ratio $e/m$ for the gaseous hydrogen ion to be 97,750 coulombs per gram mole. This value agrees within the probable experimental error with that obtained for the hydrogen ion in electrolysis.

Kirchner[5] has used still another modification. A narrow ribbon of electrons passes through slits $A$ and $B$, thence through the two pairs of parallel plates a distance $L$ apart, as indicated in Fig. 3. The same alter-

[4] W. Hammer, *Ann. d. Physik*, **43**, 653 (1914).
[5] F. Kirchner, *Phys. Zeits.*, **25**, 302 (1924).

nating potential is applied to both pairs of plates. The alternating electric fields are, therefore, in phase with each other; and the two fields are parallel. The electron stream will pass through the slit $C$ only if the potential wave is going through its zero value as the electron passes between the first pair of plates. Electrons that do get through slit $C$ will pass on to the fluorescent screen $S$, being deflected somewhat. In general there will appear two well-defined fluorescent lines on the screen, $a$ and $b$. One of these is formed by electrons which pass the last pair of plates at some time during the positive half cycle of the potential wave; the other is due to electrons which pass at the corresponding time during the negative half cycle. However, if the potential wave should be passing through another zero point as the electrons pass through the second pair of plates, the beam would be undeflected; there would result a single central fluorescent line on the screen. Under these circumstances it has taken the electron one-half period, or a multiple thereof, to travel the distance $L$. Knowing the period of the alternating

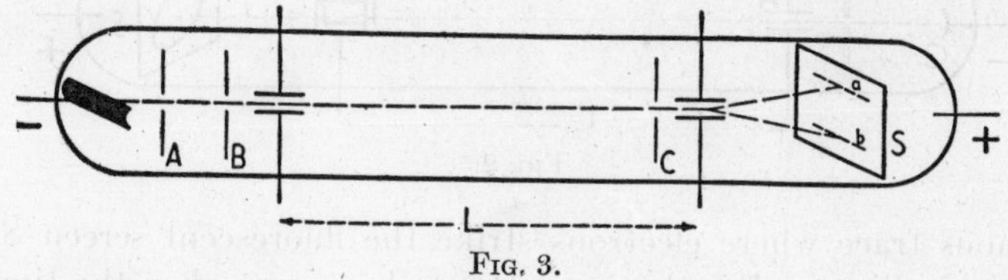


FIG. 3.

potential necessary to produce this single central line, the velocity of the electron can be calculated. Essentially this method of determining the velocity of cathode ray particles has been applied by Kirchner and by Perry and Chaffee in determinations of the ratio $e/m$ for these particles.

## 3. THE DEFLECTION OF MOVING CHARGED PARTICLES IN ELECTRIC AND MAGNETIC FIELDS

A majority of the methods used for determining the ratio $e/m$ for electrons depend upon the bending of a stream of electrons in a magnetic field, in an electric field, or in both. Let us therefore inquire concerning the force which acts upon an electron, and concerning the path described by the electron, when this electron is projected with a high velocity into such a field.

### Deflections in Electric Fields

An electron in an electric field is acted upon by a force which is independent of any velocity the electron may have; the force is the same on a moving electron as on one at rest. The magnitude of this force is $Ee$, where $E$ is the electrical field strength and $e$ the charge on the electron. The direction of this force is parallel to the electric field; it may be parallel to the electron's motion, or it may be at any angle with it, depending upon the relative directions of field and motion.

Let us consider the particular case where an electron moving with velocity $v$ enters an electric field which is perpendicular to the direction of motion. This situation is pictured in Fig. 4. In this case the electron will continue moving along the $x$ axis with its original velocity $v$. It will

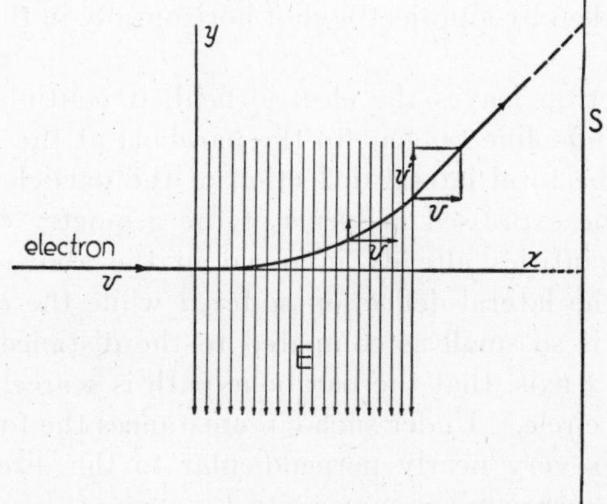


FIG. 4.—Illustrating the deflection of an electron in an electric field.

gradually acquire, however, an additional velocity component along the $y$ axis. The acceleration $a$ of the electron along the $y$ axis is

$$a = \frac{Ee}{m}$$

where $m$ is the mass of the electron. If the particle remains in the electric field for $t$ seconds, it will have acquired a final velocity $v'$ along the $y$ axis, where $v'$ is given by

$$v' = \frac{Ee}{m} t$$

Thus the electron proceeds through the field with a constant $x$ component and a gradually increasing $y$ component of velocity. In $t$ seconds the particle will have traveled a distance $vt$ along the $x$ axis; and it will have traveled a distance $\frac{1}{2}v't$ along the $y$ axis. If the origin of coordinates is chosen at the point at which the electron entered the field, then the coordinates locating the particle at any later time (provided the electron is still in the electric field) are:

$$x = vt \qquad y = \frac{1}{2}\frac{Ee}{m}t^2$$

These are the parametric equations of a parabola having its nose at the origin. The equation of this path is readily obtained in Cartesian form by eliminating $t$. Thus

$$y = \frac{1}{2}\frac{Ee}{mv^2}x^2$$

Except for the effect of air friction in the gravitational case, this path duplicates that taken by a projectile shot horizontally in the earth's gravitational field.

After the electron leaves the electric field, it continues at a constant velocity in a straight line tangent to the parabola at the point at which it left the field. The total lateral deflection of the particle upon the screen $S$ can therefore be expressed in terms of the geometry of the apparatus, together with quantities already involved in the above expressions. In many instances the lateral deflection suffered while the electron is still in the electric field is so small as compared to the distance the particle has moved along the $x$ axis, that the parabolic path is scarcely distinguishable from the arc of a circle. Under such circumstances the force acting on the electron is always very nearly perpendicular to the direction of motion. To this degree of accuracy one may write

$$Ee = m\frac{v^2}{R}$$

where $R$ is the radius of the equivalent circle, and where the entire right hand side of the equation represents the centrifugal force on the electron.

It is worth calling attention to the fact that although the electron started into the field perpendicularly, it nevertheless gained some energy while being deflected in the field. Since the velocity $v'$ is usually small as compared to $v$, and since these two are added at right angles to give the resultant velocity at any instant, it follows that the percentage change in velocity brought about by the field is usually quite small. This is not the case, of course, when electrons are projected into an electric field in such a direction that their velocity makes only a small angle with the field.

### Deflections in Magnetic Fields

When an electron moving with velocity $v$ enters a magnetic field of strength $H$ there is exerted on the electron a force urging the particle out of its line of flight. This force is at all times perpendicular both to the magnetic field and to the instantaneous direction of motion of the electron. Its magnitude depends upon the velocity, the field strength, and the angle between these. An electron at rest experiences no force in a magnetic field; the force on a moving electron is proportional to its velocity. When a conductor of length $L$ carrying a current $I$ is placed at right angles to a magnetic field $H$, it is acted upon by a force $F$ given by

$$F = HIL$$

Now a stream of moving electrons is entirely equivalent to a current flowing in the opposite direction; in fact it is the current. Consider a stream of electrons spaced an average distance $d$ apart and all moving with a velocity $v$ perpendicular to a magnetic field. From the definition of current this constitutes a current

$$I = \frac{v}{d}e$$

The force $F$ on a length $L$ of this stream is therefore

$$F = H\frac{ve}{d}L$$

But there are in this length $L/d$ electrons. Therefore,

$$\text{Force on one electron} = Hev$$

Since this force is at all times perpendicular to the instantaneous direction of motion, the path described by the electron is truly the arc of a circle. This force may therefore be equated to the centrifugal force on the electron. Thus

$$Hev = \frac{mv^2}{R}$$

where $R$ is the radius of the circular arc described in the magnetic field. The deflection suffered by an electron in a magnetic field is perpendicular to the field, whereas that suffered in an electric field is parallel to the field. If the electron leaves the magnetic field before completing a full circle, it continues in a straight line tangent to the circle at the point of exit from the field.

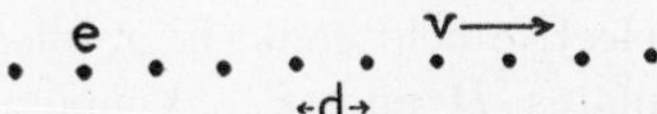


Fig. 5.—A stream of moving electrons is entirely equivalent to a current.

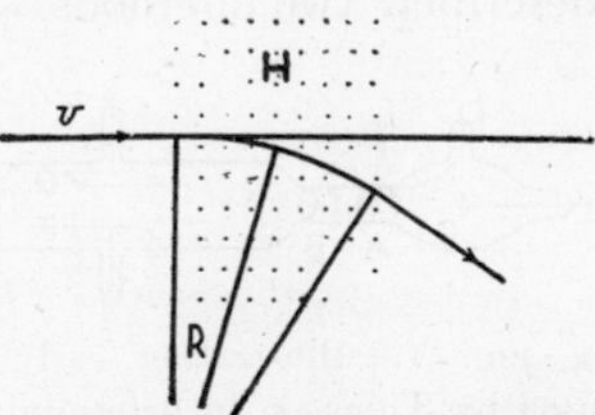


Fig. 6.—Illustrating the deflection of an electron in a magnetic field. The magnetic field is perpendicular to and directed into the paper.

In many instances an electron stream is shot into a magnetic field at other than right angles to it. Under such conditions it is only the component of the magnetic field which is perpendicular to the velocity that is effective in exerting a force on the electron. Or, if it is preferred, it is only the component of velocity which is perpendicular to the field which is effective. It should be emphasized that it is not possible in any way to change the energy of an electron by deflecting it in a magnetic field. Since the force exerted on the particle is at all times perpendicular to the instantaneous direction of motion, the magnitude of the velocity is never increased or decreased. It is only the direction of the velocity vector that is changed by a magnetic field.

## 4. THE RATIO e/m FOR ELECTRONS

The ratio of charge to mass of the electron has been measured by a variety of methods and by using electrons from a great number of different sources. Thomson was the first to make measurements of this character. In that day physicists had little idea as to the exact nature of cathode rays, and Thomson's experiments were carried out largely with the point of view of gaining information regarding the nature of these. His original experiments were described in an unusually interesting paper[2] in 1897. Most methods of determining the ratio of charge to mass fall into one of two general groups. In so-called deflection methods one observes the bending of an electron stream in electric or magnetic fields. In so-called spectroscopic methods one measures certain frequencies of the spectral lines emitted by an atom, and calculates from these the ratio $e/m$.

### Deflection Methods

*Thomson's Method.*—Among other interesting experiments, Thomson[2] described two methods for measuring the ratio $e/m$. The first of these utilized apparatus illustrated in Fig. 7. Electrons, after leaving the cathode $C$, passed through slits $A$ and $B$ and fell upon a fluorescent screen. An electric field could be applied between plates $D$ and $E$. A magnetic field, perpendicular to the electric field, was established by a current flowing in two external coils, one placed on either side of the tube. These coils, whose diameters were equal to the lengths of the plates $D$ and $E$, were placed so that magnetic and electric fields occupied approximately the same region. The directions of the fields were such that one alone deflected the electron stream upward, whereas the other alone deflected it downward. The strengths of these two fields were adjusted so that the net deflection of the electrons was zero. Under this condition the forces on the electron due to

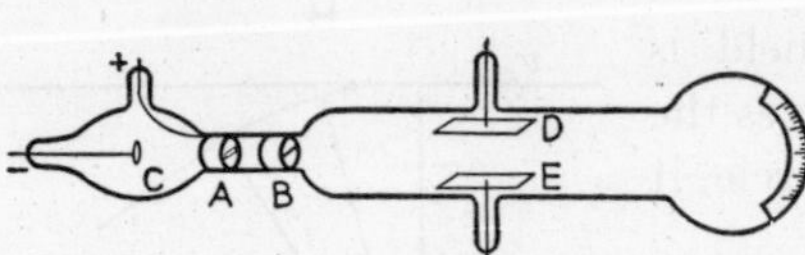

Fig. 7.—Illustrating early apparatus used by Thomson in determining $e/m$ for cathode rays.

the two fields were equal and opposite. Thus

$$Hev = Ee$$

from which

$$v = \frac{E}{H}$$

The stream of electrons was then deflected by the magnetic field alone. Under this condition

$$Hev = \frac{mv^2}{R}$$

Combining these two equations, one obtains

$$\frac{e}{m} = \frac{E}{H^2R}$$

Hence, by measuring $E$, $H$, and $R$, both the velocity and the ratio $e/m$ can be obtained. Attention should be called to the fact that all quantities in this expression must be measured in the same system of units. If it is desired to express certain of the quantities in electromagnetic units and others in electrostatic units, then a conversion factor must be introduced.

In the second method used by Thomson, cathode rays after passing through a slit were made to enter a so-called Faraday chamber. This chamber is merely a properly shielded and properly insulated conductor onto which electrons fall after coming through a small opening in the chamber. The charge communicated to the chamber in a given time was measured with an electrometer. If $N$ be the number of electrons entering the chamber and $Q$ be the total charge accumulated

$$Ne = Q$$

The same number of electrons was then made to strike a small thermocouple of known heat capacity. The energy $W$ communicated to the couple was calculated from the observed rise in temperature. This energy must come from the kinetic energy of the electrons. Thus

$$W = \tfrac{1}{2}Nmv^2$$

The electron stream was next bent in a magnetic field. For such bending

$$Hev = \frac{mv^2}{R}$$

Combining these three equations, one obtains

$$\frac{e}{m} = \frac{2W}{H^2R^2Q}$$

Since all quantities on the right can be measured, the ratio $e/m$ can be obtained.

Thomson found the velocity of cathode rays to be of the order of one-tenth that of light, and to increase with increases in potential difference across the discharge tube. After using various gases in the tube, various metals as electrodes, and various potentials applied to the tube, Thomson concluded that the ratio $e/m$ was independent of all these. He gave a numerical value of $e/m$ of the order of $10^7$ e.m.u. per gram. While more recent and refined measurements have given a somewhat higher and far more precise numerical value, they have borne out Thomson's finding of the independence of the ratio $e/m$ upon the gas and the metal electrodes used. They have shown $e/m$ to vary slightly with the velocity of the electron, but the variation is exceedingly small for all but the highest velocities. This variation will be discussed in some detail later.

*Kaufmann's Method.*—Numerous other early determinations[6–8] were carried out by various methods. While these early works were exceedingly important at the time in providing a more certain knowledge of the nature of cathode rays, many of them led to only approximate values for the ratio $e/m$. These early works have been summarized in tabular form by Thomson.[8] It is significant that identical values of $e/m$ are obtained for cathode rays, beta rays, electrons from a hot cathode and photoelectrons ejected by ultraviolet light or X-rays. This indicates that all of these particles are identical. It is interesting to inquire a bit more into the details of one of the earlier works, for essentially the same method when applied later to the study of positive rays led to the important discovery of isotopes.

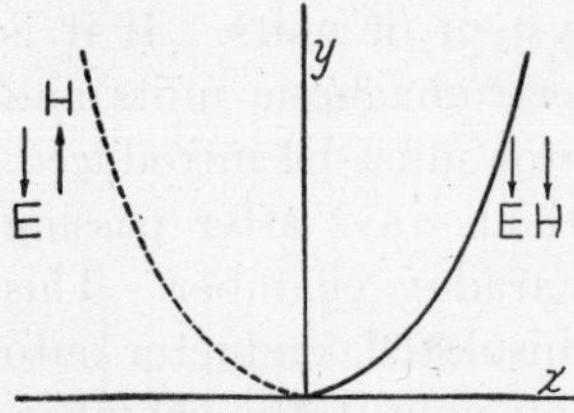

FIG. 8.—The locus of points to which electrons are deflected by coincident electric and magnetic fields is a parabola.

Shortly after 1900 Kaufmann[9] devised a method in which electrons were deflected by coincident electric and magnetic fields. Instead of cathode rays, Kaufmann used the beta rays ejected by a radioactive material. Since the two deflecting fields were parallel the resulting deflections of the electron due to the two fields were perpendicular. It is easily shown by geometry that the deviation of a particle from its original straight line of flight, due to its deflection in the arc of a circle, is closely inversely propor-

[6] W. Kaufmann, *Ann. d. Physik*, **61**, 544 (1897); **62**, 596 (1897); **65**, 431 (1898).

[7] S. Simon, *Ann. d. Physik*, **69**, 589 (1899).

[8] J. J. Thomson and G. P. Thomson, *Conduction of Electricity Through Gases* (3rd ed.; London: Cambridge University Press, 1928), Vol. I, p. 264.

[9] W. Kaufmann, *Gött. Nachr.*, **2**, 143 (1901); **3**, 291 (1902); **4**, 90, 148 (1903); *Ann. d. Physik*, **19**, 487 (1906).

tional to the radius of the circle as long as the deflection be very small. Then if in Fig. 8 $y$ be the deflection caused by the electric field and $x$ that caused by the magnetic field, one can write

$$y = k\frac{1}{R_E} = k\frac{Ee}{mv^2}$$

and

$$x = k\frac{1}{R_H} = k\frac{He}{mv}$$

where $R_E$ and $R_H$ are the radii of the circular arcs described in the electric and in the magnetic field, respectively. The constant $k$ depends upon the geometry of the apparatus; it has the same value in each equation if the two fields cover the same extent of space. Eliminating $v$ from these equations one obtains

$$y = \frac{E}{kH^2}\frac{mx^2}{e}$$

This is the equation of a parabola having its nose at the origin, the position of the undeflected beam as it enters the fields. Experimentally, one obtains only half of the parabola with given directions of fields; the remainder of the parabola can be obtained by reversing the magnetic field.

Electrons of different velocities fall at different places along the parabola. Thus, the $x$ and $y$ deflections for any one point on the curve lead to a value of $e/m$ for an electron of a definite velocity. Kaufmann's were the first data for which individual results could be obtained for definite electron velocities. These data indicated that the ratio $e/m$ varied slightly with velocity, decreasing with velocity increases. By this time there had already been advanced three different theories indicating that the mass of the electron, and therefore the ratio $e/m$, should vary with velocity. Each theory led to a slightly different manner of variation. Furthermore, each theory predicted that the ratio $e/m$ would approach a characteristic value $e/m_0$ as the velocity of the electron approached zero. This $m_0$ would then represent the rest mass of the electron. Kaufmann's data led to three different values for $e/m_0$, the value depending upon which of the three theoretical manners of variation was used in extrapolating to obtain the rest value. The three results obtained were:

Extrapolation by Abraham theory............ $e/m_0 = 1.82 \times 10^7$ e.m.u./gr.
Extrapolation by Bucherer theory............ $e/m_0 = 1.81 \times 10^7$
Extrapolation by Lorentz theory.............. $e/m_0 = 1.66 \times 10^7$

Kaufmann's work was not sufficiently precise to distinguish among the three theories by the quantitative manner of variation of $e/m$ with velocity.

The small dimensions of the photographs and the somewhat diffuse character of the parabolas prevented results of precise character.

*Classen's Method.*—Classen[10] made a marked improvement upon preceding methods in that he used a hot cathode as a source of electrons and in that he utilized a certain geometrical focusing effect possible with electrons describing semicircles in a magnetic field. His apparatus is illustrated in Fig. 9. A glass container was divided into two sections by a metal plate $M$ on the bottom of which was placed a photographic plate $P$. A hot oxide-coated cathode was placed just above a 1 mm. diameter hole located in the center of the metal plate. Electrons leaving the hot cathode were accelerated by a potential established between the cathode and the plate which served as anode. Many of these passed through the hole into the region below the anode. This region was shielded from stray electric fields by a nonmagnetic metal housing. A uniform magnetic field was established perpendicular to a line joining the cathode and the hole in the anode. Two large coils, one on either side of the apparatus, were used to obtain this field. The magnetic field causes an electron coming through the hole in the anode to describe a semicircle and strike the photographic plate. This bombardment produces an exposed spot on the plate. Reversal of the magnetic field produces a similar exposure on the opposite side of the central opening. Since the use of a hot cathode to furnish electrons permitted a high degree of evacuation, Classen felt it quite proper to calculate the velocity of the electron as it goes through the anode from the relationship

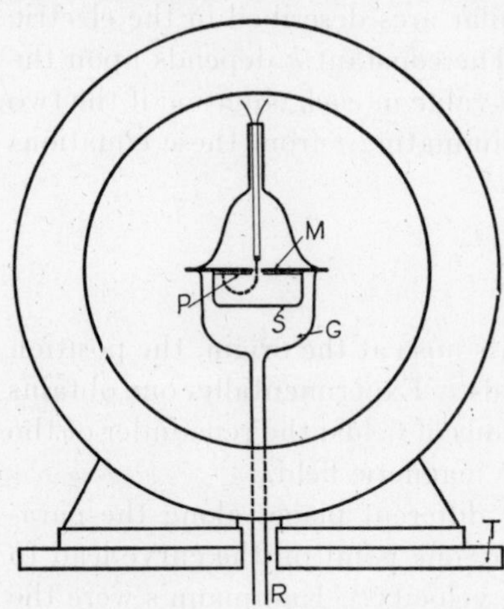


Fig. 9.—Illustrating apparatus used by Classen in determining $e/m$ for electrons coming from a heated filament.

$$\tfrac{1}{2}mv^2 = Ve$$

After passing through the opening the electron is deflected in the magnetic field in accord with the relationship

$$Hev = \frac{mv^2}{R}$$

From these two expressions, both $v$ and $e/m$ can be obtained.

[10] J. Classen, *Phys. Zeits.*, **9**, 762 (1908); *Verh. Deutsch. Phys. Gesell.*, **10**, 700 (1908).

The geometrical focusing action present in the Classen experiment is worthy of some attention; it has been utilized in many later experiments of one type or another. Let us consider, in Fig. 10, electrons which come through the hole in the anode in a somewhat divergent beam. All electrons have the same velocity except for minor variations due to the potential drop along the filament and to the thermal velocity distribution of electrons ejected from the glowing cathode. All electrons will therefore describe circles of the same radius in the magnetic field. The various circles of Fig. 10 are drawn with equal radii. The center of the circle is in each case located so that the line joining this center to the hole in the anode is perpendicular to the direction of motion of the electron as it goes through the anode. While the several electrons indicated deviate considerably at some parts of their paths, they come back surprisingly close to one another as they strike the photographic plate. This focusing action is possible only when the path described is a half circle. Such focusing allows a sharp trace on the photographic plate with a relatively large opening in the anode. The larger opening makes it possible to get a greater number of electrons through.

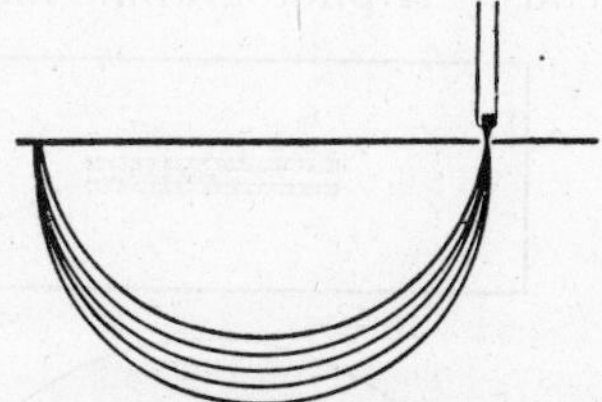

FIG. 10.—Illustrating the geometrical focusing action on electrons deflected in semicircles by a magnetic field.

Classen made measurements of $e/m$ using two different potential differences between cathode and anode. These potentials were 1,000 and 4,000 volts, corresponding to electron velocities of approximately $1.8 \times 10^9$ and $3.6 \times 10^9$ cm/sec. It appeared quite certain that $e/m$ was slightly different for electrons of these two velocities; the ratio was slightly smaller for the higher velocity. For those electrons which had been accelerated through 1,000 volts difference of potential, Classen found the ratio $e/m$ to be $(1.773 \pm 0.002) \times 10^7$. The ratio of the two values of $e/m$ found for the two velocities used was, within the limits of experimental error, that which would be expected on Lorentz's theory of mass variation. When this manner of mass variation was used to extrapolate results to zero velocity, Classen's data led to a value

$$\frac{e}{m_0} = (1.776 \pm 0.002) \times 10^7$$

Although this value has since proved to be slightly high, it was one of the first reliable values obtained.

*Bucherer's Method.*—Bucherer[11] devised a method quite different from any previously used. The arrangement of apparatus is shown in Fig. 11.

[11] A. H. Bucherer, *Verh. Deutsch. Phys. Gesell.*, **10**, 688 (1908); *Phys. Zeits.*, **9**, 755 (1908); *Ann. d. Physik*, **28**, 513 (1909).

Two optically plane circular glass plates 8 cm. in diameter and silvered on the inner surfaces, were placed one-fourth millimeter apart. A small quantity of radioactive material emitting beta particles was placed at the center of and between the plates. An electric field was established perpendicular to the plates by applying a known potential difference between the silvered surfaces. A uniform magnetic field having the direction indicated in the diagram was established by means of a current flowing through coils. A photographic film $P$ was placed on the inner surface of a circular cylinder coaxial with the glass plates and 5 cm. from the outer edges of these. Beta rays of a great variety of velocities move out from the source. As these electrons move out from the central source, they are all urged with an equal force toward one plate, say the upper one, by the electric field. But the force exerted by the magnetic field depends both upon the velocity of the beta particle and upon the direction this particle takes. If the path be parallel to the magnetic field it is not affected; if angle $\theta$ at which it leaves is between 0 and 180° the particle is urged toward the lower plate; if $\theta$ is between 180° and 360° the particle is urged toward the upper plate. It is apparent, therefore, that no beta particles will get out from between the plates for angles $\theta$ between 180° and 360°. Furthermore, a beta particle with a velocity $v$ will get out (and finally strike the photographic film) only at that angle $\theta$ for which

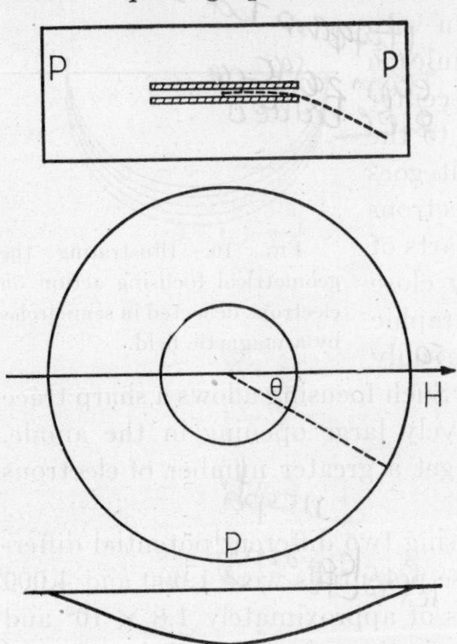

FIG. 11.—Illustrating the Bucherer method.

$$Hev \sin \theta = Ee$$

It is only at this angle that the forces on this electron due to the electric and the magnetic fields are equal and opposite. After this beta ray gets out from between plates the electric field no longer acts upon it. The remaining force due to the magnetic field causes the electron to continue along the arc of a circle until it strikes the photographic film. In this magnetic field

$$Hev \sin \theta = \frac{mv^2}{R}$$

From this and the preceding equation, along with observed values of $H$, $E$, $\theta$, and $R$, it is possible to calculate both $v$ and $e/m$.

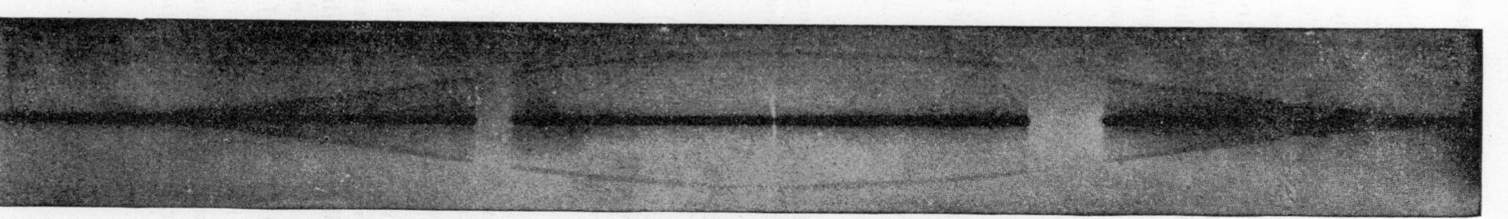

Fig. 12.—Typical photographs obtained by Bucherer. The strip of film reproduced occupied slightly over half the circumference of the apparatus. The two unexposed regions are those sections of the film shielded from the source of electrons by spacers placed between the two glass plates of the apparatus.

Fig. 12 reproduces a typical photograph obtained by Bucherer. The second half of the curve (that above the plates) is obtained by reversal of the fields. Since the exposure appearing at any one place on the film is due entirely to electrons of a particular velocity, it follows that $e/m$ can be obtained for electrons of widely different velocities; and all these values can be obtained from a single photograph. Bucherer, using electrons having speeds up to nearly 0.7 that of light, found again that the ratio $e/m$ varied with velocity. His data were sufficiently precise to show that this variation was much more closely that predicted by Lorentz than that predicted by either himself or Abraham. Using the Lorentz manner of variation for extrapolation to zero velocity, Bucherer found

$$\frac{e}{m_0} = (1.763 \pm 0.008) \times 10^7$$

These results were later verified by Wolz[12] who, using the same apparatus, found

$$\frac{e}{m_0} = (1.767 \pm 0.002) \times 10^7$$

*Busch's Method.*—In 1922 Busch[13] developed a method which depends upon the focusing of a divergent beam of electrons by means of a magnetic

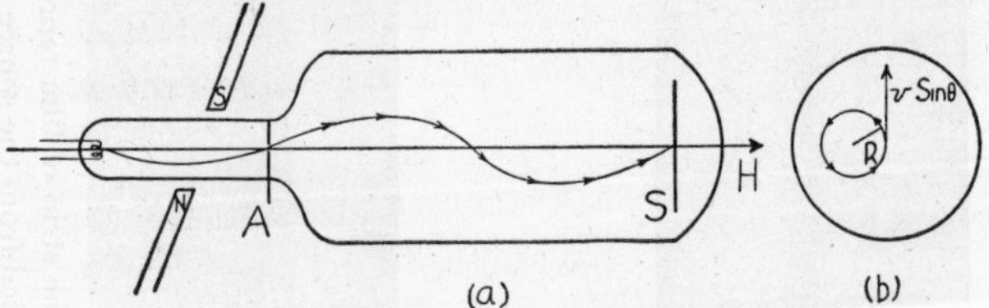


FIG. 13.—Illustrating the Busch method.

field parallel to the beam. The general method is illustrated by Fig. 13($a$). Electrons coming from a hot cathode proceed through a small hole in the anode $A$. The potential difference $V$ applied between cathode and anode determines the velocity with which electrons proceed through this opening. Since this method depends fundamentally upon focusing a beam of fairly divergent electrons, Busch placed small auxiliary magnets radially about the tube as shown. The fields due to these magnets caused electrons to proceed from cathode to anode in curved paths. As a result, the electrons leaving the hole in the anode were more divergent than they would otherwise have been. The entire tube, or at least that section from anode to fluorescent screen $S$, was placed within a uniform magnetic field produced by

[12] K. Wolz, *Ann. d. Physik*, **30**, 273 (1909).
[13] H. Busch, *Phys. Zeits.*, **23**, 438 (1922).

a long solenoid. This magnetic field was parallel to the longitudinal axis of the tube.

Let us consider one particular electron moving with a velocity $v$ in a direction making an angle $\theta$ with the axis of the tube at the instant it leaves the anode. The velocity $v$ can be represented by two components, $v \cos \theta$ parallel to the magnetic field, and $v \sin \theta$ perpendicular to the magnetic field. That component parallel to the field is not affected by the field; the electron proceeds longitudinally along the tube with a constant velocity $v \cos \theta$. The component $v \sin \theta$, however, is at all times perpendicular to the magnetic field. As a result, if one ignores for the moment the constant velocity along the axis, the electron will describe a circle in a plane perpendicular to the axis of the tube. This electron will pass through the central axis after completing one revolution. It is an interesting fact that each electron, regardless of its velocity component perpendicular to the field, and therefore regardless of its angle of divergence, requires exactly the same time to execute one complete circle. That this is the case can be seen as follows. Still ignoring the longitudinal motion along the axis of the tube, an electron with perpendicular velocity component $v \sin \theta$ will describe a circle in accord with the expression

$$Hev \sin \theta = \frac{m(v \sin \theta)^2}{R}$$

The time $t$ required for this electron to complete one circle is given by

$$t = \frac{2\pi R}{v \sin \theta}$$

If the value of $R$ be obtained from the first of these equations and substituted into the second, one finds

$$t = \frac{2\pi m}{He}$$

This expression is independent of the magnitude of the electron's velocity perpendicular to the magnetic field. Hence, all electrons in the divergent pencil, regardless of the individual angles of divergence, will complete their first circles in the same time. All will therefore come back again through the central axis at the same time.

Fig. 13($b$) shows one of the possible circles described by an electron. Those particles with a large perpendicular component of velocity describe large circles, while those with smaller perpendicular velocity components execute smaller circles. But the speedier electron completes its large circle in exactly the same time that the slower electron completes its small circle.

Since all electrons come back through the axis at the same time, it follows that if all particles have the same longitudinal velocity along the tube, then all electrons leaving the anode opening in a divergent pencil will be brought back to a sharp focus at some point along the axis. The strength of the magnetic field can be made such that this focus is at the screen $S$, a distance $L$ from the anode. If all electrons have the longitudinal velocity $v \cos \theta$, then the time required for them to travel to the screen is given by

$$t = \frac{L}{v \cos \theta}$$

If the field is adjusted so that the focus occurs at the screen, then this time is the same as that required for any electron to complete its circular path. Equating these times and solving for $e/m$, one obtains

$$\frac{e}{m} = \frac{2\pi v \cos \theta}{HL}$$

The velocity $v$ can be obtained from the expression

$$Ve = \tfrac{1}{2}mv^2$$

If $v$ be obtained from this and put into the above equation for $e/m$ one finds

$$\frac{e}{m} = \frac{8\pi^2 V \cos^2 \theta}{H^2 L^2}$$

Actually, all electrons used by Busch did not diverge at the same angle $\theta$. This angle was sufficiently small, however, that $\cos \theta$ itself was very close to unity and the variation in it was almost negligible. By this method Busch found, after extrapolation according to the Lorentz theory, a value

$$\frac{e}{m_0} = (1.768 \pm 0.0015) \times 10^7$$

Essentially this same method was used later by Wolf[14] in what constituted the most careful and precise measurements up to that time. From some seventy separate measurements Wolf found a value, after a slight correction had been applied by Birge[15] for the difference between the international and the absolute volt,

$$\frac{e}{m_0} = (1.769 \pm 0.002) \times 10^7$$

[14] F. Wolf, *Ann. d. Physik*, **83**, 849 (1927).

[15] R. T. Birge, *Rev. Mod. Phys.*, **1**, 43 (1929).

Birge,[15] in a critical survey of a number of important physical constants, weighted Wolf's determination far more heavily than other values of $e/m_0$ available at that time. Not only has the Busch method been applied with success to the measurement of $e/m_0$, but the principle underlying it has been used extensively when it is desired to focus a beam of divergent electrons.

Since Wolf's work there have been developed precision methods of measuring $e/m_0$ for electrons. Several of these are truly deflection methods and should rightfully be grouped with those discussed above. Before discussing these, however, attention should be called to an entirely different method of determining $e/m_0$, one utilizing spectroscopic data. The agreement or disagreement between results by the two entirely different methods is interesting. It at one time caused considerable theoretical speculation; and it was no doubt instrumental in the development of recent precision methods of measurement.

### Spectroscopic Methods

A little later we shall discuss briefly the mechanism by which an atom radiates or absorbs energy. Sufficient facts will be stated at this time to allow one to appreciate what is behind the spectroscopic method of determining $e/m$. Recall that a gas, when heated or excited by other means, emits a characteristic bright line spectrum. The frequencies of the numerous individual lines making up the spectrum are characteristic of the atom. No atom of any other material emits these same frequencies. In 1913 Bohr showed that it was possible, by defining certain energy levels within the atom, and by supposing that radiation is emitted or absorbed as an electron passes from one to another of these levels, to calculate with precision the actual frequencies of the emitted lines. This is possible at least for the simple atoms which can be treated rigorously with present mathematical knowledge. It has been found that these frequencies depend slightly upon, among other things, the mass of the nucleus of the atom and the strength of a magnetic field in which the radiating atom may be placed. The effect attributable to the nuclear mass or to an external magnetic field can be expressed theoretically in terms of $e/m$ and other quantities. There have resulted, therefore, two spectroscopic methods of evaluating the ratio $e/m$. Each is capable of a high degree of precision.

One of these methods utilizes experimental data on the fine structure of the lines, and the difference in the effects of the nuclear masses of hydrogen and ionized helium. This method was first applied by Paschen.[16] It was developed by Houston[17] to such a point that it gave quite accurate results,

[16] F. Paschen, *Ann. d. Physik*, **50**, 901 (1916).
[17] W. V. Houston, *Phys. Rev.*, **30**, 608 (1927).

and recently it has been used by several other workers.[18–23] Some of these more recent works have made use of the fine structure and the difference in the nuclear mass effects of ordinary and heavy hydrogen, rather than of those of hydrogen and ionized helium.

The second spectroscopic method depends upon the fact that when an atom which is radiating is placed in a strong magnetic field each characteristic spectral line is broken up into several closely spaced yet quite distinct components. This is known as the Zeeman effect. Accurate measurement of the separations of these Zeeman lines yield a value for $e/m$. This method has been used by many workers.[24–28]

### Comparison of Results by the Two Methods up to 1929

While by far the most precise determinations of $e/m_0$, by both the deflection method and the spectroscopic method, have been made within the past ten years, it is nevertheless interesting to compare results by the two entirely different methods as they appeared in 1929. Even at that time a considerable degree of apparent accuracy had been obtained by each method. Birge[15] made a critical survey of all data existing up to that time. He considered the work of Wolf[14] outstanding among the determinations by deflection methods, and that of Houston[17] and of Babcock[25] as noteworthy among spectroscopic determinations. From consideration of the probable errors associated with not only these but all existing determinations, Birge concluded at that time that the most probable values of $e/m_0$ as obtained by the two general methods were as follows:

From deflection methods.............................. $(1.769 \pm 0.002) \times 10^7$
From spectroscopic method.......................... $(1.761 \pm 0.001) \times 10^7$

Most of the individual determinations available at the time of Birge's summary are tabulated in the first part of Table I which appears several pages hence. The agreement between the two most probable values given by Birge was not all that one might expect. The most probable value obtained from deflection experiments exceeded that obtained from spectroscopic measurements by nearly three times the sum of the probable errors

18 R. C. Gibbs and R. C. Williams, *Phys. Rev.*, **44**, 1029 (1933).
19 F. H. Spedding, C. D. Shane and N. S. Grace, *Phys. Rev.*, **44**, 58 (1933).
20 C. D. Shane and F. H. Spedding, *Phys. Rev.*, **47**, 33 (1935).
21 R. C. Williams and R. C. Gibbs, *Phys. Rev.*, **48**, 971 (1935).
22 W. V. Houston, *Phys. Rev.*, **51**, 446 (1937).
23 R. C. Williams, *Phys. Rev.*, **54**, 568 (1938).
24 H. D. Babcock, *Astrophys. Jour.*, **58**, 149 (1923).
25 H. D. Babcock, *Astrophys. Jour.*, **69**, 43 (1929).
26 J. S. Campbell and W. V. Houston, *Phys. Rev.*, **39**, 601 (1932).
27 L. E. Kinsler and W. V. Houston, *Phys. Rev.*, **45**, 104 (1934).
28 L. E. Kinsler and W. V. Houston, *Phys. Rev.*, **46**, 533 (1934).

involved. While this did not mean for a certainty that the discrepancy was other than accidental, it did indicate strongly that some unknown error had crept into either one or both of the determinations. As Birge[15] pointed out, there is only one chance in nearly one hundred fifty that values having the probable errors associated with these would disagree by as much as do the two most probable values given by Birge. It was recognized that deflection experiments deal with the free electron, completely detached from any atom, whereas spectroscopic measurements deal with an electron intimately bound within an atom. It was barely possible that $e/m_0$ for free electrons might actually be different from the value for bound electrons. Such a possibility left room for a great deal of theoretical speculation. One other possible interpretation of the discrepancy occurred to many. In most of the accurate determinations by the deflection method, use had been made of the measured potential difference between cathode and anode to calculate the velocity of the electron being deflected. This assumes that all of the energy acquired by the electron in dropping through the potential difference $V$ appears as kinetic energy. This is true only if the electron loses no energy whatever in collisions with gas molecules remaining in the highly exhausted tube. If any energy is lost in such collisions the actual velocity of the electron would be slightly less than that calculated in the usual way. It can be shown that the use of this slightly incorrect velocity in deflection experiments would yield too high a value of $e/m_0$.

## 5. RECENT REFINEMENTS IN THE RATIO $e/m_0$

Since Birge's summary in 1929 there have been a number of significant determinations of this important ratio. We shall outline briefly a few of these more recent developments and call attention to the manner in which the discrepancy just discussed has been greatly reduced.

### Improvements in Free Electron Methods

*Kirchner's Method.*—Kirchner[29] refined the method he had used previously for measuring directly the velocity of cathode rays by comparing the time they required to travel a known distance with the known period of a high frequency potential wave. The accuracy attainable was greatly increased. Using this measured velocity together with the measured potential difference between cathode and anode, he was able to obtain a supposedly accurate value for $e/m_0$. These measurements gave

$$\frac{e}{m_0} = (1.770 \pm 0.002) \times 10^7$$

[29] F. Kirchner, *Phys. Zeits.*, **30**, 773 (1929).

While this determination was by a different method than any previously used, it did not clarify the discrepancy which seemed to exist between results obtained by the two general methods; rather, it emphasized this discrepancy.

Shortly after this Perry and Chaffee[30] described an experimental determination which yielded a value almost identical with that obtained from spectroscopic measurements. The method was essentially that used by Kirchner in that the velocity of the electrons was measured directly. The present workers, however, used rather high speed electrons, particles accelerated through a potential of from 10,000 to 20,000 volts. They took considerable care in obtaining a high vacuum. They chose dimensions of their apparatus in such a way as to minimize the effect of any loss of energy due to collisions with residual gas molecules. Upon combining the measured velocity with the potential difference through which the electron had fallen, and after extrapolating according to the Lorentz manner of mass variation, Perry and Chaffee found

$$\frac{e}{m_0} = (1.761 \pm 0.001) \times 10^7$$

This value is exactly that which had been given by Birge[15] as the most probable value from spectroscopic methods.

Perry and Chaffee suggested that results of previous deflection experiments were all high because of the presence of residual gas within the tube. They felt that their experiment was less sensitive to such error for several reasons. In the first place, an error of this character would be much smaller for high speed electrons than for low speed electrons; a given loss of energy would decrease the velocity of the higher speed particle by a much smaller percentage. Secondly, it was felt that the vacuum attained in this experiment was considerably better than that existing in most of the early experiments. In the third place, the method here used, together with the dimensions chosen for the apparatus, were such as to minimize any error due to residual gas. The authors pointed out that although accurate knowledge of the loss of energy of electrons in passing through a gas at low pressure is rather meager, it appears that a residual gas pressure of the order of 0.004 mm. of Hg in Wolf's apparatus would be sufficient to explain the discrepancy between his result and the spectroscopic value. Perry and Chaffee seemed to feel that the high values obtained by previous deflection experiments were in all probability due to the effect of residual gas.

There are several facts, however, which made it difficult to accept this interpretation. Perry and Chaffee did use high speed electrons, for which

[30] C. T. Perry and E. L. Chaffee, *Phys. Rev.*, **36**, 904 (1930).

the error should be relatively small. But Bucherer, Wolz, Alberti, Schaefer, Neumann and Busch used just as high speed electrons, and in several cases higher. Even so they obtained values higher than the spectroscopic value. A review of the values of $e/m_0$ obtained through use of electrons of various speeds shows no convincing trend indicating that a smaller ratio $e/m_0$ was obtained when high speed particles were used. It is true that residual gas pressures probably varied greatly from one experiment to another. But this in itself indicates that the effect of residual gas must be small; otherwise how did various workers obtain so nearly the same value? Furthermore, several early workers reported that there was no observable change in $e/m_0$, for reasonable changes in residual gas pressure. For these reasons it was felt that there was present some error other than that suggested by Perry and Chaffee. An error unsuspected at that time has since been found.

Kirchner[31] repeated his earlier work,[29] again using essentially the same method as had been used in the meantime by Perry and Chaffee. He reported a value

$$\frac{e}{m_0} = (1.7598 \pm 0.0025) \times 10^7$$

The following year[32] he applied to this value a small correction for the contact potential between cathode and anode metals. This correction lowered the previously reported value slightly and decreased the probable error, giving

$$\frac{e}{m_0} = (1.7585 \pm 0.0012) \times 10^7$$

At the same time he also carried out a new series of measurements, using an improved piezoelectric quartz crystal for controlling the period of the high frequency potential. As a result of these new measurements he obtained

$$\frac{e}{m_0} = (1.7590 \pm 0.0015) \times 10^7$$

These values obtained by Kirchner were distinctly below those obtained by earlier deflection methods. They were even slightly below the then accepted spectroscopic value. It therefore appeared from this work, together with that of Perry and Chaffee, that $e/m_0$ obtained for free electrons was certainly no higher than that obtained spectroscopically for

[31] F. Kirchner, *Ann. d. Physik*, **8**, 975 (1931).
[32] F. Kirchner, *Ann. d. Physik*, **12**, 503 (1932).

bound electrons. It is true that the method used by these workers was scarcely a deflection method, and it was essential for complete solution of the problem that someone refine a deflection method to such an extent that an equal precision could be obtained. Fortunately this has been done by three separate investigators. In connection with two of these the principal cause of the previous discrepancy between the free electron and the bound electron values has become obvious.

*Dunnington's Method.*—Dunnington[33] developed a true deflection method and at the same time preserved the all important feature of recent methods wherein the electron velocity was measured directly. The method, apparatus for which is illustrated schematically by Fig. 14, consisted essentially of accelerating electrons to a continuous range of velocities by a high frequency electric field, choosing a particular velocity of electron by deflection in a magnetic field, and measuring this velocity in terms of the distance the electron traveled and the period of the high frequency potential. The alternating potential applied between slits $A_1$ and $A_2$ serves to accelerate electrons coming from the hot filament $F$. Electrons leave $A_2$ with a wide range of velocities; the actual velocity of any electron depends upon the phase of the potential wave as this particular particle passes through slit $A_1$. A uniform magnetic field $H$ perpendicular to the plane of the paper deflects all of these electrons in circles. Electrons of only one particular velocity, however, are bent in a circle of such radius that they pass through slits $S_1$ and $S_2$ and come to slit $D_1$. The velocity of these electrons is such that

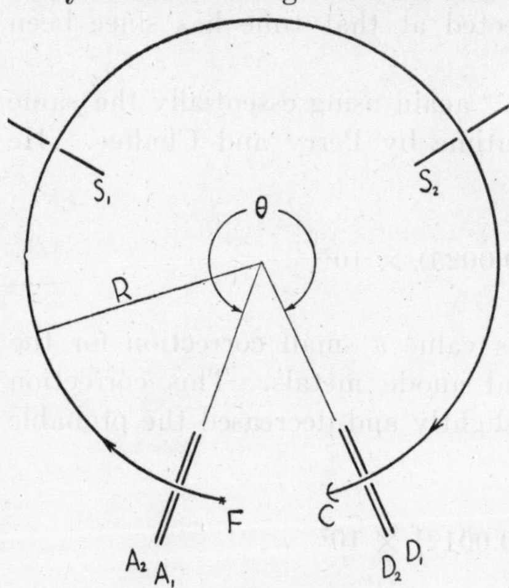


FIG. 14.—Illustrating essentials of the apparatus used by Dunnington.

$$Hev = \frac{mv^2}{R}$$

What happens to these particles after they arrive at $D_1$ depends upon the length of time they have required to travel through angle $\theta$. The same high frequency potential that is applied between $A_1$ and $A_2$ is applied simultaneously between $D_1$ and $D_2$. The connection is such that $D_1$ is always at the same potential as $A_2$. It is obvious, therefore, that an electron which has required exactly one period of the alternating potential wave to

[33] F. G. Dunnington, *Phys. Rev.*, **43**, 404 (1933).

travel from slits $A_1A_2$ to slits $D_1D_2$ will be decelerated in passing from $D_1$ to $D_2$. These electrons lose their entire energy and consequently do not reach the collector $C$. The experimental procedure is to adjust the magnetic field $H$ until a minimum number of electrons arrive at $C$. Under this condition, electrons have required exactly one period to travel from the one to the other pair of slits, and one may write

$$v = \frac{R\theta}{T} = R\theta f$$

where $\theta$ is measured in radians and where $f$ is the frequency of the potential wave. Combining the last two equations to eliminate $v$, one obtains

$$\frac{e}{m} = \frac{\theta f}{H}$$

where $H$ is now the particular field necessary for the adjustment mentioned above. It is apparent that one needs measure only an angle, a frequency, and a magnetic field in order to obtain a value for $e/m$. In this manner, Dunnington arrived at the value

$$\frac{e}{m_0} = (1.7571 \pm 0.0015) \times 10^7$$

Dunnington did not consider this result the best that could be obtained by the method and immediately set about making refinements. In the meantime it had been shown[34,35] that there are formed on or very near the metal plates between which the electric field is established, polarization charges which effectively reduce the potential used to accelerate or deflect an electron beam. Furthermore, a charge seems to accumulate on a more or less permanent insulating layer built up on a metal surface when this surface is bombarded with electrons. These effects depend upon the material of the plates, the residual gas pressure, and the intensity of electron bombardment. Equivalent potentials contributed by these effects are much greater than ordinary contact potentials between different metals. Dunnington therefore coated the entire interior of his apparatus with a thin layer of evaporated gold. But he found that even the condition of this gold film influenced to some extent the magnitude of this surface effect, and consequently the value obtained for $e/m$. The method used, however, after certain other precautions were taken to correct for this effect, was such that the residual error should be quite small. Dunnington's[36] final value reported was

[34] A. E. Shaw, *Phys. Rev.*, **44**, 1009 (1933).
[35] R. L. Stewart, *Phys. Rev.*, **45**, 488 (1934).
[36] F. G. Dunnington, *Phys. Rev.*, **52**, 475 (1937).

$$\frac{e}{m_0} = (1.7597 \pm 0.0004) \times 10^7$$

*Kretschmar's Method.*—Kretschmar[37] has obtained a value of $e/m_0$ by observing the deflection in a magnetic field suffered by photoelectrons ejected from thin metallic films by X-rays. Details of the method involve some knowledge of the photoelectric ejection of electrons, a subject to be discussed later. However, $e/m_0$ can be calculated from the observed deflection of the photoelectrons in a known magnetic field, the frequency of the X-ray used, and the X-ray absorption limits of the metal films. In this manner, Kretschmar obtained

$$\frac{e}{m_0} = (1.7570 \pm 0.0026) \times 10^7$$

*Shaw's Method.*—Shaw[34] has investigated experimentally the focusing properties of crossed electric and magnetic fields upon a beam of electrons. Apparatus used in this study is shown in Fig. 15. The essential part of the apparatus is a cylindrical condenser. An electric field is established between the plates of this condenser; a magnetic field is established parallel to a generator of the cylindrical surface. A collector $C$ was placed 127° 17′ of arc away from a slit $S$ through which electrons entered the condenser. Entering electrons were not all of exactly the same velocity; likewise they formed a somewhat divergent beam as they came through the slit. It had been shown[38] theoretically several years earlier that such an arrangement of fields should focus both for direction and velocity. That is, all electrons entering the slit, regardless of their direction within limits and regardless of their velocity within limits, should be brought to a sharp focus at a point 127° 17′ from the slit. Shaw found that with a proper combination of fields, electrons entering the slit were brought to an extremely sharp focus at the collector. It was in connection with this experimental study that Shaw found evidence for the existence of polarization and insulating layers on metal surfaces bombarded with electrons.

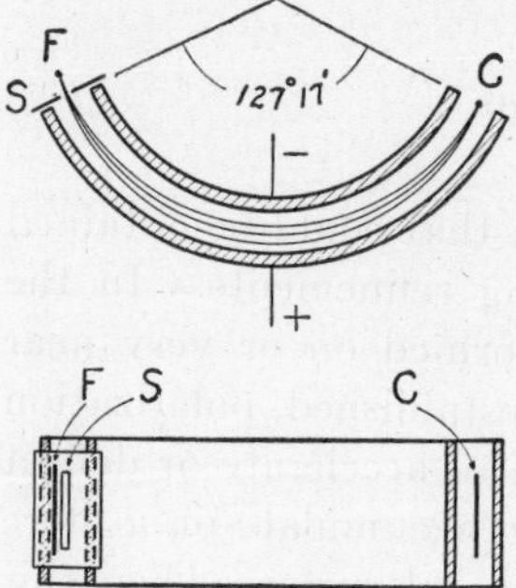


Fig. 15.—A schematic diagram of the electric and magnetic field arrangement used by Shaw.

The focusing properties of crossed electric and magnetic fields involve the quantity $e/m$. Utilizing this dependence Shaw has developed a pre-

[37] G. G. Kretschmar, *Phys. Rev.*, **43**, 417 (1933).
[38] W. Bartky and A. J. Dempster, *Phys. Rev.*, **33**, 1019 (1929).

cision method of measuring $e/m$. He has developed[39] certain supplementary focusing criteria which should eliminate entirely any uncertainties due to the peculiar insulating layers formed on metal surfaces. The method should give a value for $e/m$ entirely independent of the existence of polarization and insulating films upon critical parts of the apparatus. The final value obtained by this method is

$$\frac{e}{m_0} = (1.7571 \pm 0.0013) \times 10^7$$

While the probable error given by Shaw is not as small as that of Dunnington's work, the present method should eliminate most effectively the source of error which has no doubt been responsible for many of the discrepancies among values of $e/m_0$ reported in the literature. It seems quite certain that these errors, rather than that introduced by residual gas in the tube, were mainly responsible for the relatively large discrepancy which existed between the deflection and spectroscopic results in 1929.

**Improvements in Spectroscopic Methods**

Whereas in 1929 the free electron value of $e/m_0$ appeared definitely larger than the spectroscopic value, the recent refinements in deflection methods just discussed resulted in a value appreciably lower than the best spectroscopic value available in 1929. But improvements were being made simultaneously in the technique of spectroscopic measurements. In these methods the accuracy depends upon the careful evaluation of the frequency or wave length difference between two or more spectral lines very close together. The spacing of these lines is so close that the group appears as a single line in the simple type of spectroscope. Measurement of the separation of the closely spaced lines is therefore usually made with some form of interferometer. Since even the component lines have an appreciable width the problem arises as to just how one should locate the effective center of the line. Much of the recent work has surpassed earlier observations in accuracy because it is now better known how to locate these centers.

Improvements have been made in both spectroscopic methods. Campbell and Houston,[26] and Kinsler and Houston[27,28] have improved measurements of the separation of Zeeman lines. Certain characteristic lines of cadmium, zinc, helium, and neon have been used. Improvements have also been made in the measurement of the strong magnetic field used to produce the measured Zeeman effect. The following recent values have been reported for $e/m_0$:

Campbell and Houston[26] .......................... $(1.7579 \pm 0.0025) \times 10^7$
Kinsler and Houston[27] .......................... $(1.7570 \pm 0.0010) \times 10^7$
Kinsler and Houston[28] .......................... $(1.7570 \pm 0.0007) \times 10^7$

[39] A. E. Shaw, *Phys. Rev.*, **51**, 58, 887 (1937); **54**, 193 (1938).

These values are all definitely lower than the spectroscopic value accepted in 1929.

Refinements in the measurement of line separation have been made also in the spectroscopic method based upon the effect of nuclear mass upon the frequency of radiation. Most recent measurements have been made on the separation of lines in the ordinary and heavy hydrogen spectra rather than that of lines of the hydrogen and helium spectra. The following values of $e/m_0$ have been obtained:

| | |
|---|---|
| Spedding, Shane & Grace[19] | $(1.758 \text{ or less}) \times 10^7$ |
| Gibbs and Williams[18] | $(1.757 \pm 0.001) \times 10^7$ |
| Shane and Spedding[20] | $(1.7579 \pm 0.0003) \times 10^7$ |
| Williams and Gibbs[21] | $(1.7579 \pm 0.0003) \times 10^7$ |
| Houston[22] | $(1.7601 \pm 0.0015) \times 10^7$ |
| Williams[23] | $(1.7579 \pm 0.0004) \times 10^7$ |

The work of Williams and Gibbs consists of the recalculation of Shane and Spedding's data, applying two corrections they deem necessary. It happens that the two corrections just balance one another leaving the value of $e/m_0$ unchanged. It is interesting that these spectroscopic values are likewise all smaller than the 1929 value. Except possibly for the recent work of Houston, values obtained by the two spectroscopic methods agree accurately.

**Summary of Existing Determinations of $e/m_0$**

Several authors have published recent summaries of values of $e/m_0$ obtained by precision methods. Among these are Birge,[40] Dunnington,[41] and Bearden.[42] Just previous to these summaries Bearden[43] had published results obtained by a still different and unusually precise method. By combining measurements of indices of refraction of X-rays with the quantum theory of refraction he obtained

$$\frac{e}{m_0} = (1.7601 \pm 0.0003) \times 10^7$$

Some question arises as to whether this should be considered a free electron or a bound electron value. Bearden[43] originally classed it with the spectroscopic measurements. Birge[40] continued this classification. Later Bearden[42] argued that the determination from X-ray refraction should yield a free electron value, and both he and Dunnington[41] have averaged it with these. These three summaries give the following values:

[40] R. T. Birge, *Phys. Rev.*, **54**, 972 (1938).

[41] F. G. Dunnington, *Rev. Mod. Phys.*, **11**, 65 (1939).

[42] J. A. Bearden, *Phys. Rev.*, **55**, 584 (1939).

[43] J. A. Bearden, *Phys. Rev.*, **54**, 698 (1938).

| | |
|---|---|
| Birge | $(1.7591 \pm 0.0003) \times 10^7$ |
| Dunnington | $(1.7591 \pm 0.0002) \times 10^7$ |
| Bearden | $(1.7591 \pm 0.0008) \times 10^7$ |

Each of these is a weighted mean of all precise determinations, both free electron and spectroscopic. Birge and Dunnington each state that there is no evidence that a definite discrepancy still exists between the free electron and the spectroscopic measurements, although Dunnington[36] had maintained two years earlier that there was a discrepancy. On the other hand, Bearden obtained the above value by averaging a free electron mean of $(1.7599 \pm 0.0002) \times 10^7$ and a spectroscopic mean of $(1.7583 \pm 0.0003) \times 10^7$. Bearden feels that there still exists a very small but definite discrepancy between the two, the spectroscopic value still being the smaller. The author is not impressed by the evidence indicating an actual discrepancy at this time. It must be remembered that probable errors make allowance only for accidental errors; they do not take into account any systematic errors of measurement. Considering the numerous difficulties encountered and the many small corrections which must be made in most precision methods, it appears that there is little cause to worry about the small differences which may still exist. This is particularly true since Shaw's[39] free electron value is among the lowest and Houston's[22] spectroscopic value among the highest of the recent precision values. A rather complete summary of important determinations of the ratio $e/m_0$ is given in Table I.

## 6. THE VARIATION OF MASS WITH VELOCITY

On several occasions attention has been called to the fact that the ratio $e/m$ for an electron varies with the velocity of the particle. While it would be possible for variations in either $e$ or $m$ to account for changes in the ratio, the change has always been attributed to the mass. No concept of the dependence of mass upon velocity has yet been presented. Why should mass vary with velocity? Why even should an electron necessarily possess mass? Let us turn our attention to a brief discussion of these items, and to some of the more accurate determinations of the manner in which mass varies with velocity.

### Why Mass Must be Attributed to the Electron

A rigorous theoretical treatment of the mass of an electron and its variation with velocity would be beyond the scope of this book. It is possible to point out, however, why some mass must be assigned to the electron. Also, attention can be called to the manner in which the theory of the change of mass with velocity is developed. First, to what is the mass of an electron due? It was suggested early that perhaps the entire

TABLE I

Experimental values of the ratio $e/m_0$ for the electron. The letter *f*, wherever it occurs, indicates a free electron method or value; the letter *s* indicates a spectroscopic method or value; the letter *a* represents an average of all values both free electron and spectroscopic. Numerals indicate more specific methods as follows: (1) Known accelerating potential and deflection in magnetic field; (2) Compensating crossed electric and magnetic fields, and deflection in magnetic field; (3) Known accelerating potential and longitudinal focusing magnetic field; (4) Known accelerating potential and high frequency potential wave; (5) High frequency potential wave and magnetic field deflection; (6) Known energy of photoelectrons ejected by X-rays and magnetic field deflection; (7) Combined focusing action of electric and magnetic fields; (8) Zeeman separation; (9) Fine structure and effect of nuclear mass; (10) Measurement of index of refraction of X-rays

| Observer | Date | Method | $e/m_0 \times 10^{-7}$ |
|---|---|---|---|
| Classen[10] | 1908 | *f* (1) | 1.776 ± 0.002 |
| Bucherer[11] | 1909 | *f* (2) | 1.763 ± 0.008 |
| Wolz[12] | 1909 | *f* (2) | 1.767 ± 0.002 |
| Malassez[44] | 1911 | *f* (1) | 1.769 |
| Bestelmeyer[45] | 1911 | *f* (1) | 1.766 ± 0.001 |
| Alberti[46] | 1912 | *f* (1) | { 1.756<br>1.766 |
| Schaefer[47] | 1913 | *f* (2) | 1.765 ± 0.002 |
| Neumann[48] | 1914 | *f* (2) | 1.765 ± 0.002 |
| Paschen[16,15] | 1916 | *s* (9) | 1.768 ± 0.003 |
| Bestelmeyer[49] | 1919 | Summary | *a* 1.76 ± 0.02 |
| Busch[13] | 1922 | *f* (3) | 1.768 ± 0.0015 |
| Babcock[24] | 1923 | *s* (8) | 1.761 ± 0.001 |
| Gerlach[50] | 1926 | Summary | *a* 1.766 |
| Wolf[14,15] | 1927 | *f* (3) | 1.769 ± 0.002 |
| Houston[17] | 1927 | *s* (9) | 1.7606 ± 0.0010 |
| Kirchner[29] | 1929 | *f* (4) | 1.770 ± 0.002 |
| Babcock[25] | 1929 | *s* (8) | 1.7606 ± 0.0012 |
| Birge[15] | 1929 | Summary | { *f* 1.769 ± 0.002<br>*s* 1.761 ± 0.001 |
| Perry & Chaffee[30] | 1930 | *f* (4) | 1.761 ± 0.001 |
| Kirchner[31,32] | 1931 | *f* (4) | 1.7585 ± 0.0012 |
| Kirchner[32] | 1932 | *f* (4) | 1.7590 ± 0.0015 |
| Campbell & Houston[26] | 1932 | *s* (8) | 1.7579 ± 0.0025 |
| Dunnington[33] | 1933 | { *f* (5)<br>Summary | 1.7571 ± 0.0015<br>*a* 1.7598 ± 0.0003 |
| Kretschmar[37] | 1933 | *f* (6) | 1.7570 ± 0.0026 |
| Kinsler & Houston[27,28] | 1934 | *s* (8) | 1.7570 ± 0.0007 |
| Gibbs & Williams[18] | 1933 | *s* (9) | 1.757 ± 0.001 |
| Shane & Spedding[20] | 1935 | *s* (9) | 1.7579 ± 0.0003 |
| Williams & Gibbs[21] | 1935 | *s* (9) | 1.7579 ± 0.0003 |
| Birge[51] | 1936 | Summary | *a* 1.7576 ± 0.0003 |
| Houston[22] | 1937 | *s* (9) | 1.7601 ± 0.0015 |
| Shaw[39] | 1937 | *f* (7) | 1.7571 ± 0.0013 |
| Dunnington[36] | 1937 | { *f* (5)<br>Summary | 1.7597 ± 0.0004<br>{ *f* 1.7595 ± 0.0003<br>*s* 1.7579 ± 0.0003<br>*a* 1.7584 ± 0.0003 |
| Bearden[43] | 1938 | *s* (10) | 1.7601 ± 0.0003 |
| Williams[23] | 1938 | *s* (9) | 1.7579 ± 0.0004 |
| Birge[40] | 1938 | Summary | *a* 1.7591 ± 0.0003 |
| Dunnington[41] | 1939 | Summary | *a* 1.7591 ± 0.0002 |
| Bearden[42] | 1939 | Summary | { *f* 1.7599 ± 0.0002<br>*s* 1.7583 ± 0.0003<br>*a* 1.7591 ± 0.0008 |

44 J. Malassez, *Ann. Chim. et Phys.*, **23**, 231, 397 (1911). 45 A. Bestelmeyer, *Ann. d. Physik*, **35**, 909 (1911). 46 E. Alberti, *Ann. d. Physik*, **39**, 1133 (1912). 47 C. Schaefer, *Phys. Zeits.*, **14**, 1117 (1913). 48 G. Neumann, *Ann. d. Physik*, **45**, 529 (1914). 49 A. Bestelmeyer, *Handbuch der Radiologie*, **5**, 1 (1919). 50 W. Gerlach, *Handbuch der Physik*, **22**, 41 (1926). 51 R. T. Birge, *Nature*, **137**, 187 (1936).

mass of the electron is electromagnetic; certainly one should expect at least a portion of it to be. When an electron is set into motion a magnetic field is established about its line of flight. Energy is required to establish a magnetic field. Hence, energy is required to set the electron into motion; a definite force is necessary to accelerate the particle. Now inertia or mass is attributed to a baseball just because it takes energy to set the ball into motion, or because a certain force is required to accelerate it. One must, therefore, attribute mass to the electron merely because of the fields associated with it. This mass is referred to as electromagnetic.

It is a simple matter to calculate the electromagnetic mass which must be assigned to an electron, provided one limits this electron to a speed which is low as compared to that of light. One needs only calculate from the magnitude of the magnetic field set up about the moving electron the energy required to establish this field. Since the kinetic energy of any

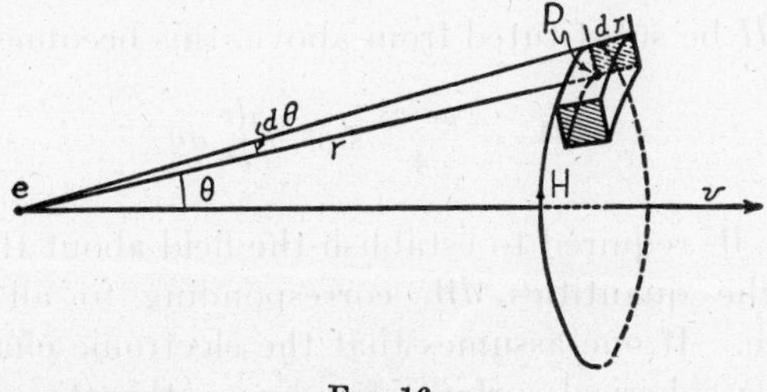


FIG. 16.

body is the work required to set this body into motion with a given velocity, the energy required to establish the magnetic field, and therefore required to set the electron into motion, can be equated to the kinetic energy. The work required to establish the magnetic field about a slowly moving electron can be obtained with the aid of Fig. 16. The moving electron constitutes an electrical current. The magnetic field lines are therefore circles about the line of flight. In the calculation of the magnetic field about a conductor carrying a current $I$, it can be shown that a small element of current length produces at point $P$ a magnetic field given by

$$H = \frac{Ids \sin \theta}{r^2}$$

It has already been shown that the quantity $Ids$ attributable to a single electron is $ev$. Consequently the magnetic field at point $P$ due to this moving electron is given by

$$H = \frac{ev \sin \theta}{r^2}$$

This field could have been obtained also by recalling that an electric field in motion sets up a magnetic field perpendicular to itself and to its direction of motion; the strength of the magnetic field is equal to the rate at which the electric flux cuts unit length of space. The component of electric field at $P$ perpendicular to the direction of motion is $(e/r^2) \sin \theta$. Then the magnetic field established is $v(e/r^2) \sin \theta$, which is the same as found above.

The energy stored in a magnetic field, or the work which must be done to establish this field, can be calculated by assigning an energy density of $\mu H^2/8\pi$ ergs/cc. of space. Within the infinitesimal annular volume element of thickness $dr$, width $r d\theta$ and circumference $2\pi r \sin \theta$, Fig. 16, the magnitude of the magnetic field strength is everywhere the same. If $dW$ represents the energy contained in this volume element, then

$$dW = \frac{\mu H^2}{8\pi} (dr\, r\, d\theta\, 2\pi r \sin \theta)$$

If the value for $H$ be substituted from above, this becomes

$$dW = \frac{\mu e^2 v^2}{4} \sin^3 \theta \frac{dr}{r^2} d\theta$$

The total energy $W$ required to establish the field about the electron is the summation of the quantities $dW$ corresponding to all similar volume elements in space. If one assumes that the electronic charge is uniformly distributed over a spherical surface of radius $a$, then to cover all space in which the magnetic field exists, the distance $r$ must be allowed to vary from $a$ to infinity while $\theta$ varies from zero to $\pi$.
Thus

$$W = {}_{\theta}\!\int_0^{\pi} {}_{r}\!\int_a^{\infty} \frac{\mu e^2 v^2}{4} \frac{dr}{r^2} \sin^3 \theta \, d\theta$$

Integrating first with respect to $\theta$ and then with respect to $r$,

$$W = \frac{\mu e^2 v^2}{4} {}_{r}\!\int_a^{\infty} \frac{dr}{r^2} \left[ -\cos \theta + \frac{1}{3} \cos^3 \theta \right]_0^{\pi} = \frac{\mu e^2 v^2}{3} {}_{r}\!\int_a^{\infty} \frac{dr}{r^2}$$

$$W = \frac{\mu e^2 v^2}{3} \left[ -\frac{1}{r} \right]_a^{\infty} = \frac{1}{3} \frac{\mu e^2 v^2}{a}$$

This represents the work that would have to be done on an electron to start it from rest and give it a velocity $v$. But by definition this is the kinetic energy of the electron. Hence

$$\frac{1}{2} mv^2 = \frac{1}{3} \frac{\mu e^2}{a} v^2 \qquad \text{from which} \qquad m = \frac{2}{3} \frac{\mu e^2}{a}$$

Really this mass is $m_0$ rather than $m$, for it will be pointed out shortly that the above deduction holds only when the electron velocity is small as compared to the velocity of light. Actually, it holds rigorously only for velocities approaching zero. Hence

$$m_0 = \frac{2}{3}\frac{\mu e^2}{a}$$

This represents only the electromagnetic mass of the electron, that mass which must be assigned to it to account for the energy required to establish the magnetic field about its line of flight. If ordinary mass be any different from that which is here called electromagnetic, then it is theoretically possible that the electron possesses additional mass of the ordinary type. There was at one time some evidence that the entire mass of the electron was electromagnetic. In the light of more recent developments the evidence no longer leads necessarily to this conclusion. There is no reason to think that an electromagnetic mass differs in any way from ordinary mass. One attributes ordinary mass to a baseball simply because he must do work on the ball to set it into motion. It is not known why the ball possessed this characteristic called mass. Mass must be attributed to the electron for exactly the same reason, but physicists have inquired a little further as to why the electron should possess mass. It is this inquiry which results in the concept of electromagnetic mass. Perhaps the mass of a baseball which is made up of atoms, which are in turn made up of positive and negative charges, is likewise due to the energy represented by fields when these charges are set into motion. The fields about these charges are complexly interwoven. Some places they reinforce while at other places they annul. Annulment may result in zero, but not less than zero, field energy at any point. Reinforcement results in a greater energy density. Some finite amount of energy is therefore stored in these overlapping fields. It is not impossible that the mass of the atom is due to just this energy.

If one supposes the mass of an electron to be entirely electromagnetic in character, it is possible to calculate the radius of the spherical surface over which the charge of the electron has been assumed to be distributed. Solving the last expression above for $a$, and inserting the accepted values of constants, one obtains

$$a = \frac{2}{3}\mu e\frac{e}{m_0} = \frac{2}{3} \times 1 \times \frac{4.803 \times 10^{-10}}{2.998 \times 10^{10}} \times 1.758 \times 10^7 = 1.88 \times 10^{-13} \text{ cm.}$$

This is the only theoretical method of estimating the radius of the assumed spherical electron.

**The Theoretical Variation of Mass with Velocity**

In the deduction of the expression for the electromagnetic mass of the electron the electric field was assumed radial from the moving electron. The magnetic field was calculated upon this supposition. Because of the finite velocity of propagation of electromagnetic fields, the electric field about a moving charge is not exactly radial. The deviation from radial distribution becomes greater as the velocity of the electron increases. The field cannot be exactly radial, for by the time a field which would appear radial from the point at which the electron was when it gave rise to this field reaches a distant point, the electron will have moved forward an appreciable distance. It turns out that the electric field is strengthened near the plane perpendicular to the direction of motion and through the electron, and is weakened at points near the line of motion, both fore and aft. The calculation of the energy necessary to establish the magnetic field about the moving electron is complicated greatly by this feature. Furthermore, the energy depends upon whether the electron in rapid motion remains spherical or whether it is flattened in the line of motion.

In order to calculate the mass of an electron moving with a velocity comparable to that of electromagnetic radiation, one would proceed much as we have done for the slow electron, except that he must now take into account the more complex distribution of electric and magnetic fields about the moving charge. Such calculations were carried out early by three different workers. Abraham[52] assumed that the electron maintains its spherical form regardless of how high a velocity it may acquire. On this assumption, and taking account of the nonradial distribution of electric field, Abraham obtained a theoretical expression for the electromagnetic mass of the electron. It turned out that the theoretical mass increased somewhat with velocity. The rate of increase was small for low velocities, becoming larger rapidly as the velocity became comparable with that of light. For very low velocities Abraham's theoretical expression approached the expression deduced here for a slowly moving electron. Since Abraham's theory has since been shown in error by experimental data, we shall not bother to write his expression for the mass variation.

Bucherer,[53] in a similar theoretical treatment, assumed the electron in motion to be shortened along that diameter parallel to the motion and increased in diameter perpendicular to the direction of motion. The changes in dimensions were assumed to be such that the volume of the electron remained constant and such that the ratio between the two dimensions was $1/\sqrt{1 - \beta^2}$, where $\beta$ is the ratio of the electron velocity to the

[52] M. Abraham, *Gött. Nachr.*, **3**, 20 (1902); *Ann. d. Physik*, **10**, 105 (1903).

[53] A. H. Bucherer, *Math. Einfuhrungen in die Elektrontheorie* (Leipzig: B. G. Teubner, 1904), p. 58.

velocity of light. The electromagnetic mass found by Bucherer also increased with velocity, but at a somewhat different rate from that predicted by Abraham. Again because experimental data have shown the Bucherer expression to be in error, the general expression for the mass variation will not be written.

Lorentz,[54] in an analogous treatment, assumed that the electron is shortened in the direction of motion in the ratio of $1/\sqrt{1-\beta^2}$, while the dimensions perpendicular to the direction of motion remained unchanged. It is of interest that this assumed foreshortening in the direction of motion is just that found necessary to explain the negative results of the Michelson-Morley ether drift experiment. It is the same foreshortening that has since been predicted by the relativity theory for any body in motion. With this assumed shape for the moving charge, Lorentz was able to show that the electromagnetic mass of an electron moving with velocity $\beta c$ is

$$m = \frac{2}{3}\frac{\mu e^2}{a\sqrt{1-\beta^2}} = \frac{m_0}{\sqrt{1-\beta^2}}$$

Experimental data have shown that the Lorentz expression describes accurately the manner in which the mass of an electron actually varies with speed.

As a matter of fact Lorentz did not obtain the expression in the form written above. He obtained two expressions for the mass, one to apply for accelerations perpendicular to the direction of motion, the other to apply for accelerations parallel to the direction of motion. He called these the transverse mass and the longitudinal mass, respectively. These masses he found to be

$$m_t = \frac{m_0}{\sqrt{1-\beta^2}} \quad \text{and} \quad m_l = \frac{m_0}{(1-\beta^2)^{3/2}}$$

The concept of these two masses was an unfortunate one, and entirely uncalled for. When properly used, the expression

$$m = \frac{m_0}{\sqrt{1-\beta^2}}$$

is valid regardless of the direction of acceleration. In the development of the theory of electromagnetic mass one obtains the one general expression universally applicable, or the two expressions, one for transverse and one

[54] H. A. Lorentz, *Versl. Akad. Wetensch.*, Amsterdam, **12**, 809 (1904); *Proc. Acad. Wetensch.*, Amsterdam, **6**, (1904); (1909); *Theory of Electrons* (Leipzig: B. G. Teubner, 1909), p. 212.

for longitudinal accelerations, accordingly as he uses Newton's second law in the form

$$\text{Force} = \frac{d(mv)}{dt} = v\frac{dm}{dt} + ma$$

or in the form

$$\text{Force} = ma$$

These two forms are equivalent only if the mass is independent of the velocity. If one uses the first statement, which is that originally given by Newton, he obtains the one universally applicable expression for mass. That is,

$$m = \frac{m_0}{\sqrt{1-\beta^2}}$$

regardless of the direction of acceleration of the electron. If one uses the second statement of Newton's law as Lorentz did, he obtains two masses for the electron, one for transverse accelerations and one for longitudinal accelerations. It will now be shown that these statements are consistent with one another by showing that the two Lorentz expressions can be obtained from the one general expression merely by a change in the form in which Newton's law is used.

To show this, consider an electron moving along the $x$ axis with a velocity $v$ equal to $\beta c$, where $c$ is the velocity of light. If $F_x$ represents the net force urging the electron aong the $x$ axis, one can write, using the first form of Newton's law along with the universally applicable expression for $m$,

$$F_x = \frac{d}{dt}(mv) = \frac{d}{dt}\left(\frac{m_0}{\sqrt{1-\beta^2}}\beta c\right) = \frac{m_0 c}{\sqrt{1-\beta^2}}\frac{d\beta}{dt} + \frac{m_0 c\beta^2}{(1-\beta^2)^{3/2}}\frac{d\beta}{dt}$$

$$= \frac{m_0 c - m_0 c\beta^2 + m_0 c\beta^2}{(1-\beta^2)^{3/2}}\frac{d\beta}{dt} = \frac{m_0}{(1-\beta^2)^{3/2}}c\frac{d\beta}{dt}$$

And since

$$c\frac{d\beta}{dt} = \frac{d}{dt}(\beta c) = \frac{dv}{dt} = a_x$$

where $a_x$ is the acceleration along the $x$ axis, this becomes

$$F_x = \frac{m_0}{(1-\beta^2)^{3/2}}a_x$$

But if the second form of Newton's law be used as it was by Lorentz,

$$F_x = m_l a_x$$

Hence, on this view of Newton's law

$$m_l = \frac{m_0}{(1 - \beta^2)^{3/2}}$$

which is the so-called longitudinal mass obtained by Lorentz. In a similar way, if $F_y$ represents the force urging the electron along the $y$ axis, perpendicular to its motion, and if $u$ represents the velocity along this $y$ axis,

$$F_y = \frac{d}{dt}(mu) = \frac{d}{dt}\left(\frac{m_0}{\sqrt{1 - \beta^2}}\,u\right) = \frac{m_0}{\sqrt{1 - \beta^2}}\frac{du}{dt} + \frac{m_0 u\beta}{(1 - \beta^2)^{3/2}}\frac{d\beta}{dt}$$

But since the axes were so chosen that the motion at the instant considered is along the $x$ axis, it is clear that the velocity $u$ along the $y$ axis is zero. This $y$ component of velocity need not, of course, remain zero; the acceleration $du/dt$ is not in general zero. Setting $u = 0$ in the last equation, and denoting the acceleration $du/dt$ by $a_y$, one obtains

$$F_y = \frac{m_0}{\sqrt{1 - \beta^2}}\,a_y$$

But if the second form of Newton's law be used,

$$F_y = m_t a_y$$

Hence, with this use of the law, the transverse mass becomes

$$m_t = \frac{m_0}{\sqrt{1 - \beta^2}}$$

which is identical with that obtained by Lorentz for transverse accelerations. Thus the two values for mass obtained by Lorentz and other early workers arose merely because of the choice of the second form of Newton's law. It is unfortunate that the concept of the two masses was ever developed, for the first form of Newton's law is now recognized as the correct one. It is interesting that the law was originally stated by Newton in this form. On this basis the electron has but one mass regardless of the direction of acceleration. It is, of course, still true that it requires a larger force to produce a given acceleration along the direction of motion than at right angles to it. That this should be the case is clear on physical grounds, for when the acceleration is in line with the motion the magnitude of the velocity is being changed more rapidly than is the case when the acceleration is transverse to the motion. It would be interesting to know whether Newton stated his law as he did merely by accident, or because he actually foresaw the possibility of the dependence of mass upon velocity and purposely made his statement the more general to cover it.

We can now point out just what evidence physicists had at one time for thinking the mass of the electron is entirely electromagnetic in character. On the Lorentz theory the electromagnetic mass should vary with velocity in accord with the expression

$$m = \frac{m_0}{\sqrt{1 - \beta^2}}$$

Nothing has been said of any additional mass the electron may possess, or as to whether this additional mass should vary with velocity. Now experimentally, as will be pointed out immediately, the entire mass of an electron has been found to vary accurately in accord with Lorentz's expression. One is then driven to accept one of two conclusions. Either the electronic mass is entirely electromagnetic, or any additional mass the electron may have varies with velocity in accord with the same law. At the time of these developments it seemed a fair, though not certain, conclusion that the entire mass was electromagnetic. There was at that time no evidence that ordinary mass ever varied with velocity. Since then, however, the theory of relativity has been developed, and it makes certain predictions as to mass variation. On the theory of relativity, which has been amply justified by experiments of various types, it turns out that all mass, regardless of its nature, should vary in accord with the expression

$$m = \frac{m_0}{\sqrt{1 - \beta^2}}$$

Hence, the conclusion that the electronic mass is purely electromagnetic is no longer necessary. But let it be emphasized again that even today there is no evidence that electromagnetic mass is fundamentally any different from mass in the ordinary sense of the word.

### Experimental Evidence of the Change of Mass with Velocity

The theoretical change of mass with velocity occurs to any measurable extent only at velocities comparable with the velocity of light. It is only the electron that can be given a velocity high enough in the laboratory to make this mass variation sufficiently large to study accurately. Changes in the mass of a high speed electron are evidenced by changes in the ratio $e/m$. Several workers have secured convincing data on the manner in which the ratio $e/m$ varies with velocity.

*Bucherer's Method.*—Although several workers previous to Bucherer had obtained some evidence that the ratio $e/m$ does vary with the velocity, Bucherer[11] was the first to extend measurements to sufficiently high velocities to make possible any decision as to which theory of mass variation came nearest to describing experimental findings. By the method already outlined in our discussion of $e/m_0$, Bucherer made measurements of the changes in the ratio $e/m$ for beta particles having velocities up to near 0.7 that of light.

According to the Lorentz theory a particle of this velocity should have a mass some forty percent greater than the rest mass. It is from measurements on high speed particles that one can best decide which of the three theories of mass variation describes most accurately the actual behavior, for the change of mass becomes large only at high speeds. Decision as to the most appropriate theory can be made by calculating the value of $m_0$ from the observed values of $m$ at various velocities, using first one and then another of the theoretical expressions for this analytical extrapolation. If any theory describes accurately the actual manner of mass variation, then extrapolation by that theory will lead always to the same value of $m_0$ regardless of the velocity at which the measurements were carried out. Bucherer saw immediately that his own theory did not agree with the observations; he therefore withdrew it. The relative merits of the Abraham and Lorentz theories can be judged from Table II. Values in this table are reproduced from Bucherer's work.

TABLE II

A comparison of the Abraham and Lorentz theories according to the data of Bucherer

| $\beta$ | $e/m_0$, Abraham | $e/m_0$, Lorentz |
|---|---|---|
| 0.3173 | $1.726 \times 10^7$ | $1.752 \times 10^7$ |
| 0.3787 | 1.733 | 1.761 |
| 0.4281 | 1.723 | 1.760 |
| 0.5154 | 1.706 | 1.763 |
| 0.6870 | 1.642 | 1.767 |

These data indicate strongly that the Lorentz theory is much the better. This theory leads to an extrapolated value of $e/m_0$ which is nearly constant. On the other hand, the value obtained on the basis of the Abraham concept decreases noticeably as the velocity of the electron increases.

Experiments similar to these were repeated a few years later by Neumann.[48] Beta rays having velocities up to 0.8 that of light were used. A number of improvements in detail of apparatus and technique were made. These more extensive observations again supported the Lorentz theory, as is evident from Fig. 17. Not only was this theory the best of the group, but it appeared to describe accurately the actual manner in which the mass varies. It is true that some recent work[55] indicates that these early results may have been influenced to a considerable degree by the scattering of

[55] C. T. Zahn and A. H. Spees, *Phys. Rev.*, **53**, 357, 365 (1938).

electrons as they strike the inner surfaces of the two plates between which the electric field was established. It has been suggested that the Bucherer-Neumann interpretation may have been unwarranted. The fact remains that, although the Bucherer-Neumann conclusions may have been questionable, other experiments have shown conclusively that the Lorentz theory is correct.

*Hupka's Method.*—Hupka[56] obtained convincing evidence using an entirely different method and utilizing cathode rays having velocities up to 0.524 that of light. These electrons were directed through a small pinhole opening across which a fine cross hair was placed. After being bent by a magnetic field they fell upon a fluorescent screen. The shadow

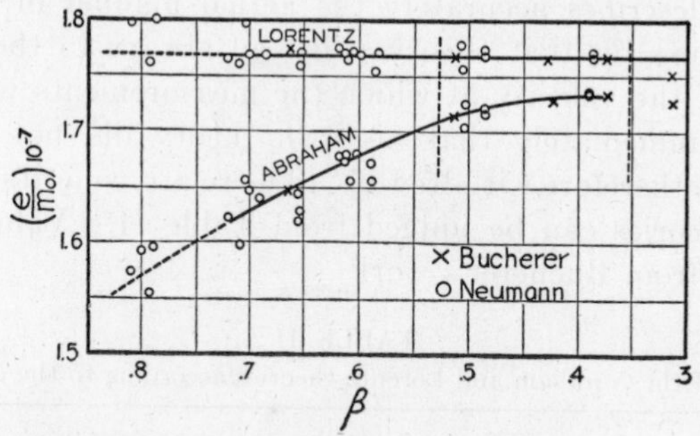


FIG. 17.—A comparison of the experimentally observed manner of variation of $e/m$ with velocity with the manners of variation predicted by Lorentz and by Abraham. Values of $e/m_0$ obtained through extrapolation should, for the correct theory, lead to a horizontal line.

of the cross hair appeared on this screen. The cross hair of a microscope was focused on this shadow. Hupka then changed the potential difference through which the electrons fell, thus changing the velocity, and then changed also the magnetic field just enough to keep the shadow of the cross hair exactly in the same place. The ratio of the two values of $e/m$ for the two velocities can be calculated from the ratios of the potential differences and the magnetic fields required in the two cases to keep the deflection constant. The method is not suitable for obtaining an accurate value of $e/m_0$, but it does yield accurate values for the ratio of masses at different velocities. Hupka shows some six pages of data strikingly in accord with the Lorentz theory.

*Guye and Lavanchy's Method.*—Cathode rays having velocities up to 0.48 that of light were studied by Guye and Lavanchy.[57] They used crossed electric and magnetic fields of such strength as to balance their effects upon the path of the electron. While again the method did not

[56] E. Hupka, *Ann. d. Physik*, **31**, 169 (1910).

[57] C. E. Guye and C. Lavanchy, *Comptes Rendus*, **161**, 52 (1915).

permit of an accurate value of $e/m_0$, it did yield accurate ratios of $m/m_0$. Table III is taken from the work of these observers.

TABLE III

Comparison of observed and calculated values of $m/m_0$ for electrons of various velocities, as taken from the work of Guye and Lavanchy. Δ represents the difference between an observed and a calculated value

| Abraham theory | | | | Lorentz theory | | | |
|---|---|---|---|---|---|---|---|
| $\beta$ | $m/m_0$ observed | $m/m_0$ calculated | Δ | $\beta$ | $m/m_0$ observed | $m/m_0$ calculated | Δ |
| 0.2588 | 1.035 | 1.027 | .008 | 0.2581 | 1.041 | 1.035 | .006 |
| 0.2816 | 1.036 | 1.033 | .003 | 0.2808 | 1.042 | 1.042 | .000 |
| 0.3038 | 1.040 | 1.039 | .001 | 0.3029 | 1.046 | 1.049 | −.003 |
| 0.3107 | 1.042 | 1.040 | .002 | 0.3098 | 1.048 | 1.052 | −.004 |
| 0.3168 | 1.048 | 1.042 | .006 | 0.3159 | 1.054 | 1.054 | .000 |
| 0.3260 | 1.053 | 1.045 | .008 | 0.3251 | 1.059 | 1.058 | .001 |
| 0.3311 | 1.057 | 1.047 | .010 | 0.3302 | 1.063 | 1.060 | .003 |
| 0.3365 | 1.054 | 1.049 | .005 | 0.3356 | 1.060 | 1.062 | −.002 |
| 0.3443 | 1.060 | 1.051 | .009 | 0.3433 | 1.066 | 1.065 | .001 |
| 0.3472 | 1.059 | 1.053 | .006 | 0.3462 | 1.065 | 1.066 | −.001 |
| 0.3561 | 1.064 | 1.055 | .009 | 0.3551 | 1.070 | 1.069 | .001 |
| 0.3640 | 1.061 | 1.058 | .003 | 0.3630 | 1.067 | 1.073 | −.006 |
| 0.3824 | 1.072 | 1.065 | .007 | 0.3813 | 1.079 | 1.082 | −.003 |
| 0.3905 | 1.078 | 1.069 | .009 | 0.3894 | 1.085 | 1.086 | −.001 |
| 0.3985 | 1.084 | 1.072 | .012 | 0.3972 | 1.091 | 1.090 | .001 |
| 0.4055 | 1.089 | 1.074 | .015 | 0.4044 | 1.096 | 1.094 | .002 |
| 0.4108 | 1.094 | 1.077 | .017 | 0.4097 | 1.101 | 1.096 | .005 |
| 0.4159 | 1.093 | 1.079 | .014 | 0.4147 | 1.100 | 1.099 | .001 |
| 0.4198 | 1.093 | 1.080 | .013 | 0.4186 | 1.100 | 1.101 | −.001 |
| 0.4282 | 1.103 | 1.084 | .019 | 0.4270 | 1.110 | 1.106 | .004 |
| 0.4394 | 1.107 | 1.089 | .018 | 0.4382 | 1.114 | 1.112 | .002 |
| 0.4481 | 1.113 | 1.093 | .020 | 0.4468 | 1.120 | 1.117 | .003 |
| 0.4604 | 1.115 | 1.099 | .016 | 0.4591 | 1.122 | 1.126 | −.004 |
| 0.4728 | 1.130 | 1.105 | .025 | 0.4714 | 1.137 | 1.134 | .003 |
| 0.4842 | 1.132 | 1.111 | .021 | 0.4829 | 1.139 | 1.142 | −.003 |

In the case of the Abraham theory the difference between the observed and calculated values of $m/m_0$ are all positive; and these differences grow rather large at the higher velocities. On the Lorentz theory the differences are about as often positive as negative; the sum of the positive errors is nearly equal to the sum of the negative ones. Furthermore. there is no indication that the error increases at the higher velocities. These facts indicate that the errors are not inherent in the theory; the Lorentz theory describes accurately the observed variation.

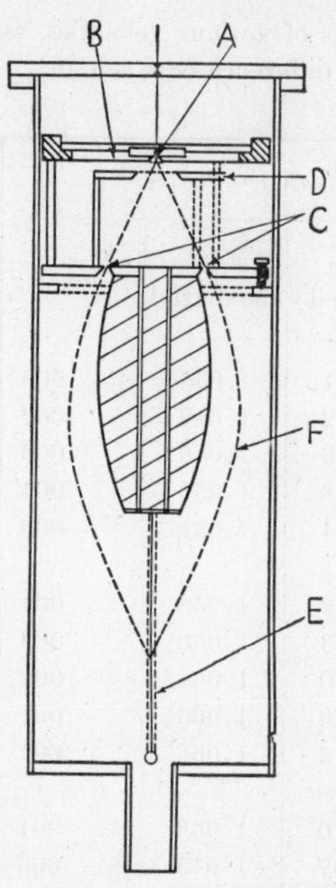


Fig. 18.—Illustrating the apparatus used by Tricker. Beta rays coming from the radioactive source $A$ are slightly accelerated or decelerated by a potential applied to $B$. After passing the grounded plate $D$, they proceed through the circular slit $C$. They are brought to a focus on the photographic film $E$ by a longitudinal magnetic field.

*Tricker's Method.*—While the measurements of Hupka and of Guye and Lavanchy are not susceptible to errors due to electron reflection as are those of Bucherer and Neumann, they do not extend to as high velocities. Tricker[58] has employed an entirely different method to study electrons having velocities up to 0.8 that of light. Essentials of the method are indicated in Fig. 18. Beta rays from a thin deposit of radioactive material were allowed to pass through an accelerating or decelerating potential difference of 5,000 volts, and thence through a narrow annular slit. These divergent beta rays were brought to a focus on the axis of the apparatus by means of a magnetic field parallel to this axis. The focusing action of this longitudinal magnetic field has already been discussed in connection with Busch's method of determining $e/m$. The position of the focus was recorded on a photographic film placed along the axis. Photographs of the focus were taken under two conditions: (1) When the 5,000 volts was applied in such a direction as to accelerate the beta rays; (2) When this same potential was applied in such a direction as to decelerate the particles. A typical photographic record is reproduced in Fig. 19. Since the 5,000 volts accelerating potential is small as compared to the initial energy of the beta rays, around 500,000 volts, $e/m$ remained essentially constant regardless of the application of the accelerating or decelerating potential. From the displacement of focus occasioned by reversal of the applied potential, the value of $e/m$ can be calculated for a beta ray of the velocity used. Measurements extending up to velocities 0.8 that of light were entirely in accord with the Lorentz theory. The accuracy in mass measurements was within one or two percent, which was sufficient to distinguish between the Lorentz and other theories. This accuracy is essentially the same as that obtained by Bucherer and Neumann, but the method seems much freer from possible uncertainties.

[58] R. A. R. Tricker, *Proc. Roy. Soc.*, A, **109**, 384 (1925).

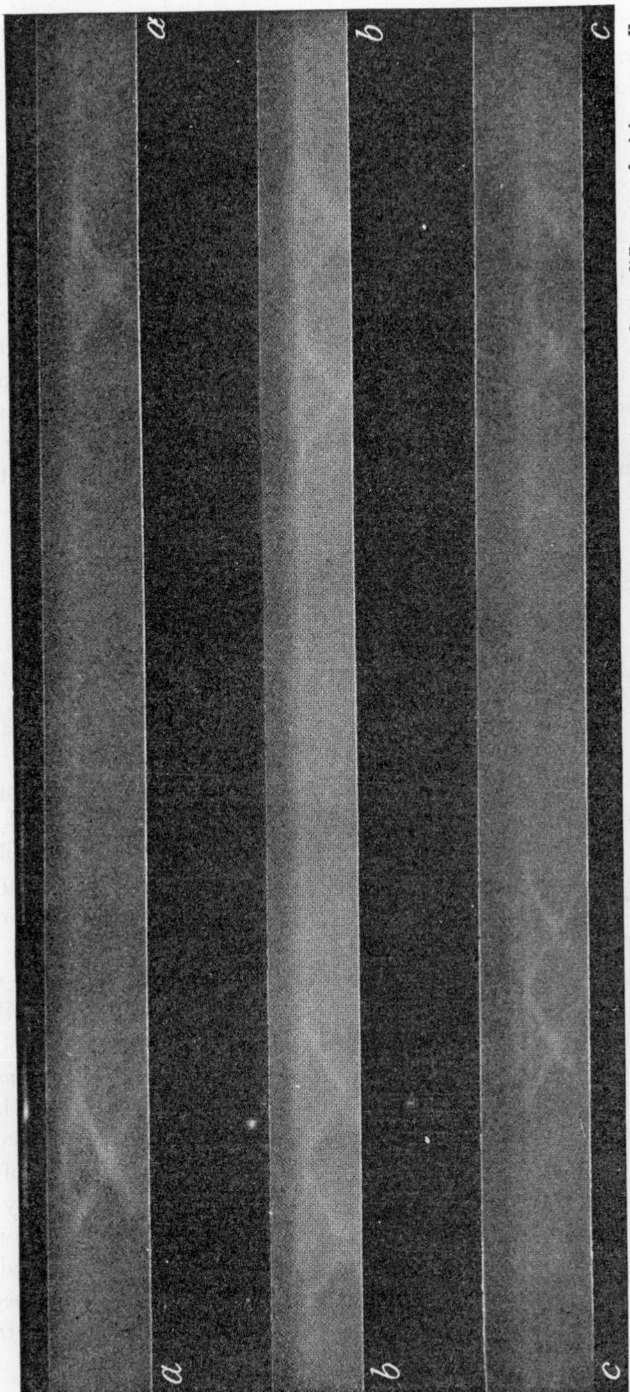


FIG. 19.—Typical photographs obtained by Tricker. On film *a* are shown the places at which beta rays of two different velocities normally come to a focus when no accelerating or decelerating electric field is used. Film *b* shows these foci when an accelerating and a decelerating potential is used. Film *c* is similar to *b*, except that it records beta rays of a different velocity.

*Zahn and Spees' Method.*—Recently Zahn and Spees[55] have suggested a modification of the Bucherer-Neumann method which is much freer from possible errors due to reflection from condenser plates. The general method is illustrated by Fig. 20. A uniform magnetic field perpendicular to the plane of the paper allows only one velocity of beta ray coming from source $S$ to pass through slits $S_1$ and $S_2$ and enter the small space between two heavy aluminum plates ½ mm. apart. If the electric field between plates be adjusted to the proper value, the forces on the electron due to the magnetic and the electric fields balance. Under this condition the electron emerges from the plates and, after further deflection in the magnetic field, enters a Geiger counter tube which registers the number of particles entering. The experimental procedure consists of finding, for a given magnetic field, that electric field between plates which results in a maximum number of particles arriving at the counter per unit time. The method represents an improvement over the Bucherer-Neumann arrangement in that relatively few of the electrons strike the plates. Zahn and Spees have applied this method, using beta rays of velocity approximately 0.75 that of light. The results are entirely consistent with the Lorentz theory. While the accuracy they attained is of the same order as that in the Bucherer-Neumann work, one and one-half percent, this work is apparently free from the uncertainties associated with the earlier measurements.

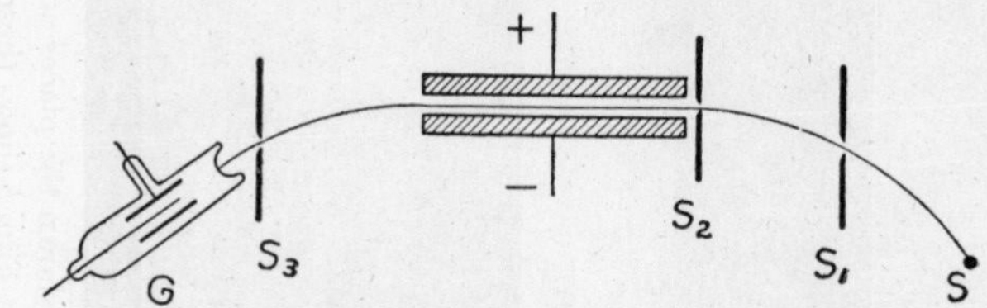

FIG. 20.—Illustrating the method used recently by Zahn and Spees.

All these experiments leave no doubt that the mass of an electron varies with velocity. Furthermore, they show that the manner of variation is given accurately by the Lorentz expression. While it is to be regretted that such measurements do not extend to higher velocities than the highest yet studied, still there is no reason to suspect that one would find at higher velocities a manner of variation any different from that observed over the velocity range already covered. It is interesting that the theory of relativity leads to the conclusion that mass should vary with velocity, and that the manner of variation is exactly that predicted earlier by Lorentz. There is one important difference, however. Lorentz's theory treated only of electromagnetic mass, of mass attributable to a charged particle because of the energy represented by the fields about it. The relativity theory treats mass in general, with no specification of what may be responsible for the property. It is true that Lorentz presented arguments that all mass is probably electromagnetic in character. If these arguments are accepted, his theory would lead one to suppose that all mass varies with velocity. The relativity theory predicts this directly.

While no mass such as a baseball or rifle bullet has ever been given a sufficient velocity to make the necessary tests, nature has furnished us one excellent example. The various planets execute elliptical orbits about the sun as focus. While most of these elliptical orbits are nearly circular, the axes of the ellipses can nevertheless be recognized and located in space. This is true for the planet Mercury, the one nearest the sun. It has long been known that this planet does not describe a true ellipse. The orbit might be described as an ellipse whose major axis rotates constantly in the plane of the orbit. While rotation of this axis is caused in part by perturbations due to other planets, there remains a residual rotation of some forty-three seconds of arc per century after all known perturbing forces are taken into account. This residual is known to an accuracy of three or four seconds. There was no logical interpretation of this residual rotation before the advent of the relativity theory. If, however, account is taken of the variation of mass of the planet Mercury with the velocity in its orbit, it turns out that one would expect this mass variation to produce a rotation of almost exactly the residual observed. This is rather convincing evidence of the change of mass with velocity for ordinary matter. No one doubts that all mass changes in exactly this same way.

### More Exact Expression for Kinetic Energy

The simple expression $\frac{1}{2}mv^2$ for the kinetic energy of a moving body was deduced on the supposition that the mass of a body is constant. Since mass actually varies with velocity this simple expression is only an approximation. It is permissible to use it only for velocities which are small compared to that of light. Furthermore, one cannot obtain the correct expression simply by substituting $m_0/\sqrt{1 - \beta^2}$ for $m$ in the usual expression. The work done in setting a body into motion with velocity $v$ will depend not only upon the final mass corresponding to this velocity, but also upon the intermediate values of mass as the velocity is being increased from zero to $v$.

The correct expression for kinetic energy is easily obtained. The kinetic energy of a body is defined as the work which must be done on the body to increase its velocity from zero to that value $v$ for which the kinetic energy is desired. Thus

$$\text{K.E.} = \int f\,ds = \int \frac{d(mv)}{dt}\,ds = \int \frac{ds}{dt}\,d(mv)$$

But $m = m_0/\sqrt{1 - \beta^2}$, $v = \beta c$, and $ds/dt = v = \beta c$. Then

$$\text{K.E.} = \int_0^\beta \beta c \, d\left(\frac{m_0 \beta c}{\sqrt{1 - \beta^2}}\right) = m_0 c^2 \int_0^\beta \frac{\beta}{(1 - \beta^2)^{3/2}} \, d\beta = m_0 c^2 \left[\frac{1}{\sqrt{1 - \beta^2}}\right]_0^\beta$$

$$\text{K.E.} = m_0 c^2 \left(\frac{1}{\sqrt{1 - \beta^2}} - 1\right)$$

This is the general expression for kinetic energy. By expanding the first term in the parenthesis in a power series it is possible to show that the entire expression approaches $\frac{1}{2}mv^2$ for small velocities. For small velocities either expression can be used; for high velocities the general one must be used.

## Chapter 5

# POSITIVE RAYS—ISOTOPES

## 1. WHAT ARE POSITIVE RAYS?

In 1886 Goldstein[1] first observed streams of luminous gas back of a perforated cathode in a discharge tube. These streams proceeded in straight lines from the apertures in the perforated cathode. They were called "Kanalstrahlen" or canal rays. It is now known that the luminosity of the gas results from the passage of ionizing particles. It is these particles themselves that constitute the canal rays. These rays produce fluorescence of the glass walls of a discharge tube or of a suitable screen. That they have considerable energy is shown by the fact that they heat bodies upon which they impinge. The particles can be deflected by electric or magnetic fields, though Goldstein did not succeed in his original efforts to deflect them. Wien[2] first succeeded in producing deflections by electric and magnetic fields. It was from the directions of deflection in these fields that it was concluded that the streams consist of positively charged particles. That the particles carry a positive charge has been verified since, by catching the particles on a conductor connected to an electroscope; the electroscope acquires a positive charge.

Since these canal rays can be deflected by electric and magnetic fields it is possible to determine the velocity and the ratio $e/m$ for the particles constituting the stream. Wien[2,3] made a number of early studies of this character. He found values of $e/m$ very much smaller than that for the electron; the velocities of the particles were likewise much smaller. By studying canal rays in various gases it was found that $e/m$ depended upon the atomic weight of the gas used, being smaller for the heavier gases. The velocity of the particles was likewise smaller for the heavier gases. The largest value of $e/m$ found was for hydrogen, approximately $10^4$ e.m.u./gram. Values for other gases were invariably lower. The actual value found for any gas was of the same order of magnitude as the value of $e/m$ found for the current carrier in electrolysis of solutions. Experiments of this character showed convincingly that these canal rays were streams of positively charged

[1] E. Goldstein, *Ber. Preuss. Akad. Wiss.*, **39**, 691 (1886).

[2] W. Wien, *Ann. d. Physik*, **65**, 440 (1898).

[3] W. Wien, *Ann. d. Physik*, **8**, 244 (1902); **33**, 871 (1910); **39**, 519 (1912); *Phys. Zeits.*, **11**, 377 (1910).

ions. These ions are atoms of the gas which have, in their vigorous treatment in the discharge tube, lost one or more electrons. The mass of the ion is very little different from the mass of the atom. These positively charged particles are now called positive rays. Wien found that positive rays came through an opening in the cathode with a wide range of velocities. In his experiments these velocities ranged from $10^7$ or $10^8$ cm/sec. downward. The more or less continuous range of velocities indicated that these positive ions often do not retain their charge through the entire Crookes dark space. This is now a recognized fact. The particles often change charge during their journeys to the cathode, or during their travels beyond.

Several early workers[4] determined the velocities of positive ray particles by observing the Doppler effect shown by the light they emit upon becoming neutralized. If the light is viewed in line with the direction of motion it appears of slightly different wave length than when viewed normal to the direction of motion. From the distribution of light at displaced wave lengths the distribution of velocities can be estimated. This method likewise shows that there are particles of various velocities present. The velocity of any particle depends both upon the distribution of potential throughout the Crookes dark space and upon where the positive ion was formed in the dark space. The maximum velocity corresponds to that which an ion acquires in falling through the entire cathode fall of potential.

The nature of the positive ray particle, the velocity of the particle, and the ratio $e/m$ have been studied by several distinct and powerful methods. The three classical methods are those of Thomson, Dempster and Aston. These, together with several more recent refinements, will be discussed briefly. All but the most recent methods and results have been discussed in detail elsewhere.[5]

## 2. METHODS OF STUDYING THE RATIO e/m FOR POSITIVE RAYS

### Thomson's Parabola Method

The first method of positive ray analysis was a parabola method devised by Thomson.[6] The important researches carried out by this versatile experimenter led to a much clearer understanding of phenomena in the discharge, and to the important discovery of isotopes among the lighter elements. Thomson employed a method utilizing coincident and coterminous electric and magnetic deflecting fields. Fig. 1 represents the essen-

[4] See: J. J. Thomson, *Rays of Positive Electricity* (2nd ed.; London: Longmans, Green & Co., 1921), pp. 148–165; H. Krefft, *Ann. d. Physik,* **75**, 513 (1924); *Phys. Zeits.*, **25**, 352 (1924); F. W. Aston, *Mass Spectra and Isotopes* (3rd ed.; London: E. Arnold & Co., 1933).

[5] F. W. Aston, *Mass Spectra and Isotopes* (3rd ed.; London: E. Arnold & Co., 1933).

[6] J. J. Thomson, *Phil. Mag.*, **13**, 561 (1907); **18**, 821 (1909); **20**, 752 (1910); **21**, 225 (1911); **24**, 209, 668 (1912). Or for summaries of work see: J. J. Thomson, *Proc. Roy. Soc.*, A, **89**, 1 (1914); *Rays of Positive Electricity* (2nd ed.; London: Longmans, Green and Co., 1921).

tial features of his apparatus. A discharge was maintained by applying a potential difference of the order of 30,000 volts between the anode and the cathode $C$. Positive ions formed in the gas were accelerated toward the cathode. Some of them continued through the long narrow opening in this cathode. An electric field was established between the iron plates $L$ and $M$ which were insulated from $P$ and $Q$ by thin sheets of mica. A magnetic field was established by the electromagnet, the plates $L$ and $M$ serving again as magnetic poles. In this way practically coincident and coterminous electric and magnetic fields were obtained. The resultant deflection of the positive rays was observed visually on a fluorescent screen $H$, or photographed by replacing $H$ with a photographic plate. The difficulties encountered in the development of this apparatus into its final form can be appreciated only by reference to Thomson's series of papers. One troublesome feature was the cathode with its long narrow opening to define sharply the positive ray beam. The face of the cathode was a hemisphere of aluminum having a funnel shaped depression where the positive ions entered. The shape of this face influences greatly the distribution of the strong electric field near the cathode, and thereby affects the number of positive particles entering. The remainder of the cathode was brass. The central tube running through the cathode was about 7 centimeters long and of the order of a few tenths of a millimeter in diameter. This central hole was not only difficult to construct accurately, but it continually filled with silt produced by ion bombardment. The cathode was cooled by running water in the jacket $J$.

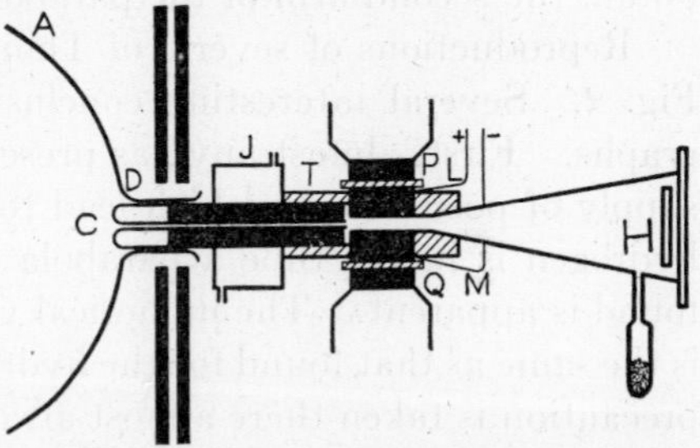


Fig. 1.—Illustrating the original Thomson method of studying positive rays. The remainder of the discharge tube $A$ to the left, including the anode, is not shown.

Since the electric and magnetic fields through which the positive particles pass are parallel, the resulting deflections caused by the individual fields are perpendicular to one another. Just as in Kaufmann's work with cathode rays, the locus of points at which positive rays of the same $e/m$ but different velocities fall upon the photographic plate is a parabola. The deflections in the two fields are in accord with the expressions

$$Ee = \frac{mv^2}{R_E} \qquad \text{and} \qquad Hev = \frac{mv^2}{R_H}$$

If $x$ represents the lateral deflection on the photographic plate produced by the magnetic field, and $y$ represents the deflection produced by the electric field, then

$$x = k\frac{1}{R_H} = \frac{kHe}{mv} \quad \text{and} \quad y = k\frac{1}{R_E} = \frac{kEe}{mv^2}$$

where $m$ is the mass of the positive ray particle, $e$ the charge carried by this particle, and $k$ a constant depending upon the dimensions of the apparatus. If $v$ be eliminated from these two equations

$$y = \frac{E}{kH^2}\frac{m}{e}x^2$$

Thus positive rays of a given $e/m$ fall along the arc of a parabola regardless of the velocity of the ray. The value of $e/m$ can be determined from the constants of the parabola. To facilitate measurements it was usual to obtain the second arm of the parabola by reversing the magnetic field.

Reproductions of several of Thomson's early photographs are shown in Fig. 2. Several interesting conclusions can be drawn from these photographs. First, almost any gas present in the discharge tube will provide a supply of positive ions which lead to a characteristic parabola. Whenever hydrogen is in the tube a parabola yielding the largest value of $e/m$ ever found is apparent. The numerical value of $e/m$ for this hydrogen parabola is the same as that found for the hydrogen ion in electrolysis. Unless special precaution is taken there almost always appear parabolas yielding values of $e/m$ ½, ⅟12, ⅟16, ⅟28, and ⅟44 that found for hydrogen. Thomson interpreted these as being due to the molecule of hydrogen, the atom of carbon, the atom of oxygen, the molecule of carbon monoxide, and the molecule of carbon dioxide, respectively. Parabolas can be found for any gas, including the inert gases, by introducing that gas into the discharge. They have been found also for many complex molecules.

The second piece of evidence indicated by the photographs is that many ions may bear other than a single positive charge. Fig. 2 (*b*) shows parabolas corresponding to doubly charged carbon, oxygen, and mercury. Particles responsible for these traces are atoms which have lost two electrons. Parabolas are often found which correspond to atoms which have lost 3, 4, or 5 electrons; the mercury ion bearing a charge of 8 units is often found. Fig. 2(*c*) shows parabolas corresponding to mercury ions bearing positive charges of 2, 3, 4, 5, 6 and 7 elementary units. So-called negative parabolas often appear, parabolas produced by negative ions striking the photographic plate. In order that these particles could have passed through the cathode with a high velocity they must have borne a positive charge while passing through the potential difference across the discharge tube. Since the position on the photographic plate shows that they bore a negative charge while passing through the deflecting fields, these particles must have lost

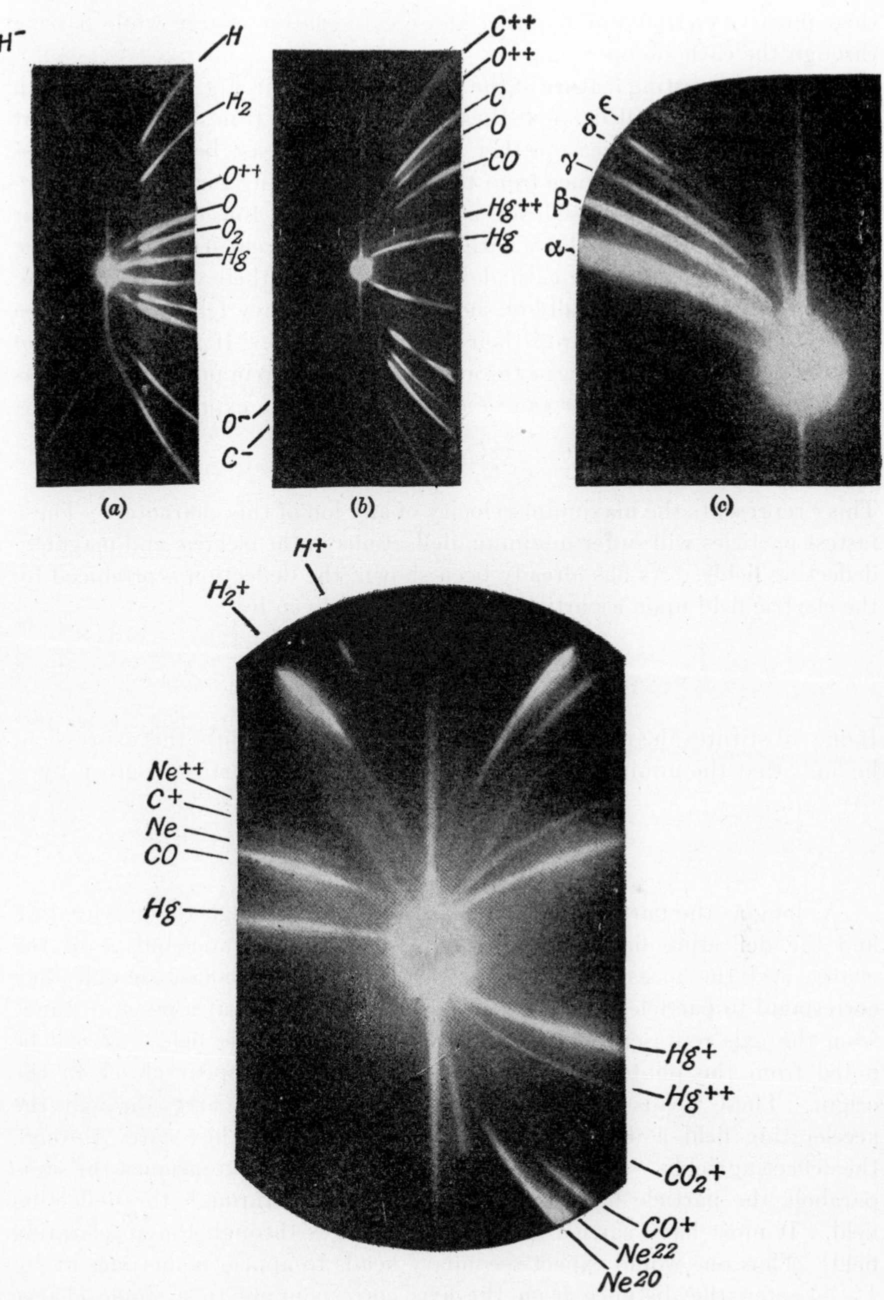


FIG. 2.—Early positive ray parabolas obtained by Thomson.

their positive charge and acquired an excess negative charge while passing through the cathode opening.

A third interesting feature of the parabolas shown in Fig. 2 has to do with their more or less well defined "heads." It is clear from (*a*) and (*b*) that most of the parabolas cease rather abruptly, or at least become much less intense, at a certain distance from the axis representing zero electric deflection. The presence of these heads is to be expected. Ions of any particular kind come through the cathode with a wide range of velocity. If they have fallen through most of the cathode fall of potential their velocity is large; if they were formed originally at such a point that they fell through only a portion of this potential drop their velocity is small. If a positive ion of mass $m$ carries a single charge $e$ through the entire drop in potential $V$ across the discharge, its velocity $v$ can be obtained from the expression

$$\tfrac{1}{2}mv^2 = Ve$$

This $v$ represents the maximum velocity of any ion of this character. These fastest particles will suffer minimum deflections in the electric and magnetic deflecting fields. As has already been shown, the deflection $y$ produced by the electric field upon a particle of velocity $v$ is given by

$$y = \frac{kEe}{mv^2}$$

If one substitutes the maximum velocity obtained above into this expression, he finds that the minimum deflection suffered by any particle is given by

$$y_{\min} = \frac{kE}{2V}$$

As long as the particle carries the same charge through the accelerating and the deflecting fields this minimum deflection is independent of the charge and the mass of the particle. Thus all parabolas, though they correspond to particles of different masses, should cease at a given distance from the axis representing zero deflection in the electric field. It will be noted from the photographs that occasional heads appear closer to the origin. These heads are caused by particles which carry through the accelerating field a different charge than that which they carry through the deflecting fields. Since the secondary head is on an extension of the same parabola the particle has carried the usual charge through the deflecting field. It must have carried 2, 3, 4, etc., charges through the accelerating field. Thus one would expect secondary heads to appear sometimes at ½, ⅓, ¼, etc., the distance from the axis corresponding to a single charge carried through the discharge. Such secondary heads are found. This indicates that during their journeys through the discharge some particles have carried 2, 3, 4, or even 8 in the case of mercury, elementary charges through the discharge; and they have lost all but one of these in passing through the cathode.

The fourth significant piece of evidence, and the most important of all, is illustrated by Fig. 2(*d*). It has to do with the neon parabolas, the one intense one marked $Ne^{20}$ and the much less intense one marked $Ne^{22}$. Thomson, before the Royal Institute in 1913, described this finding as follows: "I now turn to the photograph of the lighter constituents; here we find the lines of helium, of neon (very strong), of argon, and in addition there is a line corresponding to an atomic weight 22, which cannot be identified with the line due to any known gas. I thought at first that this line, since its atomic weight is one-half that of $CO_2$, must be due to a carbonic acid molecule with a double charge of electricity, and on some of the plates a faint line at 44 could be detected. On passing the gas slowly through tubes immersed in liquid air the line at 44 completely disappeared, while the brightness of the one at 22 was not affected. The origin of this line presents many points of interest; there are no known gaseous compounds of any of the recognized elements which have this molecular weight. Again, if we accept Mendeleef's Periodic Law, there is no room for a new element with this atomic weight. The fact that this line is bright in the sample when the neon line is extraordinarily bright, and invisible in the other when the neon is comparatively feeble, suggests that it may possibly be a compound of neon and hydrogen, $NeH_2$, though no direct evidence of the combination of these inert gases has hitherto been found. I have two photographs of the discharge through helium in which there is a strong line, 6, which could be explained by the compound $HeH_2$, but, as I have never again been able to get these lines, I do not wish to lay much stress on this point. There is, however, the possibility that we may be interpreting Mendeleef's law too rigidly, and that in the neighborhood of the atomic weight of neon there may be a group of two or more elements with similar properties, just as in another part of the table we have the group iron, nickel, and cobalt. From the relative intensities of the 22 line and the neon line we may conclude that the quantity of the gas giving the 22 line is only a small fraction of the quantity of neon."

This highly important finding, when confirmed, had far-reaching consequences. Since the early years scientists had hoped that all atomic weights would finally prove to be multiples of that of some common building stone. But as the years progressed it became increasingly obvious that their existed many fractional atomic weights. On the other hand, many more of them were close to whole numbers than one could reasonably expect on any accidental distribution. With Thomson's finding in mind, could it be that elements in general, or at least those with fractional atomic weights, are made up of two or more components each having a whole number atomic weight? Perhaps the atomic weight ordinarily measured represents merely an average of all the components going to make up this element. This has proved to be the case. The several components of any element are called isotopes. All isotopes of an element occupy the same position in the periodic table; they all have the same atomic number, but each component has a different atomic weight. Thomson's finding excited much interest in this field. Unfortunately, his apparatus was not the most satisfactory for accurate quantitative investigation. Two other methods more suitable in certain respects were soon developed. One of these was devised by Dempster in this country, the other by Aston in England.

**Dempster's Direction Focusing Method**

Dempster[7] employed a method similar to that used by Classen for the measurement of $e/m$ of electrons. The apparatus is illustrated in Fig. 3. Positive ions were obtained from heated filaments coated with suitable salts, or by actual volatization of metallic atoms from a pure metal or from some suitable compound containing the atom desired. The vaporized atoms were ionized by bombardment with electrons from a secondary heated filament. The resulting positive ions were accelerated by a potential applied between the source and the slit. After passing through the slit the positive ray stream was bent in a semicircle by a magnetic field perpendicular to the plane of the paper. This arrangement utilized the geometrical focusing action discussed in connection with Classen's work.

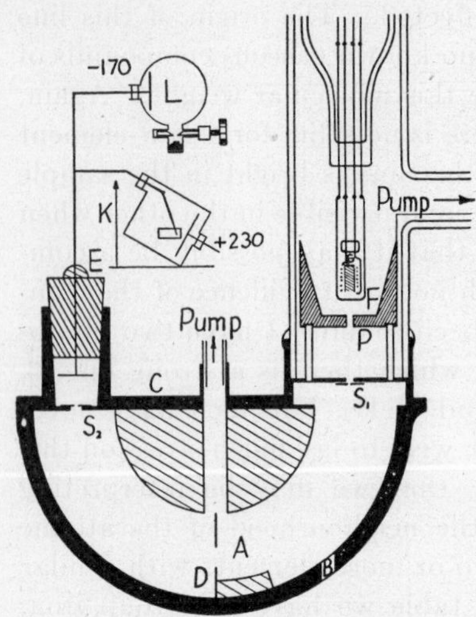


FIG. 3.—Illustrating the Dempster apparatus for studying positive rays.

If $m$ be the mass of the positive ion given off from the source, $e$ the charge carried by this ion, and $V$ the accelerating potential difference applied between the source and slit, then

$$Ve = \tfrac{1}{2}mv^2$$

[7] A. J. Dempster, *Phys. Rev.*, **11**, 316 (1918); *Science*, **52**, 559 (1920); *Proc. Nat. Acad. Sci.*, **7**, 45 (1921); *Phys. Rev.*, **18**, 415 (1921); **19**, 431 (1922); **20**, 631 (1922); **21**, 209 (1923).

During the deflection in the magnetic field

$$Hev = \frac{mv^2}{R}$$

Combining these two equations,

$$e/m = \frac{2V}{H^2R^2}$$

Since the radius of the circle must be a definite value in order that the particles will enter the second slit and be detected by the electroscope, it is clear that particles of only one particular value of $e/m$ will be received for a given combination of accelerating potential and magnetic field. Dempster's procedure was to keep the magnetic field strength constant and vary the accelerating potential, observing for each potential the positive ion current coming through the second slit and onto the electroscope. Since the current to the electroscope is proportional to the number of positive ions reaching it per unit time, and since each accelerating potential corresponds to a definite mass of particle reaching the electroscope, a curve can be plotted with the number of particles arriving per second as ordinate and the atomic weight of these particles as abscissa. Fig. 4 represents the results[8] obtained for a source giving off magnesium ions. It is typical of many other curves obtained by Dempster.

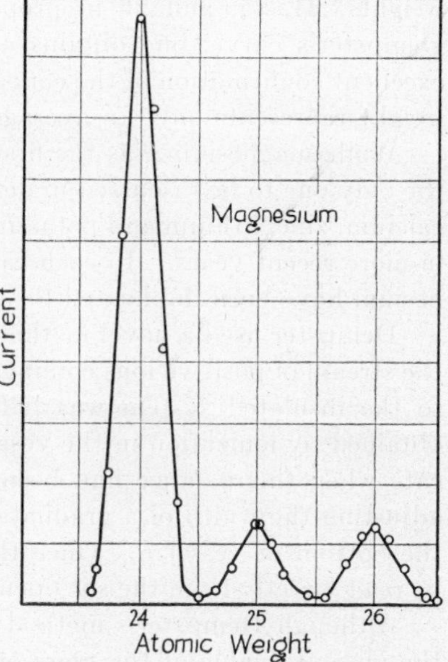


Fig. 4.—Showing the three isotopes of Mg.

The results shown in Fig. 4 leave no doubt that magnesium is a mixture of at least three components, each present in appreciable extent. There are magnesium atoms of atomic weights almost exactly 24, 25, and 26. The atomic weight of magnesium as determined by ordinary methods is 24.32. Although the width of these early curves was such that one could not say definitely that there are no magnesium atoms of atomic weight 24.32, it appeared from the first that the existence of these was highly improbable. The width of the original curves could be accounted for largely by the size

[8] A. J. Dempster, *Science*, **52**, 559 (1920); *Phys. Rev.*, **18**, 421 (1921).

of the slit openings. Similar curves have since been made extremely narrow by suitable refinements in apparatus. These show definitely that no atom exists with an atomic weight differing much from a whole number. It was suspected immediately that the chemically determined atomic weight 24.32 represented merely a weighted mean of the several kinds of magnesium atoms present. Except for certain corrections which were probably small in the case of magnesium, and which were largely eliminated[9] in later work, the heights of the maxima of the curve are proportional to the number of atoms of the respective weights present. If one combines atoms of atomic weights, 24, 25, and 26 in proportion to the heights of the maxima of Dempster's curve, one obtains a mean atomic weight of 24.34. This is excellent confirmation of the concept that the chemically determined atomic weight represents only an average.

While magnesium was the first metal to be analyzed by Dempster, and the only one to be discussed in detail here, similar findings were made upon calcium, zinc, lithium and potassium. Many others have been investigated in more recent years. In each case the general findings discussed for magnesium have been duplicated for the other elements studied.

Dempster used a novel method of measuring the current contributed by the stream of positive ions coming through slit $S_2$. The positive ion current to the insulated system was balanced by an equal negative ion current obtained by ionization in the vessel $L$. The electroscope was used to indicate when this balance had been obtained. The balance was secured by adjusting the width of a graduated slit above some radioactive material in the bottom of vessel $L$. Once this system was calibrated, currents could be read directly from the slit opening required for balance.

Although Dempster's method theoretically might be used to determine the absolute value of the mass of an atom, it is never so used in accurate work. Such procedure would require measurement of the magnetic field strength, knowledge of the lack of uniformity of the field, and various other measurements associated with the apparatus. All of these would introduce errors, some of which might be serious. Since the entire table of atomic weights is based upon the arbitrary assignment of 16.0000 as the atomic weight of oxygen, it is both easier and better to reckon all other atomic weights as directly as possible relative to this. This procedure is followed in all methods of positive ray analysis.

### Aston's Velocity Focusing Method

Simultaneously with the development of Dempster's method of positive ray analysis Aston[10] started an outstanding series of researches in this field.

[9] A. J. Dempster, *Phys. Rev.*, **20**, 631 (1922).

[10] F. W. Aston, *Proc. Camb. Phil. Soc.*, **19**, 317 (1919); *Phil. Mag.*, **38**, 707 (1919); **39**, 449, 611 (1920).

Upon reading his early papers one is impressed with the deliberate and careful manner in which the method and apparatus were developed. Whereas Dempster had used apparatus allowing direction but not velocity focusing, Aston employed a method providing velocity but not direction focusing. Dempster used particles all of which had closely the same velocity but whose directions diverged appreciably after passing through the slit into the deflecting field; this divergent beam was brought to a focus by the geometrical focusing action already discussed. Aston used a beam of positive ions very carefully limited in direction but having a considerable range of velocities. Particles of the same $e/m$ but different velocities were then brought to a focus by an ingenious combination of electric and mag-

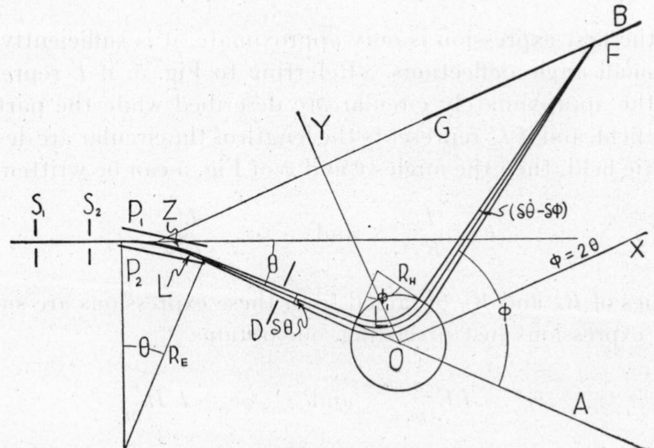


**Fig. 5.—Illustrating the Aston mass spectrograph. (Although it is not clear from the diagram, $Z$ represents the mid-point of the electric field.)**

netic deflecting fields. Hence the method has been called a velocity focusing method.

The essentials of Aston's method are illustrated in Fig. 5. Positive rays were produced in a discharge tube not shown. After arriving at the cathode a very thin ribbon of positive ions passed through slits $S_1$ and $S_2$ and thence into the electric field between plates $P_1$ and $P_2$. It is interesting to note the way in which Aston avoided use of a long narrow tube which caused Thomson so much grief in his earlier work. As the ribbon of positive rays passed through the electric field it was spread out into a divergent beam, the slower ions being deflected through a greater angle $\theta$. The ion stream then entered a magnetic field perpendicular to the plane of the paper in the sketch. The direction of this magnetic field was such as to produce a deflection in the opposite direction to that produced by the electric field. Again the slower particles are bent the more. If the magnetic deflection be sufficient, those particles with low velocity and those particles with high velocity will be brought back to some common point $F$. That is, with proper design of apparatus it is possible to focus particles of a given $e/m$ but various velocities at some point $F$ on a photographic plate. Particles of a different $e/m$ would be focused at some other point.

A rigorous mathematical treatment of this focusing action has been developed.[11] A simple approximate treatment is sufficient for our purpose. The deflections of a particle in the electric and the magnetic field correspond to the respective expressions

$$Ee = \frac{mv^2}{R_E} \qquad \text{and} \qquad Hev = \frac{mv^2}{R_H}.$$

Although the first expression is only approximate, it is sufficiently near the truth for small angle deflections. Referring to Fig. 5, if $L$ represents the length of the approximately circular arc described while the particle is in the electric field, and if $L'$ represents the length of the circular arc described in the magnetic field, then the angles $\theta$ and $\phi$ of Fig. 5 can be written

$$\theta = \frac{L}{R_E} \qquad \text{and} \qquad \phi = \frac{L'}{R_H}$$

If the values of $R_E$ and $R_H$ obtained from these expressions are substituted in the two expressions just preceding, one obtains

$$\theta v^2 = LE\frac{e}{m} \qquad \text{and} \qquad \phi v = L'H\frac{e}{m}$$

Thus over the small range of $\theta$ allowed by the auxiliary diaphragm $D$, the quantities $\theta v^2$ and $\phi v$ are constant for all particles of a given $e/m$. That is, the deflections $\theta$ and $\phi$ vary for particles of different velocity in such a way as to keep these two products constant. Expressing this fact analytically

$$\theta v^2 = A \qquad \text{and} \qquad \phi v = B$$

where $A$ and $B$ are constants. Differentiating these expressions,

$$\frac{d\theta}{\theta} = -2\frac{dv}{v} \qquad \text{and} \qquad \frac{d\phi}{\phi} = -\frac{dv}{v}$$

Hence

$$\frac{d\theta}{\theta} = 2\frac{d\phi}{\phi}.$$

Thus the fractional angular separation produced by the electric field for two particles of slightly different velocities is twice the fractional angular

[11] F. W. Aston and R. H. Fowler, *Phil. Mag.*, **43**, 514 (1922).

separation produced for the same particles by a magnetic field. Since the angles $\phi$ and $\theta$ are opposite, it follows that if $\phi$ is made equal to $2\theta$, particles of all velocities would proceed onward in parallel paths. But the beam would be wide. By making $\phi$ larger than $2\theta$ this beam can be converged to a point $F$. It will now be shown that this can be done.

Let $\delta\theta$ represent the angular separation of the slowest and the fastest particles getting through the diaphragm $D$. Then if $a$ be the distance from $Z$ to $O$ the actual width of the beam at $O$ is $a\,\delta\theta$. This considers the entire effect of the electric field localized at $Z$ and that of the magnetic field localized at $O$. This procedure would have to be justified in any rigorous treatment. If these extreme particles are now converged by an angle $\delta\phi$ by the magnetic field, the angular separation beyond point $O$ will be $(\delta\theta - \delta\phi)$. If $r$ represents any distance beyond $O$ in the direction $\phi$, the width of the beam at distance $r$ will be

$$\text{Width} = a\,\delta\theta + r(\delta\theta - \delta\phi) = \delta\theta\left[a + r\left(1 - \frac{\delta\phi}{\delta\theta}\right)\right]$$

But it has been shown that $\delta\phi/\delta\theta = \phi/2\theta$. Making this substitution, and setting the width of the beam equal to zero for a focus, one obtains

$$a + r\left(1 - \frac{\phi}{2\theta}\right) = 0$$

or

$$2a\theta = r(\phi - 2\theta)$$

Particles of the same $e/m$ but of various velocities will come to a focus when this condition is satisfied. In polar coordinates with origin at $O$ and base line $OA$, this focus $F$ will be at point $r$, $\phi$. Relative to axes $OX$ and $OY$ the rectangular coordinates of $F$ will be $r\cos(\phi - 2\theta)$ and $r\sin(\phi - 2\theta)$. If the angle $(\phi - 2\theta)$ be sufficiently small $\sin(\phi - 2\theta)$ is approximately equal to $(\phi - 2\theta)$. To this accuracy the $y$ coordinate is $r(\phi - 2\theta)$. But for a focus of the particles

$$r(\phi - 2\theta) = 2a\theta$$

Therefore the focus $F$ is at the point $r\cos(\phi - 2\theta)$, $2a\theta$. Since the $y$ coordinate is constant the various foci for particles of different $e/m$ all fall on a straight line parallel to the axis $OX$ and a distance $2a\theta$ away. But the distance the particles have been deflected from their original line of flight by the electric field by the time they have reached the origin $O$ is approximately $a\theta$. Since the constant $y$ coordinate of the locus of foci is just twice this, it is clear that the straight line representing positions of these foci passes through the point $Z$. Hence, if a photographic plate $GF$ is placed along the line $ZB$ making angle $\theta$ with line $S_1S_2$, particles of various $e/m$ values will be in focus at different places along the plate. This simple theory has many approximations, but a more rigorous treatment[11] leads to essentially the same conclusions. Experimentally these have proved correct within practical limits even when quite large circular magnetic pole pieces are used.

It is interesting to recognize the analogy between the effects of the electric and magnetic fields in Aston's apparatus and those of the flint and crown glass in an achromatic prism or lens. Positive rays of various velocities take the place of the white light made up of various colors. The electric field takes the place of the strongly dispersive flint glass, producing a large separation of components for a small average angle of deviation. The magnetic field takes the place of the weakly dispersive crown glass which, to counterbalance the previous dispersion, must produce a larger average

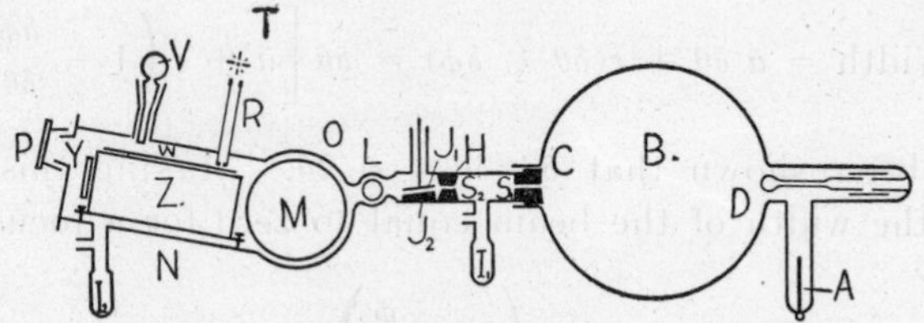


FIG. 6.—Aston's first mass spectrograph.

deviation. The combined action of the two glasses in the lens focuses different colored lights, which travel with different velocities in the glass, at the same point; and at the same time some net deflection is produced. The combined action of the two fields in Aston's apparatus focuses particles of different velocity at the same point; and again a net deflection is produced.

Fig. 6 shows a more complete sketch of Aston's apparatus. Positive ions of the desired gas are produced in the discharge tube $B$ by admitting a small quantity of gas. The arrangement of slits, electric field, and magnetic field has already been discussed. $I_1$ and $I_2$ represent two charcoal traps for keeping the gas pressure at a low value at all points to the left of the cathode. $W$ represents the photographic plate. A source of light at $T$ produces a fiducial mark upon the plate; this is used later in measurements of the relative positions of exposed lines. Fig. 7 is a reproduction of typical early photographs obtained by Aston. Exposure $I$ shows the two lines due to Ne, an intense one at 20 and a weak one at 22. There is no line at 20.2, the chemically determined atomic weight of Ne. In photographs not shown the corresponding doubly charged Ne lines were found at 10 and 11. Thus Thomson's finding as regards the composition of Ne was confirmed. Exposures II, III, and IV show Cl lines at 35, 37, 17.5 and 18.5. The first two are produced by singly charged ions; the last two are due to doubly charged Cl ions. Lines at 36 and 38 are often found when Cl is in the tube, but hydrogen must be present also. These two lines are due to two kinds of HCl, one formed with the $Cl^{35}$ and the other with $Cl^{37}$.

Aston made no attempt to determine the absolute value of $e/m$ from his mass spectrograph data. He took the value 16.0000 for oxygen and evaluated all other masses directly or indirectly in terms of this. While the mass scale over certain parts of the photographic plate was essentially linear, this relationship could not be trusted to the accuracy desired. Several methods were available for comparing masses. The position of a line on the photographic plate depends upon both the electric field and the magnetic field used for deflecting particles causing the trace. If the

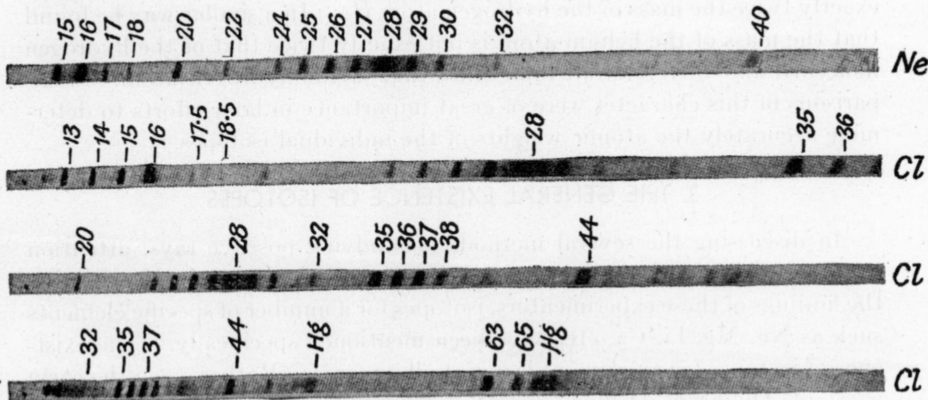

FIG. 7.—Typical early photographs obtained by Aston.

potential $V$ across the condenser and the magnetic deflecting field $H$ cause a particle of mass $m$ to fall at a certain place on the photographic plate, and if a potential $V'$ and a field $H'$ are required to bring particles of mass $m'$ to this same point, then it can be shown that

$$\frac{m'}{m} = \frac{V}{V'}\frac{H'^2}{H^2}$$

Theoretically then it is possible to compare two masses $m$ and $m'$ by varying either the potential or the magnetic field until both masses fall, one at a time, at the same place on the photographic plate. Because of several difficulties encountered in changing the magnetic field by known amounts, it is preferable to make this comparison by varying only the potential across the condenser.

Aston has used a modification of this procedure in much of his work. Suppose it is desired to compare two masses one of which is essentially twice the other. If the mass ratio were exactly two, the traces of the two particles could be made to coincide by using a potential $V$ to deflect one of them and a potential $2V$ to deflect the other. When two lines overlap, however, it is difficult to tell just how much they lack of being in true coincidence. Aston therefore used potentials slightly different from $2V$ to deflect the second particle. One of these was slightly larger than $2V$, the other smaller by the same amount. There resulted therefore three traces on the photographic plate, one corresponding to one mass and two corresponding to the second mass. If the first was not midway between the second two, the masses were not exactly in the ratio of 2:1. The amount of dissymmetry gave a measure of the amount by which the one failed being exactly twice the other. This general method is known as bracketing. Following this procedure Aston found that the hydrogen molecule $H_2$ has exactly twice the mass of the hydrogen atom $H_1$. In a similar way he found that the mass of the helium atom is not exactly twice that of the hydrogen molecule, and therefore not four times that of the hydrogen atom. Comparisons of this character were of great importance in later efforts to determine accurately the atomic weights of the individual isotopes.

## 3. THE GENERAL EXISTENCE OF ISOTOPES

In discussing the several methods of studying positive rays, attention has been called repeatedly to the existence of isotopes. In interpreting the findings of these experimenters, isotopes for a number of specific elements such as Ne, Mg, Li, Ca, etc. have been mentioned specifically. The existence of isotopes for an element is not at all unusual. Rather, even the early work of Thomson, Dempster, and Aston showed that it was the usual situation. A large number of the elements had been investigated within a few years after these pioneering works, and a majority of these had been found to have isotopes. By 1924, according to Aston,[12] 48 elements had been investigated and 25 of these had been found to be composed of two or more isotopes. Since then all elements have been investigated more carefully, both with the mass spectrograph and by other methods to be discussed later, with the result that stable isotopes have been found for practically all the elements. Numerous tables can be found in the literature.[13–16] Table I gives a rather complete list of known stable isotopes and their relative abundance. These are taken largely from a summary of both stable and radioactive isotopes by Livingood and Seaborg.[16] Specific references to original works are given in this summary.

[12] F. W. Aston, *Isotopes* (2nd ed.; London: E. Arnold & Co., 1924), p. 107.

[13] Report of the Committee on Atoms, *Rev. Sci. Instr.*, **7**, 334 (1936).

[14] R. Grégoire, *Jour. de Physique et le Radium*, **9**, 419 (1938).

[15] O. Hahn, S. Flügge and J. Mattauch, *Phys. Zeits.*, **41**, 1 (1940).

[16] J. J. Livingood and G. T. Seaborg, *Rev. Mod. Phys.*, **12**, 30 (1940).

TABLE I

A complete list of the stable isotopes and their relative abundance. Those followed by an asterisk occur naturally but are radioactive

| Element | Atomic number | Atomic weight | Relative abundance % |
|---|---|---|---|
| H | 1 | 1 | 99.98 |
| | | 2 | .02 |
| He | 2 | 3 | $10^{-5}$ |
| | | 4 | 100 |
| Li | 3 | 6 | 7.9 |
| | | 7 | 92.1 |
| Be | 4 | 9 | 100 |
| B | 5 | 10 | 18.4 |
| | | 11 | 81.6 |
| C | 6 | 12 | 98.9 |
| | | 13 | 1.1 |
| N | 7 | 14 | 99.62 |
| | | 15 | .38 |
| O | 8 | 16 | 99.76 |
| | | 17 | .04 |
| | | 18 | .20 |
| F | 9 | 19 | 100 |
| Ne | 10 | 20 | 90.00 |
| | | 21 | .27 |
| | | 22 | 9.73 |
| Na | 11 | 23 | 100 |
| Mg | 12 | 24 | 77.4 |
| | | 25 | 11.5 |
| | | 26 | 11.1 |
| Al | 13 | 27 | 100 |
| Si | 14 | 28 | 89.6 |
| | | 29 | 6.2 |
| | | 30 | 4.2 |
| P | 15 | 31 | 100 |
| S | 16 | 32 | 95.0 |
| | | 33 | .74 |
| | | 34 | 4.2 |
| | | 36 | .016 |
| Cl | 17 | 35 | 75.4 |
| | | 37 | 24.6 |
| A | 18 | 36 | .307 |
| | | 38 | .061 |
| | | 40 | 99.632 |
| K | 19 | 39 | 93.3 |
| | | 40* | .012 |
| | | 41 | 6.7 |
| Ca | 20 | 40 | 96.96 |
| | | 42 | .64 |
| | | 43 | .15 |
| | | 44 | 2.06 |
| | | 46 | .0033 |
| | | 48 | .19 |
| Sc | 21 | 45 | 100 |
| Ti | 22 | 46 | 7.95 |
| | | 47 | 7.75 |
| | | 48 | 73.45 |
| | | 49 | 5.51 |
| | | 50 | 5.34 |
| V | 23 | 51 | 100 |
| Cr | 24 | 50 | 4.49 |
| | | 52 | 83.77 |
| | | 53 | 9.43 |
| | | 54 | 2.30 |
| Mn | 25 | 55 | 100 |
| Fe | 26 | 54 | 6.04 |
| | | 56 | 91.57 |
| | | 57 | 2.11 |
| | | 58 | .28 |

TABLE I. (*Continued*)

| Element | Atomic number | Atomic weight | Relative abundance % |
|---|---|---|---|
| Co | 27 | 57 | .17 |
| | | 59 | 99.83 |
| Ni | 28 | 58 | 68.0 |
| | | 60 | 27.2 |
| | | 61 | .1 |
| | | 62 | 3.8 |
| | | 64 | .9 |
| Cu | 29 | 63 | 68 |
| | | 65 | 32 |
| Zn | 30 | 64 | 50.9 |
| | | 66 | 27.3 |
| | | 67 | 3.9 |
| | | 68 | 17.4 |
| | | 70 | .5 |
| Ga | 31 | 69 | 61.2 |
| | | 71 | 38.8 |
| Ge | 32 | 70 | 21.2 |
| | | 72 | 27.3 |
| | | 73 | 7.9 |
| | | 74 | 37.1 |
| | | 76 | 6.5 |
| As | 33 | 75 | 100 |
| Se | 34 | 74 | .9 |
| | | 76 | 9.5 |
| | | 77 | 8.3 |
| | | 78 | 24.0 |
| | | 80 | 48.0 |
| | | 82 | 9.3 |
| Br | 35 | 79 | 50.6 |
| | | 81 | 49.4 |
| Kr | 36 | 78 | .35 |
| | | 80 | 2.01 |
| | | 82 | 11.53 |
| | | 83 | 11.53 |
| | | 84 | 57.10 |
| | | 86 | 17.47 |
| Rb | 37 | 85 | 72.3 |
| | | 87* | 27.7 |
| Sr | 38 | 84 | .56 |
| | | 86 | 9.86 |
| | | 87 | 7.02 |
| | | 88 | 82.56 |
| Y | 39 | 89 | 100 |
| Zr | 40 | 90 | 48 |
| | | 91 | 11.5 |
| | | 92 | 22 |
| | | 94 | 17 |
| | | 96 | 1.5 |
| Cb | 41 | 93 | 100 |
| Mo | 42 | 92 | 15.5 |
| | | 94 | 8.7 |
| | | 95 | 16.3 |
| | | 96 | 16.8 |
| | | 97 | 8.7 |
| | | 98 | 25.4 |
| | | 100 | 8.6 |
| Ru | 44 | 96 | 5 |
| | | 98 | ? |
| | | 99 | 12 |
| | | 100 | 14 |
| | | 101 | 22 |
| | | 102 | 30 |
| | | 104 | 17 |
| Rh | 45 | 101 | .08 |
| | | 103 | 99.92 |
| Pd | 46 | 102 | .8 |
| | | 104 | 9.3 |
| | | 105 | 22.6 |
| | | 106 | 27.2 |
| | | 108 | 26.8 |
| | | 110 | 13.5 |
| Ag | 47 | 107 | 52.5 |
| | | 109 | 47.5 |

TABLE I (*Continued*)

| Element | Atomic number | Atomic weight | Relative abundance % |
|---|---|---|---|
| Cd | 48 | 106 | 1.4 |
| | | 108 | 1.0 |
| | | 110 | 12.8 |
| | | 111 | 13.0 |
| | | 112 | 24.2 |
| | | 113 | 12.3 |
| | | 114 | 28.0 |
| | | 116 | 7.3 |
| In | 49 | 113 | 4.5 |
| | | 115 | 95.5 |
| Sn | 50 | 112 | 1.1 |
| | | 114 | .8 |
| | | 115 | .4 |
| | | 116 | 15.5 |
| | | 117 | 9.1 |
| | | 118 | 22.5 |
| | | 119 | 9.8 |
| | | 120 | 28.5 |
| | | 122 | 5.5 |
| | | 124 | 6.8 |
| Sb | 51 | 121 | 56 |
| | | 123 | 44 |
| Te | 52 | 120 | <.1 |
| | | 122 | 2.9 |
| | | 123 | 1.6 |
| | | 124 | 4.5 |
| | | 125 | 6.0 |
| | | 126 | 19.0 |
| | | 128 | 32.8 |
| | | 130 | 33.1 |
| I | 53 | 127 | 100 |
| Xe | 54 | 124 | .094 |
| | | 126 | .088 |
| | | 128 | 1.90 |
| | | 129 | 26.23 |
| | | 130 | 4.07 |
| | | 131 | 21.17 |
| | | 132 | 26.97 |
| | | 134 | 10.54 |
| | | 136 | 8.95 |

| Element | Atomic number | Atomic weight | Relative abundance % |
|---|---|---|---|
| Cs | 55 | 133 | 100 |
| Ba | 56 | 130 | .101 |
| | | 132 | .097 |
| | | 134 | 2.42 |
| | | 135 | 6.59 |
| | | 136 | 7.81 |
| | | 137 | 11.32 |
| | | 138 | 71.66 |
| La | 57 | 139 | 100 |
| Ce | 58 | 136 | <1 |
| | | 138 | <1 |
| | | 140 | 90 |
| | | 142 | 10 |
| Pr | 59 | 141 | 100 |
| Nd | 60 | 142 | 25.95 |
| | | 143 | 13.0 |
| | | 144 | 22.6 |
| | | 145 | 9.2 |
| | | 146 | 16.5 |
| | | 148 | 6.8 |
| | | 150 | 5.95 |
| Sm | 62 | 144 | 3 |
| | | 147 | 17 |
| | | 148* | 14 |
| | | 149 | 15 |
| | | 150 | 5 |
| | | 152 | 26 |
| | | 154 | 20 |
| Eu | 63 | 151 | 49.1 |
| | | 153 | 50.9 |
| Gd | 64 | 152 | .2 |
| | | 154 | 1.5 |
| | | 155 | 20.7 |
| | | 156 | 22.6 |
| | | 157 | 16.7 |
| | | 158 | 22.6 |
| | | 160 | 15.7 |

TABLE I (*Continued*)

| Element | Atomic number | Atomic weight | Relative abundance % |
|---|---|---|---|
| Tb | 65 | 159 | 100 |
| Dy | 66 | 158 | .1 |
| | | 160 | 1.5 |
| | | 161 | 21.6 |
| | | 162 | 24.6 |
| | | 163 | 24.6 |
| | | 164 | 27.6 |
| Ho | 67 | 165 | 100 |
| Er | 68 | 162 | .25 |
| | | 164 | 2.0 |
| | | 166 | 35.2 |
| | | 167 | 23.5 |
| | | 168 | 29.3 |
| | | 170 | 9.8 |
| Tm | 69 | 169 | 100 |
| Yb | 70 | 168 | .06 |
| | | 170 | 2 |
| | | 171 | 8.8 |
| | | 172 | 23.5 |
| | | 173 | 16.7 |
| | | 174 | 37.2 |
| | | 176 | 11.8 |
| Lu | 71 | 175 | 97.5 |
| | | 176* | 2.5 |
| Hf | 72 | 172 | <.1 |
| | | 174 | .3 |
| | | 176 | 5 |
| | | 177 | 19 |
| | | 178 | 28 |
| | | 179 | 18 |
| | | 180 | 30 |
| Ta | 73 | 181 | 100 |
| W | 74 | 180 | .2 |
| | | 182 | 22.6 |
| | | 183 | 17.3 |
| | | 184 | 30.1 |
| | | 186 | 29.8 |
| Re | 75 | 185 | 38.2 |
| | | 187 | 61.8 |
| Os | 76 | 184 | .018 |
| | | 186 | 1.59 |
| | | 187 | 1.64 |
| | | 188 | 13.3 |
| | | 189 | 16.1 |
| | | 190 | 26.4 |
| | | 192 | 41.0 |
| Ir | 77 | 191 | 38.5 |
| | | 193 | 61.5 |
| Pt | 78 | 192 | .8 |
| | | 194 | 30.2 |
| | | 195 | 35.3 |
| | | 196 | 26.6 |
| | | 198 | 7.2 |
| Au | 79 | 197 | 100 |
| Hg | 80 | 196 | .15 |
| | | 198 | 10.1 |
| | | 199 | 17.0 |
| | | 200 | 23.3 |
| | | 201 | 13.2 |
| | | 202 | 29.6 |
| | | 204 | 6.7 |
| Tl | 81 | 203 | 29.1 |
| | | 205 | 70.9 |
| Pb | 82 | 204 | 1.48 |
| | | 206 | 23.59 |
| | | 207 | 22.64 |
| | | 208 | 52.29 |
| Bi | 83 | 209 | 100 |
| Th | 90 | 232* | 100 |
| Pa | 91 | 231* | |
| U | 92 | 234* | .006 |
| | | 235* | .71 |
| | | 238* | 99.28 |

It is apparent that there exist a large number of stable isotopes. There are 286 listed in the table, 8 of which are radioactive. Twenty-one elements have but one stable isotope. Each of these have one or more isotopes which can be produced artificially and which are radioactive. Those elements with the greatest number of stable isotopes are Sn with 10 and Xe with 9. Inspection of the table shows that in general the elements of even atomic number have a greater number of isotopes than have those of odd atomic number. In fact, elements of odd atomic number never have more than two stable isotopes. As late as 1936 it appeared that H and K, both of odd atomic number, each had three stable isotopes. It has since been found, however, that one of each group is radioactive. $K^{40}$ was shown[17,18] in 1937 to be radioactive. The radioactivity of $H^3$ has even more recently been demonstrated.[19–22] This leaves no element of odd atomic number with more than two stable isotopes.

## 4. ACCURATE DETERMINATION OF ATOMIC WEIGHTS OF INDIVIDUAL ISOTOPES

### Are Atomic Weights of Isotopes Exactly Whole Numbers?

It had always been the hope of chemists and physicists that the atomic weights of all elements would prove to be whole numbers. It would be extremely simple if all atomic weights were whole multiples of that of hydrogen. More than a century ago Dalton assumed that all atoms of any element were alike. A few years later Prout suggested that the atoms of all elements were made up of groups of H atoms. Multiple atomic weights would be a direct consequence of these two postulates. Before the discovery of isotopes such gross fractional atomic weights as those of Ne and Cl made it appear impossible that such could be the case. With the discovery of isotopes, however, all of these gross differences from whole numbers were removed, and many conceived that it might still be possible to have essentially whole number atomic weights. Even the early studies of Aston showed, however, that the weight of hydrogen was not exactly one, and that helium was not exactly four times hydrogen. In general all other isotopes seemed to be at least very close to whole numbers. Aston's original apparatus was not sufficiently accurate to show, except in a few cases, that there was any actual divergence from whole numbers. In a few cases, however, the observed divergence was appreciably greater than the probable

[17] W. R. Smythe and A. Hemmendinger, *Phys. Rev.*, **51**, 178 (1937)

[18] A. Bramley and A. K. Brewer, *Phys. Rev.*, **53**, 502 (1938).

[19] T. W. Bonner, *Phys. Rev.*, **53**, 711 (1938).

[20] R. Sherr, L. G. Smith and W. Bleakney, *Phys. Rev.*, **54**, 388 (1938).

[21] L. W. Alvarez and R. Cornog, *Phys. Rev.*, **56**, 613 (1939); **58**, 197 (1940).

[22] R. D. O'Neal and M. Goldhaber, *Phys. Rev.*, **58**, 574 (1940).

error of measurement. It therefore became important to determine with more precision the actual atomic weights of the individual isotopes of many elements. Accurate determinations of these have proved possible by two distinct and wholly unrelated methods. The first of these was due to refinements in the mass spectrograph. The second method, which was developed in 1935, evaluates the masses of atoms from observed energies associated with nuclear disintegrations. The masses of the same atoms have in many cases been determined by both methods, and a comparison of results is exceedingly interesting. Let us consider the methods and the results associated with each type of determination.

**Atomic Weights from Positive Ray Studies**

*Aston's Accurate Atomic Weights of* 1927.—The mass spectograph originally constructed by Aston and used for a number of years, was able to resolve two lines corresponding to masses differing by 1 part in 130, and the accuracy of atomic weight measurements was approximately 1 part in 1000. This resolution was sufficient to investigate the isotopes of all but the heavier elements, and the accuracy was sufficient to show that with the exception of hydrogen the atomic weights of all isotopes were integers within 1 or 2 parts in 1000. As early as 1921 Aston recognized the necessity for an instrument of greater resolving power (to enable investigation of the isotopes of the heavier elements) and of greater accuracy in measurement of atomic weights (to investigate possible deviations of isotope atomic weights from whole numbers). Construction was begun upon an instrument in 1921 which, when finished in 1926, was able to resolve two lines corresponding to masses differing by only 1 part in 600, and which allowed measurements of atomic weights with an accuracy of 1 part in 10,000. In the meantime Costa[23] had developed an instrument permitting an accuracy of 1 part in 3000.

Aston's[24] new apparatus was of essentially the same design as that used earlier. The changes in detail can be appreciated only by reference to the original paper. Greater resolving power and accuracy were made possible by the use of narrower slits, curved plates for producing the electric field, and an elaborate electromagnet. Whereas the old slits had been 10 cm. apart and 0.05 mm. wide, the new ones were placed 20 cm. apart and were only 0.02 mm. wide. The use of curved plates which could be placed relatively close together allowed a sufficiently strong electric field to be established with a relatively low and accurately measurable potential difference. The electromagnet producing the magnetic field was designed particularly to avoid changes in field strength due to changes in resistance of the winding

[23] J. L. Costa, *Ann. de Physique*, **4**, 425 (1925).
[24] F. W. Aston, *Proc. Roy. Soc.*, A, **115**, 487 (1927).

and permeability of the core with heating. The individual deflections produced by the electric and magnetic fields were doubled. And finally, more carefully tested and refined methods of photographing and comparing the traces produced by different masses were used.

Results obtained with the new mass spectrograph are shown in Table II. These results made it certain that atomic weights are in general not quite whole numbers; but they are very close to whole numbers. For some isotopes the atomic weight is just under an integer; for others it is slightly larger than an integer. These divergences are many times greater than the probable errors associated with their measurement; they were recognized as real. While in more recent years most of these divergences have been still

TABLE II
Aston's accurate atomic weights of 1927

| Atom | Packing fraction $\times 10^4$ | Atomic weight |
|---|---|---|
| H | $77.8 \pm 1.5$ | 1.00778 |
| He | $5.4 \pm 1$ | 4.00216 |
| $Li^6$ | $20.0 \pm 3$ | 6.012 |
| $Li^7$ | $17.0 \pm 3$ | 7.012 |
| $B^{10}$ | $13.5 \pm 1.5$ | 10.0135 |
| $B^{11}$ | $10.0 \pm 1.5$ | 11.0110 |
| C | $3.0 \pm 1$ | 12.0036 |
| N | $5.7 \pm 2$ | 14.008 |
| O | 0.0 | 16.0000 |
| F | $0.0 \pm 1$ | 19.0000 |
| $Ne^{20}$ | $0.2 \pm 1$ | 20.0004 |
| $Ne^{22}$ | (2.2 ? | 22.0048) |
| P | $-5.6 \pm 1.5$ | 30.9825 |
| $Cl^{35}$ | $-4.8 \pm 1.5$ | 34.983 |
| $A^{36}$ | $-6.6 \pm 1.5$ | 35.976 |
| $Cl^{37}$ | $-5.0 \pm 1.5$ | 36.980 |
| $A^{40}$ | $-7.2 \pm 1$ | 39.971 |
| As | $-8.8 \pm 1.5$ | 74.934 |
| $Kr^{78}$ | $-9.4 \pm 2$ | 77.926 |
| $Br^{79}$ | $-9.0 \pm 1.5$ | 78.929 |
| $Kr^{80}$ | $-9.1 \pm 2$ | 79.926 |
| $Kr^{81}$ | $-8.6 \pm 1.5$ | 80.926 |
| $Kr^{82}$ | $-8.8 \pm 1.5$ | 81.927 |
| $Kr^{83}$ | $-8.7 \pm 1.5$ | 82.927 |
| $Kr^{84}$ | $-8.5 \pm 1.5$ | 83.928 |
| $Kr^{86}$ | $-8.2 \pm 1.5$ | 85.929 |
| I | $-5.3 \pm 2$ | 126.932 |
| $Sn^{120}$ | $-7.3 \pm 2$ | 119.912 |
| $Xe^{134}$ | $-5.3 \pm 2$ | 133.929 |
| $Hg^{200}$ | $+0.8 \pm 2$ | 200.016 |

more precisely determined, it is nevertheless proper at this time to look into Aston's interpretation of these.

*Aston's Original Packing Fraction Curve.*—While it was clear that atomic weights were not exactly whole multiples of any fundamental unit, still physicists could not give up the concept that the nuclei of various atoms were formed always of the same fundamental building stones. It was therefore necessary to look for some logical interpretation of the small divergences from multiple atomic weights. At that time the existence of the positron and the neutron was unknown. Quite naturally it was supposed that all nuclei were made up of protons and electrons. The number of protons in a given nucleus was supposed to be equal to the mass number of that nucleus. The number of electrons within the nucleus was thought to be equal to the mass number less the atomic number. This combination of protons and electrons would provide a nuclear mass approximately correct, together with a net positive nuclear charge equal to the atomic number. Earlier experimental evidence, which will be discussed later, had shown that the net positive charge on the nucleus of any atom is equal to the atomic number of that atom. The question was, therefore, when a number of protons and electrons are combined closely to form a nucleus, why is the mass of the combination less than the sum of the individual masses? If one conceives the mass of the electron to be represented by the energy content of the fields about it, and if one regards the mass of the proton in the same light, it is to be expected that closely grouped charges would have a combined mass different from the sum of the individual masses. For example, it can be shown that if two opposite charges are brought sufficiently close together, their fields will interact in such a way as to reduce the total energy content and thus reduce the mass. Such interactions of fields are entirely negligible at distances comparable with those between the nucleus and any planetary electron of an atom, but the effect might be appreciable for cases in which charges are packed as closely as they are within the nuclei of atoms. Evidence to be discussed later shows clearly that the nucleus of even a heavy atom certainly does not exceed $10^{-12}$ or $10^{-13}$ cm. in diameter. All of the particles making up one nucleus must be packed within this region.

If one conceives of the helium nucleus being made up of four protons and two electrons he would expect the resultant mass of helium to be less than four times that of hydrogen. If one were to tear the helium nucleus apart piece by piece, separating the components to appreciable distances, a considerable increase of mass would result, and in the meantime one would have done a considerable amount of work. Does this increase of mass represent simply a form of energy? That is, are mass and energy interchangeable? Such an interpretation was suggested in our study of the increase of mass of the electron at velocities approaching that of light.

The entire equivalence of mass and energy is also one of the conclusions of the Einstein theory of relativity. In fact it is there predicted that if a mass $m$ is converted into energy the amount of energy resulting is $c^2$ times the mass, or $mc^2$.

If this packing effect is real, it should exist in varying amounts for the nuclei of all atoms. Aston therefore calculated from his observed divergences of atomic weights from whole numbers, a quantity which he called the "packing fraction." This fraction was computed by dividing the small divergence from the nearest whole number atomic weight by this whole number. On the proton-electron concept of nuclear structure this represented the packing effect per proton in the nucleus. The curve obtained by Aston is shown in Fig. 8. The mere fact that the packing fractions for the

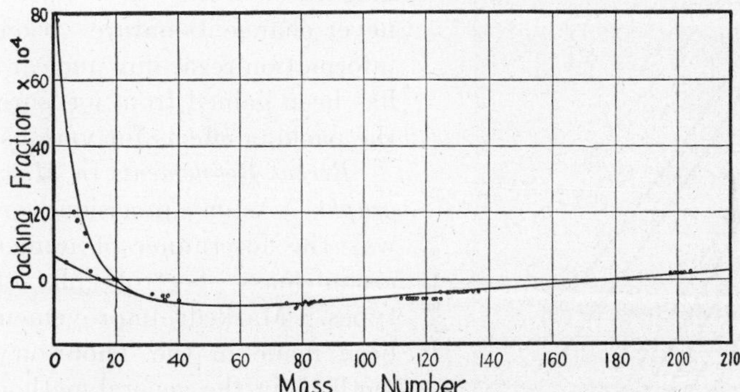


FIG. 8.—The original packing fraction curve obtained by Aston.

various elements fall upon a smooth curve shows definitely that this fraction is a function of the mass number of the element. No consistent deviation from this single smooth curve is evident except for the elements He, C, and O. Judging from the probable errors associated with Aston's measurements it appeared that data for these atoms really do fall below a curve drawn through the other light elements. It is interesting to note that these three atoms have atomic weights which are multiples of four. While still more accurate data have shown the packing fraction curve to be somewhat less simple than that found by Aston, it has borne out the fact that He, C, and O have notably small packing fractions. More recent evidence bearing upon this will be presented shortly.

Although the original interpretation of the small divergences from whole number atomic weights was phrased in terms of the packing effect in a nucleus made up of protons and electrons, the same fundamental idea is good for any concept of nuclear structure. Since the discovery of the positron and the neutron there exist a number of different ways in which one can conceive the nucleus to be constructed. It could be built from protons and electrons alone. Or only protons and neutrons might be used in the structure. Another possibility is a group of neutrons and positrons only. A large number of possibilities occur if one admits the use of more than two fundamental particles in the structure. It is not certain today which one of the nuclear structure concepts is correct, but an ever increasing amount of evidence speaks strongly in favor of the proton-neutron structure. Regardless of which model may prove correct, the fundamental arguments underlying the packing effect still hold. The component parts of the nucleus would be expected to influence the magnitude of this effect, but they could never change its nature. Considerable information regarding nuclear structure has been gained from measurements of the packing effects for various atoms.

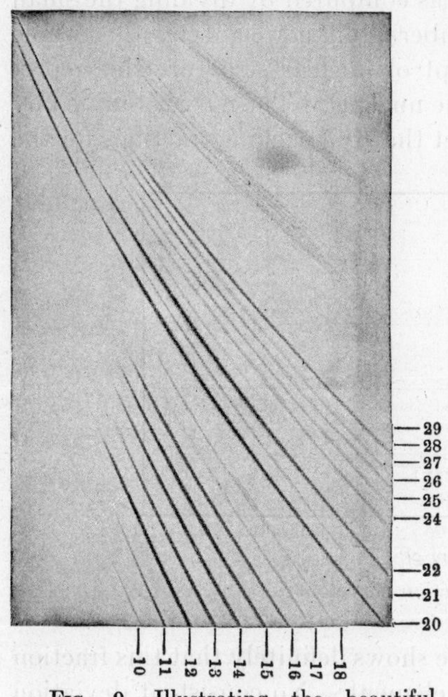


FIG. 9.—Illustrating the beautiful parabolas obtained recently by Harmsen. Note the three neon traces at 20, 21 and 22.

*Recent Refinements in Mass Spectrographs.*—Aston's precision work of 1927 was the forerunner of numerous precision mass spectrographs of several types. Marked improvements have been made in the Thomson parabola method, in the general method typified by Dempster's early apparatus, and in the method of which Aston's apparatus is typical. While improvements in the parabola method have led to no precision measurements of atomic weights, it is nevertheless interesting to see the degree of resolution and sharpness of photographic traces which have been attained today. Fig. 9 reproduces some beautiful parabolas obtained by Harmsen.[24a] The two parabolas corresponding to $Ne^{20}$ and $Ne^{22}$ are widely separated in this photograph. The much fainter trace at 21 is due to still another isotope of Ne. Fig. 10(*a*) reproduces similar parabolas obtained by Lukanow and Schütze[25] for a number of hydrocarbon molecules. These workers obtained a resolving power of approximately 1 part in 600. That the resolution was excellent for the parabola method is indicated in Fig. 10(*b*), where a small

[24a] H. Harmsen, *Zeits. f. Physik*, **82**, 589 (1933).
[25] H. Lukanow and W. Schütze, *Zeits. f. Physik*, **82**, 610 (1933).

section of the parabolas due to the singly charged hydrogen molecule and the doubly charged helium atom are clearly resolved.

Bainbridge developed a mass spectrograph of a somewhat different type that gave unusual accuracy and resolving power. The apparatus resembled

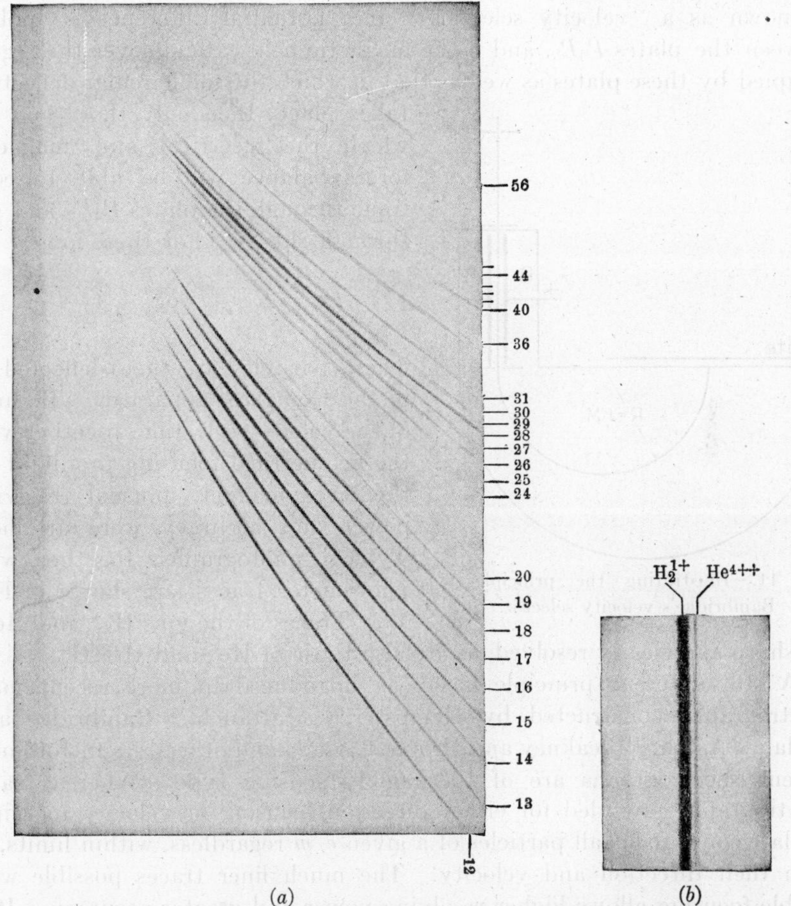


FIG. 10.—(*a*) Parabolas due to various hydrocarbon ions. (*b*) The resolved traces of singly charged molecular H and doubly charged atomic He.

that of Dempster in that the positive ions were bent in semicircles by a magnetic field. In fact the original apparatus[26] was intended to embody the same principle as that used by Dempster. Its original main feature was a very large electromagnet designed to give a large and uniform mag-

[26] W. F. G. Swann, *Jour. Frank. Inst.*, **210**, 751 (1930).

netic field. With this large apparatus of considerably increased resolving power a critical search was made for unknown isotopes. Shortly, however, Bainbridge[27] modified the apparatus in a very essential respect. The new principle incorporated is shown schematically in Fig. 11. The apparatus selects ions of one velocity only. That section which performs this function is known as a "velocity selector." If a potential difference is applied between the plates $P_1P_2$, and if the magnetic field extends over the region occupied by these plates as well as that in which the semicircular deflection takes place, then only those ions for which the electrical and magnetic forces balance will be able to continue through the plates $P_1P_2$ and get through slit $S_3$. For these ions

$$Ee = Hev \qquad \text{or} \qquad v = \frac{E}{H}$$

These particles are then deflected as in the Dempster apparatus. Because of the velocity selection, together with the geometrical focusing produced by the large magnet, unusual resolving power and accuracy were attained. Typical photographs, together with photometer traces, are shown in Fig. 12. Traces of the ions $H_2^+$ and $He^{++}$ are sharp and clearly resolved, as are also those of $He^+$ and $H^2HH^+$.

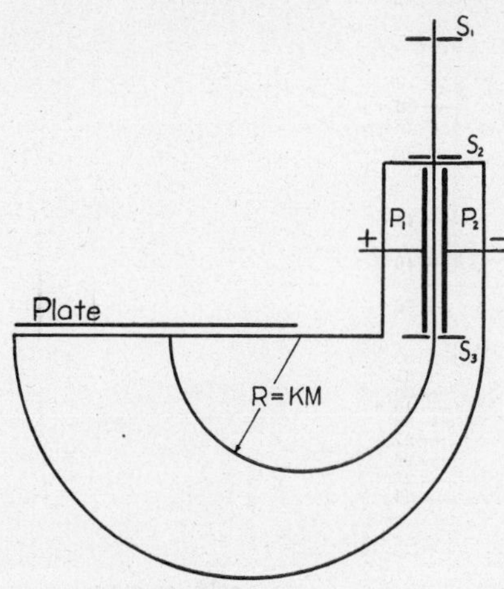

FIG. 11.—Illustrating the principle of Bainbridge's velocity selector.

A still different principle has been introduced in more recent mass spectrographs constructed by Dempster,[28] Mattauch,[29] Bainbridge and Jordan,[30] Aston,[31] Bleakney and Hipple,[32] Asada and others,[33] and Jordan.[34] Recent spectrographs are of the double-focusing type. Whereas early spectrographs provided for either direction focusing or velocity focusing, the later ones focus all particles of a given $e/m$ regardless, within limits, of both their direction and velocity. The much finer traces possible with double-focusing allows higher resolving power and greater accuracy. It is

[27] K. T. Bainbridge, *Jour. Frank. Inst.*, **215**, 509 (1933).

[28] A. J. Dempster, *Proc. Amer. Phil. Soc.*, **75**, 755 (1935); *Phys. Rev.*, **51**, 67 (1937).

[29] J. Mattauch, *Phys. Rev.*, **50**, 617 (1936).

[30] K. T. Bainbridge and E. B. Jordan, *Phys. Rev.*, **50**, 282 (1936).

[31] F. W. Aston, *Proc. Roy. Soc.*, A, **163**, 391 (1937).

[32] W. Bleakney and J. A. Hipple, *Phys. Rev.*, **53**, 521 (1938).

[33] T. Asada, T. Okuda, K. Ogata and S. Yoshimoto, *Proc. Phys. Math. Soc.*, Japan, **22**, 41 (1940).

[34] E. B. Jordan, *Phys. Rev.*, **57**, 1072 (1940); **58**, 1009 (1940).

possible to acquire to some extent this double-focusing in a variety of ways. Fig. 13, showing the apparatus used by Bainbridge and Jordan,[30] illustrates

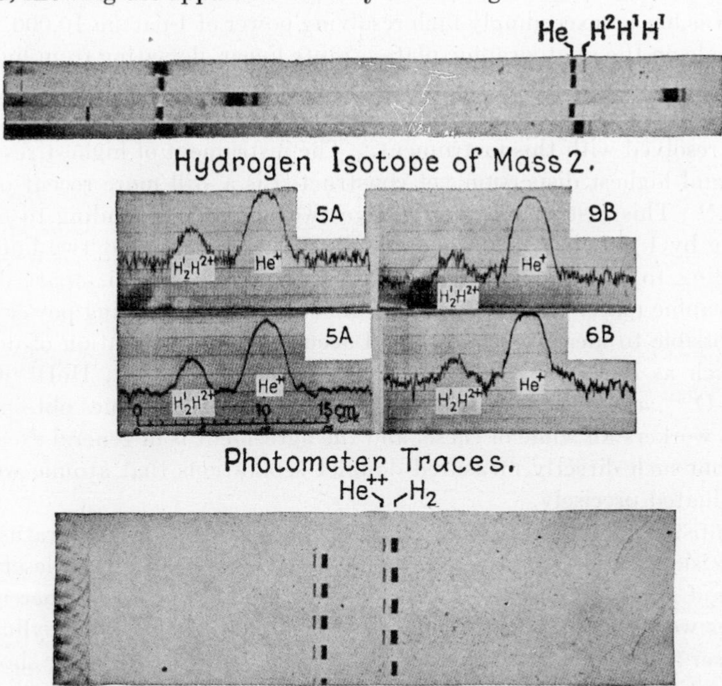


FIG. 12.—Typical photographs and photometer traces obtained by Bainbridge.

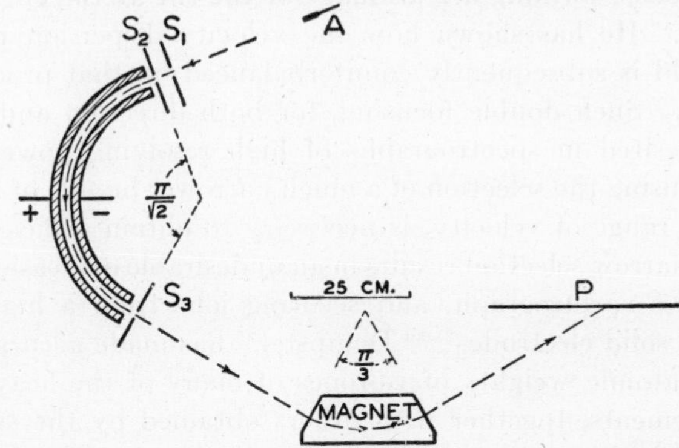


FIG. 13.—Illustrating the precision method used recently by Bainbridge.

the general method. An electrical deflection within the cylindrical condenser extending over an angle $\pi/\sqrt{2}$ is followed by a magnetic deflection through an angle $\pi/3$. The dispersion produced by the electric deflection is counterbalanced by that produced by the magnetic deflection. The apparatus has an exceedingly high resolving power of 1 part in 10,000. The mass scale on the photographic plate is quite linear, deviating from linearity by only 1 part in 7,000 over a distance of 14 cm. on the photographic plate. Closely spaced lines corresponding to particles of nearly equal $e/m$ are clearly resolved with this instrument. The instrument of highest resolving power and highest dispersion yet constructed is a still more recent one by Jordan.[34] This instrument will resolve two lines corresponding to masses differing by 1 part in 30,000, and the dispersion is such that two lines corresponding to masses differing by 1 percent fall 14.6 mm. apart on the photographic plate. With these instruments of high resolving power it has been possible to measure directly and accurately the separation of doublet lines such as $H_2^+$-$He^{++}$, $H^2HH^+$-$He^+$, $H_2^+$-$H^{2+}$, $H_3^{2+}$-$C^{12++}$, $HeH^{2+}$-$C^{12++}$, $C^{12}H_4^+$-$O^{16+}$, and $C^{12}H_2^+$-$N^{14+}$. Jordan[34] has compared values obtained by various workers for some of these, and the agreement is in general excellent. It is from such directly measured doublet separations that atomic weights are evaluated precisely.

Dempster has likewise made marked improvements in apparatus used for precision studies of atomic weights. He had previously described[28] a method quite similar to that since used by Bainbridge, wherein the particles were first deflected through 90° by an electric field in a cylindrical condenser and thence through 180° by a magnetic field. He later showed[28] mathematically how this arrangement of fields will produce both direction and velocity focusing. One particular velocity of particle in the divergent bundle of rays entering the electric field through a slit is sorted out and brought to a focus, forming a real image of the slit at the entrance to the magnetic field. He has shown how the velocity dispersion produced by the electric field is subsequently counterbalanced by that produced in the magnetic field. Such double focusing, for both direction and velocity, is much to be desired in spectrographs of high resolving power. Without this double focusing the selection of a much narrower bundle of rays, having a very narrow range of velocity, is necessary to obtain sufficient resolving power. This narrow selection results in an undesirable decrease in intensity. Using this mass spectrograph, and securing ions from a high frequency spark between solid electrodes[28,35] Dempster[36] has made accurate measurements of the atomic weights of isotopes of many of the heavy elements. These measurements, together with others obtained by the same method and usually with the same apparatus, comprise by far the most extensive accurate observations on the heavy elements.

[35] A. J. Dempster, *Rev. Sci. Instr.*, **7**, 46 (1936).
[36] A. J. Dempster, *Phys. Rev.*, **53**, 64 (1938).

Numerous other workers have used modifications of the original Dempster apparatus. Fig. 14 shows experimental results obtained by Bleakney.[37] The strong peak corresponding to the triatomic molecule of H is interesting.

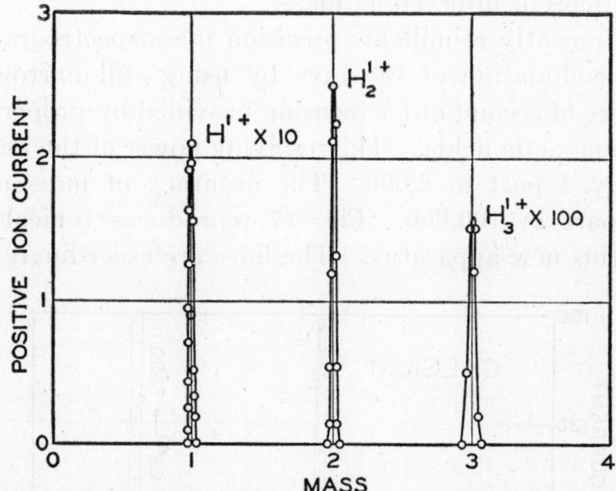


FIG. 14.—Showing the relative abundance, under the working conditions, of the mono-, dia-, and triatomic molecules formed from the normal hydrogen atom of mass 1.

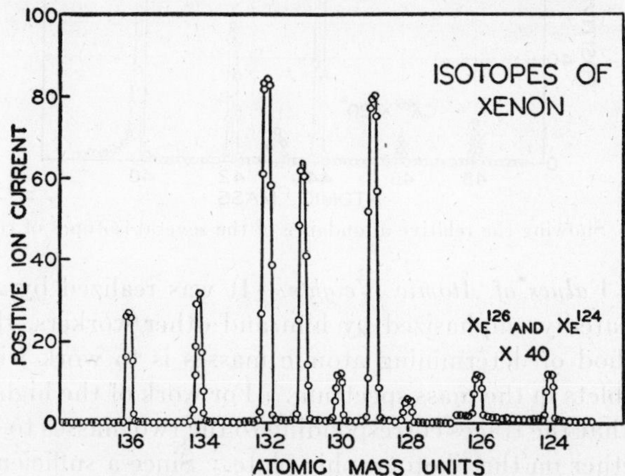


FIG. 15.—Reproducing results of a study of the relative abundance of the isotopes of Xe. Data for the isotopes of masses 124 and 126 have been multiplied by 40 before being plotted; otherwise these two peaks would scarcely be evident on the diagram.

Some evidence for the existence of this molecule had been obtained early by Thomson. In the meantime its existence had been shown in numerous ways. Fig. 15 shows recent results obtained by Nier[38] for Xe. The 9

[37] W. Bleakney, *Phys. Rev.*, **41**, 32 (1932).

[38] A. O. Nier, *Phys. Rev.*, **52**, 933 (1937).

isotopes of Xe are clearly defined. Fig. 16 shows similar results by the same author[39] for Ca. The remarkable thing about these figures is the sharpness of the peak corresponding to a particular isotope, and the complete lack of any particles of intervening mass.

Aston[31] has recently rebuilt his precision mass spectrograph, obtaining more accurate collimation of the rays by using still narrower slits, and taking advantage of second order focusing provided by proper arrangement of electric and magnetic fields. The resolving power of the new instrument is approximately 1 part in 2,000. The accuracy of mass measurements approaches 1 part in 100,000. Fig. 17 reproduces typical photographs obtained with this new apparatus. The lines are exceedingly sharp.

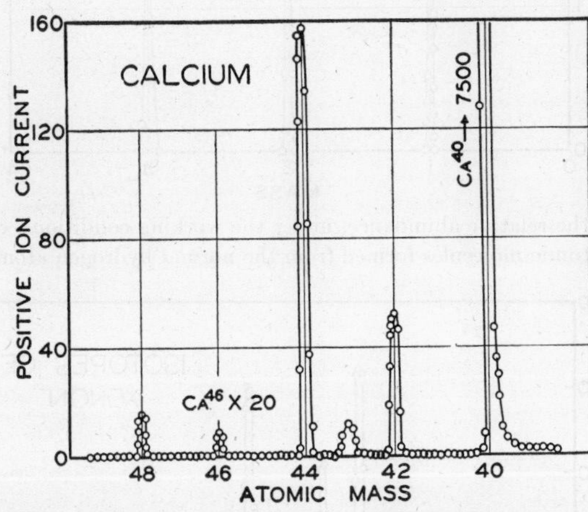


**Fig. 16.**—Showing the relative abundance of the several isotopes of calcium.

*Numerical Values of Atomic Weights.*—It was realized by Aston,[24] and has been repeatedly emphasized by him and other workers, that the only precision method of determining atomic masses is to work with naturally occurring doublets in the mass spectrum. For work of the highest precision it is essential that the traces corresponding to the two masses to be compared fall close together on the photographic plate. Since a sufficient number of complex ions had not then been observed, it was necessary in the early work to cause these traces to fall together by some artificial method such as changing the electric deflecting field. This and other similar procedures introduced additional errors. Aston[24] noticed a serious polarization effect near the condenser plates to which the potential producing the electric field was applied. This appears to have been the same effect as one of those which have caused so many discrepancies in supposedly precise determina-

[39] A. O. Nier, *Phys. Rev.*, **53**, 282 (1938).

tions of the ratio $e/m$ for electrons. While this and other small errors can be largely eliminated by proper experimental procedure, it is nevertheless

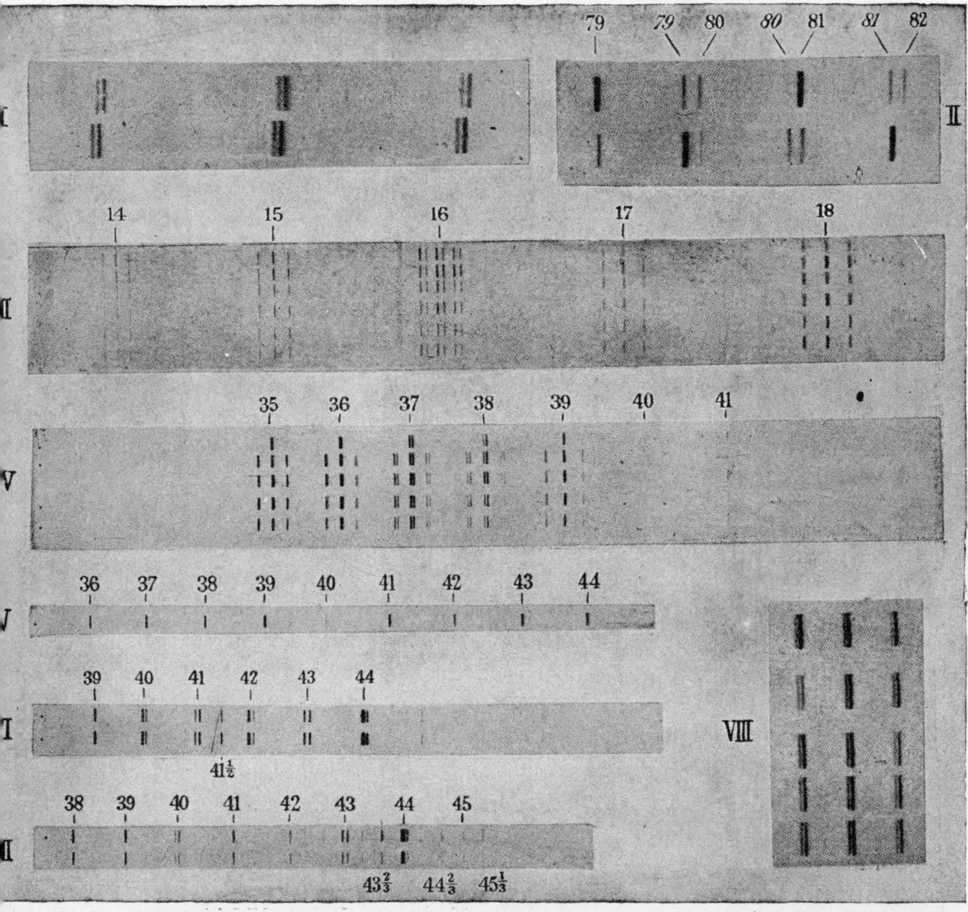


FIG. 17.—I. The doublet formed by the heavy hydrogen atom and the diatomic molecule of ordinary drogen. II. Lines due to the bromine isotopes and their hydrides photographed with a series shift of unit. III. One of the photographs used in measurement of the O-$CH_4$ doublet. IV. Comparison of chlorine isotopes with hydrocarbon molecules of the $C_3$ group. V. Lines of the $C_3$ group; the one at is due mainly to $CO_2$. VI. Spectra of the $C_3$ group of lines and those of doubly charged krypton. I. Spectra of the $C_3$ group of lines and those of triply charged xenon. VIII. The doublet $S^{32}$-$O_2$. For ater detail of description, see Aston.[31]

much better to make comparisons of masses which naturally fall very close together.

It is possible today to photograph, completely resolved, many naturally occurring doublets. Some of these have been shown in Figs. 12 and 17. In order to make clear how these natural doublets are used, a few specific examples will be mentioned. The atomic weights of H and He might be compared by measuring the separation of the two closely spaced lines corresponding to $He^{++}$ and $H_2^+$. Aston[40] pointed out the advantages of this particular comparison when he first observed the line due to $He^{++}$. Or, ordinary hydrogen might be compared with heavy hydrogen through use of the doublet $H_2$-$H^2$, as was done by Bainbridge and Jordan,[30] and then these hydrogens compared with He by measuring[41] the separation of the doublet $HHH^2$-He. The atomic weight of $Li^6$ might be obtained by comparison with the line corresponding to $H_3^2$. Then through use of the two doublets $C^{++}$-$H_3^2$ and O-$CH_4$, as Aston[42] has pointed out, all these atomic weights can be expressed in terms of O = 16.000000 through measurements of doublet separation alone. Since unusual ions as $H_2$, $H_3$, $H^2$, $HH^2$, $HHH^2$, $H_3^2$, $HH^2O$, $H_2^2O$, $He^{++}$ and $C^{++}$ have been observed, and since the ions H, C, N, O, $N_2$, OH, $OH_2$, $NH_2$, $NH_3$, CH, $CH_2$, $CH_3$, $CH_4$, and CO are commonly observed, it is clear that there are in many instances several alternate methods of making these and other comparisons finally in terms of O. All recent precise determinations have been confined to measurements on naturally occurring doublets.

Although it is entirely beyond the scope of this work to trace the way in which atomic weights of the various isotopes were modified as first one and then another observer made a worthwhile contribution, there are one or two significant facts that should be mentioned. For a number of years after Aston's[24] original precision work there was every reason to believe that results obtained at that time were entirely trustworthy. In the main they have certainly proved so. In this work it was necessary, however, to compare He with O through use of the lines $He^+$ and $O^{++}$; and H had to be compared with He through use of the lines corresponding to $H_2^+$ and $He^+$. The only accurate measurement of doublet separation that could be made was that for the doublet O-$CH_4$. Although Aston made every effort to obtain the O/He and the He/H ratios accurately, there was a real chance that some appreciable error might exist in one or both of these. For the next several years all atomic weights up to and including $Li^7$ were determined with respect to He, and thence converted to the O = 16.000000 scale through use of Aston's O/He ratio. Atomic weights of 8 or above were determined more directly in terms of O. It therefore became increasingly important that the O/He ratio be known accurately.

The original ratios found by Aston[24] were

$$\frac{He}{H} = 3.97126 \quad \text{and} \quad \frac{O}{He} = 3.99784$$

[40] F. W. Aston, *Nature*, **130**, 21 (1932).
[41] K. T. Bainbridge, *Phys. Rev.*, **41**, 115 (1932); **42**, 1 (1932).
[42] F. W. Aston, *Nature*, **135**, 541 (1935).

Some years later Bainbridge[43] reported excellent confirmation of one of these ratios. He obtained

$$\frac{\mathrm{He}}{\mathrm{H}} = 3.971283 \pm 0.000042$$

This was obtained from measurement of doublet separation and should have been entirely reliable. It duplicated almost exactly the earlier value found by Aston. Shortly after this there was developed an entirely independent method of evaluating atomic weights of individual isotopes. The basis of the method will be discussed shortly. For the present, however, it is sufficient to remark that several inconsistencies appeared in atomic weights measured by the two methods. These discrepancies never appeared when one confined his attention in each case to measurements involving only those isotopes having atomic weights above 8. Neither did they appear if one confined his attention to measurements of isotopes of atomic weights below 7. But the moment any measurements involved the use of isotopes falling in both groups, inconsistencies appeared. An entirely self-consistent set of atomic masses could be obtained only if it were supposed that the O/He ratio was slightly in error. This led Aston to renew his efforts. After considerable modification of his spectrograph, and after numerous measurements of the separations of various naturally occurring doublets, Aston[42] became convinced that both the O/He and He/H ratios were slightly in error. After final measurements he reported[44] values of atomic weights which lead to the ratios

$$\frac{\mathrm{He}}{\mathrm{H}} = 3.97166 \qquad \text{and} \qquad \frac{\mathrm{O}}{\mathrm{He}} = 3.99609$$

These recent atomic weights obtained by Aston[44,31] are among the most reliable values available today. The remarkable agreement of the original Bainbridge He/H ratio with the previous Aston value, which was later shown by Aston to be incorrect, was entirely accidental. It is an excellent illustration of how careful one must be in accepting without question any physical measurement just because it has been duplicated accurately by one other observer.

A high order of accuracy has been attained in recent mass spectrograph measurements of atomic weights. The probable errors associated with many of the recent measurements are only a few parts in 100,000. Table III, taken from the work of Aston,[31] illustrates the order of accuracy to which isotopic masses are known today from mass spectrograph studies. A

[43] K. T. Bainbridge, *Phys. Rev.*, **43**, 103 (1933).
[44] F. W. Aston, *Nature*, **137**, 357 (1936).

more extensive table, including many comparative values, will be given later. Although the 1927 Aston[24] values were at that time recognized to be of relatively high precision, the present atomic weights are known to a still much higher order of accuracy.

TABLE III

Aston's precision atomic weights of 1937. Provisional values are given in parentheses

| Symbol | Packing fraction × $10^4$ | Atomic weight |
|---|---|---|
| $H^1$ | +81.2 | 1.00812 ± 0.00004 |
| $H^2$ | +73.55 | 2.01471 ± 0.00007 |
| $He^4$ | + 9.77 | 4.00391 ± 0.00016 |
| $B^{10}$ | +16.1 | 10.0161 ± 0.0003 |
| $C^{12}$ | + 2.96 | 12.00355 ± 0.00015 |
| $N^{14}$ | + 5.28 | 14.0073 ± 0.0004 |
| ($O^{18}$ | + 3.2 | 18.0057 ± 0.0002) |
| $F^{19}$ | + 2.36 | 19.0045 ± 0.0005 |
| $Ne^{20}$ | − 0.70 | 19.9986 ± 0.0006 |
| ($Al^{27}$ | − 3.3 | 26.9909) |
| $Si^{28}$ | − 4.90 | 27.9863 ± 0.0007 |
| $Si^{29}$ | − 4.7 | 28.9864 ± 0.0008 |
| $P^{31}$ | − 5.30 | 30.9863 ± 0.0005 |
| $S^{32}$ | − 5.53 | 31.9823 ± 0.0003 |
| $Cl^{35}$ | − 5.71 | 34.9800 ± 0.0008 |
| $Cl^{37}$ | − 6.10 | 36.9775 ± 0.0008 |
| $A^{36}$ | − 6.10 | 35.9780 ± 0.0010 |
| $A^{40}$ | − 6.15 | 39.9754 ± 0.0014 |
| $Kr^{78}$ | − 7.30 | 77.9430 ± 0.0020 |
| $Kr^{82}$ | − 7.70 | 81.9369 ± 0.0015 |
| $Kr^{84}$ | − 7.60 | 83.9362 ± 0.0015 |
| $Kr^{86}$ | − 7.40 | 85.9363 ± 0.0015 |
| ($Sn^{118}$ | − 5.8 | 117.930) |
| ($Sn^{120}$ | − 5.8 | 119.930) |
| $Xe^{129}$ | − 4.46 | 128.9424 ± 0.0020 |
| ($Xe^{132}$ | − 4.4 | 131.942) |
| ($Hg^{200}$ | + 1.4 | 200.028) |

There is one further fact which should be mentioned in connection with these accurate atomic weights. The chemical scale of atomic weights is constructed on the basis of assigning the value 16.000000 to O. This was done before anyone thought seriously of the possible existence of isotopes. It is known today that O is composed of three isotopes, one of atomic weight 16, one 17, and one 18. It is rather fortunate that 99.76% of all O is of atomic weight 16. The $O^{17}$ component constitutes only 0.04% of the total. $O^{18}$ is present to the extent of 0.20%. It is obvious that what is assigned the value 16.000000 on the chemical scale is really a mixture of these isotopes, whereas the physical scale, on which all accurate atomic weights obtained from mass spectrograph or nuclear studies are specified, has taken the atomic weight of the one isotope $O^{16}$ as equal to 16.000000. Atomic weights specified on the chemical scale and on the physical scale are therefore slightly different. The only way one can obtain the ratio of atomic weights on the two scales is to make use of knowledge of the percentage of various isotopes present in some element for which the atomic weights are known accurately on both scales. The logical choice is of course O itself. If the above percentages are taken as correctly representing the constitution of ordinary O, then its mean atomic weight on the physical scale would be 16.0044. This is 1.00027 times its atomic weight on the chemical scale. A very recent redetermination of the percentages of the several oxygen isotopes by Murphey[45] has yielded for the ratio between the two scales the value $(1.000275 \pm 0.000009)$. Thus all chemical atomic weights would have to be increased by 27 parts per 100,000 to be corrected to the physical scale.

## Atomic Weights from Nuclear Disintegration Studies

*Basis of the Method.*—It has been mentioned that there was developed in 1935 an entirely independent method of evaluating the atomic masses of the individual isotopes. The method has proved an exceedingly accurate one. It depends upon a quantitative study of the energies associated with the artificial disintegration of matter. For centuries past it had been the hope of physicists and chemists that some way might be found by which one element could be made over into an entirely different element. In the early years this desire had been aimed more particularly at the costly noble metals. No success of any kind had been attained until 1920. In that year Rutherford succeeded beyond all doubt in disintegrating in the laboratory such supposedly stable elements as nitrogen, aluminum, phosphorous and others. While workers following him succeeded in disintegrating other materials, no further important advance came until within the last decade physicists learned how to produce charged particles having energies of several million electron volts. With these energetic particles it has become a relatively easy matter to disintegrate almost any atom. Detailed studies of the products of disintegration have been made by use of Wilson cloud expansion photographs and by other methods. Instead of knowing merely that atoms can be disintegrated, it is known also in a great majority of cases just what new atoms or other particles are formed by the disintegration.

No details of nuclear disintegration will be discussed at present. Some of the more fundamental observations connected with these studies will be taken up later. For the present, attention will be called to only a few facts, enough to allow one to appreciate the basis of the nuclear disintegration

[45] B. F. Murphey, *Phys. Rev.*, **59**, 320 (1941).

method of evaluating atomic masses. By way of a specific example consider the bombardment of Li with energetic H nuclei. These nuclei can be given known high energies by allowing them to fall through known potential differences. It has been found that when $Li^6$ is bombarded with nuclei of heavy hydrogen, called deuterons, the $Li^6$ nucleus absorbs the bombarding $H^2$ nucleus and immediately disintegrates into two He atoms. The occurrence of such a disintegration is indicated by writing

$$_3Li^6 + {}_1H^2 \rightarrow {}_2He^4 + {}_2He^4$$

wherein the subscript preceding the chemical symbol indicates the atomic number and the superscript following the symbol refers to the atomic weight of the isotope concerned. A similar disintegration takes place when $Li^7$ is bombarded with protons. This is represented by writing

$$_3Li^7 + {}_1H^1 \rightarrow {}_2He^4 + {}_2He^4$$

There can be no question but what disintegrations of this character are produced in the laboratory. On many occasions they have been studied in detail by cloud expansion photographs. In the above reactions the tracks of the two He nuclei leaving the point of disintegration have been photographed. Fig. 18 reproduces a photograph by Dee and Walton.[46]

The products of disintegration leave the point at which they are formed with considerable kinetic energy. These energies can be determined experimentally, as for example, from the lengths of tracks in the cloud chamber. They can be evaluated also by other methods. Measurement of these energies allows one to check, by direct experiment upon a single disintegration, whether the law of conservation of energy holds. It allows one to decide definitely whether the decrease of mass resulting from the disintegration is truly represented by a net amount of energy released. If $Li^7$ is bombarded with protons of 300,000 electron volts energy the two resulting He atoms are found to possess kinetic energies of 8,700,000 electron volts each. Or more exactly,[47,48] the total energy of the two alpha particles ejected is $17.13 \times 10^6$ electron volts more than that of the incident proton. Taking Aston's[44,31] mass spectrograph values for the atomic weights of $H^1$ and $He^4$ as 1.00812 and 4.00391 respectively, and taking Bainbridge and Jordan's[49] value of 7.01822 for the atomic weight of $Li^7$, one calculates that the disintegration has resulted in a loss of mass equal

[46] P. I. Dee and E. T. S. Walton, *Proc. Roy. Soc.*, A, **141**, 733 (1933).

[47] M. L. E. Oliphant, A. R. Kempton and E. Rutherford, *Proc. Roy. Soc.*, A, **149**, 406 (1935).

[48] M. S. Livingston and H. A. Bethe, *Rev. Mod. Phys.*, **9**, 373 (1937). Masses given by these authors are most probable values; some are mass spectrograph values while others are from nuclear observations.

[49] K. T. Bainbridge and E. B. Jordan, *Phys. Rev.*, **51**, 384 (1937).

to 0.01852 atomic mass units. In calculating this loss of mass one really should use the masses of the nuclei rather than those of the atoms. The "atomic weight" of electrons on the $O^{16} = 16.000000$ scale is 0.00055. This amount should therefore be subtracted for each planetary electron possessed by each atom concerned. It is obvious, however, that the same total would be subtracted from both the original and the final products, thus

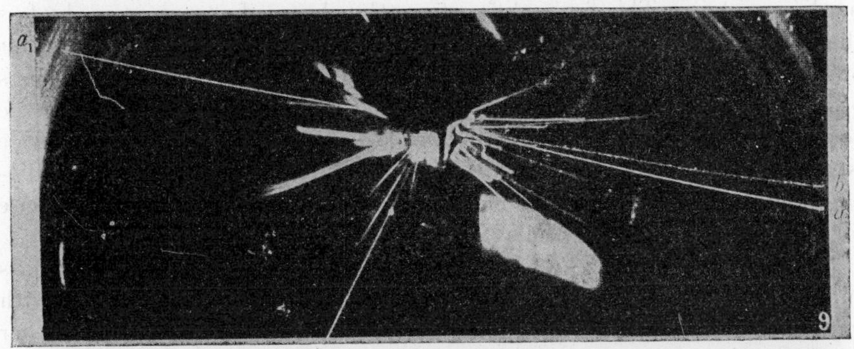


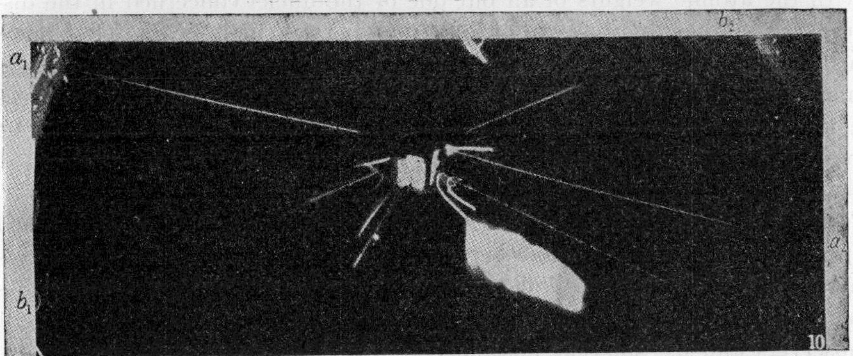


**Fig. 18.**—$a_1a_2$ in each photograph represent a pair of alpha particles resulting from the bombardment of $Li^6$ with deuterons. $b$ in the upper photograph is probably the track of a fast proton. $b_1b_2$ in the lower photograph represent alpha particles of shorter range than $a_1a_2$; they are probably those due to the bombardment of $Li^7$ with protons.

leaving the mass difference unchanged. If mass is truly a form of energy and if the two are interchangeable in accord with the expression

$$\text{Energy in ergs} = c^2 \text{ (mass in grams)}$$

then this loss of mass represents $(2.99776 \times 10^{10})^2 \times 0.01852 = 1.664 \times 10^{19}$ ergs of energy. That is, assuming the correctness of the mass energy equivalence concept, one would expect this net amount of energy to be released during the disintegration of one gram atom of $Li^7$. Dividing this energy by $6.023 \times 10^{23}$, the number of atoms per gram atom, it is found that $2.763 \times 10^{-5}$ ergs of energy should appear for every $Li^7$ nucleus which disintegrates. This energy can be converted to electron volts by writing

$$\frac{V}{299.8} \times 4.8029 \times 10^{-10} = 2.763 \times 10^{-5}$$

from which $V = 17.25 \times 10^6$ electron volts. That is, the two ${}_2He^4$ nuclei together should possess this much more kinetic energy than did the bombarding proton. This figure differs from the observed energy excess by less than 1%. Oliphant, Kempton and Rutherford[50] have made comparisons of this type for the energies involved in a large number of disintegrations of light elements. These and other comparisons leave no doubt as to the correctness of the mass energy equivalence concept. The same equivalence is also shown[51] by similar calculations involving the heavy natural radioactive elements. While mass measurements in general are far less precise for these heavy elements, the agreement is good.

The nuclear method of evaluating atomic weights utilizes this mass energy equivalence together with the observed energies associated with various disintegrations. If one knows the disintegration energies, together with the atomic weights of all but one of the nuclei concerned in the disintegration, the atomic weight of this remaining one can be evaluated. Since a large number of disintegration reactions involving all of the lighter elements have been studied, it follows that the atomic weights of all of these could be evaluated with respect to $O^{16} = 16.000000$. This has been done by numerous workers.

*Numerical Results and Comparison of Atomic Weights by the Two Methods.* A comparison of results obtained by the nuclear method with those obtained from mass spectrograph studies serves as an excellent check on the accuracies attained. Table IV is a sufficiently complete list of accurate atomic weights of the light elements to show the agreement of results obtained by different observers and by different methods. For any one isotope the values are arranged in approximately chronological order. Those values printed in italics have been obtained by the nuclear disintegration method. All other values are from mass spectrograph studies. The agreement between results by the two entirely different methods is remarkable. The consistency with which various observers obtain essentially the same value is likewise significant. The precision attained with either the mass spectrograph or the nuclear method exceeds by far that which has been attained by any chemical or other physical method. Furthermore, both of these methods give atomic weights of the individual isotopes of an element, whereas the more common older methods yield only the mean atomic weight for all the isotopes present for any element.

[50] M. L. E. Oliphant, A. R. Kempton and E. Rutherford, *Proc. Roy. Soc.*, A, **150, 241** (1935).
[51] N. Feather, *Rep. on Prog. in Phys.*, **3**, 70 (1936).

TABLE IV

A summary of accurate determinations of the atomic masses of individual isotopes of the lighter elements. All values in normal type are mass spectrograph results. Values printed in italics have been obtained through nuclear studies. Some nuclear determinations of course make use of certain mass spectrograph values for the more accurately known isotopes. Values for any one isotope of an element are arranged in approximately chronological order. For the most probable atomic masses of the isotopes one can scarcely do better than accept the values given by Livingston and Bethe.[48] For the atoms $He^3$, $C^{14}$, and $N^{13}$ Bethe's[59] more recent values should be substituted. For the elements from Ne to A the recent values given by Pollard[79] may be used. Not all of the isotopes listed in this table are stable; some are radioactive. The radioactive isotopes are marked with an asterisk

| Atom | Z | A | Atomic weight | Reference |
|---|---|---|---|---|
| H | 1 | 1 | 1.0079 | 23 |
| | | | 1.00778 | 24 |
| | | | 1.007775 | 43 |
| | | | *1.0081* | 50 |
| | | | *1.00807* | 52 |
| | | | 1.0081 | 42 |
| | | | 1.00812 | 44, 31 |
| | | | *1.0081* | 53 |
| | | | *1.0082* | 54 |
| | | | 1.0081 | 55 |
| | | | *1.0081* | 56 |
| | | | 1.00815 | 49 |
| | | | *1.00815* | 57 |
| | | | 1.00813 | 48 |
| | | 2 | 2.01353 | 41 |
| | | | 2.01351 | 41 |
| | | | 2.01363 | 58 |
| | | | *2.0142* | 50 |
| | | | *2.01423* | 52 |
| | | | 2.0148 | 42 |
| | | | 2.01471 | 44, 31 |
| | | | *2.0147* | 53 |
| | | | *2.01445* | 54 |
| | | | *2.0147* | 56 |
| | | | 2.01478 | 49 |
| | | | *2.01476* | 57 |
| | | | 2.01473 | 48 |
| | | 3* | *3.0152* | 47 |
| | | | *3.0161* | 50 |
| | | | *3.01610* | 52 |
| | | | *3.0171* | 53 |
| | | | *3.0170* | 56 |
| | | | *3.01701* | 57 |
| | | | *3.01705* | 48 |

TABLE IV (*Continued*)

| Atom | Z | A | Atomic weight | Reference |
|---|---|---|---|---|
| He | 2 | 3 | *3.0172* | 50 |
| | | | *3.01699* | 52 |
| | | | *3.0171* | 53 |
| | | | *3.0171* | 56 |
| | | | *3.01712* | 57 |
| | | | *3.01707* | 48 |
| | | | *3.01700* | 19 |
| | | | *3.01711* | 59 |
| | | 4 | 4.00216 | 24 |
| | | | *4.0034* | 50 |
| | | | *4.00336* | 52 |
| | | | 4.0041 | 42 |
| | | | 4.00391 | 44, 31 |
| | | | *4.0039* | 53 |
| | | | *4.00377* | 54 |
| | | | *4.0034* | 60 |
| | | | *4.0040* | 56 |
| | | | 4.00395 | 49 |
| | | | *4.00395* | 57 |
| | | | 4.00389 | 48 |
| | | | 4.00386 | 61 |
| | | 6* | *6.0208* | 48 |
| Li | 3 | 6 | 6.009 | 23 |
| | | | 6.012 | 24 |
| | | | 6.0145 | 62 |
| | | | *6.0143* | 47 |
| | | | *6.0163* | 50 |
| | | | *6.01614* | 52 |
| | | | *6.0167* | 53 |
| | | | *6.0168* | 54 |
| | | | *6.0161* | 60 |
| | | | *6.0170* | 56 |
| | | | *6.01689* | 57 |
| | | | *6.01686* | 48 |
| | | | *6.01655* | 63 |
| | | | *6.01670* | 73 |
| | | | *6.01682* | 74, 75 |
| | | 7 | 7.012 | 23 |
| | | | 7.012 | 24 |
| | | | 7.0146 | 62 |
| | | | *7.0148* | 47 |
| | | | *7.0170* | 50 |
| | | | *7.01694* | 52 |

TABLE IV (*Continued*)

| Atom | Z | A | Atomic weight | Reference |
|---|---|---|---|---|
| | | | *7.0180* | 53 |
| | | | *7.0176* | 54 |
| | | | *7.0170* | 60 |
| | | | *7.0182* | 56 |
| | | | 7.01822 | 49 |
| | | | *7.01821* | 57 |
| | | | 7.01818 | 48 |
| | | | *7.01799* | 73 |
| | | | *7.01784* | 74, 75 |
| | | 8* | *8.0190* | 53 |
| | | | *8.0195* | 56 |
| | | | *8.0251* | 48 |
| Be | 4 | 8* | *8.0071* | 50 |
| | | | *8.0078* | 53 |
| | | | *8.0070* | 60 |
| | | | *8.0080* | 56 |
| | | | *8.0081* | 64 |
| | | | *8.00795* | 57 |
| | | | *8.00792* | 48 |
| | | | *8.00739* | 63 |
| | | | *8.00753* | 73 |
| | | | *8.00766* | 74, 75 |
| | | 9 | *9.0138* | 50 |
| | | | *9.0135* | 52 |
| | | | *9.0149* | 53 |
| | | | *9.0146* | 54 |
| | | | *9.0139* | 60 |
| | | | *9.0149* | 56 |
| | | | 9.01517 | 65 |
| | | | *9.0150* | 64 |
| | | | *9.01506* | 57 |
| | | | *9.01504* | 48 |
| | | | *9.01491* | 66 |
| | | | *9.01459* | 63 |
| | | | *9.01474* | 73 |
| | | | *9.01486* | 74, 75 |
| | | 10* | *10.0149* | 50 |
| | | | *10.0164* | 53 |
| | | | *10.0154* | 60 |
| | | | *10.0163* | 56 |
| | | | *10.0168* | 64 |
| | | | *10.01629* | 57 |

TABLE IV (*Continued*)

| Atom | Z | A | Atomic weight | Reference |
|---|---|---|---|---|
| | | | *10.01671* | 48 |
| | | | *10.0165* | 78 |
| B | 5 | 10 | 10.0135 | 24 |
| | | | *10.0143* | 50 |
| | | | *10.0146* | 52 |
| | | | *10.0161* | 53 |
| | | | *10.0161* | 54 |
| | | | 10.0161 | 67, 31 |
| | | | *10.0152* | 60 |
| | | | *10.0160* | 56 |
| | | | 10.01633 | 65 |
| | | | 10.01631 | 48 |
| | | | *10.01579* | 73 |
| | | 11 | 11.0110 | 24 |
| | | | 11.0107 | 68 |
| | | | *11.0110* | 50 |
| | | | *11.0111* | 52 |
| | | | *11.0128* | 53 |
| | | | *11.0126* | 54 |
| | | | *11.0117* | 60 |
| | | | *11.0128* | 56 |
| | | | 11.01295 | 65 |
| | | | *11.01289* | 57 |
| | | | 11.01292 | 48 |
| | | | *11.01244* | 73 |
| | | 12* | *12.0153* | 53 |
| | | | *12.0179* | 56 |
| | | | *12.019* | 48 |
| C | 6 | 11* | *11.0143* | 53 |
| | | | *11.0150* | 56 |
| | | | *11.01526* | 48 |
| | | 12 | 12.000 | 23 |
| | | | 12.0036 | 24 |
| | | | *12.0027* | 50 |
| | | | *12.0037* | 52 |
| | | | 12.0048 | 42 |
| | | | 12.0035 | 44 |
| | | | *12.0036* | 53 |
| | | | *12.0040* | 54 |
| | | | *12.0037* | 60 |
| | | | *12.0040* | 56 |

TABLE IV (*Continued*)

| Atom | Z | A | Atomic weight | Reference |
|---|---|---|---|---|
| | | | 12.00355 | 69, 31 |
| | | | 12.00428 | 49 |
| | | | 12.00402 | 65 |
| | | | *12.00396* | 57 |
| | | | 12.00398 | 48 |
| | | 13 | *13.0069* | 52 |
| | | | *13.0073* | 53 |
| | | | *13.0075* | 54 |
| | | | *13.0069* | 60 |
| | | | *13.0076* | 56 |
| | | | 13.0079 | 49 |
| | | | *13.00761* | 57 |
| | | | 13.00761 | 48 |
| | | 14* | *14.0077* | 60 |
| | | | *14.0078* | 56 |
| | | | *14.00767* | 48 |
| | | | *14.00763* | 59 |
| | | | *14.00780* | 77 |
| N | 7 | 13* | *13.0096* | 53 |
| | | | *13.0100* | 60 |
| | | | *13.0100* | 56 |
| | | | *13.01004* | 48 |
| | | | *13.01008* | 59 |
| | | 14 | 14.008 | 24 |
| | | | *14.0076* | 52 |
| | | | *14.0073* | 53 |
| | | | *14.0075* | 54 |
| | | | 14.0073 | 67, 31 |
| | | | *14.0076* | 60 |
| | | | *14.0075* | 56 |
| | | | 14.0076 | 49 |
| | | | *14.00738* | 57 |
| | | | 14.00750 | 48 |
| | | 15 | *15.0053* | 52 |
| | | | *15.0048* | 53 |
| | | | *15.0046* | 54 |
| | | | 15.0040 | 29 |
| | | | *15.0053* | 60 |
| | | | *15.0049* | 56 |
| | | | 15.0050 | 49 |
| | | | *15.00465* | 57 |
| | | | 15.00489 | 48 |

TABLE IV (*Continued*)

| Atom | Z | A | Atomic weight | Reference |
|---|---|---|---|---|
| | | 16* | *16.0066* | 56 |
| | | | *16.011* | 48 |
| O | 8 | 15* | *15.0079* | 56 |
| | | | *15.0078* | 48 |
| | | 16 | 16.000000 | Standard |
| | | | *16.000000* | Standard |
| | | 17 | *17.0040* | 52 |
| | | | *17.0046* | 53 |
| | | | *17.0040* | 60 |
| | | | *17.00450* | 48 |
| | | 18 | 18.0037 | 29 |
| | | | *18.0065* | 60 |
| | | | 18.0057 | 69, 31 |
| | | | 18.00369 | 48 |
| F | 9 | 17* | *17.0073* | 53 |
| | | | *17.0078* | 60 |
| | | | *17.0076* | 48 |
| | | 18* | *18.0056* | 48 |
| | | 19 | 19.0000 | 24 |
| | | | *19.0045* | 53 |
| | | | 19.0045 | 67, 31 |
| | | | *19.0040* | 60 |
| | | | 19.00452 | 48 |
| | | 20* | *20.006* | 48 |
| Ne | 10 | 20 | 20.0004 | 24 |
| | | | 19.9967 | 68 |
| | | | 19.9986 | 67, 31 |
| | | | *19.9994* | 60 |
| | | | 19.99881 | 48 |
| | | 21 | *20.999* | 60 |
| | | | 21.00013 | 65 |
| | | | 20.99968 | 48 |
| | | | *21.00018* | 79 |
| | | 22 | 22.0048 | 24 |
| | | | 21.9947 | 68 |
| | | | *21.9977* | 60 |
| | | | *21.9985* | 70 |
| | | | *21.9989* | 71 |

TABLE IV (*Continued*)

| Atom | Z | A | Atomic weight | Reference |
|---|---|---|---|---|
| | | | 21.99870 | 65 |
| | | | 21.99864 | 48 |
| Na | 11 | 22* | *21.9996* | 60 |
| | | | *22.0002* | 48 |
| | | 23 | *22.9980* | 60 |
| | | | *22.9972* | 71 |
| | | | *22.9961* | 48 |
| | | | *22.99680* | 79 |
| | | 24* | *23.9974* | 48 |
| Mg | 12 | 24 | *23.9938* | 70 |
| | | | *23.9939* | 71 |
| | | | *23.9924* | 48 |
| | | | *23.99189* | 79 |
| | | 25 | *24.9938* | 48 |
| | | | *24.99277* | 79 |
| | | 26 | *25.9908* | 71 |
| | | | *25.9898* | 48 |
| | | | *25.99062* | 79 |
| | | 27* | *26.9921* | 48 |
| Al | 13 | 26* | *25.9929* | 48 |
| | | 27 | 26.9909 | 67, 31 |
| | | | *26.9899* | 48 |
| | | | *26.98960* | 79 |
| | | 28* | *27.9903* | 48 |
| | | 29* | *28.9904* | 48 |
| Si | 14 | 27* | *26.9931* | 48 |
| | | 28 | 27.9860 | 67 |
| | | | 27.9863 | 31 |
| | | | 27.9866 | 48 |
| | | | *27.98639* | 79 |
| | | 29 | 28.9864 | 67, 31 |
| | | | 28.9866 | 48 |
| | | | *28.98685* | 79 |

TABLE IV (*Continued*)

| Atom | Z | A | Atomic weight | Reference |
|---|---|---|---|---|
| | | 30 | *29.9845* | 70 |
| | | | *29.9844* | 71 |
| | | | *29.9832* | 48 |
| | | | *29.98294* | 79 |
| | | 31* | *30.9862* | 48 |
| P | 15 | 30* | *29.9882* | 48 |
| | | 31 | 30.9825 | 24 |
| | | | *30.9844* | 70 |
| | | | 30.9836 | 31 |
| | | | 30.9843 | 48 |
| | | | *30.98457* | 79 |
| | | 32* | *31.9841* | 48 |
| S | 16 | 32 | *31.9812* | 70 |
| | | | 31.9823 | 31 |
| | | | 31.9823 | 48 |
| | | | *31.98306* | 79 |
| | | 33 | *32.9818* | 76 |
| | | | *32.98260* | 79 |
| | | 34 | *33.9799* | 70, 72 |
| | | | *33.9802* | 71 |
| | | | *33.978* | 48 |
| | | | *33.97974* | 79 |
| Cl | 17 | 34* | *33.981* | 48 |
| | | 35 | 34.983 | 24 |
| | | | 34.9796 | 68 |
| | | | 34.9800 | 31 |
| | | | *34.9803* | 48 |
| | | | *34.98107* | 79 |
| | | | 34.9790 | 80 |
| | | 37 | 36.980 | 24 |
| | | | 36.9777 | 68 |
| | | | 36.9775 | 31 |
| | | | 36.9779 | 48 |
| | | | *36.97829* | 79 |
| | | | 36.9779 | 80 |
| | | 38* | *37.981* | 48 |

TABLE IV (*Continued*)

| Atom | Z | A | Atomic weight | Reference |
|---|---|---|---|---|
| A | 18 | 36 | 35.976 | 24 |
| | | | 35.9780 | 69, 31 |
| | | | *35.97852* | 79 |
| | | 38 | *37.9753* | 70, 72 |
| | | | *37.974* | 48 |
| | | | *37.97544* | 79 |
| | | 40 | 39.971 | 24 |
| | | | 39.9754 | 67, 31 |
| | | | 39.97580 | 65 |
| | | | 39.97504 | 48 |
| | | | 39.9757 | 80 |

[52] H. A. Bethe, *Phys. Rev.*, **47**, 633 (1935).

[53] M. L. E. Oliphant, *Nature*, **137**, 396, 407 (1936).

[54] J. D. Cockcroft and W. B. Lewis, *Proc. Roy. Soc.*, A, **154**, 261 (1936).

[55] K. T. Bainbridge and E. B. Jordan, *Phys. Rev.*, **49**, 883 (1936).

[56] T. W. Bonner and W. M. Brubaker, *Phys. Rev.*, **50**, 308 (1936).

[57] G. Mano, *Soc. Roumaine de Physique, Bull.* 38, **69**, 51 (1937). Masses given by this author represent most probable values obtained from both nuclear and mass spectrograph observations.

[58] K. T. Bainbridge, *Phys. Rev.*, **44**, 57 (1933).

[59] H. A. Bethe, *Phys. Rev.*, **53**, 313 (1938).

[60] H. A. Bethe and R. F. Bacher, *Rev. Mod. Phys.*, **8**, 175 (1936).

[61] K. T. Bainbridge, *Phys. Rev.*, **53**, 922 (1938).

[62] K. T. Bainbridge, *Phys. Rev.*, **44**, 56 (1933).

[63] S. K. Allison, E. R. Graves, L. S. Skaggs and N. M. Smith, *Phys. Rev.*, **55**, 107, 599 (1939).

[64] J. H. Williams, R. O. Haxby and W. G. Shepherd, *Phys. Rev.*, **52**, 1031 (1937).

[65] E. B. Jordan and K. T. Bainbridge, *Phys. Rev.*, **51**, 385 (1937).

[66] S. K. Allison, L. S. Skaggs and N. M. Smith, *Phys. Rev.*, **54**, 171 (1938).

[67] F. W. Aston, *Nature*, **137**, 613 (1936).

[68] K. T. Bainbridge, *Phys. Rev.*, **43**, 378, 424 (1933).

[69] F. W. Aston, *Nature*, **139**, 922 (1937).

[70] E. Pollard and C. J. Brasefield, *Nature*, **137**, 943 (1936).

[71] E. Pollard and C. J. Brasefield, *Phys. Rev.*, **51**, 11 (1937).

[72] E. Pollard and C. J. Brasefield, *Phys. Rev.*, **50**, 890 (1936).

[73] S. K. Allison, *Phys. Rev.*, **55**, 624 (1939).

[74] S. K. Allison, L. S. Skaggs and N. M. Smith, *Phys. Rev.*, **56**, 288 (1939).

[75] N. M. Smith, *Phys. Rev.*, **56**, 548 (1939).

[76] E. Pollard, *Phys. Rev.*, **56**, 961 (1939).

[77] E. Pollard, *Phys. Rev.*, **56**, 1168 (1939).

[78] E. Pollard, *Phys. Rev.*, **57**, 241 (1940).

[79] E. Pollard, *Phys. Rev.*, **57**, 1186 (1940); a table of atomic masses from $Ne^{20}$ to $Fe^{57}$.

[80] T. Okuda, K. Ogata, K. Aoki and Y. Sugawara, *Phys. Rev.*, **58**, 578 (1940).

The atomic weights of a large number of the heavy elements have also been determined with precision. Elements beyond argon have not been included in Table IV for several reasons. A table including all of the isotopes of the heavier elements would become quite long. For the heavy elements there exist measurements by few observers on any one isotope. Comparisons of results by different observers and different methods are therefore not possible in general. Dempster's recent mass spectrograph has proved exceedingly useful for studies of isotopes of large atomic weight. Practically all of the accurate measurements that have been made upon these have utilized this or similar apparatus. Dempster himself has been responsible for a great number of the atomic weights now available. Numerical values of these and other atomic weights can be found throughout the literature.[31,36,79,81–87]

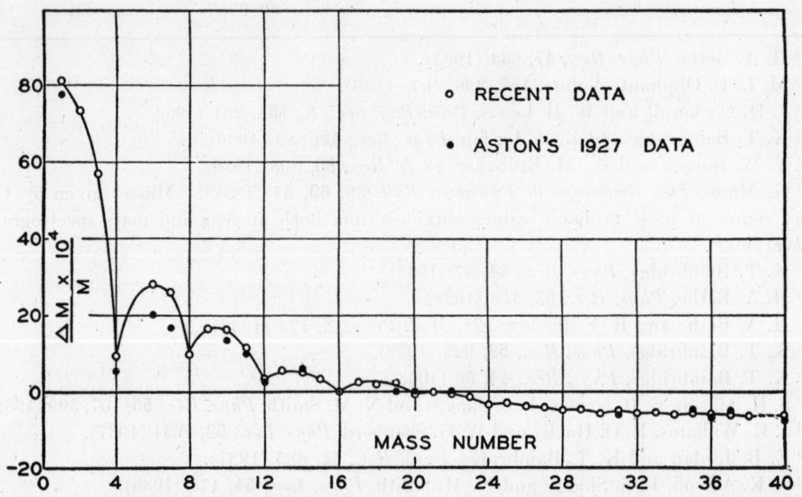


Fig. 19.—A packing fraction curve, $\Delta m/m$ versus $m$, for the light elements, using recent accurate atomic weights.

## Packing Fraction Curve for the Elements

Recent precision atomic weights make it possible to plot in much greater detail a packing fraction curve similar to that originally given by Aston. Fig. 19 is plotted from the atomic weights given by Livingston and Bethe[48,59]

[81] A. J. Dempster, *Phys. Rev.*, **53,** 869 (1938).
[82] A. C. Graves, *Phys. Rev.*, **55,** 238, 863 (1939).
[83] A. J. Dempster, *Nature*, **138,** 120 (1936).
[84] J. Mattauch, *Naturwiss.*, **25,** 170, 189 (1937).
[85] F. W. Aston, *Nature*, **140,** 149 (1937); **141,** 1096 (1938).
[86] W. L. Davidson, *Phys. Rev.*, **57,** 244 (1940).
[87] T. Okuda, K. Ogata, H. Kuroda, S. Shima and S. Shindo, *Phys. Rev.*, **59,** 104 (1941).

and by Pollard.[79] Aston's original values[24] are shown for the sake of comparison. These original values follow the present curve surprisingly well. Fig. 20, reproduced from the work of Dempster,[81] shows a similar curve for the heavy elements. Although it may not appear so, this curve is a continuation of that for the light elements. The second curve is plotted to a much more extended scale than is the first. The range of packing fractions covered by the light elements is so great that it precludes the use of this extended scale.

In 1936 Oliphant[53] pointed out some striking features of a curve obtained by plotting the divergence of the atomic weight of an isotope from the nearest whole number against this whole number. Such a curve contains the same information as that shown by the usual packing fraction curve. But in Oliphant's plot the entire divergence from the nearest whole number

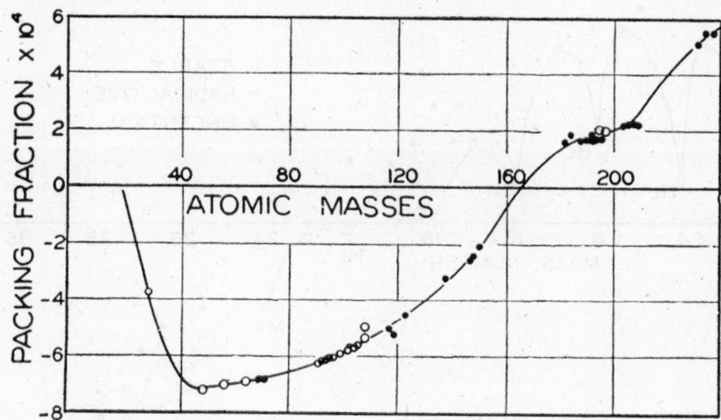


Fig. 20.—Packing fraction curve for the heavy elements, as given by Dempster.

is represented as ordinate, whereas in the usual packing fraction curve the ordinate is this divergence divided by the mass number. A curve similar to that originally given by Oliphant, and later extended by others,[70,79] plotted from the more recent atomic weights of Livingston and Bethe[48,59] and of Pollard,[79] is shown in Fig. 21. The remarkable feature of this curve is the consistency with which atoms having atomic weights which are multiples of four fall below the general trend of the curve. This tendency is marked for those elements below Ne, and it continues somewhat up to A. There is not a single exception to the rule that an element with atomic weight some multiple of four shows an unusually small mass divergence. In this connection it is interesting that even the early work of Aston[24] showed the atoms $He^4$, $C^{12}$ and $O^{16}$ to be distinctly below the packing fraction curve drawn through other atoms. These early observations were therefore consistent with the present curve. The fact that all light atoms with atomic weights some whole multiple of $He^4$ have minima divergences suggests that these atoms may be unusually stable. Perhaps the nuclei of these contain $He^4$ nuclei as entities. The effect becomes smaller as one goes to heavier atoms; it almost completely disappears in the neighborhood of A.

One further observation is quite significant. Included on this plot are a number of isotopes which are not stable. These atoms are radioactive. Immediately they are formed they proceed to disintegrate into some other material which is stable. Many of these radioactive atoms fall distinctly above the curve drawn through the stable isotopes. The fact that they

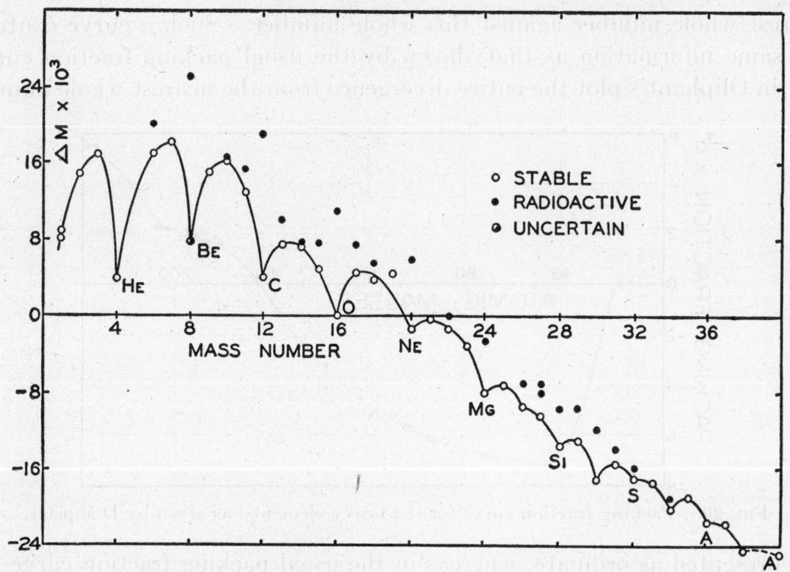


FIG. 21.—A curve (similar to Oliphant's) of $\Delta m$ versus $m$ for the light elements, using recent accurate atomic weights.

possess this excess energy represented by the larger than normal mass is responsible for their subsequent disintegration. In general those materials which fall far above the curve disintegrate into stable atoms more rapidly than those which have but a small excess mass. Those which fall near the curve disintegrate very slowly.

## 5. OTHER METHODS OF DETECTING ISOTOPES

The study of positive rays is not the only method available for detecting the existence of isotopes, although this method has yielded a wealth of important information that would not have been obtained in any other way. Too much knowledge from other fields is interwoven in the application of these other methods to permit a detailed discussion of them here. For the present purpose it is sufficient to call attention to the several methods and to bring out in a crude way the general basis on which each is founded.

The existence of isotopes was really well established before the pioneering work of Thomson, Dempster and Aston. The fact that there existed some forty radioactive materials, all among the heavier elements, had been known for years. And it had been recognized that in many cases two radioactive materials giving easily distinguishable radioactive radiations could not be separated by any chemical means. As early as 1910 Soddy[88] remarked: "... the complete identity of ionium thorium and radiothorium, of radium and mesothorium 1, of lead and radium D, may be considered already established. ... The recognition that elements of different atomic weights may possess identical properties seems destined to have its most important application in the region of inactive elements, where the absence of a second radioactive nature makes it impossible for chemical identity to be individually detected. Chemical homogeneity is no longer a guarantee that any supposed element is not a mixture of several of different atomic weights, or that any atomic weight is not merely a mean number. The consistency of atomic weight, whatever the source of material, is not a complete proof of homogeneity. ..." The actual existence of isotopes among the radioactive heavy elements seemed proved. But the great importance of the isotopic structure of all elements, and a real understanding of this structure, was not realized until mass spectrograph studies had demonstrated the existence of isotopes for the lighter inactive elements. In these studies the evidence was irrefutable. There seems no question, however, that isotopes were discovered originally through marked differences in their radioactive properties.

There exist several isotope effects which can be observed in the spectral emission of atoms. A gas when heated or otherwise excited gives out a characteristic bright line spectrum. The lines are located at frequencies or wave lengths characteristic of the atom which emits them. It appeared for some years that there was no detectable difference between the line spectra of radioactive isotopes. Aronberg[89] finally succeeded in finding for two isotopes of lead a difference of 0.0044 A° in the characteristic line at 4058.00 A°. This is an extremely small but detectable shift. The observation was confirmed shortly by Merton[90] who found a difference of $(0.0050 \pm 0.0007)$. Merton also observed a similar effect for the isotopes of thallium. Details of the various isotope effects upon spectral emission have been summarized elsewhere.[91] Only the essential ideas will be pre-

[88] F. Soddy, *Chem. Soc. Ann. Rep.*, 285 (1910).

[89] L. Aronberg, *Astrophys. Jour.*, **47**, 96 (1918).

[90] T. R. Merton, *Proc. Roy. Soc.*, A, **96**, 388 (1920).

[91] F. W. Aston, *Mass Spectra and Isotopes* (3rd ed.; London: E. Arnold & Co., 1933), pp. 193–218.

sented here. There are two reasons for which one might expect the characteristic line spectra of isotopes to be slightly different. As will be shown later, these lines are emitted when a planetary electron transfers itself from one energy level to another which is nearer the nucleus. The frequency of the radiation is determined by the change of energy. Now the amount by which the energies corresponding to two levels differ is determined almost entirely by the electrical configuration of the nucleus, together with the charge and the mass of the electron itself. These energies are practically independent of the mass of the atom and therefore of the mass of the nucleus. But the mass of the nucleus does enter in a very minor way. As a result one would expect the frequencies of characteristic lines for two isotopes to be slightly different. Although this difference should be very small, it should be easily observable for the lighter elements. It is through this effect that Urey, Brickwedde and Murphy[92] discovered the existence of heavy hydrogen, a hydrogen isotope of mass two. Fig. 22, reproduced from this work, definitely shows a line attributable to this isotope. But the line is very weak, indicating a very small percentage of this isotope in normal hydrogen. The intensity of this line was increased many times by increasing the concentration of the heavy isotope through fractional distillation.

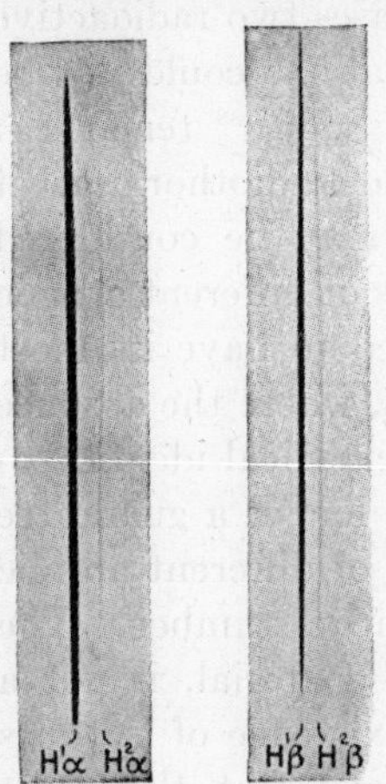


FIG. 22.—Showing the doubling of the $H_\alpha$ and $H_\beta$ lines of the Balmer series due to the presence of the H isotope of mass 2.

There is a second reason for a slight difference in the line spectra of isotopes. In order to interpret properly several complicated features of spectral emission it has been found necessary to suppose that there is associated with the nucleus a certain spin. The magnetic moment associated with this spin varies from one atom to another. Since the nuclei of two isotopes differ in structure, one would suspect that the spin moment might be different for the two. Now the existence of this nuclear magnetic moment influences to a very slight degree the energy associated with any particular electron transition. Various possible couplings between the spin moment and the electron give rise to several possibilities. As a result there appears a so-called hyperfine structure in the line spectra. A line is really made up of a number of very closely spaced lines. With special apparatus it has been possible to resolve these lines and measure their separations. Two isotopes which have different nuclear spin moments give different hyperfine structure patterns. Considerable isotopic data has been obtained from studies of hyperfine structure.

[92] H. C. Urey, F. G. Brickwedde and G. M. Murphy, *Phys. Rev.*, **40**, 1 (1932).

The complete spectrum emitted by polyatomic molecules is far more complex than the simple line spectra emitted by atoms. In general the complete spectrum emitted by polyatomic molecules can be divided into three subdivisions, electronic bands, vibration bands, and rotation bands. The energy change which a certain molecular configuration undergoes when this molecule emits radiation depends largely upon the shift of an electron from one energy level to another. For polyatomic molecules, however, there are two other possible energy changes. Even in a simple diatomic molecule there may be energy represented by vibration of the two atomic nuclei along the line joining them; and this energy may change during the emission of radiation. Likewise, there may be energy of rotation about an axis perpendicular to the line joining the atoms of a molecule; and again this energy may change during emission. The electronic energy changes are in general much larger than the others; and the vibrational changes are in turn much greater than the rotational changes. Emission of radiant energy may result from a change in any one of these energies, or from a net change brought about by simultaneous changes in any combination of the three. As will be pointed out later, the frequency of the radiation emitted is proportional to the net energy change the atom or molecule undergoes. The electronic bands occur in or near the visible. This is true whether the line is given out by a pure electronic transition or by a vibrational or rotational change superimposed upon this. The vibrational bands occur well into the infrared. This is true for lines emitted by purely vibrational changes or for those emitted by a combination of rotational and vibrational changes. The pure rotation bands occur far in the infrared. Since no electronic or vibrational energy changes take place, the net energy change is small and the frequency is low. Although these pure rotational bands are so far in the infrared that they are difficult to study they have nevertheless been observed in a number of cases.

Fortunately, the effect of isotopic mass upon the vibration-rotation bands is much greater than that upon the electronic bands. It is obvious that the vibrational energy of a diatomic or other polyatomic molecule depends markedly upon the masses of the atomic nuclei; it would therefore be quite different for two isotopes. For example, the vibrational energy of a molecule of $HCl^{35}$ would be appreciably different from that of the molecule $HCl^{37}$. In a similar manner the rotational energy depends upon the moment of inertia of the molecule. This also is appreciably different for the two molecules mentioned. As a result there exists both a vibrational and a rotational isotope effect in band spectra. If two isotopes are present there is a doubling of the spectral pattern attributable to one isotope. Frequencies of spectral lines corresponding to the second isotope are offset slightly with respect to the first. This is illustrated by Fig. 23 which reproduces[93] one of the vibration-rotation bands for HCl. Thus it is possible to detect the presence of isotopes through a study of the vibration-rotation band spectra. The method is in fact quite sensitive, and a number of rare isotopes have been discovered in this way. The existence of heavy hydrogen was confirmed[94] through a study of the band spectra of HCl; a band attributable to $H^2Cl$ was found. The heavier isotopes of oxygen, $O^{18}$ and $O^{17}$, were actually discovered[95,96] through band spectra studies. Among other isotopes discovered in a similar way are $N^{15}$ and $C^{13}$. Not only is it possible to detect or confirm the existence of an isotope by band

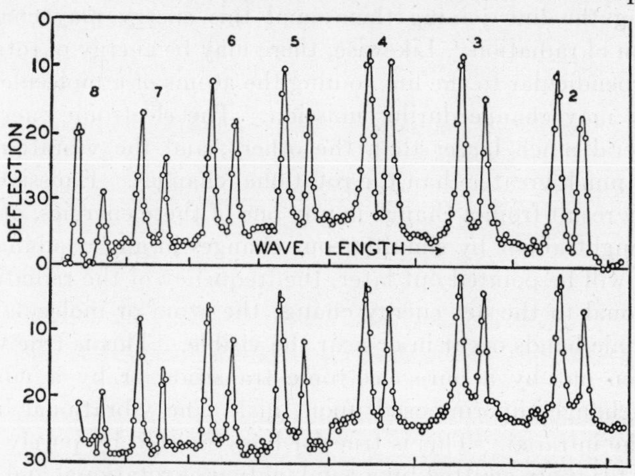


FIG. 23.—Showing the *R* branch of the HCl band spectrum in the infrared under high resolving power.

spectra studies, but relatively accurate measurements can often be made of its abundance and its atomic weight relative to other isotopes present. For example, the atomic weight of heavy hydrogen, $H^2$, was found[94] to be $(2.01367 \pm 0.00010)$. This calculation was based upon the early mass spectrograph value $H^1 = 1.00778$. Since this value has since been revised upward, so should be the value for $H^2$. In a similar way the atomic weights $O^{17} = 17.0029$ and $O^{18} = 18.0065$ were obtained. All of these agreed quite favorably with other values available at the time. Thus spectroscopic evidence has been quite valuable in furthering the knowledge of isotopes.

The question of the relative abundance of isotopes in nature is an interesting one. It has long been known[97] that elements of even atomic

[93] J. D. Hardy and G. B. B. M. Sutherland, *Phys. Rev.*, **41**, 471 (1932).

[94] J. D. Hardy, E. F. Barker and D. M. Dennison, *Phys. Rev.*, **42**, 279 (1932).

[95] W. F. Giauque and H. L. Johnston, *Nature*, **123**, 318, 831 (1929).

[96] H. D. Babcock, *Nature*, **123**, 761 (1929).

[97] W. D. Harkins, *Jour. Amer. Chem. Soc.*, **39**, 856 (1917).

number make up far the greater share of matter. These elements preponderate in a marked degree both in the earth's crust and in meteorites. They are perhaps ten times more abundant than are those of odd atomic number. The light elements are in general much more abundant than the heavy. Certain elements such as He, Ne, A, and Kr are exceedingly rare. Since the discovery of isotopes the further question of the relative abundance of individual isotopes has arisen. Results of many studies of this and similar questions have been summarized elsewhere.[98,99] There appear to be a number of elements for which the isotopes of median mass numbers are far more abundant than are those considerably removed from this median number. On the other hand, there exist a group of elements for which the lighter isotopes seem far the more abundant. Apparently many family resemblances in isotopic structure exist for various elements throughout the periodic table. It is also interesting that there exists[99] in nature an unusual abundance of atoms having masses some multiple of 8. Of the nine most abundant types of atoms, $O^{16}$, $Si^{28}$, $Al^{27}$, $H^1$, $Na^{23}$, $Ca^{40}$, $Fe^{56}$, $K^{39}$ and $Mg^{24}$, four have atomic weights some multiple of 8.

## 6. THE SEPARATION OF ISOTOPES

The fact that each element found in nature has always the same atomic weight, even though it is made up of a number of isotopes of various masses, suggests that it might be difficult to separate the isotopes of an element by any simple process. The theoretical problem of such separation has been of importance since the first discovery of isotopes. Once it is possible to produce a real separation there is no telling what practical applications may spring up. Today numerous isotopes have been separated to a sufficient degree and in sufficient quantities for physical and chemical research. Almost complete separation has been accomplished for a few. Several of these nearly pure isotopes are now being used with some success in various biological and physiological studies.

There are several ways in which it is possible to produce at least a partial separation of isotopes. The early methods have been discussed admirably by Aston,[100] while the later works have been summarized by Urey[101] and by Walcher.[102] For the present purpose it will be sufficient to call attention to a few of the more important methods of separation, and to point out the

[98] G. Hevesy, *Chemical Analysis by X-Rays and its Applications* (New York: McGraw-Hill, 1932).

[99] F. W. Aston, *Mass Spectra and Isotopes* (3rd ed.; London; E. Arnold & Co., 1933), pp. 177–185.

[100] F. W. Aston, *Mass Spectra and Isotopes* (3rd ed.; London: E. Arnold & Co., 1933), pp. 219–233.

[101] H. C. Urey, *Rep. on Prog. in Phys.*, **6,** 48 (1939).

[102] W. Walcher, *Ergeb. d. exakt. Naturwiss.*, **18,** 155 (1939).

degree of separation that has been accomplished. These methods may be classified[102] as: (1) Separation by electrolysis; (2) Separation by diffusion; (3) Separation by fractional distillation; (4) Separation by chemical exchange reactions; (5) Separation by thermal diffusion; (6) Separation by centrifugal action; (7) Separation by the mass spectrograph; (8) Separation by photochemical action.

Theoretically, the rate at which a gas diffuses through a porous material or through an opening depends upon the mass of the atoms of the diffusing gas. The velocity of diffusion is inversely proportional to the square root of the mass of the atom. It appears, therefore, that if a gas such as neon, which is composed mainly of the two isotopes 20 and 22, were allowed to diffuse repeatedly through a porous material or through an opening, relatively more of the lighter isotope should be found in the one sample, while more of the heavier isotope should remain in the residue. Unfortunately the separation is extremely slow, for the square roots of the masses of the two isotopes of neon differ by only five percent. But with the exception of the isotopes of hydrogen, which were entirely unknown in the earlier days, no gas seemed to offer a better possibility. It is quite natural therefore that the first efforts toward separation were made upon Ne. Aston[100] attempted to separate Ne by a series of fractional diffusions before the existence of the Ne isotopes had been definitely proved. After a long and tedious series of fractionations, an analysis of the two end fractions, theoretically those of greatest and least density, yielded atomic weights of 20.28 and 20.15 as against the normal atomic weight of 20.2. While the change in atomic weight observed in these experiments was small, in the light of later developments it appears that a partial separation was actually accomplished. Although the evidence was far from conclusive at the time, the difference in atomic weights of the two end fractions appeared entirely too large to attribute to experimental error. It was roughly what was expected on the theory of diffusion.

A somewhat similar separation was accomplished early for HCl gas. Part of this is made up from $Cl^{35}$ and part from $Cl^{37}$. Harkins,[103] after repeated fractionations by diffusion, in which the volume of gas was reduced from the original 19,000 liters to a few cc., found the heavier fraction to yield an atomic weight of 35.512 for the Cl. Since the normal atomic weight of Cl is 35.457, an increase of 0.055 had thus been effected. A few years later it was reported[104] that Cl with an atomic weight as low as 35.418 had been obtained. While changes in atomic weight effected by these tedious fractionations were not large, the results left no doubt that a partial separation had actually been accomplished.

[103] W. D. Harkins and A. Hayes, *Jour. Amer. Chem. Soc.*, **43**, 1803 (1921).
[104] W. D. Harkins and F. A. Jenkins, *Jour. Amer. Chem. Soc.*, **48**, 58 (1926).

Comparable success was attained early by another method. It can be shown that the rate of evaporation from a liquid surface depends upon the mass of the atoms of the liquid; this rate is inversely proportional to the square root of the mass of the atom. Hence, if a liquid consists of two isotopes, the evaporated material should be relatively rich in the lighter isotope and the residue should contain more than the normal amount of the heavy isotope. Brönsted and Hevesy[105] applied this method to the separation of Hg. Liquid Hg was allowed to evaporate in vacuum. The upper surface of the containing vessel, which surface was only a few cm. from that of the liquid Hg, was cooled with liquid air. Practically all atoms evaporated from the liquid Hg surface struck this cooled surface and condensed thereon. Accurate density measurements were then made upon the evaporated and the residue samples. After repeated fractionations during which the volume of Hg was reduced by a factor of 100,000, these workers reported densities of 0.99974 and 1.00023 that of ordinary Hg for the two end fractions. Hönigschmid and Birckenbach,[106] separating Hg by this same method, found end fractions of densities 0.999824 and 1.000164 that of ordinary Hg. These correspond to atomic weights of (200.564 $\pm$ 0.006) and (200.632 $\pm$ 0.007), whereas the atomic weight of ordinary Hg is (200.61 $\pm$ 0.006). Brönsted and Hevesy[107] obtained a partial separation for Cl using essentially the same method. By evaporating a solution of HCl in water they produced a change of 0.024 units difference between the atomic weights of the two end fractions. Thus this general method again produced without question a partial separation, but the end samples were far from pure isotopes. In fact, they were just measurably different from the usual mixture of isotopes. The one sample had been enriched slightly in the lighter isotope, whereas the other had been similarly enriched in the heavier isotope.

More recent efforts[101,102] toward nearly complete separation of isotopes have been rewarded with much greater success. Hertz,[108] employing gaseous diffusion at low pressure through a special porous material, succeeded in producing a real separation for the isotopes of Ne. He produced a light end fraction which contained less than one percent of the heavy isotope. This represented a real separation, for the heavy isotope of normal Ne represents roughly ten percent of the total. The heavy end fraction was found to contain approximately 70% $Ne^{22}$ and 30% $Ne^{20}$. Hertz[109] and his associates have since succeeded in isolating $Ne^{22}$ almost completely

[105] J. N. Brönsted and G. Hevesy, *Nature*, **106**, 144 (1920); *Phil. Mag.*, **43**, 31 (1922).
[106] O. Hönigschmid and L. Birckenbach, *Chem. Ber.* **56**, 1219 (1923).
[107] J. N. Brönsted and G. Hevesy, *Nature*, **107**, 619 (1921).
[108] G. Hertz, *Zeits. f. Physik*, **79**, 108, 700 (1932).
[109] H. Harmsen, G. Hertz and W. Schütze, *Zeits. f. Physik*, **90**, 703 (1934).

from the lighter isotopes of this element. In a similar manner the heavy hydrogen isotope $H^2$ has been obtained[110] in a spectroscopically pure state by repeated diffusions. The separation of hydrogen isotopes presents far less difficulty than that of heavier elements, for the percentage difference of mass is relatively great for the components of hydrogen. The same method has yielded[111] methane of which 16% was $C^{13}H_4$, whereas the normal concentration of the $C^{13}$ isotope in methane is only 1%. It has also yielded nitrogen of which 6% was $N^{14}N^{15}$, whereas the normal concentration of the $N^{15}$ isotope in nitrogen is only 0.6%.

One of the most effective methods of separation in many cases is that of thermal diffusion introduced by Clusius and Dickel.[112] In this method the gas comprised of two or more isotopes is placed between two vertical parallel walls. The one wall is kept hot and the other cold. Diffusion results in a concentration of the heavier isotope near the cold wall and of the lighter isotope near the hot wall. Due to thermal convection there is a flow of the colder gas, which is rich in the heavier isotope, downward near the cold wall, and a flow of the warmer gas, which is rich in the lighter isotope, upward near the hot wall. This results in a concentration of the heavier isotope at the bottom and of the lighter isotope at the top of the apparatus. Using this method Clusius and Dickel[113] produced 99.6% pure $Cl^{35}$ and 99.4% pure $Cl^{37}$. Two different samples of $Cl^{35}$ had atomic weights of 35.021 and 34.979. One sample of $Cl^{37}$ had an atomic weight of 36.956. A comparison of these atomic weights with those determined by the mass spectrograph for the two isotopes shows how nearly complete was the separation. Other isotopes have been separated[101] by the same method. Among these [114–116] is $C^{13}$. The separation of this isotope is of particular interest because of its use as a tracer in biological work. Watson[115] has recently estimated the cost of production of $C^{13}$ at a concentration of 20% at $300 per gram exclusive of labor, when the separation is made by the thermal diffusion process. While this method is less economical for the separation of $C^{13}$ than is another method to be discussed immediately, it does have certain advantages for biological laboratories.

Pronounced separation of isotopes has also been produced in a number of instances by a chemical method known as the exchange reaction method. Consider the particular case of the nitrogen isotopes, the separation of which

[110] G. Hertz, *Naturwiss.*, **21**, 884 (1933).
[111] D. E. Wooldridge and W. R. Smythe, *Phys. Rev.*, **50**, 233 (1936).
[112] K. Clusius and G. Dickel, *Naturwiss.*, **26**, 546 (1938).
[113] K. Clusius and G. Dickel, *Naturwiss.*, **27**, 148, 487 (1939).
[114] A. O. Nier, *Phys. Rev.*, **57**, 30 (1940).
[115] W. W. Watson, *Phys. Rev.*, **56**, 703 (1939); **57**, 899 (1940); *Science*, **93**, 473 (1941).
[116] H. L. Schultz and W. W. Watson, *Phys. Rev.*, **58**, 1047 (1940).

by this method was first investigated by Urey and Aten.[117] Because of the very small difference in chemical properties attributable to isotopes, it is necessary to employ rather unusual methods to effect a chemical separation. Consider the exchange reaction

$$N^{15}H_3 + N^{14}H_4^+ = N^{14}H_3 + N^{15}H_4^+$$

wherein the ammonia $NH_3$ is in each case in gaseous form and where the ammonium ion $NH_4^+$ is obtained from an ammonium salt in water solution. This reaction is allowed to proceed in a fractionating column much like that used for distillation. The process is often referred to as a two-phase counter-current process. The two phases in this case are the gaseous and the liquid. The counter-current designation comes from the fact that, in this case, ammonium salt in water solution flows down a fractionating column, and ammonia gas, freed at the bottom by the addition of sodium hydroxide, passes up the column.

If K be the equilibrium constant for the above reaction, then

$$\frac{(N^{15}H_4^+)(N^{14}H_3)}{(N^{15}H_3)(N^{14}H_4^+)} = K = \frac{(N^{15}H_4^+)/(N^{14}H_4^+)}{(N^{15}H_3)/(N^{14}H_3)}$$

where the parentheses represent the concentrations of the materials inclosed therein. Now it has been shown that in general the equilibrium constants for such exchange reactions are not exactly unity.[101] Furthermore, it has been shown that if the constant is not unity for a given reaction then a partial separation of isotopes will result, the one being concentrated in the gaseous phase and the other in the liquid phase. The greater the divergence of the constant from unity the more rapid the separation. Since the constant has been found to differ from unity by a significant amount only for the lighter atoms, it is only for the light atoms that a real separation can be effected by the method. Since it has also been found that the constant approaches unity more closely as the temperature is raised, the process must be carried out at a low temperature if it is to be most effective in producing a separation. By this method the isotopes $H^2$, $Li^7$, $C^{13}$ and $N^{15}$ have been produced in significant concentrations. Concentrations as high as 25% of $C^{13}$ in sodium cyanide have been produced,[118] and at the rate of 0.15 grams of $C^{13}$ per day. The normal concentration of this isotope is only 1.06%. A concentration of 72.8% of $N^{15}$ has been produced.[119] Concentrations of 50% of $N^{15}$ can be produced at the rate of several grams per day. The chemical method is the most rapid and the most economical method of

[117] H. C. Urey and A. H. W. Aten, *Phys. Rev.*, **50**, 575 (1936).

[118] C. A. Hutchinson, D. W. Stewart and H. C. Urey, *Jour. Chem. Phys.*, **8**, 532 (1940).

[119] H. C. Urey and Others, *Jour. Chem. Phys.*, **6**, 296 (1938); **7**, 34 (1939).

separating a number of important isotopes. It has been estimated[101] that $C^{13}$ and $N^{15}$ can be produced for $15 per gram.

The discovery of heavy hydrogen, an isotope of mass two, was encouraged by an accidental error in the early value for the atomic weight of hydrogen. Recall that Aston[24] had obtained a value (1.00778 ± 0.00015) for the atomic weight of $H^1$. At that time the most probable value[120] from chemical determinations was (1.00777 ± 0.00002). These figures, being in perfect agreement, seemed to indicate that no heavier isotopes of hydrogen existed. The subsequent discovery of the two heavier isotopes of oxygen changed the situation materially. As has already been pointed out, the existence of these meant that the physical and chemical scales of atomic weight were slightly different. To express any physical value on the chemical scale it is necessary to divide by the factor 1.00027. Thus Aston's value, when converted to the chemical scale, was 1.00750. This was appreciably smaller than the chemically determined atomic weight; what had appeared to be perfect agreement thus proved to be false. It was pointed out[121] that, in order to remove this inconsistency, one must suppose that H contains some heavier isotopes. A careful search for these by Urey, Brickwedde and Murphy[92] revealed the presence of $H^2$. The abundance of this isotope was judged to be of the general order of that necessary to bring the mean atomic weight of ordinary hydrogen up to the value observed chemically. It is interesting that, whereas an apparent discrepancy stimulated greatly the discovery of heavy hydrogen, this discrepancy itself was later shown[42] to be due to a small experimental error. It was shown that the original mass spectrograph value was slightly low, and this in spite of the fact that Aston's value had been confirmed accurately by Bainbridge.[43] When the new spectrograph value of 1.0081 was converted to the chemical scale, it agreed so nearly with the chemically determined value that there was no longer any reason to suppose the existence of a heavier isotope of hydrogen. Thus a certain discrepancy had encouraged a search for unknown isotopes of hydrogen. Heavy hydrogen had been found. And then the theoretical need for heavy hydrogen was removed through elimination of a small experimental error. Aston[42] remarked that he would never regret the slightly low value obtained for hydrogen in 1927, since it played such an essential part in encouraging the search for $H^2$.

The isotopes of hydrogen have been separated by several methods. The first method employed was that of fractional distillation near the triple point. This method of separation was used by the discoverers to concentrate the heavy isotope in samples to be examined spectroscopically. In more recent years an elaborate system of fractional distillation, employing a huge dis-

[120] R. T. Birge, *Rev. Mod. Phys.*, **1**, 20 (1929).

[121] R. T. Birge and D. H. Menzel, *Phys. Rev.*, **37**, 1669 (1931).

tillation column, has been used with success in concentrating other relatively rare isotopes, such as those of oxygen and nitrogen. Under the direction of Urey this process has yielded samples of surprising enrichment of certain isotopes.

Commercially, the most important method of separation of the heavy hydrogen isotope is that of electrolysis. It was found by Washburn and Urey[122] in 1932 that electrolytic cells used for the production of hydrogen and oxygen contained much greater than normal concentrations of heavy hydrogen, and that this method could be used for the production of almost pure heavy water. Lewis and MacDonald[123,124] almost immediately produced concentrated heavy water by this method of electrolysis. Since then almost pure heavy water has been produced in large quantities. As the heavy water is taken from ordinary water the density of the remaining water decreases below the ordinary value. Water of density 21 parts per million less than that of ordinary water has been produced. This water has supposedly been freed from all molecules containing the heavy hydrogen isotope. Such observations indicate that the concentration of $H^2$ in ordinary hydrogen is approximately one part in 5,000.

The theory of electrolytic separation is not entirely clear. One would immediately suspect that the different rates of diffusion of the two isotopes, or the difference in the mobilities of their ions, might be responsible. Apparently, however, these are relatively unimportant factors.[125,126] The most important factor seems to be connected with the transfer of an electron from the cathode metal to the solution, and the simultaneous adsorption of the H atom by the electrode. The energies involved in this process are apparently different for ordinary and for heavy hydrogen. This subject has been discussed in some detail by Urey and Teal.[125]

Because of the widespread use of heavy water, and because it is one of the few compounds which can be produced in practically pure isotopic form, it is interesting to compare a few of the properties of heavy water with those of ordinary water. Many of these properties have been summarized elsewhere.[125] A few of the more fundamental ones are shown in Table V. It should be understood that the heavy water commonly spoken of is really only one of a number of possible heavy waters. Since there exist two stable isotopes of hydrogen and three of oxygen it follows that there are 9 distinct kinds of water possible. Probably all of these exist to some extent, though the scarcity of certain isotopes leads to very small concentrations of most of

[122] E. W. Washburn and H. C. Urey, *Proc. Nat. Acad. Sci.*, **18**, 496 (1932).

[123] G. N. Lewis and R. T. MacDonald, *Jour. Chem. Phys.*, **1**, 341 (1933).

[124] G. N. Lewis, *Jour. Amer. Chem. Soc.*, **55**, 1297 (1933).

[125] H. C. Urey and G. K. Teal, *Rev. Mod. Phys.*, **7**, 34 (1935).

[126] R. H. Fowler, *Proc. Roy. Soc.*, A, **144**, 452 (1934).

them. The one heavy water ordinarily spoken of is that made from two atoms of the hydrogen isotope of mass two, called deuterium, together with one atom of $O^{16}$. This is the heavy water that has been obtained in practically pure form and which is widely advertised commercially.

TABLE V
Comparative properties of ordinary and heavy water

| Property | $H_2O$ | $H_2^2O$ |
|---|---|---|
| Specific gravity at 25° C relative to ordinary water at 25° C | 1.0000 | 1.1079 |
| Temperature of maximum density | 4.0° C | 11.6 |
| Dielectric constant | 81.5 | 80.7 |
| Surface tension | 72.75 dynes/cm. | 67.8 |
| Viscosity at 10° C | 13.10 millipoises | 16.85 |
| Melting point | 0.000° C | 3.802 |
| Boiling point (76 cm. of Hg pressure) | 100.00° C | 101.42 |
| Heat of fusion | 1436 cal/mole | 1510 |
| Heat of vaporization at 25° C | 10,484 cal/mole | 10,743 |
| Refractive index at 20° C for NaD line | 1.33300 | 1.32828 |

Another possible method of isotope separation is that of centrifuging. The theory of this was given by Aston and Lindemann in 1919. Numerous early attempts at separation by this method were unsuccessful. Recently Beams[127] and his associates have developed an extremely high speed type of centrifuge and have applied it to the separation of isotopes. With this apparatus it has been possible to obtain[128,129] appreciable separation for a number of materials. The percentage separation yet produced is small. and about that indicated by theory.

It has always been realized that the ideal way to obtain isotopes in a pure state is through use of a mass spectrograph. Such an instrument concentrates particles of different masses at different places. If these particles could be caught separately, one would have samples of the pure isotopes. The difficulty of application is that an insufficient number of particles can be trapped in any reasonable length of time. In recent years, however, certain designs[130,131] of mass spectrographs have provided unusually intense positive ion currents, and the Li isotopes have been separated in sufficient quantities

[127] J. W. Beams and Others, *Rev. Sci. Instr.*, **6**, 299 (1935); *Jour. App. Phys.*, **8**, 795 (1937); *Rev. Mod. Phys.*, **10**, 245 (1938).

[128] J. W. Beams and Others, *Phys. Rev.*, **50**, 491 (1936); **51**, 384 (1937); **55**, 591 (1939); **56**, 266 (1939).

[129] R. F. Humphreys, *Phys. Rev.*, **56**, 684 (1939).

[130] L. H. Rumbaugh and Others, *Phys. Rev.*, **45**, 724 (1934); **49**, 882 (1936); **50**, 681 (1936).

[131] M. L. Oliphant, E. S. Shire and B. M. Crowther, *Proc. Roy. Soc.*, A, **146**, 922 (1934).

for certain work. Using this method of separation, Smythe and Hemmendinger[17] have succeeded in collecting sufficient samples of the several K isotopes to prove that $K^{40}$ is the isotope which is responsible for the radioactive properties of K. While it will never be possible to collect large samples by the mass spectrograph method, it may well provide sufficient quantities of pure isotopes to allow at least certain types of studies.

## Chapter 6

# PHOTONS—THE PHOTOELECTRIC EFFECT —RADIATION AND ABSORPTION

Serious studies of the nature of light date back at least to the seventeenth century. In the early days the generally accepted concept was that a light beam consisted of a stream of rapidly moving corpuscles emitted by the source. This view was held by Newton. Satisfactory interpretation of such simple phenomena as straight line propagation, reflection and refraction were possible on this view. About this same time, however, Huygens formulated his wave theory of light. This likewise accounted in a simple manner for reflection and refraction, but straight line propagation was not at that time evident on this view. Studies of diffraction and interference effects, started by Young early in the nineteenth century, soon turned the tide strongly in favor of the wave theory. After Maxwell brought forward his quantitative treatment of the electromagnetic wave theory in 1864, the case seemed conclusive. About 1900, however, there began to appear a number of difficulties with the simple wave theory. It was because of these that Planck proposed a radical change of view, at least as regards the process of radiation and absorption. He proposed that radiant energy is emitted and absorbed in bundles, or quanta, not continuously as the wave theory would have it. This idea was extremely fruitful during the ensuing years, and its basic correctness seems to have been proved beyond a doubt. Thus we have returned to a form of corpuscular theory, one in which the corpuscles are definite quantities of energy. This does not mean that the wave theory has been discarded; it is still necessary to account for many phenomena. But so is the quantum theory equally essential to account for other observed phenomena. The concept of energy quanta received one of its earlier convincing confirmations from the phenomenon of emission and absorption of radiant energy by gaseous atoms. Other equally convincing evidence came from studies of photoelectricity, the emission of electrons from metal surfaces illuminated with ultraviolet light. Still other evidence came from studies of ionization and resonance potentials, and from studies of the scattering of X-rays. These studies will now be discussed at sufficient length that the underlying concepts may be made clear.

## 1. THE EMISSION AND ABSORPTION OF RADIANT ENERGY

### General Information Regarding Emission from Gases

The mechanism by which atoms emit and absorb radiant energy is of considerable significance. Attempts to analyze this phenomenon have played a large part in formulating the present mechanical model of the atom. At the same time they have led to highly accurate quantitative evidence of the basic correctness of the quantum theory concept of emission and absorption.

All gases when heated or otherwise excited emit characteristic bright line spectra. Energy is radiated from an excited atom only at certain well-defined frequencies, or wave lengths. Many of these wave lengths are in or near the visible. Atoms of any one material emit many lines; that is, they emit radiation of many well-defined frequencies. These emission lines are extremely sharp, appearing to occur at nearly single frequencies rather than over a frequency band of appreciable width. The bright line spectrum of any gas is characteristic of the atoms of that material; no other atom emits the same group of lines. Also, a gas radiates this characteristic line spectrum, entirely unaltered, when mixed physically with other gases. The absence of the line spectrum characteristic of any particular gas is a sensitive test of the purity of a sample as regards possible contamination by this gas. A gas has also a characteristic line absorption spectrum. That is, if light of all wave lengths is sent through a gas, the gas absorbs light only at sharply defined characteristic wave lengths. A gas absorbs when cool exactly those wave lengths which it itself emits when hot. This absorption spectrum is not altered by a physical mixing of other gases with the one being studied. Each gas present adds its own characteristic absorption.

Polyatomic molecules, that is, molecules composed of two or more atoms, have spectra quite distinct from that of the atom. The single hydrogen atom, for example, emits one line spectrum; the hydrogen molecule emits a different line spectrum. Let us confine our attention for the moment to the spectrum characteristic of the hydrogen atom. At least four distinct groups, or series, of lines have been observed. The spacing of lines, as regards wave length, within any one group progresses in a regular order; as one proceeds to shorter and shorter wave lengths the lines occur closer and closer together. The lines become so close at the shorter wave lengths that they appear to overlap, the wave length approaching a definite lower limit. Such a group of lines is called a series. Fig. 1 reproduces[1] a photograph of one of the series for atomic hydrogen. This is called the Balmer series. Several of these lines are in the visible, and the remainder are in the near

[1] G. Herzberg, *Ann. d. Physik*, **84**, 565 (1927); *Atomic Spectra and Atomic Structure* (New York: Prentice-Hall, 1937).

ultraviolet. The longest and the shortest wave lengths are 6563 and 3646 A°, respectively. Hydrogen also emits another group, the Lyman series, all of the lines of which are far in the ultraviolet. Still another series, the Paschen, occurs in the infrared. A few lines of a fourth series, the Brackett, and of the fifth series, the Pfund, have been observed still farther in the infrared. Atoms other than hydrogen also emit characteristic series of lines, but the frequencies and the spacings of these lines are quite different from those for hydrogen.

Although it had been possible, even before the advent of the quantum theory, to find many empirical relationships among the lines constituting the bright line spectrum of a gas, no success whatever had been attained in correlating these lines with atomic structure. There existed no concept as to why the atom emitted just these particular frequencies, nor did there exist any worthwhile picture of the mechanism by which it emitted them.

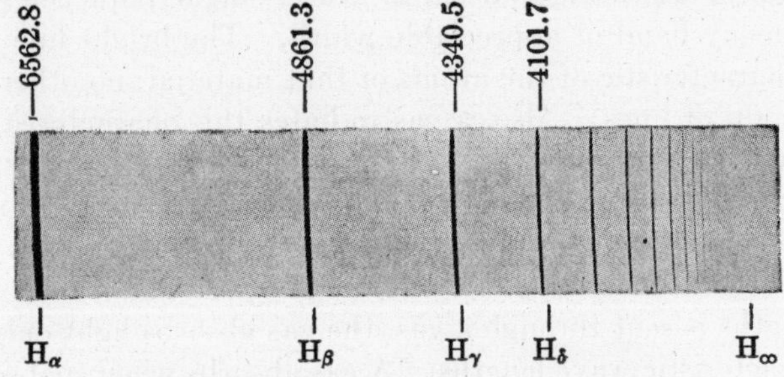


FIG. 1.—The Balmer series of atomic hydrogen.

It was years after Planck's original suggestion that energy was emitted and absorbed in discrete amounts $h\nu$, that Bohr[2] first succeeded in applying these ideas to the problem of line spectra. The results caused revolutionary changes in the concepts of atomic structure.

Previous to Bohr's contribution there was little exact knowledge on which to base any concept of the structure of an atom. It was fairly certain that the atom contained both positive and negative charges, but one could only guess at the relative locations of these within the atom. Was the positive charge near the outer extremities of the atom, or was it deep within? J. J. Thomson had suggested a model in which the positive charge was distributed uniformly throughout a spherical region, and in which the electrons were in various shells within this region. On the other hand, Rutherford[3] had suggested that the atom consists of a positively charged nucleus surrounded by electrons. Since then it has become possible to obtain fairly direct and entirely convincing experimental evidence, which will be discussed

[2] N. Bohr, *Phil. Mag.*, **26**, 1, 476 (1913).

[3] E. Rutherford, *Phil. Mag.*, **21**, 669 (1911).

in a later chapter, that all of the positive charge on an atom is located in an extremely small and centrally located region called the nucleus, and that the outer part of the atom consists of so-called planetary electrons, the number of these being different for different atoms.

But this experimental evidence was not yet available in 1913. Nevertheless, Bohr assumed that an atom consists of a small, centrally located and positively charged nucleus, and that electrons rotate about this nucleus much as the planets rotate about the central sun. The simplest atom, hydrogen, was assumed to consist of one proton as a central nucleus; there was one planetary electron rotating about this. The helium atom was supposed to consist of a small central nucleus made up of particles having a total mass approximately four times that of the proton and a net positive charge the equal of two electrons; there were two planetary electrons rotating about this nucleus. Other atoms were assumed to be constructed in a similar manner. The greater the atomic number the greater is the number of planetary electrons. It is now known that the number of planetary electrons associated with any particular atom is equal to the atomic number of that atom.

### The Classical Concept of Radiation

Before proceeding to Bohr's interpretation of the emission of radiant energy, it is well to point out what little success had been attained by the classical theory. The planetary model of the atom supposes that the various electrons belonging to the atom rotate in orbits about the central nucleus. It can easily be shown mathematically that if one relatively light body moves about a second relatively massive one, and if the two bodies attract one another with a force inversely proportional to the square of the distance between them, then the light body will move in a circle, an ellipse, a parabola, or a hyperbola, having its focus at the massive body. If a system is to be permanent, then of course the path must be either a circle or an ellipse. All of the planets describe ellipses with the sun at one focus. The planet moves always with such an angular velocity, and at such a distance from the sun, that the centrifugal force outward is exactly balanced by the force of attraction between the two masses. It is conceived that the planetary electron of the atom executes a similar orbit about the nucleus as focus. In this way a dynamically stable atom results.

Before the work of Bohr there appeared to be serious objections to such an atom model. Think of an electron rotating with constant angular velocity in a circle about the nucleus. This electron is accelerated toward the center of the circle. Now it is shown in classical electrodynamics that an accelerated electric charge radiates energy as an electromagnetic wave. The frequency of the radiation should be the same as that with which the acceleration repeats itself. It follows that the frequency of radiation should be the same as the frequency with which the electron rotates in its orbit. On classical theory this radiation might represent one of the characteristic lines emitted by the atom. There are, however, two serious difficulties. Even an atom as simple as hydrogen emits many characteristic frequencies; and how could the rotation of the one planetary electron possessed by hydrogen be responsible for all of these? Furthermore, if this rotating electron does radiate energy, then from the law of conservation of energy one would expect the energy of the electron itself to decrease. In doing this the electron moves in closer to the nucleus. A continuously radiating electron would therefore spiral gradually inward. Such an atom would not be a stable system. This concept of radiation was therefore untenable.

**Bohr's Theory of Radiation**

Recognizing the insurmountable difficulties of the classical concept of radiation, Bohr[2] proposed an entirely new theory in 1913. Let us proceed with the development of the basic theory as applied to the simplest of all atoms, an atom having but one planetary electron. There is only one normal atom which meets this requirement, and this is the hydrogen atom. An ionized atom of helium would also meet the requirement, for one of its customary two electrons has been taken away in the ionization process. A doubly ionized lithium atom would also meet the requirement, for there remains but one planetary electron. Bohr assumed that such an atom consists of a small but massive and positively charged nucleus, about which rotates a single planetary electron in an orbit such that the centrifugal force is always balanced by the electrical force of attraction between the electron and the nucleus. While balance of forces might be met by either an elliptical or a circular orbit, let the present discussion be limited to circular orbits only. Bohr supposed that this centrally accelerated electron does not radiate as classical electrodynamics would lead one to suspect. In this way the atom remains a stable system with the electron rotating in a fixed orbit. Now the centrifugal force and the electrical force of attraction can balance for any radius of orbit provided the electron moves with the appropriate velocity. Bohr assumed, however, that only certain of the infinite number of orbits were possible. The only ones possible were assumed to be those for which the angular momentum of the electron was some whole multiple of $h/2\pi$, where $h$ is the universal

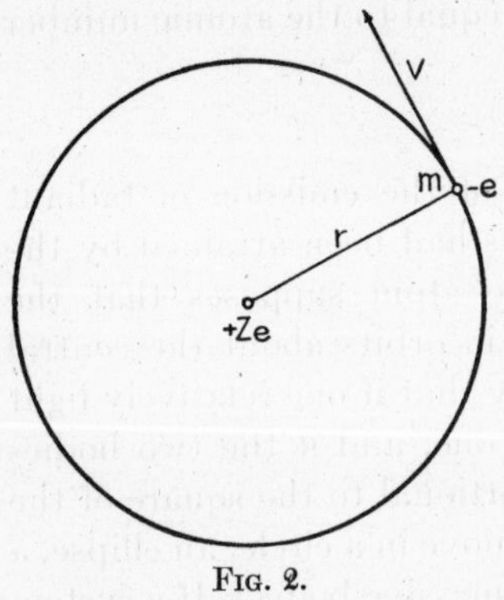

FIG. 2.

constant introduced some years earlier by Planck in his theory of the distribution of energy radiated from a black body. Referring to Fig. 2, a balance between the centrifugal force and the force of attraction is obtained when

$$\frac{mv^2}{r} = \frac{Ze^2}{r^2}$$

It is apparent from this that the kinetic energy of the electron is given by

$$\text{K.E.} = \frac{1}{2}mv^2 = \frac{Ze^2}{2r}$$

Now Bohr assumed that the angular momentum, or the moment of momentum, must be some integer times $h/2\pi$. Thus, the electron can exist only in those orbits for which

$$mvr = \frac{nh}{2\pi}$$

where $n$ is some whole number. If one solves this equation for $v$, substitutes this value for $v$ in the equation for the kinetic energy, and solves the resulting equation for $r$, he finds that

$$r = \frac{n^2h^2}{4\pi^2mZe^2}$$

Thus, according to Bohr's assumption, the electron can rotate only in those orbits which have radii given by this last expression. The radii of these permitted orbits are obtained by giving $n$ the values 1, 2, 3, 4, etc. These radii are in the ratio of the squares of small whole numbers.

Since the electron is in the field of the nucleus it also possesses potential energy. This potential energy is given by

$$\text{P.E.} = \frac{Ze}{r}(-e) = \frac{-Ze^2}{r}$$

The total energy $W$ of the electron is, therefore

$$W = \text{K.E.} + \text{P.E.} = \frac{Ze^2}{2r} - \frac{Ze^2}{r} = \frac{-Ze^2}{2r}$$

If the value of the permitted radius $r$ be substituted into this, one obtains

$$W = -\frac{2\pi^2mZ^2e^4}{h^2}\frac{1}{n^2}$$

This represents the discrete energies permitted by Bohr's assumption. An electron is supposed to exist in a stable state with any one of these energies, that is, in any one of these permissible orbits.

Bohr further assumed that monochromatic radiation of energy is brought about by the electron jumping from one orbit into some inner orbit. He assumed that the frequency of this radiation was such that when multiplied by the constant $h$, the product is equal to the change in the energy of the electron. That is, if $W_i$ is the energy of an electron in its initial permitted state, and if $W_f$ is the energy of the electron in its final permitted state, then

$$h\nu = W_i - W_f$$

in which $\nu$ is the frequency of radiation and $h$ is the same constant as entered previously. Substituting in this equation the values of $W_i$ and $W_f$ for the two states, and solving for the frequency $\nu$, one obtains

$$\nu = \frac{2\pi^2 m Z^2 e^4}{h^3}\left(\frac{1}{n_f^2} - \frac{1}{n_i^2}\right)$$

The numbers $n_i$ and $n_f$ may be any integers, but for radiation of energy $n_i$ must be larger than $n_f$. $n = 1$ corresponds to the innermost orbit; $n = 2$ corresponds to the next orbit out from the nucleus, etc. In terms of the $K$, $L$, $M$, etc., energy levels, $n = 1$ corresponds to the $K$ shell, $n = 2$ to the $L$ shell, $n = 3$ to the $M$ shell, etc.

Before attempting a comparison between this theory and experiment, attention should be called to one slight correction which is necessary. It has been supposed that the nucleus remains stationary and that the electron rotates about it. Although even a nucleus of hydrogen is 1837 times as massive[4] as the electron, this nucleus will not remain absolutely at rest. The electron and the nucleus will rotate about their common center of mass. The motion of the nucleus will of course be small as compared to that of the electron, and the resulting correction should be small. Consideration of this correction due to the motion of the nucleus leads to the introduction of a factor $\dfrac{1}{\left(1 + \dfrac{m}{M}\right)}$, where $M$ is the mass of the nucleus. The correction amounts to 1 part in 1837 for hydrogen. The corrected expression for the frequency of radiation is then

$$\nu = \frac{2\pi^2 m Z^2 e^4}{\left(1 + \frac{m}{M}\right) h^3}\left(\frac{1}{n_f^2} - \frac{1}{n_i^2}\right)$$

[4] R. T. Birge, A Mimeographed, "*Consistent Set of Values of the General Physical Constants*," as of August, 1939.

This expression is commonly written

$$\nu = RZ^2\left(\frac{1}{n_f^2} - \frac{1}{n_i^2}\right)$$

where the constant $R$ is known as the Rydberg constant. This constant takes on slightly different values for different atoms, depending upon the mass $M$ of the nucleus.

Let us now turn to experimental evidence bearing upon the equation derived for the frequency of emitted radiation. Consider the spectral data available for atomic hydrogen. In particular, consider those emission lines representing the Balmer series. The fourth column of Table I gives the observed wave lengths, as collected by Saha[5], of the lines of this series that have been measured. Not a line between the wave lengths 6563 and 3657 A° has been omitted.

Now if one puts into the Bohr expression for frequency the values of the known physical constants, including the $Z$ and $M$ appropriate for hydrogen, if $n_f$ is given the fixed value 2, and if $n_i$ is allowed to take on the values 3, 4, 5, 6, etc., one gets consecutively frequencies corresponding to the wave lengths of the observed lines. Unfortunately, the known constants in the Bohr expression cannot be measured individually with the same degree of precision as can the wave lengths of spectral lines. A real test of the form of the Bohr expression for frequency can best be made, therefore, by using a value of the constant $R$ obtained directly from spectroscopic data. The best value of this constant for hydrogen, determined experimentally, is[4]

$$R_H = 109{,}677.747 \pm 0.008.$$

Using essentially this value of $R_H$, assigning $n_f$ the fixed value 2, and allowing $n_i$ to take on the values 3, 4, 5, 6, etc., Saha[5] calculated the theoretical wave lengths in air shown in the third column of Table I. The known index of refraction of air for each wave length was used to convert the calculated wave lengths in vacuum to those in air. The agreement between the calculated and the observed wave lengths is remarkable. Every one of the thirty-six observed Balmer lines is accounted for by the Bohr expression, and the wave length of each is given accurately. Accepting the Bohr concept of emission, therefore, the various lines of the Balmer series are emitted when electrons move from the various outer energy levels indicated in Fig. 3, always into a common final level corresponding to $n_f = 2$. Absorption of radiant energy occurs when the electron moves from an inner to an

[5] M. N. Saha and N. K. Saha, *A Treatise on Modern Physics* (Allahabad and Calcutta: The Indian Press, 1934), Vol. I, pp. 319–360.

TABLE I

Comparison of the calculated and observed wave lengths of the Balmer series of lines for atomic hydrogen, as collected by Saha.[5] Wave lengths are those in air, and are given in A°. Saha used a value 109,678.696 for the Rydberg constant for hydrogen, and a value approximately 1.00028 (varying slightly with wave length) for the index of refraction of air, in evaluating the calculated wave lengths

| Name of line | Value of $n_i$ | Calculated wave length | Observed wave length |
|---|---|---|---|
| $H_\alpha$ | 3 | 6562.793 | 6562.8473<br>6562.7110 |
| $H_\beta$ | 4 | 4861.327 | 4861.3578<br>4861.2800 |
| $H_\gamma$ | 5 | 4340.466 | 4340.497<br>4340.429 |
| $H_\delta$ | 6 | 4101.738 | 4101.7346 |
| $H_\epsilon$ | 7 | 3970.075 | 3970.0740 |
| | 8 | 3889.052 | 3889.0575 |
| | 9 | 3835.387 | 3835.397 |
| | 10 | 3797.900 | 3797.910 |
| | 11 | 3770.633 | 3770.634 |
| | 12 | 3750.154 | 3750.152 |
| | 13 | 3734.371 | 3734.372 |
| | 14 | 3721.948 | 3721.948 |
| | 15 | 3711.973 | 3711.980 |
| | 16 | 3703.855 | 3703.861 |
| | 17 | 3697.154 | 3697.159 |
| | 18 | 3691.557 | 3691.553 |
| | 19 | 3686.834 | 3686.833 |
| | 20 | 3682.810 | 3682.825 |
| | 21 | 3679.355 | 3679.372 |
| | 22 | 3676.354 | 3676.378 |
| | 23 | 3673.761 | 3673.76 |
| | 24 | 3671.478 | 3671.42 |
| | 25 | 3669.466 | 3669.50 |
| | 26 | 3667.384 | 3667.69 |
| | 27 | 3666.097 | 3666.10 |
| | 28 | 3664.679 | 3664.69 |
| | 29 | 3663.405 | 3663.42 |
| | 30 | 3662.258 | 3662.24 |
| | 31 | 3661.221 | 3661.34 |
| | 32 | 3660.280 | 3660.33 |
| | 33 | 3659.423 | 3659.68 |
| | 34 | 3658.641 | 3658.81 |
| | 35 | 3657.926 | 3658.00 |
| | 36 | 3657.269 | 3657.25 |
| | ∞ | 3645.981 | |

outer energy level. The concept makes clear why the frequencies of the absorption lines are exactly the same as those of the emission lines.

Although it is commonly stated that gases emit only bright line spectra, this is not exactly true. They do not emit continuous spectra in the sense that a hot solid does, but they do emit in certain regions a somewhat restricted continuous distribution of energy. For example, atomic hydrogen emits a continuous spectrum restricted to the region of wave lengths just shorter than the shortest wave length of the Balmer series. One might properly inquire into the origin of this. On the Bohr picture the shortest Balmer line is emitted when an electron drops from a relatively long way off, theoretically from infinity, into the level defined by $n_f = 2$. This electron

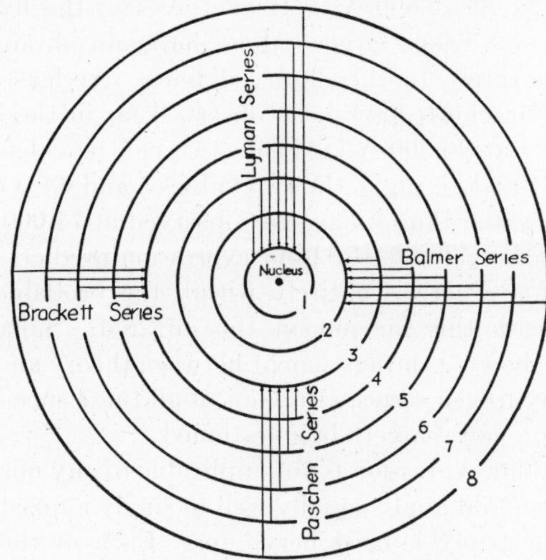


FIG. 3.—Indicating the origins of the several line series of atomic hydrogen.

had no energy, either potential or kinetic, before moving in. Now suppose instead that a free electron with some kinetic energy of thermal agitation should drop into the same final orbit. It would give up more energy in the transition and, on the Bohr concept, would cause radiation of somewhat greater frequency. Since free electrons exist with all possible energies of thermal agitation, one would expect some radiation at all frequencies above that corresponding to the shortest Balmer line. Since the thermal energy is relatively small for a great majority of the free electrons, the resulting continuous spectrum would extend, in any measurable intensity, for only a short way below the shortest line of the series. Similar continuous spectra, often called recombination spectra, should accompany other series, and it has been found that they do. Their positions and extent are in general agreement with the Bohr interpretation.

The success of the Bohr concept did not stop with an interpretation of the Balmer series of hydrogen. On this picture of emission, why could electrons not jump from various levels into the innermost level? And would such transitions not lead to another series of lines? If in the Bohr expression $n_f$ is given the fixed value 1, and $n_i$ is allowed to take on the values 2, 3, 4, 5, etc., there is obtained a series of lines falling entirely in the ultraviolet. The observed lines of the Lyman series correspond accurately to the wave lengths calculated by giving $n_f$ the fixed value 1. Electron transitions giving rise to this series are also indicated in Fig. 3.

A number of hydrogen lines have also been observed in the infrared. Most of these fall in the Paschen series, the members of which have wave lengths of the order of 10,000 A°. If one gives $n_f$ the fixed value 3 and allows $n_i$ to take on various larger values, he again obtains wave lengths corresponding accurately to the observed lines. At least two lines of a fourth series, the Brackett, have been observed far in the infrared, one at 40,500 and another at 26,300 A°. These two can be calculated by giving $n_f$ the fixed value 4 and giving $n_i$ the two values 5 and 6. One member of a fifth probable series, the Pfund, has been observed at 74,000 A°. Giving $n_f$ the value 5 and $n_i$ the value 6, the Bohr expression predicts a line at 74,578 A°. The discrepancy here is entirely within the probable error of wave length measurements this far out in the infrared. Saha[5] has collected quantitative data showing the agreement between theory and experiment for all of the known hydrogen series. In view of all these successes the form of the Bohr expression can scarcely be questioned.

Although the Bohr expression is not applicable to any normal atom other than hydrogen, it should apply equally well to singly ionized helium, doubly ionized lithium, or triply ionized beryllium. Each of these has but one remaining planetary electron; it is a hydrogen-like atom. It differs from hydrogen only in that it has a larger nuclear charge and nuclear mass. Previous to Bohr's development certain lines constituting a series known as the Pickering had been attributed to some form of hydrogen. Subsequent to Bohr's work it was shown[6–8] that these lines were emitted by ionized helium. The wave lengths of these observed lines are given accurately by the Bohr expression when $Z$ is given the value 2, $M$ the mass of the helium nucleus, $n_f$ the fixed value 4, and when $n_i$ is allowed to take on higher integers. The quantitative agreement is comparable to that for the Balmer series of hydrogen. Alternate lines of the Pickering series of helium coincide almost exactly with the Balmer lines of hydrogen. But the correspondence is not exact; the Pickering lines fall at slightly shorter wave lengths. The

[6] A. Fowler, *Proc. Roy. Soc.*, A, **90**, 426 (1914).
[7] E. J. Evans, *Phil. Mag.*, **29**, 284 (1915).
[8] F. Paschen, *Ann. d. Physik*, **50**, 901 (1916).

difference in wave lengths, roughly 2 A°, is just accounted for by the smaller effect of the factor $\left(1 + \frac{m}{M}\right)$ for helium. For the same reason the Balmer series for heavy hydrogen, atomic weight 2, does not coincide exactly with that for ordinary hydrogen of atomic weight 1. Lines for heavy hydrogen fall between the normal Balmer and Pickering lines. Other series for ionized helium have since been found at shorter wave lengths. The observed lines of these three series can be calculated accurately by assigning $n_f$ the fixed values 3, 2, or 1, and allowing $n_i$ to take on higher values in each case. But few data are available on the spectra of doubly ionized lithium and triply ionized beryllium. The characteristic emission lines of these fall far in the ultraviolet. Certain lines have been observed[9] for each of these, however, and the observed wave lengths correspond closely to those calculated from the Bohr expression.

Let us now compare the value of $R$ obtained directly from spectroscopic data with the value calculated from individual determinations of the constants involved in the Bohr expression. Theoretically the Rydberg constant for hydrogen is given by

$$R_H = \frac{2\pi^2 me^4}{\left(1 + \frac{m}{M}\right) h^3}$$

Methods by which the constants $e$ and $e/m$, and thence $m$, can be determined accurately have already been discussed. There are a variety of ways in which the constant $h$ can be evaluated. Some of these will become evident shortly. In the earlier days of the Bohr theory it appeared that the value of the Rydberg constant calculated from the above expression agreed quite satisfactorily with the experimental value obtained directly from spectroscopic data. In recent years, however, there have been appreciable changes in the accepted values of two of our fundamental constants, $e$ and $e/m$. These changes have been brought about by more precise experimental methods and technique. Unfortunately these newer values, even though more accurate, do not lead to as good agreement between the calculated and the observed Rydberg constant as did the earlier values. If one uses present accepted values[4] of the individual constants, the theoretical Rydberg constant for hydrogen is $R_H = 110{,}410$ provided the quantity $\nu$ is expressed as the number of waves per centimeter instead of the number per second. When so expressed it is called the wave number. The wave number is obviously the reciprocal of the wave length. The value of $R$ for hydrogen determined experimentally, directly from spectroscopic data, is[4]

[9] A. Ericson and B. Edlén, *Zeits. f. Physik*, **59**, 656 (1930)

$R_H = 109{,}677.747 \pm 0.008$. Thus the value calculated from individual determinations of the constants involved is ⅔ of 1 percent higher than that observed directly. Although the discrepancy is not large, it is much greater than probable errors of measurement lead one to expect.

This discrepancy is at present receiving much attention.[4,10,11] The real reason behind it is not known, though it is generally supposed that the error may lie in the direct determination of the ratio $h/e$, and hence in the value of $h$ used in the theoretical calculation. While there exist what are supposed to be precise methods of evaluating the ratio $h/e$, methods other than spectroscopic, it is supposed that some unrecognized error exists in either the experiment or the theory behind it. It is of course possible that some small correction factor has been omitted in the Bohr theory of radiation, but most workers regard this as doubtful. It is to be hoped that the real source of the small discrepancy will be revealed in the near future. Much can often be gained from efforts designed to clear up an apparent discrepancy. For example, the original discrepancy between the oil drop value of $e$ and the value observed indirectly from X-ray wave length measurements was finally attributed to an incorrect value for the viscosity of air; newer viscosity measurements have removed the discrepancy. In a similar way an apparent discrepancy between values of $e/m$ obtained by deflection methods and by spectroscopic methods, led to recognition of certain unsuspected errors present in previous deflection methods; elimination of these errors has removed the discrepancy. It is interesting that the slight changes in constants introduced as these discrepancies were eliminated, are just those mainly responsible for the present difficulty as regards the Rydberg constant. Let us hope for equal success in clearing up the present discrepancy between the value of $h/e$ obtained by direct experiment and the value necessary to make the calculated Rydberg constant agree with the observed.

## Sommerfeld's Theory of Fine Structure

It was probably noticed in Table I that two observed wave lengths were given for each of the first three Balmer lines. Actually, all of these lines are multiplets, consisting of two or more lines exceedingly close together. The separation is far less than 1 A°. The strong NaD line doublet, with a separation of approximately 6 A°, is a matter of common knowledge; it is easily resolved by good spectrometers. The separation of the several components of the $H_\alpha$ line is not more than 1/50 of this, and some members of the multiplet are still much closer; such multiplets can be resolved only with the best spectroscopes. This multiplicity is referred to as the fine structure of the line. The details of fine structure differ from one element

[10] J. W. M. DuMond, *Phys. Rev.*, **56**, 153 (1939).
[11] F. G. Dunnington, *Rev. Mod. Phys.*, **11**, 65 (1939).

to another, both as regards the number of lines in the multiplet and the spacing of these lines.

In Bohr's original treatment of emission from a hydrogen-like atom the orbits in which the electron was permitted to exist were all regarded as circles. It is known, however, that a dynamically stable system is entirely possible if the electron executes an elliptical orbit. On classical theory an ellipse of any eccentricity is possible. Sommerfeld[12] extended the Bohr theory to include elliptical orbits, but only those of certain eccentricities. An electron executing an elliptical orbit has, in addition to its angular momentum, a component of momentum along the radius vector drawn from the nucleus to the instantaneous position of the electron. The selection of permitted ellipses was made by postulating that this radial component of momentum must also be quantized. Any permitted elliptical orbit was therefore defined by two independent integers, an azimuthal and a radial quantum number. Through introduction of the radial quantum number the ellipses permitted were reduced to a few. These few all have the same major axis but different, though well defined, eccentricities. Details regarding these permitted elliptical orbits can be found in numerous more specialized works.[13,14,15] It turned out that only one orbit was permissible for an electron in the $K$ level; this was a circle. Two orbits were permissible for an electron in the $L$ level, a circle and an ellipse. Three orbits were permitted an electron in the $M$ level, a circle and two ellipses.

If no account is taken of the variation of the mass of the electron with velocity, the energies of electrons in the various orbits of any one main level turn out to be exactly equal. But an electron executing an elliptical orbit has a variable velocity; it moves faster when in that part of the ellipse near the nucleus, which is at one of the foci, than when in a part of the orbit farther from the nucleus. Furthermore, the mass of an electron changes with velocity. Sommerfeld took into account this variation in mass. When this is done it turns out that electrons in the various orbits of any one main level have slightly different energies. The energy depends upon the eccentricity of the orbit. It should be emphasized that these differences in energy are small. Theoretically then, each of the main Bohr energy levels within an atom is composed of several closely spaced sublevels.

When an electron jumps from the third to the second main level the atom emits the Balmer line $H_\alpha$; but, as Sommerfeld pointed out, the frequency of this line should depend slightly upon the sublevel from which the

[12] A. Sommerfeld, *Ann. d. Physik*, **51**, 1 (1916).

[13] H. E. White, *Introduction to Atomic Spectra* (New York: McGraw-Hill, 1934).

[14] F. K. Richtmyer, *Introduction to Modern Physics* (New York: McGraw-Hill, 1928).

[15] A. Sommerfeld, *Atomic Structure and Spectral Lines* (3rd ed. rev.; London: Methuen & Co., 1934), Vol. I.

electron comes and the sublevel to which it goes, in the third and the second main levels respectively. That is, the line $H_\alpha$ should be a multiplet consisting of several very closely spaced lines. One would think that this multiplet might consist of 6 components. There were introduced early, however, rather arbitrary selection rules which forbid a number of these. These selection rules place certain restrictions upon the amounts by which the azimuthal and radial quantum numbers can change during an electron transition. Applying these selection rules, one concludes theoretically that $H_\alpha$ should be a multiplet consisting of three lines, two of these very close together. The characteristic spacing of lines, that between a certain pair of the 6 mathematically possible, was calculated to be 0.365 per cm. This represents the difference between the wave numbers of the two lines. Although $H_\alpha$ is indicated in Table I as a doublet, this is merely because it is impossible to separate distinctly the more closely spaced lines; a third component is unquestionably present, and there are probably more. Futhermore, the experimentally observed separation[16–19] is almost exactly that calculated. For example, one recent experiment[18] gave an average characteristic spacing of 0.338. It does appear that the observed separation may be slightly less than that calculated. The Sommerfeld theory of fine structure was equally successful in interpreting the structure of other hydrogen lines and of the lines of ionized He.

The Bohr-Sommerfeld picture was extended far beyond what one would infer from our brief discussion. An additional quantum number was introduced, making a total of three, which had the effect of limiting the angular orientations of orbits with respect to any characteristic direction associated with the atom. This introduced a still more complex sublevel structure of the main energy levels. Although we are about to remark on several shortcomings of the Bohr-Sommerfeld orbital picture of the atom, this picture has been of inestimable value in developing and correlating knowledge of atomic processes. Without it physicists would never have arrived at the even more satisfactory, though more complex, interpretation in favor today. Actually, the Bohr-Sommerfeld theory was rigorously applicable only to a hydrogen-like atom, an atom with but one planetary electron. Even one added electron introduced a three body problem, a problem not yet subject to rigorous mathematical analysis. Through use of analogy and empirical relationships it was possible to extend it in a general way to heavier atoms. But there appeared certain difficulties. For example, although the fine structure interpretation appeared to work admirably for hydrogen and

[16] G. M. Shrum, *Proc. Roy. Soc.*, A, **105**, 259 (1924).
[17] W. V. Houston, *Astrophys. Jour.*, **64**, 81 (1926).
[18] F. H. Spedding, C. D. Shane and N. S. Grace, *Phys. Rev.*, **47**, 38 (1935).
[19] W. V. Houston, *Phys. Rev.*, **51**, 446 (1937).

ionized helium, it did not work satisfactorily for the heavier elements. More recent work has shown that it did not completely describe the multiplicity of lines for even a hydrogen-like atom. Nevertheless, the Bohr-Sommerfeld picture has been one of the most valuable concepts. Certain important aspects of the concept have remained, and will no doubt continue to remain, intact. The Bohr-Sommerfeld theory put upon a firm foundation the concept of discrete enegry levels within an atom and the emission and absorption of radiant energy in photons, quanta of energy $h\nu$. No one has since questioned seriously either the existence of discrete energy levels or the photon characteristic of emission and absorption. And physicists have stuck fast to Bohr's original idea that the frequency of the emitted radiation is determined by the energy change accompanying the transition of an electron from one state to another. More recent developments have only served to define in a less arbitrary manner the discrete energy levels.

**More Recent Theories of the Atom**

The purpose of this section has been primarily to present evidence for the photon character of radiation. The Bohr-Sommerfeld picture of emission and absorption has been introduced mainly as a means to this end. It is not our purpose to go into the intricate details of spectroscopy, or into modern concepts of the atom. But there have been important developments since the Bohr-Sommerfeld theory, and the existence of these should at least be recognized. One of the first of these was the introduction of the spinning electron.[20] It was conceived that, due to spin, the electron possessed a magnetic moment. This moment, including its direction, would help to determine the energy of the electron in a given level. Sublevels were therefore introduced by this spin. It was in terms of this spinning electron that Goudsmit and Uhlenbeck[20] first succeeded in explaining some of the fine structure details that appeared anomalous on the Bohr-Sommerfeld theory. The concept of the spinning electron has proved valuable also in interpreting other atomic properties, magnetism for example.

Other developments have proposed treatments entirely foreign to the Bohr-Sommerfeld picture, and these have led to even more satisfactory results from an analytical point of view. They have not led, however, to a physical atom model comparable with that of Bohr in simplicity or clarity. These modifications were started when de Broglie[21] proposed that particles, such as electrons, possessed many of the properties of waves. He concluded theoretically that a particle of mass $m$ moving with a velocity $v$ would behave as a wave having a wave length $\lambda = h/mv$. It has since been demon-

[20] S. Goudsmit and G. E. Uhlenbeck, *Physica*, **5,** 266 (1925); *Nature*, **117,** 264 (1926).
[21] L. de Broglie, *Phil. Mag.*, **47,** 446 (1924); *Comptes Rendus*, **180,** 498 (1925).

strated experimentally that electrons do, under suitable conditions, exhibit wave properties. They can be diffracted, just as can light, and in accord with the de Broglie equation. Fundamental experimental evidence bearing upon this behavior will be discussed in a later chapter. As a result of such evidence, the de Broglie equation has become one of the most fundamental in modern theories.

Several newer forms of quantum theory followed. The most important of these was that initiated by Schrödinger[22] and now known as wave mechanics. Starting with the de Broglie equation for the wave length associated with the electron, and making use of the fact that all waves satisfy a certain differential equation known as the wave equation, Schrödinger deduced a very general differential equation that must be satisfied by an electron in an atom. This is called the Schrödinger wave equation. It involves, among other things, the total energy $W$ of the electron in the atom. Modern theory consists, therefore, of solving [13,23] this differential equation subject to certain conditions characteristic of a particular atom. The equation has a number of solutions. These solutions yield a number of possible values for the energy $W$. These represent the permitted energy states of the electron. Just as on the Bohr theory, emission or absorption of radiant energy is supposed to accompany the transition of the electron to a lower or to a higher energy state.

On wave mechanics the electron is not regarded as a localized particle. Rather, it is a distribution of charge extending over a wide region. The distribution of charge density in the space surrounding the nucleus can be obtained from the Schrödinger wave equation. There are various possible positions of the maximum in this distribution curve, positions corresponding to the various possible energy states. Whereas the discrete energy states were defined by the artificial introduction of three quantum numbers in the Bohr-Sommerfeld theory, they are here defined by three integers which appear quite naturally in the solution of the wave equation. The orbits of the Bohr-Sommerfield picture are not retained as such in the wave theory. It is interesting, however, that there is a definite correspondence between the radii of the Bohr-Sommerfeld orbits and the distances at which the electron distribution function has its maxima. The newer theory leads to a group of discrete energy levels just as did the earlier quantum theory. But the newer theory does not associate these energy levels with electron orbits. Although the newer wave mechanics theory has displaced the Bohr-Sommerfeld theory for purposes of rigorous treatment, it is still found exceedingly convenient and fairly reliable to think generally in terms of the orbital atom model.

[22] E. Schrödinger, *Ann. d. Physik*, **79**, 361, 489, 734 (1926); *Phys. Rev.*, **28**, 1049 (1926).
[23] M. Born, *Atomic Physics* (New York: G. E. Stechert & Co., 1936).

## 2. IONIZATION AND RESONANCE POTENTIALS

### General Information

Direct experimental evidence for the existence of discrete energy levels, as postulated by Bohr, is obtained from studies of the ionization and resonance potentials of gases. On the Bohr concept an atom emits radiant energy when one of its electrons drops from some outer energy level into one closer to the nucleus. Since the potential energy of an electron is smaller when it is in a level near the nucleus, it is natural that the electron should normally exist in the lowest available level. Before an atom can emit radiant energy it is therefore necessary to displace this electron from its normal state to some outer energy level. This process is said to excite the atom. This excitation can be accomplished in a number of ways, one of the simplest of which is by heating the gas to a high temperature. The collisions of atoms executing their thermal motions are usually such that no change in kinetic energy results from collision; the collisions are perfectly elastic. Such collisions can never result in the excitation of an atom. It is possible that a few atoms having thermal energies much higher than the average may occasionally collide inelastically, that one atom may spend a part of its kinetic energy in raising the electron of another atom to a higher energy level. The electron of this second atom may be taken entirely away from the nucleus; the atom may be ionized. Or the electron may just be raised to a higher energy level, still remaining a part of the excited atom. In either case the atom would emit radiation when its electron returns to its normal level.

It is conceivable also that electrons passing through a gas might lose energy to the atoms in two ways. A collision between an electron and an atom might result merely in a change in the division of kinetic energy between the two. The electron might give some of its kinetic energy to the atom; occasionally it might gain a little from the atom. Such collisions are referred to as elastic. There is no change in the potential energy of the atom. It is equally conceivable that other collisions might result in a net loss of kinetic energy. The colliding electron might detach an electron from the atom it strikes, thus ionizing it. This requires energy, and this energy must come from the original kinetic energy of the electron. Such a collision is called an inelastic collision. Some kinetic energy has been transformed into potential energy. Inelastic collisions can occur without complete ionization of the atom. The energy of an electron is increased somewhat without detaching this electron from the nucleus; that is, the electron is raised to a higher energy level within the atom. The energy necessary to accomplish this must again come at the expense of the kinetic energy of the colliding electron.

In order to look into the process of inelastic collisions, consider a tube similar to that shown in Fig. 4. Let this tube be filled with some gas, say He, at rather low pressure. Electrons are emitted from the heated filament $F$. Electrode $G$, which will be called the grid, consists of a wire mesh; it can be held at any desired potential $V$ above that of the filament. A plate $P$ is held at a potential slightly negative, perhaps 0.5 volts, with respect to the grid. Let the spacing of electrodes and the gas pressure be such that there occur a negligible number of collisions between electrons and He atoms in the region between the filament and the grid. Because of the relative spacing of electrodes, a great majority of collisions will occur between $G$ and $P$. Starting with the grid at the same potential as the filament, let the potential difference $V$ between the two be increased gradually, observing all the while the current to the plate. Electrons leaving the filament are accelerated,

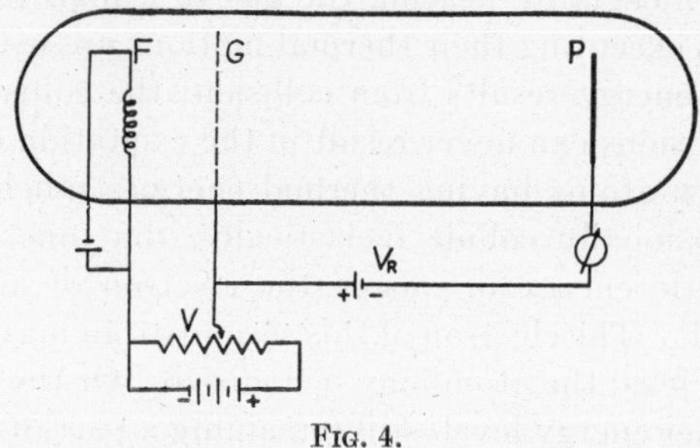


FIG. 4.

arriving at $G$ with an energy given by $\frac{1}{2}mv^2 = Ve$. Although some of these strike the wires of the grid, many of them pass through the openings and proceed toward the plate. Since there is but a very small electric field between $G$ and $P$, these continue with a nearly constant velocity $v$. If they do not lose any appreciable amount of energy in collisions with He atoms, they finally reach the plate and are registered by a sensitive current-measuring instrument. Nothing unsuspected happens as $V$ is increased from zero up to 19.75 volts. The current to $P$ continues to increase all the while. Electrons coming through the grid are able to proceed to the plate. In fact they are able, because of the energy $Ve$ given them, to drive themselves to the plate even though the retarding potential $V_R$ be increased to a value nearly equal to $V$. The electrons, in their collisions with atoms, have apparently lost an inappreciable part of their energy. As the accelerating potential $V$ is increased slightly above 19.75 volts, however, the plate current decreases. This decrease occurs even if the retarding potential $V_R$ be only a few tenths of a volt, say 0.5. Those electrons that fail to reach the plate must therefore have lost practically all of their energy in a collision. Thus an electron with less than 19.75 electron volts of energy cannot give up any of this to a He atom in an inelastic collision. If the electron has just 19.75 volts energy and makes an inelastic collision with a He atom, it gives up its entire energy. Furthermore, it is found that an electron with more than this required amount of energy gives up just 19.75 volts and retains the rest itself. The energy represented by this potential is called a critical potential.

Helium atoms also absorb other definite amounts of energy, 20.55, 21.2, 22.9, 23.6, etc., and 24.5 electron volts. But they will absorb no intermediate values. In a similar way mercury atoms will absorb 4.68, 4.9, 5.47, 5.76, 6.73, etc., and 10.38 volts, while they absorb no intermediate values. And so it is with all other atoms. They all absorb energy inelastically only in definite amounts. These amounts are interpreted as those required to move an electron from one Bohr orbit to another, from the normal energy level to some higher energy level. Such values are called critical potentials. The largest of the group is the ionization potential; it is the energy necessary to extract the electron completely from the atom. The smaller values are called resonance, or excitation, potentials; they are the energies necessary to shift the electron outward one or more orbits from its normal level. There are of course many resonance potentials for a given atom. There is but one ionization potential, unless one considers multiple ionization.

The emission of a spectral line has been interpreted as due to an electron jumping from one energy level into some lower level; the frequency of emission has been assumed proportional to the energy change between the initial and the final level. Data substantiating this interpretation have already been presented. Following the same concept, a resonance potential should represent the energy required to move an electron from one energy level to some outer level. If this is true there should exist a simple relationship between the frequency of a given spectral line and a resonance potential observed for the same gas. If $W_i$ and $W_f$ represent the energy of the electron in an outer and an inner level respectively, then in emission $h\nu = W_i - W_f$. If $V$ represents the measured resonance potential corresponding to a transfer from level $W_f$ to level $W_i$, then $Ve = W_i - W_f$. Hence, one would expect to find that $h\nu = Ve$. From this equation one should be able to calculate resonance potentials from the frequencies of observed lines. These calculated potentials might then be compared with those observed directly by electrical methods. This comparison would serve as a good check upon the fundamental concept.

## Methods of Measuring Critical Potentials

Shortly after 1900 Lenard[24] suggested a method of measuring certain critical potentials of a gas. It was only after Bohr had given his picture

[24] P. Lenard, *Ann. d. Physik*, **8**, 149 (1902).

of the atom, however, that any real progress was made. Since then a great many experimental methods have been developed. Summaries of both the earlier[25] and the more recent[26,27] methods are available in the literature. A typical early method which allows measurement of both resonance and ionization potentials, and allows one to distinguish between these, is that used by Davis and Goucher.[28] This method, as slightly modified later,[25] utilizes a tube with five electrodes, a hot filament $F$, three wire gauze grids $G_1$, $G_2$, and $G_3$, and a plate $P$. The essential arrangement of electrodes is illustrated in Fig. 5. The potential $V_A$ accelerates electrons emitted from the filament; this potential is variable. Between $G_1$ and $G_2$ is a very small retarding potential $V_a$, perhaps 0.1 volt. This is to cause positive ions which might be formed in this region to drift toward $G_2$. Since $V_a$ is very small, electrons coming through $G_1$ proceed toward $G_2$ with a constant velocity until they make an inelastic collision. They can never reach $G_3$, however, for $V_R$ is made sufficiently large to prevent this.

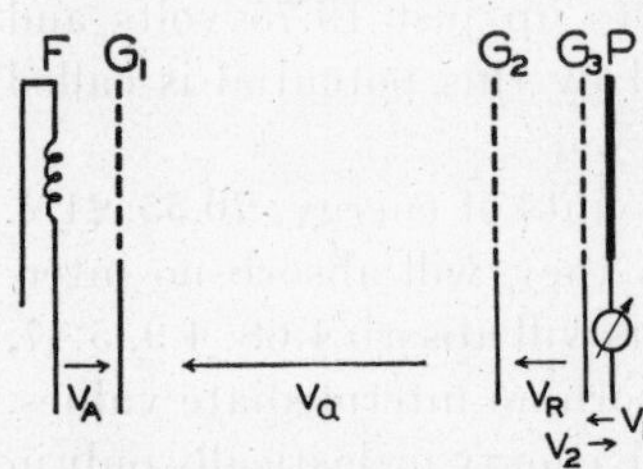


FIG. 5.—Illustrating the electrode arrangement in the modified Davis and Goucher method of measuring critical potentials. The direction of the arrow associated with each potential indicates the direction an electron is urged in this region.

When an electron makes a collision between $G_1$ and $G_2$ the collision may result in excitation or ionization of the atom, depending upon the magnitude of the accelerating potential $V_A$. If it results only in excitation there are no ions formed. The excited atom will soon radiate energy, however, as its electron falls back to its normal energy level. This radiation will fall upon various parts of the tube, in particular upon $G_3$ and $P$. Now we shall soon see that many metals eject electrons, called photoelectrons, when radiation falls upon them. Plate $P$ and grid $G_3$ are made of a material photoelectrically active at the frequencies of radiation encountered here. A small reversible potential of approximately two volts is applied between $G_3$ and $P$. If this is applied in such a direction as to urge electrons from $P$ to $G_3$, as indicated by $V_1$ in Fig. 5, then those photoelectrons ejected by $P$ will go over to $G_3$. Since electrons leave the plate this plate will acquire a positive charge. If the potential between $P$ and $G_3$ be applied in such a direction as to urge electrons toward $P$, as indicated by $V_2$, then the plate will acquire a negative charge due to the radiation. Those photoelectrons emitted from

[25] K. T. Compton and F. L. Mohler, *Bull. Nat. Res. Coun.*, **9**, 1–60 (1924).

[26] H. D. Smyth, *Rev. Mod. Phys.*, **3**, 347 (1931).

[27] M. N. Saha and N. K. Saha, *A Treatise on Modern Physics* (Allahabad and Calcutta: The Indian Press, 1934), Vol. I, pp. 611–619.

[28] B. Davis and F. S. Goucher, *Phys. Rev.*, **10**, 101 (1917).

$P$ are stopped by the potential $V_2$ and return to $P$. Electrons emitted by $G_3$ are urged to the plate $P$. Hence, the plate acquires a negative charge. Thus the plate current change corresponding to a resonance potential may be either positive or negative depending upon whether potential $V_1$ or $V_2$ is used. If, however, an electron produces ionization between $G_1$ and $G_2$, the behavior is quite different. Although the newly formed negative ion can never reach the plate, because of the retarding potential $V_R$, the positive ion will be urged toward the plate. Since $V_R$ is larger than $V_1$ or $V_2$, this positive ion will reach the plate regardless of whether $V_1$ or $V_2$ be applied. Thus ionization is accompanied by a positive increase in plate current regardless of the direction of the potential applied between $G_3$ and $P$. Fig. 6 reproduces[25] results obtained for mercury vapor. These results show quite clearly two resonance potentials, one at 4.9 and another at 6.7. They show an ionization potential at 10.4 volts.

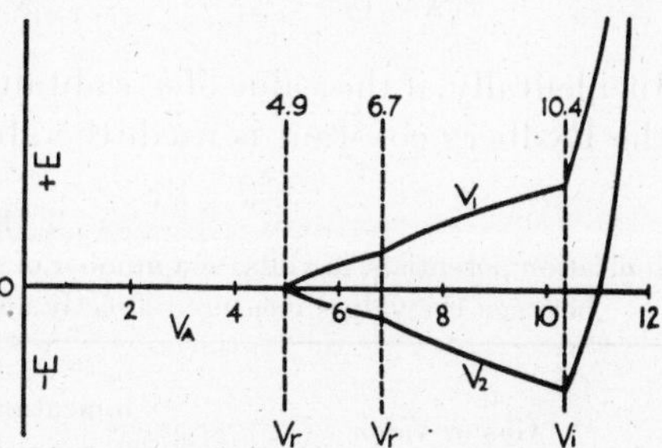

FIG. 6.—Indicating certain critical potentials of mercury vapor, as obtained by the Davis and Goucher method.

## Experimental Results

Using a variety of methods similar to that discussed, various workers have determined directly the ionization potentials of many gases and vapors.[25,26,29] Values obtained for a number of the more common gases and vapors are shown in the second column of Table II. It is interesting that He has the largest ionization potential known. Another interesting observation is the gradual decrease in ionization potential among the inert gases He, Ne, A, Kr, and Xe, as one proceeds to gases of higher atomic number.

In order to test the physical concept of the connection between an ionization potential and the frequency of the shortest wave length radiation the normal atom is capable of radiating, a comparison of observed and calculated ionization potentials is advisable. It has already been argued that the critical potential $V$ required to excite a line of frequency $\nu$ should be given by the expression

$$Ve = h\nu \qquad \text{or} \qquad V = \frac{h}{e}\,\nu$$

It has already been remarked that the values of the constant $h/e$ obtained by

[29] *International Critical Tables* (New York: McGraw-Hill, 1929), Vol. VI, p. 70.

different methods are not entirely consistent. If we use what appears to be a precise value of $h/e = (1.3762 \pm 0.0003) \times 10^{-17}$ obtained from certain X-ray studies,[30] and if we agree to express λ in A° and $V$ in volts, we find

$$V = \frac{h}{e}\frac{c}{\lambda} = \frac{1.3762 \times 10^{-17} \times 2.99776 \times 10^{10} \times 299.776}{\lambda \times 10^{-8}} = \frac{12367}{\lambda}$$

Incidentally, if the value of $h/e$ obtained from experimental determination of the Rydberg constant is used, the above numerical constant is replaced[4] by

TABLE II

Ionization potentials, in volts, of a number of common gases and vapors. Note the agreement between the values measured directly and those calculated from spectroscopic data

| Gas or vapor | Ionization potential determined electrically | Ionization potential calculated from spectroscopic data |
|---|---|---|
| H | 13.54 | 13.56 |
| $H_2$ | 15.9 | ..... |
| O | 13.5 | 13.58 |
| $O_2$ | 13. | ..... |
| N | 14.5 | 14.49 |
| $N_2$ | 16.3 | ..... |
| He | 24.5 | 24.52 |
| Ne | 21.5 | 21.54 |
| A | 15.7 | 15.72 |
| Kr | 13.3 | 13.97 |
| Xe | 11.5 | 12.11 |
| Li | ..... | 5.37 |
| Na | 5.13 | 5.12 |
| K | 4.1 | 4.33 |
| Rb | 4.1 | 4.17 |
| Cs | 3.9 | 3.89 |
| Mg | 7.75 | 7.63 |
| Ca | 6.01 | 6.10 |
| Zn | 9.3 | 9.36 |
| Cd | 8.92 | 8.96 |
| Hg | 10.38 | 10.41 |

12395. Differences of this magnitude are of no consequence for our present purpose, for electrical determinations of ionization potentials are not precise. If the highest frequency emitted by a normal atom is used in the above

[30] J. DuMond and V. Bollman, *Phys. Rev.*, **51**, 400 (1937).

expression for the critical potential $V$, the resulting potential will represent the theoretical ionization potential for the atom. The third column of Table II lists a few of the calculated ionization potentials. The agreement between the values observed directly by electrical methods and those calculated from spectroscopic data is excellent. Saha[31] has given an extensive table of ionization potentials calculated in this way.

TABLE III

Comparison of directly observed resonance potentials with those calculated from the wave lengths of spectral lines. Resonance potentials are given in volts and wave lengths in A°. Those potentials marked (I) are ionization potentials

| Gas or vapor | Resonance potential determined electrically | Wave length of associated line | Resonance potential calculated from frequency of this spectral line |
|---|---|---|---|
| H | 10.15 | 1215.7 | 10.17 |
| | 12.05 | 1026.0 | 12.05 |
| | 12.70 | 972.7 | 12.71 |
| | 13.00 | 949.7 | 13.02 |
| | 13.17 | 937.8 | 13.19 |
| | 13.27 | 930.8 | 13.29 |
| | ..... | ..... | .... |
| | 13.54 (I) | 911.8 | 13.56 (I) |
| Hg | 4.68 | 2656 | 4.66 |
| | 4.9 | 2537 | 4.87 |
| | 5.47 | 2271 | 5.45 |
| | 5.76 | 2150 | 5.75 |
| | 6.73 | 1849 | 6.69 |
| | 7.73 | 1604 | 7.71 |
| | 8.64 | 1436 | 8.61 |
| | 9.79 | 1269 | 9.75 |
| | .... | .... | .... |
| | 10.38 (I) | 1188 | 10.41 (I) |

Although no resonance potentials are listed in Table II, some have been measured electrically for many materials. As a further check upon the connection between resonance potentials and spectral emission, one might compare a series of electrically determined resonance potentials of some gas with the theoretical resonance potentials calculated from the frequencies of the spectral series lines emitted by this gas. Direct measurement of the critical potentials of atomic hydrogen present the difficulty of having first to

[31] M. N. Saha and N. K. Saha, *A Treatise on Modern Physics* (Allahabad and Calcutta: The Indian Press, 1934), Vol. I, p. 674.

dissociate the normal hydrogen molecule. These measurements have been made,[32] however, by carrying on the experiment in a very high temperature furnace. A sufficiently high temperature, 2800° K, was maintained that the molecular hydrogen was largely dissociated due to thermal energies. It was therefore possible to obtain directly the resonance potentials of atomic hydrogen. These are shown in the second column of Table III.

Now one would expect that the smallest amount of energy that could be absorbed by the hydrogen atom would be that required to move an electron from its normal energy level characterized by the Bohr quantum number $n = 1$, out to the next energy level for which $n = 2$. After this energy is absorbed the atom should emit the longest wave length of the Lyman series, a line having an observed wave length of 1215.7 A°. The next resonance potential should correspond to the next line of the Lyman series, the one emitted when an electron jumps from the $n = 3$ level to the $n = 1$ level. Other resonance potentials should correspond to other lines of this series. Finally, the ionizing potential, representing the work required to move an electron from the $n = 1$ level to the $n = \infty$ level, should correspond to the short wave limit of the Lyman series. In fact it is observed that the emission of each of these lines does set in at the corresponding resonance potential. The wave lengths of the six longest Lyman series lines, together with that of the series limit, are shown in the third column of Table III. If one calculates the lowest resonance potential of atomic hydrogen, that corresponding to the longest line of the Lyman series, he obtains

$$V = \frac{12367}{\lambda} = \frac{12367}{1215.7} = 10.17 \text{ volts}$$

Similar calculations for other lines of the Lyman series lead to the resonance potentials listed in the last column of Table III. The agreement between measured and calculated values is remarkable. Table III shows also a similar comparison of observed and calculated resonance potentials for mercury vapor. An abundance of data of this character speaks strongly in favor of the Bohr concept of emission and absorption of energy, and of the photon as a unit of radiant energy.

## 3. THE PHOTOELECTRIC EFFECT

### Metals Illuminated with Visible or Ultraviolet Light

*Early History.*—In 1864 Maxwell predicted that energy would be radiated from an electric circuit in which an oscillatory current was maintained. In 1887 Hertz succeeded in detecting this radiation. It is this radiation that is used in present day radio transmission. In order to detect this new radia-

[32] P. S. Olmstead and K. T. Compton, *Phys. Rev.*, **22**, 559 (1923).

tion Hertz used an electric circuit in series with which there was a spark gap. With proper adjustment of the circuit a spark was found to jump across this gap. This spark represented reception of energy from the transmitter which was located across the room. It was observed by Hertz[33] that this spark gap could be made to break down with a larger separation of electrodes if the light from the spark at the transmitter were allowed to fall upon the electrodes of the receiving gap. Although the reason for this was not understood at the time, it was no doubt due to the photoelectric effect of the ultraviolet light from the transmitter spark falling upon the metal electrodes of the receiving gap.

Hertz's discovery was the forerunner of a long series of investigations,[34,35] many of the earlier of which were subject to errors introduced by various experimental difficulties not then realized. Certain fundamental findings were established in spite of these difficulties. Hallwachs[36] immediately showed that when ultraviolet light is allowed to fall on a zinc plate connected to a negatively charged electroscope, as indicated in Fig. 7, the electroscope discharges rapidly. Electrons are emitted from the surface of the zinc and repelled by the negative charge on this plate; the negative charge on the plate is thus reduced. An uncharged plate gradually acquires a small positive charge when illuminated by ultraviolet light; electrons are ejected until the plate becomes sufficiently positive to cause subsequently ejected electrons to return immediately to the plate. The positive potential assumed by such a plate is not large; it is of the order of a few volts. A positively charged electroscope is not discharged[37] by the action of the light, for although electrons may be ejected by the light they all return immediately because of the attraction of the positive plate. It was shown[38,39] quite early

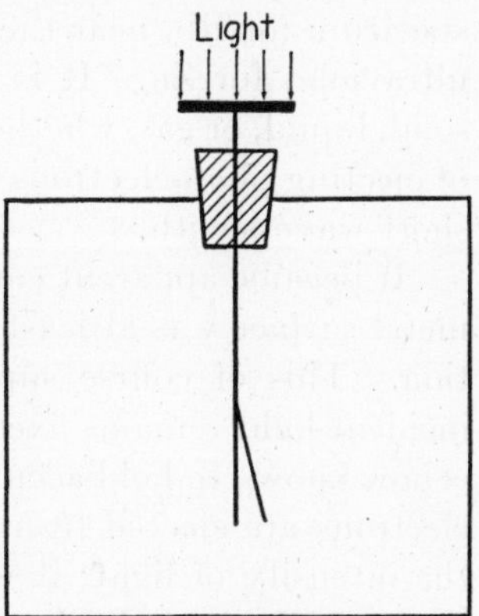


FIG. 7.—Illustrating the discharge of a negatively charged zinc plate by shining ultraviolet light upon it.

[33] H. Hertz, *Wied. Ann.*, **31**, 983 (1887).

[34] J. J. Thomson and G. P. Thomson, *Conduction of Electricity Through Gases* (3rd ed.; London: Cambridge University Press, 1928), Vol. I, pp. 435–482.

[35] A. L. Hughes and L. A. DuBridge, *Photoelectric Phenomena* (New York: McGraw-Hill, 1932).

[36] W. Hallwachs, *Wied. Ann.*, **33**, 301 (1888).

[37] J. Elster and H. Geitel, *Wied. Ann.*, **38**, 40, 497 (1889); **41**, 161 (1890); **42**, 564 (1891); **43**, 225 (1892); **52**, 433 (1894); **55**, 684 (1895).

[38] P. Lenard, *Wien. Ber.*, **108**, 1649 (1899); *Ann. d. Physik*, **2**, 359 (1900); **8**, 149 (1902)

[39] J. J. Thomson, *Phil. Mag.*, **48**, 547 (1899).

that the negatively charged particles ejected by the ultraviolet light are identical with the cathode rays in a discharge tube; they are electrons. It soon became apparent that many metals possess this photoelectric property, and that light over a wide range of wave lengths is capable of ejecting the photoelectrons. It was soon possible to arrange a number of metals in the order of decreasing activity to ultraviolet light. These ran[37] Rb, K, Na, Li, Mg, Th, and Zn. This order of metals is the same as that in the Volta series for contact potentials. The most electro-positive metals are the most active photoelectrically to ultraviolet light.

Photoelectrons are ejected from a given metal only if the wave length of the light is shorter than a certain critical value. The maximum wave length capable of ejecting photoelectrons, known as the long wave length limit, is characteristic of the material. It is well toward the red of the visible spectrum for Rb, near the middle of the visible for Na, and in the invisible ultraviolet for Zn. It is now known that all materials, whether they be solid, liquid, or gas, whether they be conductor or nonconductor, are capable of ejecting photoelectrons if they are illuminated by radiation of sufficiently short wave length.

It became apparent early that the photoelectric current given off from a metal surface was at least closely proportional to the intensity of illumination. This of course supposes that the wave length distribution of the incident light remains fixed as the intensity is varied. This proportionality is now known to hold accurately. The maximum energy with which photoelectrons are ejected from a given metal surface is entirely independent of the intensity of light; it was found[38] to depend, however, upon the source from which the light came. Observers soon began to illuminate surfaces with monochromatic light[40] of various wave lengths in an effort to find just how the energy of the emitted electrons depends upon the wave length. It was found that the energy of the fastest electron ejected from a given surface depends entirely upon the wave length of the incident light. The shorter this wave length the greater is the maximum energy.

All electrons emitted are not ejected with the same velocity. By placing nearby a metal gauze at a potential slightly lower than that of the surface, it is possible to determine the velocities with which the electrons are ejected. An electron ejected with a particular velocity is able to drive itself against a definite potential difference before being brought to rest. One therefore measures the number of photoelectrons that arrive at the gauze against various retarding potentials. The energy of the speediest electron is given directly by the greatest retarding potential through which any electron is able to drive itself. The manner in which the number of electrons arriving

[40] E. Ladenburg, *Phys. Zeits.*, **9**, 504 (1907).

at the gauze increases as the retarding potential is made smaller, allows one to determine the distribution of electron velocities of ejection. It is found that electrons are ejected over a continuous range of velocities varying from zero up to a definite maximum. A majority are ejected with velocities much much less than this maximum, the greatest number coming off with a velocity something like 0.4 of the maximum. It is the maximum velocity of ejection that is determined entirely, for a given metal, by the wave length of the exciting light.

The literature contains much early data indicating that the photoelectric properties of a given material depend upon the length of time the surface has been illuminated. Surfaces were therefore said to show a fatigue effect. Both the magnitude of the photoelectric current and the long wave length limit of the material appeared to change with the length of time the surface was illuminated. This behavior is now recognized as being due to varying degrees of contamination of the surface with adsorbed or chemically active gases. Illumination produced photo-chemical changes of the surface, and thereby changed the surface being studied. An oxidized Na surface has properties quite different from a freshly cut surface; a carefully out-gassed surface is photoelectrically quite different from one which has not been out-gassed. When surfaces which have been carefully cleaned and out-gassed are studied in high vacuum there appears no evidence whatever for a fatigue effect.

During the past fifteen years the photoelectric cell has found wide and important applications[41] in research, in industry, and in connection with many more or less common contrivances. In its simplest form such a cell consists only of a photoelectrically active surface and a second nonactive electrode placed within a glass envelope. In many cases the cell is thoroughly exhausted. It is then quite stable, not at all critical in operation; it has a sensitivity independent of the potential placed across it, provided this potential is not too low. Many other cells contain certain gases. The advantage of the gas filled cell is its much greater sensitivity. For a given illumination the gas filled cell will furnish a current from five to ten times that obtainable from one of the high vacuum type. This increase in current comes through ionization by collision of the gas filling the cell; the photoelectric current itself is no larger than in the vacuum type. Since the extent of ionization by collision depends upon the potential applied to the cell, the sensitivity changes markedly with the applied potential. For this reason the gas filled cell is much more critical in operation than is the vacuum type. Cells of both types are used extensively. They provide a means of changing variations in light intensity into variations in electric

[41] A. L. Hughes and L. A. DuBridge, *Photoelectric Phenomena* (New York: McGraw-Hill, 1932), pp. 466–493.

current. These electric currents can then be amplified and made to perform various tasks.

*Einstein's Interpretation of the Effect.*—It was not until 1905 that any worthwhile interpretation of the photoelectric effect was offered. The wave theory of radiation offered no logical explanation. On this theory it would seem that the energy with which the electron is ejected should certainly depend upon the intensity of illumination. The electric field associated with an intense light beam is much greater than that of a low intensity beam, and this stronger field should eject the electron with a greater velocity. But it does not do so; the velocity of ejection is independent of the intensity of light. Shortly after Planck had established rather firmly his quantum theory of black body radiation, Einstein[42] offered an entirely new theory of the photoelectric effect. For satisfactory interpretation of black body radiation, Planck had found it necessary to assume that radiant energy is not emitted and absorbed continuously by matter, but that emission and absorption of energy occurs always in energy quanta of definite size. For radiation of frequency $\nu$ the energy of each quantum was given by the product $h\nu$, where $h$ is a constant, approximately $6.6 \times 10^{-27}$ erg-sec. Applying this concept to the photoelectric effect Einstein suggested that when light of frequency $\nu$ strikes a metal surface, the radiant energy is absorbed in energy quanta of size $h\nu$. If this energy is transferred to an electron within the metal, as Einstein assumed, then the absorbing electron will acquire an energy equal to $h\nu$. It appeared probable that the electron would have to expend some of this energy in getting out through the surface of the metal. The amount of energy necessary might well be more for an electron coming from a considerable depth beneath the surface than for one coming from the outermost layer of atoms constituting the surface. If $w$ represents the minimum amount of energy necessary to free an electron from the surface, then the maximum kinetic energy that the ejected electrons could have, should be

$$\tfrac{1}{2}mv^2_{\text{max}} = h\nu - w$$

This is known as the Einstein photoelectric equation.

When it is recalled that there had so far been established very little evidence that interchanges of energy between radiant energy and matter always take place discontinuously, in energy quanta of size $h\nu$, and when it is recalled that the quantitative photoelectric data available at the time of Einstein's suggestion were both meager and unreliable, it appears bold indeed that Einstein should have offered such an interpretation. But the real advances in science have come from those who have the courage to

[42] A. Einstein, *Ann. d. Physik*, **17**, 132 (1905); **20**, 199 (1906).

think originally. Since Einstein's suggestion many data[34,35,43–53] have shown the correctness of his interpretation. His equation has been verified for the photoelectric emission from numerous metals illuminated with light over a wide range of frequencies. It has also been found to hold for photoelectrons ejected from either gases or metals by the action of either X-rays or gamma rays.

*Millikan's Verification of the Einstein Equation.*—Einstein's photoelectric equation makes several quantitative predictions. First, the equation predicts that the maximum energy of emission is determined entirely by the frequency of the exciting light; it is independent of the intensity of excitation. Second, the equation predicts a definite value for the maximum energy of ejection. Third, it predicts that the curve relating the kinetic energy of the most speedy electrons ejected to the frequency of the exciting light is a straight line. Fourth, it predicts the existence of a long wave length limit; no photoelectrons will be ejected unless the frequency of exciting light is sufficiently great that $h\nu$ is equal to or greater than $w$. These as well as a number of other conclusions which follow from the Einstein concept are subject to experimental test. The first entirely trustworthy experiment designed to test the Einstein equation was one performed by Millikan.[48] The results of this careful study were of great significance.

Millikan's elaborate experimental arrangement permitted the removal in high vacuum of all surface films from the surface to be studied, the measurement of retarding potentials and corresponding photoelectric currents due to these film free surfaces, and the almost simultaneous measurement of the contact potential difference between the test surface and the metal of which the electron receiver was made. Fig. 8 reproduces the essentials of the experimental apparatus. Blocks of three different test materials, Na, Li, and K, were mounted in such a way that any one of the surfaces could be turned toward the scraper $K$, toward the quartz window $Q$, or toward the plate $S$. After the entire system was thoroughly evacuated the material to be studied was first cleaned. The armature $M$ was rotated magnetically until the scraper $K$ was pressed firmly against the surface to be cleaned.

[43] A. L. Hughes, *Phil. Trans. Roy. Soc.*, **212**, 205 (1912).
[44] K. T. Compton, *Phil. Mag.*, **23**, 579 (1912).
[45] O. W. Richardson and K. T. Compton, *Phil. Mag.*, **24**, 575 (1912).
[46] W. H. Kadesch, *Phys. Rev.*, **3**, 367 (1914).
[47] W. H. Kadesch and A. E. Hennings, *Phys. Rev.*, **8**, 221 (1916).
[48] R. A. Millikan, *Phys. Rev.*, **7**, 18, 355 (1916).
[49] P. E. Sabine, *Phys. Rev.*, **9**, 210 (1917).
[50] R. A. Millikan, *Phys. Rev.*, **18**, 236 (1921).
[51] P. Lukirsky and S. Prilezaev, *Zeits. f. Physik*, **49**, 236 (1928).
[52] A. R. Olpin, *Phys. Rev.*, **36**, 251 (1930).
[53] G. N. Glasoe, *Phys. Rev.*, **38**, 1490 (1931).

This pressure was developed by means of the threaded section shown attached to $M$. The scraper was then rotated by means of the armature

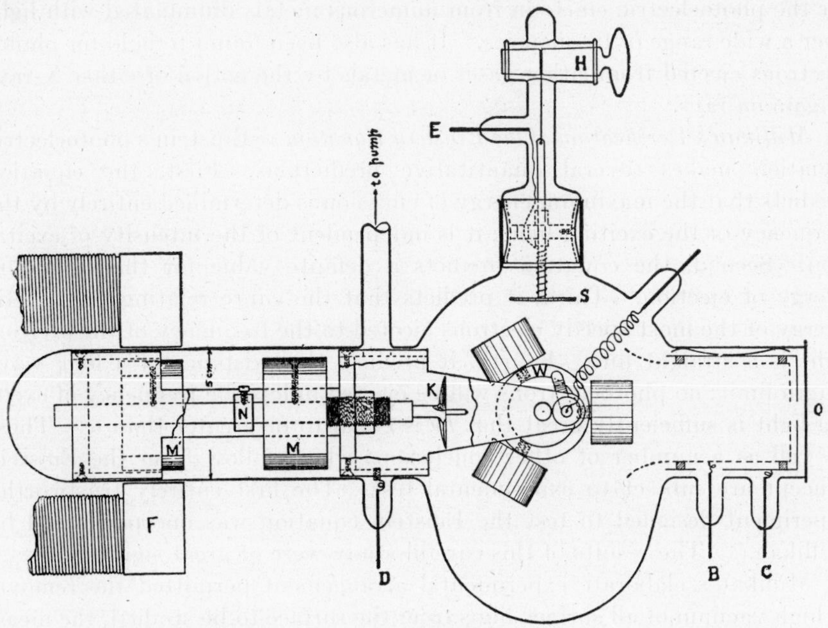


Fig. 8.—Millikan's apparatus for the study of the photoelectric effect.

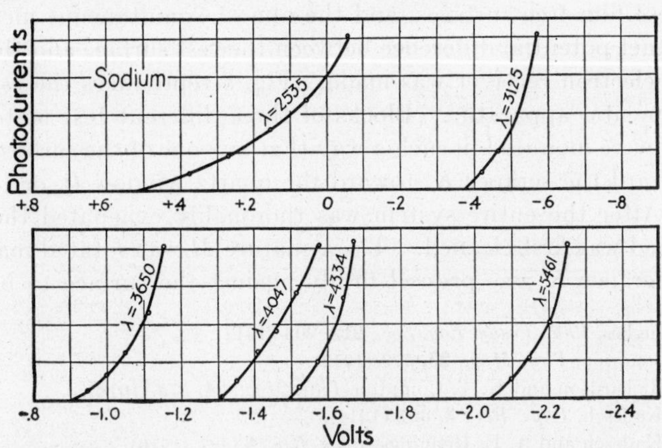


Fig. 9.—Showing the photocurrents observed for various retarding potentials. All curves are for a Na surface. Any one curve represents results obtained for monochromatic illumination of the indicated wave length.

$M'$. Thus a fresh surface was prepared in high vacuum. The test surface was then faced toward the monochromatic light coming through the quartz window $Q$. Various retarding potentials were applied between the surface being studied and the gauze connected to $B$. The photoelectric current to the gauze was measured for each of these potentials. Such measurements were made for a number of different wave lengths of monochromatic light. The results for any one wave length were then plotted as shown in Fig. 9. The intercept of any one curve on the potential axis, when corrected for the contact potential between the test surface and the electron receiver, gives the retarding potential against which the most speedy electrons ejected by light of this wave length can drive themselves. The measurement of contact potential was made by a standard method, after rotating the test surface until it was close to an auxiliary platinum plate $S$. The electron receiver was carefully constructed of a material which was not photoelectrically active at the wave lengths used.

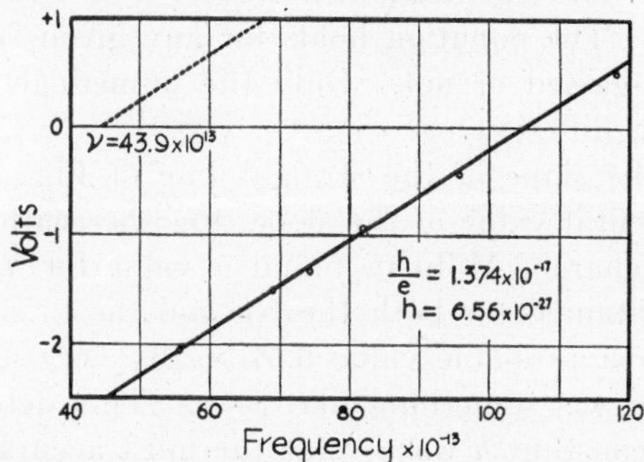


FIG. 10.—Experimental test of the Einstein equation, using a Na surface.

If $V$ represents the retarding potential just necessary to stop the most speedy electron ejected by illumination of frequency $\nu$, then according to the Einstein equation

$$Ve = h\nu - w$$

Observed values of $V$ were plotted against the corresponding frequencies $\nu$. On theory the resulting curve should be a straight line with slope $h/e$ and intercept $-w/e$. The six values of $V$ obtained for Na from the intercepts in Fig. 9 are shown plotted against the corresponding frequencies in Fig. 10. The resulting curve is quite accurately a straight line. Although the values plotted in this figure have not yet been corrected for contact potential, this fact does not affect either the shape or the slope of the curve. It does alter the position of the intercept on the frequency axis. When each observation is corrected for the contact potential, the entire curve is shifted into a new position indicated by the dashed line near the top of Fig. 10. Similar results were obtained for the Li surface. Accident prevented obtaining data on K.

The observations on Na and Li, however, bear out the Einstein equation quite accurately as regards the manner in which the maximum energy of ejection varies with the frequency of the illumination.

The intercept of the experimental curve on the frequency axis gives the theoretical low frequency, or long wave length, limit for the metal being studied. In the case of Na for example, Fig. 10 indicates that this critical frequency should be $4.39 \times 10^{14}$. This corresponds to a wave length of 6830 A°. By using various wave lengths just below and just above this value, Millikan found that this did truly represent the long wave length limit of the material. Any shorter wave length excited photoelectrons; no longer wave length caused ejection of these photoelectrons. It is true that the long wave length limit observed by Millikan is appreciably greater than that now accepted for a carefully cleaned and thoroughly out-gassed Na surface. This fact does not detract, however, from Millikan's test of the Einstein equation. The equation holds for any given surface, whether it be thoroughly out-gassed or not. Only the numerical value of the long wave length limit is different.

Theoretically the slope of the straight line of Fig. 10 should be $h/e$. Using the experimental value of the slope, together with the known value for the electronic charge, Millikan found a value for $h$. Essentially the same value was obtained for both the Na and the Li surfaces. Millikan reported as the most probable value $6.57 \times 10^{-27}$ erg-sec. The probable error in this value was something like ½%. This determination of the value of Planck's constant $h$ was by far the most accurate then available. Thus Millikan's experimental test of the Einstein photoelectric equation not only proved the correctness of the equation, but it also provided a much more accurate value for one of the important fundamental constants of nature.

Using the experimental value of $h$ along with the experimental value of the low frequency limit, it was possible to express the work function $w$ of the metal in usual energy units. If $\nu_0$ represents the low frequency limit, then $h\nu_0 = w$. The value of $w$ obtained by Millikan for a freshly cleaned but not out-gassed Na surface was $2.88 \times 10^{-12}$ ergs. This is equivalent to 1.80 electron volts. That is, the minimum energy necessary for an electron to get out of a clean surface of metallic Na is that which an electron would acquire in dropping freely through a potential difference of 1.8 volts. It is now known that the work function for a thoroughly out-gassed Na surface is somewhat larger than this, perhaps slightly over 2 volts. It is of course clear that the long wave length limit of a material is larger if that material has a small work function. It is probable that changes in photoelectric behavior produced by surface impurities are brought about largely through changes in this work function.

More recent studies,[51,52] perhaps more precise than Millikan's, have only served to emphasize the correctness of the Einstein equation. These studies have likewise provided accurate values of the constant $h$. Whereas Millikan obtained the value $6.57 \times 10^{-27}$, supposedly good to ½%, more recently reported values are $6.543 \times 10^{-27}$ and $6.541 \times 10^{-27}$. The accuracy claimed for the two last values is from 0.1 to 0.2%. There are a number of methods of determining the constant $h$ other than that involving the photoelectric effect. Attention will be called to one of the more accurate of these in a later chapter on X-rays. After a critical examination of the values of $h$ obtained by all methods up to 1929, Birge[54] concluded that the most probable value was $(6.547 \pm 0.009) \times 10^{-27}$ erg-sec. It will be noticed that this is essentially the value obtained from studies of the photoelectric effect.

Attention should be called to the fact that determination of the constant $h$ from photoelectric data really comes through a direct evaluation of the ratio $h/e$ from experimental data. The constant $h$ is then obtained by combining this ratio with the known value of $e$. Since the above values of $h$ were calculated the accepted value of the electronic charge has been raised by some ⅔ of 1%. Using the same ratio $h/e$ then, this higher value of $e$ leads to a higher value for $h$. This change alone raises the Birge 1929 most probable value to $6.592 \times 10^{-27}$. In addition there has arisen considerable question[4,10,11] as to just what the best value of $h/e$ may be. Several apparently precise methods of determining it yield results which differ by approximately 0.2%. Although this discrepancy is not large, it is much greater than the probable errors of the determinations indicate that it should be. As a result, the present value of the constant $h$ is somewhat in doubt. One recently quoted value[11] is $6.610 \times 10^{-27}$ erg-sec; another[4] is $(6.6236 \pm 0.0024) \times 10^{-27}$.

*Other Interesting Aspects of the Effect.*—It has been shown[48,50] that the Einstein photoelectric equation allows one to express the contact potential between two metals in terms of the work functions of these metals. The work function for a given metal expressed in electron volts is of course given by $h\nu_0/e$. The work function can therefore be determined by observing the long wave length limit of the material. It has been found,[50,53] in full accord with the Einstein equation, that the measured contact potential difference between two metals is the difference in their photoelectric work functions. Using extremely pure electrolytic Fe and Ni, for example, Glasoe[53] found work functions of $(4.71 \pm 0.02)$ and $(4.93 \pm 0.02)$ electron volts, respectively. A simultaneous measurement of the contact potential difference between the two metals yielded $(0.21 \pm 0.01)$ volt. This is

[54] R. T. Birge, *Rev. Mod. Phys.*, **1**, 1 (1929).

quite accurately the difference between the two work functions expressed in electron volts.

It has long been known that metals emit electrons when heated to sufficiently high temperatures. Richardson[55] has shown theoretically that the electron current from unit area of a heated metal should be given by an expression of the form

$$i = AT^2\epsilon^{-\frac{b}{kT}}$$

where $k$ is the Boltzmann gas constant and $A$ and $b$ are constants characteristic of the metal. The quantity $b$ is called the thermionic work function. This constant represents the energy required to carry a free electron from within the metal to a point well outside the surface. Actually, Richardson deduced an expression for the thermionic current on two different assumptions. If one supposes that the number of free electrons in a metal is independent of temperature, and if one also assumes that these share equally with the atoms in the energy of thermal agitation, then one can calculate the number of electrons which have energies sufficient to do the work necessary to get them through the surface of the metal. The resulting expression for the thermionic current is not quite that written above; the temperature factor occurs as $T^{1/2}$ instead of $T^2$. If, however, one supposes that the number of free electrons is a function of temperature, as one can argue thermodynamically it should be, then one obtains the equation written above. Since the exponential term varies far more rapidly with temperature than does $T^{1/2}$ or $T^2$, it is impossible to judge from experimental data which power of $T$ is proper. Newer theories of the behavior of electrons in metals lead physicists to favor[56–58] strongly the form involving $T^2$.

The general form of this equation, known as Richardson's equation, has been found to be in agreement with experimental data.[57,58] From observation of the thermionic currents given off by a metal when heated to various temperatures, the value of $b$ can be determined. This is of the order of a few electron volts for the common metals. The question naturally arises as to whether this thermionic work function is the same as the photoelectric work function for the same surface. Unfortunately the magnitude of each work function varies greatly with even slight contamination of the surface. Probably mainly for this reason, results reported for each constant by various early observers varied widely. Even today a trustworthy answer

[55] O. W. Richardson, *Emission of Electricity from Hot Bodies* (2nd ed.; London: Longmans, Green & Co., 1921), pp. 29–37.

[56] K. K. Darrow, *Rev. Mod. Phys.*, **1**, 90 (1929).

[57] S. Dushman, *Rev. Mod. Phys.*, **2**, 381 (1930).

[58] J. A. Becker, *Rev. Mod. Phys.*, **7**, 95 (1935).

to the question can be obtained only from studies in which both work functions have been determined nearly simultaneously for the same carefully out-gassed surface. The most trustworthy data are available for Pt. The first reliable value for the thermionic work function of platinum was obtained by DuBridge.[59] After carefully cleaning and out-gassing the platinum specimen, DuBridge found a thermionic work function (6.27 ± 0.05) volts and a photoelectric work function of 6.30 volts. This is excellent agreement, indicating that the two work functions are idential. Hughes and DuBridge[60] and Becker[58] have summarized in tabular form the photoelectric and thermionic properties of a goodly number of materials which have been rather carefully studied. In many cases the agreement between the photoelectric and the thermionic work functions is by no means as good as that indicated by the values quoted above for platinum. When one considers only those materials which have been carefully out-gassed, and for which the same observer has made measurements of the two work functions on what there is reason to believe is exactly the same surface, the agreement is striking. Table IV shows values[58,60] which have been determined under these conditions. There can be little doubt of the equality of these two work functions when they are determined for exactly the same surface.

TABLE IV

A comparison of the photoelectric and the thermionic work functions obtained simultaneously for a given surface

| Metal | Photoelectric work function | Thermionic work function |
|---|---|---|
| Pd | 4.96 | 4.99 |
| Pt | 6.30 | 6.27 |
| Rh | 4.57 | 4.58 |
| Mo | 4.15 | 4.14–4.17 |

Temperature changes normally encountered have no significant effect upon the photoelectric behavior of a metal. It is true that early studies did indicate rather large variations of both photoelectric current and long wave length limit with changes of temperature. Subsequent investigations have shown, however, that most of these observations were affected greatly by gases absorbed on the surface. By far the greatest part of the apparent temperature effect was due to a change in the nature of the surface; the amount of absorbed gas depends greatly upon the temperature. It has been found that surfaces carefully out-gassed show no measurable variation

[59] L. A. DuBridge, *Phys. Rev.*, **29**, 451 (1927); **31**, 236 (1928); **32**, 961 (1928).

[60] A. L. Hughes and L. A. DuBridge, *Photoelectric Phenomena* (New York: McGraw-Hill, 1932), pp. 75–78.

in either photoelectric current or long wave length limit over a considerable range of temperature near that of their normal surroundings. A significant variation has been found, however, at high temperatures. Some studies have been carried up to 1250° C. At high temperatures, even after the most careful out-gassing, Pt,[59] Co,[61] and Rh,[62] show a definite increase in photoelectric current with increases in temperature. While workers have frequently found a decrease in photoelectric sensitivity with increase in temperature, it is generally suspected that these results have been brought about by failure to free the surface from gases. It has also been found that the long wave length limit of carefully out-gassed Pt,[59] Au,[63] Ag,[64] and Ta[65] shifts slightly toward the red with increases in temperature. This shift is something of the order of 100 A° for a temperature change of 500 C°. As a result of this shift in the long wave length limit with temperature, which represents a decrease in work function, enormous increases in photoelectric current with increases in temperature are observed when the wave length of the illumination is but slightly shorter than the long wave length limit of the metal. Theoretical consideration[66] of these temperature effects indicates that they are brought about through changes in the thermal energies of electrons within the metal. The recent observation[67] that the thermionic work function for *W* shows a small increase of 0.00006 electron volts per C° rise in temperature may be important in this connection. The photoelectric and the thermionic work functions cannot be identical if the former decreases and the latter increases with increases in temperature.

Although it is known that the presence of adsorbed gas on a surface often affects greatly the photoelectric behavior of the surface, it is impossible to formulate any very general rules regarding such behavior. A survey[60] of the observed effects of various gases on various metals shows that some gases increase photoelectric emission, other gases decrease it, and still others have no effect. The photoelectric behavior is known to depend upon the gas truly absorbed by the metal rather than upon the gas surrounding it. As a result the problem is difficult, and many inconsistent results have been reported.

Another interesting study connected with the photoelectric effect has to do with the possible existence of a time lag between the instant the surface is first illuminated and the instant it starts emitting photoelectrons.

[61] A. B. Cardwell, *Proc. Nat. Acad. Sci.*, **15**, 544 (1929).
[62] E. H. Dixon, *Phys. Rev.*, **37**, 60 (1931).
[63] L. W. Morris, *Phys. Rev.*, **37**, 1263 (1931).
[64] R. P. Winch, *Phys. Rev.*, **37**, 1269 (1931).
[65] A. B. Cardwell, *Phys. Rev.*, **38**, 2041 (1931).
[66] R. H. Fowler, *Phys. Rev.*, **38**, 45 (1931).
[67] A. L. Reimann, *Proc. Roy. Soc.*, A, **163**, 499 (1937); *Science Suppl.*, **90**, 14 (1939).

Information regarding this has been obtained by illuminating a surface intermittently for very short intervals of time. One study[68] showed that there was no lag as great as $10^{-7}$ sec. A more recent study[69] has shown that the photoelectric current starts within $3 \times 10^{-9}$ sec. after the surface is illuminated, and that it ceases within $10^{-8}$ sec. after the illumination is cut off. No lag whatever has been found. These times represent merely upper limits established by the method and apparatus. The absence of any measurable lapse of time between the instant of illumination and the start of the photoelectric current is entirely consistent with the quantum theory interpretation of the photoelectric effect; it is not in accord with the classical theory in which the electron must gradually accumulate energy from the wave front until it has a sufficient amount to enable it to pass through the surface. Even with the lowest intensity of illumination for which it is possible to measure the photoelectric current, this current starts immediately. On quantum theory this means that a certain few of the electrons immediately absorb a large amount of energy, an amount $h\nu$. If one supposes, according to classical theory, that the electron must gradually accumulate this energy from the wave, then it is logical to expect a measurable lag in the start of the photoelectric current. If one assumes that an electron can absorb energy only from that part of the wave front which strikes a single atom, then for very low intensity it would take years for the electron to absorb sufficient energy to be ejected. It has been shown[70] theoretically that an absorber the size of the electron will absorb energy from an area of the wave front of the order of $\lambda^2$. Even with absorption of this area of the wave front there would still be a lag of several hours for very low intensity blue light. But experimentally there is no lag. It is necessary, therefore, either to accept the quantum concept that a few electrons absorb an energy $h\nu$ and others absorb none, or to assume that the individual electrons can absorb energy from parts of the wave front many centimeters distant from the absorbing electron. The evidence is strongly in favor of the quantum concept.

### Materials Illuminated with X-rays or γ-rays

*Solids.*—X-rays and γ-rays are also capable of ejecting photoelectrons from materials, either solids or gases. The process is identical with that already discussed for ultraviolet light. The Einstein equation holds just as certainly for the case of X-rays and γ-rays as it does for light. There is just one essential difference, one brought in by the fact that the energy quantum for an X-ray frequency is much larger than that corresponding to a

[68] E. Marx and K. Lichtenecker, *Ann. d. Physik,* **41,** 124 (1913).
[69] E. O. Lawrence and J. W. Beams, *Phys. Rev.,* **32,** 478 (1928).
[70] Lord Rayleigh, *Phil. Mag.,* **32,** 188 (1916).

light frequency. Whereas the energy of a quantum is about 1.8 electron volts for red light, 3.1 for blue light, and 90 for the shortest ultraviolet radiation, it is of the order of 125,000 electron volts for X-rays of average wave length, say 0.1 A°. This is more than sufficient to overcome the surface work function for any material. In fact it is sufficient to eject electrons from deeper levels of any of the atoms. Whereas light can eject electrons only if they are practically free from atoms, X-rays and $\gamma$-rays can eject electrons from the $M$, $L$, and $K$ levels of the atom as well. As a result, the work function $w$ takes on a number of values for the same material. The largest of these represents the work to extract a $K$ electron from the atom; the smallest is that required to get a free electron out through the surface. When monochromatic X-rays or $\gamma$-rays are allowed to fall upon a thin film of metal, electrons having a number of well defined energies are ejected. Since many of these electrons have very high velocities, the kinetic energy can no longer be written $\frac{1}{2}mv^2$. It is necessary to use the expression which takes account of the fact that the mass increases with velocity; that is, one must write

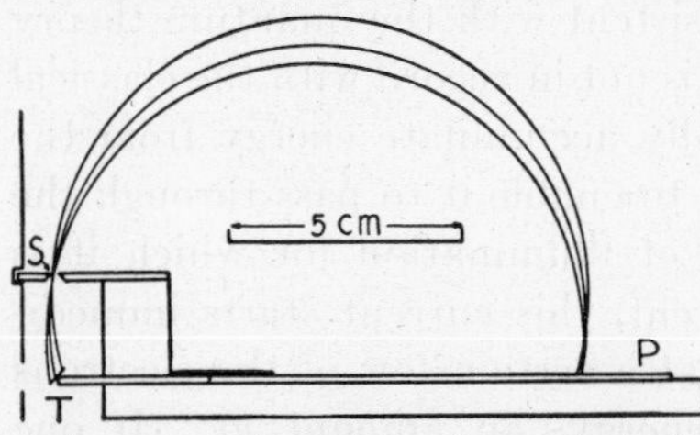

FIG. 11.—Illustrating the method of determining the velocities of high speed photoelectrons. Photoelectrons emitted from the surface $T$ are bent in a circular path, by a magnetic field perpendicular to the plane of the paper, and strike the photographic film $P$.

$$\text{K.E.} = m_0c^2\left[\frac{1}{\sqrt{1-\beta^2}} - 1\right]$$

Using this in the Einstein equation,

$$m_0c^2\left[\frac{1}{\sqrt{1-\beta^2}} - 1\right] = h\nu - w$$

where $w$ may take on any one of a number of definite values characteristic of an atom. The numerical values of $w$ are known accurately for a majority of atoms from studies of X-ray spectra. The experimentally determined velocities of photoelectrons ejected by a known frequency are just those one calculates from the Einstein equation when one uses first one and then another of these values of $w$. There exists a low frequency limit, or long wave length limit, corresponding to each discrete energy level within the atom. A certain frequency may be able to eject an $L$ but not a $K$ electron from a given material.

The fact that the Einstein equation holds accurately for photoelectric ejection by X-rays and $\gamma$-rays has proved a valuable aid in determining the wave lengths of $\gamma$-rays. One allows the $\gamma$-ray to fall upon a thin film of some metal for which the various energy levels are known. The velocities of the resulting photoelectrons are then determined, usually by the method[71] illustrated in Fig. 11. Having the velocity of one group of photoelectrons, one could calculate the frequency of the incident $\gamma$-ray if he could be certain from which level in the atom these electrons came. Fortunately, the energy difference between successive levels varies greatly from one material to another. Hence, by observing the photoelectrons ejected from several materials, it is possible to judge with certainty the level from which each group of electrons came. When one succeeds in assigning the origins of the various groups of electrons to the proper levels, the values calculated

TABLE V

**Showing data on photoelectrons ejected from various materials and from various atomic levels by a single $\gamma$-ray having a wave length of 0.0352 A°. All energies, including $h\nu/e$ for the gamma ray, are given in kilovolts. Gamma ray wave lengths are given in A°.**

| Material | Energy of photoelectron | Assumed level | Known work function for this level | Calculated $h\nu/e$ | Calculated wave length |
|---|---|---|---|---|---|
| Ag | ..... | K | ..... | 348 | .0354 |
| Ta | ..... | K | ..... | 344 | .0358 |
| W | 276 | K | 69 | 345 | .0357 |
| Pt | 265 | K | 78 | 343 | .0359 |
| | 269 | K | 78 | 347 | .0355 |
| | 275 | K | 78 | 353 | .0349 |
| | 340 | $L_{III}$ | 12 | 352 | .0350 |
| | 352 | M | 3.0 | 355 | .0347 |
| Au | ..... | K | ..... | 348 | .0354 |
| Pb | 258 | K | 87 | 345 | .0357 |
| | 260 | K | 87 | 347 | .0355 |
| | 260.9 | K | 87.4 | 348.3 | .0354 |
| | 263.8 | K | 87.4 | 351.2 | .0351 |
| | 265 | K | 87 | 352 | .0350 |
| | 332.9 | $L_I$ | 15.8 | 348.7 | .0354 |
| | 337.9 | $L_{III}$ | 13.0 | 350.9 | .0352 |
| | 350.2 | M | 3.2 | 353.4 | .0349 |
| | 353.6 | N | 0.5 | 354.1 | .0348 |
| U | 231 | K | 115 | 346 | .0356 |
| | 238 | K | 115 | 353 | .0349 |

[71] H. Robinson, *Proc. Roy. Soc.*, A, **104**, 455 (1923).

for the frequency of a $\gamma$-ray from data on the various groups must come out the same. When it does, one is quite certain that his assignments are correct. Results[72] of such measurements are shown in Table V. All of the photoelectrons for which data are quoted in the table were ejected by a single $\gamma$-ray having a wave length of 0.0352 A°. That the Einstein equation holds accurately for this process is evident from the agreement of wave lengths for this $\gamma$-ray as calculated from photoelectric data on various materials. Furthermore, wave lengths evaluated in this manner agree with those measured directly by reflection from crystal surfaces. The photoelectric method has been found the more convenient and the more precise for determining wave lengths of the shorter $\gamma$-rays.

*Gases.*—Gases also exhibit a photoelectric effect when illuminated with ultraviolet light, X-rays, or $\gamma$-rays. The general behavior is entirely similar to that discussed above. Whereas ultraviolet light is capable of ejecting only the outermost electrons, X-ray and $\gamma$-ray photons have sufficient energy to eject electrons from the deeper energy levels. If a pulse of X-rays is sent through a Wilson cloud chamber just preceding an expansion of this chamber, the tracks of photoelectrons ejected from the gaseous atoms can be seen. By observing the ranges of these tracks it is possible to evaluate approximately the energy with which the electrons are ejected. When the work $w$ required to eject an electron from the appropriate level of the atom is added to the kinetic energy of the ejected electron, the total energy obtained is equal to $h\nu$ within the limit of error. Thus the Einstein equation is again found to hold.

If one calculates the entire energy that could fall upon any one atom during the short pulse of X-rays, assuming that the X-ray energy spreads out as a wave, it is found that this is often much less than the energy of the photoelectron ejected from the atom. Just as in the case of metals illuminated with ultraviolet light, it is found that the photoelectron has often absorbed far more energy than one would expect, on the wave hypothesis, to come even close to it. Certain of the electrons immediately absorb a large amount of energy, $h\nu$, whereas others absorb none. Thus again it appears that radiant energy is not only emitted and absorbed in quanta of size $h\nu$ but these discrete photons may proceed individually in quite definite directions. Further evidence concerning this will be pointed out shortly. X-rays are absorbed in passing through a gas by means of the ejection of high speed photoelectrons. Each photon of X-rays gives up its entire energy to an electron. This high speed photoelectron in turn gives up its energy by forming ions along its path; the photoelectron gradually comes to rest. It is now clear why a photograph of a Wilson cloud chamber through which an X-ray beam is traveling shows no definite path for the X-ray, but

[72] A. F. Kovarik and L. W. McKeehan, *Bull. Nat. Res. Coun.*, **10**, 120 (1925).

does show tracks of innumerable electrons proceeding in all directions and all originating within the geometrical boundaries of the X-ray beam.

It is interesting to inquire briefly into the direction in which a photoelectron is ejected from an atom. Many experimental studies[73,74] have shown that a majority of these are ejected in a direction nearly perpendicular to the direction of the X-ray beam. For an unpolarized beam the distribution of ejected electrons is symmetrical about the direction of travel of the X-ray. For a plane polarized beam the distribution is no longer symmetrical; a majority of the electrons are ejected in a direction parallel to the electric vector of the wave representing the X-ray. It is interesting that, although the ejection process clearly follows the concepts of the quantum theory, it is necessary to revert to the classical wave theory to formulate any clear-cut concept dealing with the general direction of ejection.

It has been remarked that for an unpolarized X-ray beam a majority of the photoelectrons are ejected in directions nearly perpendicular to that of the X-ray beam. Peculiarly, more are ejected in the forward direction than in the backward direction.[73,74] That is, the direction in which a maximum number of electrons are ejected makes an angle somewhat less than 90° with the forward direction of the X-ray beam. This is indicated by Fig. 12, a reproduction of the electron distribution observed by Anderson.[75] Many experiments of this type show that the average forward component of ejection increases with increasing frequency of the incident X-ray. On the quantum theory one would expect a majority of the electrons to be ejected in a somewhat forward direction. The photon gives up to the electron not only its energy but also its momentum. A photon having an energy $h\nu$ and moving with the velocity of light $c$ would possess a momentum $h\nu/c$ in the direction of motion. Qualitatively at least, the forward component of the direction of ejection appears to be in accord with the idea that the electron must absorb this forward momentum. The increase in the forward component with increasing X-ray frequency is also in qualitative accord with this concept. Quantitative agreement is not obtained, however, on this simple picture of the process. The observed asymmetry in the forward direction is definitely larger than that expected on this concept. Modern wave mechanics treatment of this problem does lead[73,74,76] to a theoretical asymmetry in close agreement with that observed.

[73] A. L. Hughes and L. A. DuBridge, *Photoelectric Phenomena* (New York: McGraw-Hill, 1932), pp. 404–414.

[74] A. H. Compton and S. K. Allison, *X-Rays in Theory and Experiment* (2nd ed.; New York: D. Van Nostrand, 1935), pp. 564–582.

[75] C. D. Anderson, *Phys. Rev.*, **35**, 1139 (1930).

[76] G. Wentzel, *Zeits. f. Physik*, **40**, 574 (1926); **41**, 828 (1927).

In fact the solid line curve of Fig. 12 was not drawn as the best curve representing the observed points; it represents the theoretical distribution of photoelectrons. A similar preponderance of photoelectrons in a forward direction has also been observed for very thin films of metal irradiated with X-rays. In fact it was here that the phenomenon was first discovered. If X-rays are shone on one side of a very thin film, more electrons are ejected from the back surface of the film than from the surface facing the source of X-rays. This again is attributed to the fact that the electron must absorb not only the energy but also the momentum of the incident photon.

There are many other aspects of photoelectric phenomena and many more intricate details of those we have mentioned, that provide valuable information. Our purpose of illustrating the photon character of radiation,

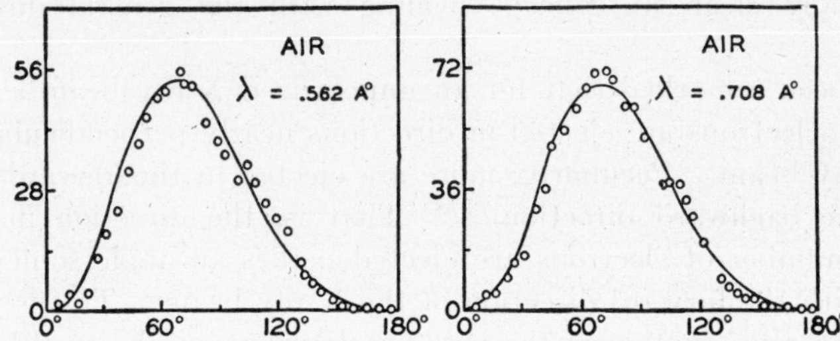


FIG. 12.—Showing that more photoelectrons are ejected in a forward than in a backward direction.

as exemplified in the basic photoelectric process, has been served sufficiently well, however, by this brief discussion of the more fundamental photoelectric phenomena. The photoelectric effect contributed some of the earliest and most convincing evidence for the existence of the photon. The photon character of radiation would certainly have been accepted without this evidence, but its acceptance would no doubt have been delayed for some years.

## 4. THE SCATTERING OF X-RAYS

Some of the more fundamental findings and concepts of X-rays will be discussed briefly in a following chapter. Studies of emission and absorption of X-rays provide further convincing evidence for the photon character of radiant energy, and for the existence of discrete energy levels within the atom. This evidence is so nearly parallel to that which has already been discussed in connection with visible and ultraviolet radiation, however, that its inclusion at this time is unnecessary. There is one phenomenon of X-rays, however, that provides quite another line of evidence regarding the photon character of radiant energy, one which has no clear-cut parallel in light. This has to do with the phenomenon of scattering. The evidence it provides as to the photon character of radiation is so important that it is advisable to discuss this phenomenon here at sufficient length to bring out the fundamental concept involved.

Everyone is familiar with the fact that visible light can be scattered by minute particles of matter such as dust or fog. Although when light of all wave lengths is scattered there often results a change in effective color in certain directions, it is recognized that this is due directly to the fact that blue light is more effectively scattered in all directions than is red light. It is for this reason that the sun appears unusually red at sunset; and for the same reason the sky always appears blue. But it is equally well recognized that if monochromatic light is scattered, there is no change in color. That is, although the light may be scattered in all directions, the color, and hence the wave length, is entirely unchanged by the scattering process.

X-rays are also scattered by matter, largely by the electrons associated with the atoms of the scattering material. In the early days no fundamental difference between this process and that of light scattering was recognized. On classical theory one pictures the X-ray as an electromagnetic wave having associated with it varying electric and magnetic fields. Electrons of the scattering material are supposed to be set into vibration by the varying electric field. These vibrating, and hence accelerated, electrons are then supposed to re-radiate the energy in all directions. This re-radiated energy represents the scattered X-rays. On this concept it is clear that the frequency of the vibrating electron, and hence the frequency of the scattered radiation, should be exactly the same as that of the incident radiation. The wave length of the scattered X-rays should then be exactly the same regardless of the direction in which the X-ray is scattered, and this should be equal to the wave length of the X-ray incident upon the scattering material. It was soon found, however, that this was not actually the case. In general the wave length of X-rays is increased when the rays are scattered, and the increase is definitely measurable. This finding was quite inconsistent with the classical view.

In 1922, A. H. Compton[77] suggested an entirely different interpretation of the scattering process. The quantum theory had by this time secured an unmistakable foothold in the fields of spectroscopy and photoelectricity; the concept of the photon seemed quite necessary. It was therefore natural that attempts should be made to apply the concept to other phenomena. Compton assumed that X-ray energy travels as photons, in quanta of energy $h\nu$. He supposed that the energy is scattered by electrons within the scattering material, electrons some of which behave essentially as if they are free. Referring to Fig. 13, let the incident photon come from the left towards a free electron at point $P$. The energy of this photon is $h\nu$; its

[77] A. H. Compton, *Bull. Nat. Res. Coun.*, **4**, 1–56 (1922); *Phys. Rev.*, **21**, 207, 483 (1923).

momentum[78] is $h\nu/c$, where $c$ is the velocity of light, the velocity with which the photon travels. When this quantum is scattered by the free electron, let the scattered quantum move off in some direction making an angle $\phi$ with the direction of the incident quantum. And let us suppose that the scattering electron recoils from the "collision" with a velocity $\beta c$ in some direction $\theta$. The photon must in general lose energy as it is scattered, for it gives some energy to the electron. Now the only way in which a photon might decrease its energy would be to decrease the frequency associated with it. Let the energy of the scattered photon be $h\nu'$, where the frequency $\nu'$ is in general less than $\nu$. Compton assumed that the laws of conservation of energy and conservation of momentum hold for the interaction between the photon and the scattering electron. From the law of conservation of energy

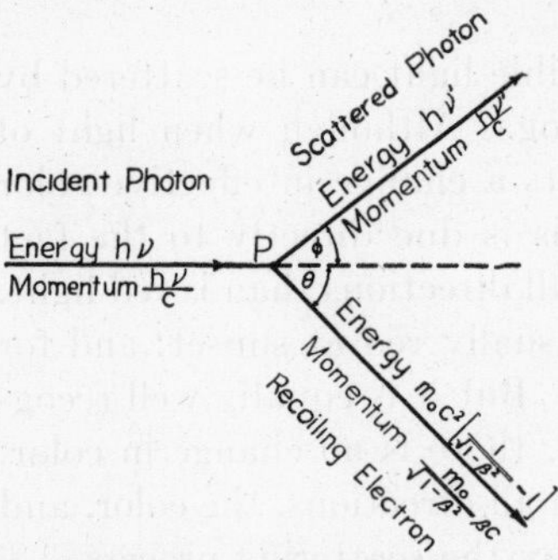


FIG. 13.—Illustrating a supposed "collision" between an X-ray photon and a free electron.

$$h\nu = h\nu' + m_0c^2\left[\frac{1}{\sqrt{1-\beta^2}} - 1\right]$$

From the law of conservation of momentum, considering first the components of momenta along the original direction of the incident photon,

$$\frac{h\nu}{c} = \frac{h\nu'}{c}\cos\phi + \frac{m_0\beta c}{\sqrt{1-\beta^2}}\cos\theta$$

And considering components of momenta perpendicular to this direction

$$0 = \frac{h\nu'}{c}\sin\phi - \frac{m_0\beta c}{\sqrt{1-\beta^2}}\sin\theta$$

We thus have three equations in four unknowns, $\nu'$, $\phi$, $\beta$, and $\theta$. It is possible to eliminate completely any two of these, obtaining a relationship between the remaining two. For example, the equations can be solved for the frequency of the scattered photon, $\nu'$, in terms of the angle $\phi$ at which the energy is scattered. It is clear that the frequency will be decreased upon scattering; the wave length of the scattered radiation will be longer

[78] On the mass-energy equivalence concept a mass $m$ is equivalent to an energy $E = c^2m$. The mass one must assign to the photon can therefore be obtained from $h\nu = mc^2$. The momentum to be assigned the photon is therefore $mc = h\nu/c$.

than that of the incident radiation. By solving the above equations it is found[77,79] that the increase in wave length, $\Delta\lambda$, is given by

$$\Delta\lambda = \frac{2h}{mc} \sin^2 \frac{1}{2} \phi = 0.04853 \sin^2 \frac{1}{2} \phi$$

where recent[4] values of the constants $h$, $m$ and $c$ have been used to evaluate the numerical constant, and where it is agreed that $\Delta\lambda$ is to be expressed in A°.

Compton's theory of the scattering by free electrons thus leads to the remarkable conclusion that the wave length of the scattered radiation should be greater than that of the incident radiation. Furthermore, the increase in wave length should vary from 0 for energy scattered straight forward to 0.04853 A° for that scattered directly backward; and the increase should vary as the square of the sine of one-half the angle of scattering. In addition the theory predicts that the increase in wave length should be independent of the wave length of the incident radiation, and independent of the nature of the scattering material. Many careful experiments[79] bear out these conclusions in all detail. The wave length is increased during the scattering process, and it is increased in accord with the theoretical expression derived by Compton. Only a few years ago what Compton[79] regarded as the best experimental observations[80] showed the increase in wave length to be

$$\Delta\lambda = (0.04848 \pm 0.00008) \sin^2 \tfrac{1}{2}\phi$$

The numerical constant of this experimentally confirmed relationship agrees remarkably well with the theoretical constant 0.04853. The precise value of the theoretical constant depends slightly upon which experimental values of $h/e$ and $e/m$ one accepts. While the value of $e/m$ is known with precision, the value of $h/e$ is open to some question. In calculating the above theoretical constant the value[4] $h/e = (1.3793 \pm 0.0002) \times 10^{-17}$ obtained from the Rydberg constant has been used. If one uses instead the value[30] $h/e = (1.3762 \pm 0.0003) \times 10^{-17}$ obtained directly from X-ray measurements, the theoretical constant of the Compton expression becomes 0.04842. The agreement with the experimental value is still entirely satisfactory. It should be remarked that Ross and Kirkpatrick[81] find a somewhat lower value of this constant, (0.04760 ± 0.00006). In fact they feel that the original Compton expression is not exactly correct, that a small term should be subtracted to take account of the fact that the scattering

[79] A. H. Compton and S. K. Allison, *X-Rays in Theory and Experiment* (2nd ed.; New York: D. Van Nostrand, 1935), pp. 200–237.

[80] N. S. Gingrich, *Phys. Rev.*, **36**, 1050 (1930).

[81] P. A. Ross and P. Kirkpatrick, *Phys. Rev.*, **45**, 223 (1934); **46**, 668 (1934).

electron is not entirely free. This proposed correction term, and hence the change of wave length accompanying scattering, depends upon the wave length being scattered. When this correction term is included in the Compton expression, Ross and Kirkpatrick find for the multiplier $2h/mc$ the value $(0.04836 \pm 0.00008)$.

Even more direct evidence as to the correctness of this concept of scattering has been secured, photographic evidence that quanta do proceed in quite definite directions and do produce recoil electrons when they are scattered. The scattering process has been allowed to take place in a cloud chamber. The path of the recoil electron can be observed visually or photographically. Although a photon does not leave a continuous track,

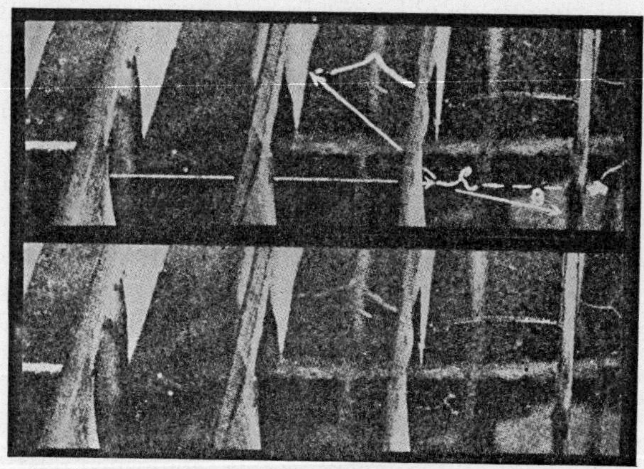

Fig. 14.—Showing the track of a recoil electron and that of a photoelectron ejected by the scattered photon. Lead sheets have been placed in the chamber to increase the chance that the scattered photon will eject a photoelectron within the chamber. The lower figure reproduces the original photograph; the upper figure has been retouched by Compton.

the direction of the scattered quantum can also be determined from such a photograph. After traveling a short distance the photon will often be absorbed by an atom with the resultant emission of a photoelectron. The track of this photoelectron can be observed visually or recorded photographically. The direction taken by the scattered photon is then that of a line drawn through the point at which the recoil electron track starts and the point at which the photoelectron was produced. Such a photograph is reproduced[82] in Fig. 14. There can be no doubt of the existence of the recoil electron; and there is likewise no doubt that the scattered photon proceeds to a definite point where it ejects a photoelectron.

Many other experimental tests of the Compton theory of scattering can be devised, some as regards the relative angles at which the recoil electron

[82] A. H. Compton and A. W. Simon, *Phys. Rev.*, **26**, 289 (1925).

and the scattered photon leave the point of scattering, some as regards the energy of the recoiling electron, and others as regards the simultaneity of the appearance of the recoil electron and the scattered photon. All of these features have been investigated[79] and the results are in full accord with the Compton theory. They leave no doubt as to the correctness of the concept. It is true that this scattering process has been treated by Schrödinger[83,79] on the modern wave theory of the electron. The theoretical results are identical with those obtained by Compton on the particle concept. Certainly the Compton treatment gives a much clearer picture of the process. The important bearing the Compton work had upon modern physical concepts is evidenced by the fact that the Nobel Prize was awarded in recognition of the work. Studies in this field seem to leave no doubt of the photon character of radiant energy.

[83] E. Schrödinger, *Ann. d. Physik*, **82**, 257 (1927).

## Chapter 7

# X-RAYS

It was during the course of a systematic search for a possible radiation capable of traversing matter opaque to ordinary light that Roentgen[1] discovered the X-ray in 1895. Roentgen had been studying the ultraviolet light given off from an electrical discharge passing through a rather highly evacuated tube, and had been using crystals of platinum barium cyanide spread over a paper screen to detect the presence of radiation too short to affect the eye. These crystals fluoresce when illuminated with radiation of sufficiently short wave length. Having covered the discharge tube completely with opaque paper, Roentgen found that the screen continued to fluoresce. The intensity of fluorescence was found to decrease when heavy obstacles were interposed between the discharge tube and the screen, but some radiation was able to penetrate considerable thicknesses of matter. It was evident that this was some new radiation of unknown nature and origin, a radiation excited in some manner in the discharge tube. Roentgen called this "X-rays," a name indicating the then unknown character of the radiation.

Roentgen thought that the X-rays he observed came from the glass walls of his discharge tube, and they no doubt did. It is now known that X-rays are given off from any material when properly excited. The excitation is usually accomplished by bombardment with high speed electrons, although irradiation with other X-rays will likewise cause a material to emit X-rays. Roentgen found immediately that obstacles interposed in the path of this new radiation cast shadows upon the fluorescent screen. The shadow is due to the partial absorption of the radiation by the obstacle. The discoverer of this new radiation foresaw its probable importance to medical science.

Roentgen at once attempted to determine many of the properties of X-rays. He found that the radiation could not be deflected by electric or magnetic fields; hence, it did not consist of charged particles. His attempts to reflect and refract the rays were unsuccessful. Early attempts of other workers to observe diffraction effects were also unconvincing. However, it has since been shown that it is possible to reflect, refract, and

[1] W. C. Roentgen, *Sitzungsber. der Würtzburger Physik-Medic. Gesellsch.*, (1895); reprinted in *Ann. d. Physik*, **64**, 1 (1898); translated by A. Stanton, *Science*, **3**, 227, 726 (1896).

diffract the radiation, that it produces interference phenomena, and that it can be polarized. The radiation not only causes fluorescence, but affects a photographic plate and produces ionization in gases. It can therefore be detected visually, photographically, or electrically. It has already been stated in an earlier section that X-rays eject photoelectrons from metals or gases on which they impinge. The subject of X-rays has now been developed so extensively that we can touch here upon but a few of the more fundamental and interesting properties, leaving to more specialized works[2] the complete development of the subject.

## 1. GENERAL PROPERTIES OF X-RAYS

### Their Production

X-rays are produced whenever high speed electrons are stopped abruptly by allowing them to impinge upon a target of some material. It makes no difference what kind of a target the electrons strike, X-rays are produced. Targets made of materials of high atomic number give much more intense X-rays. The higher the speed of the electron stopped the more penetrating are the X-rays produced. X-ray tubes consist essentially of a source of electrons, some means of giving these electrons high speeds, and a target on which the electrons strike. The X-rays are given out from the point where the electrons strike this target.

There are two general types of X-ray tube, the gas tube and the Coolidge tube. The former consists of a concave metal cold cathode facing a metal target. A small amount of gas, at a pressure of the order of a few tenths of a micron, is purposely left in the tube. A potential difference of the order of 50 to 100 kilovolts is applied across the tube. Just as in the discharge tube at higher pressures, this causes electrons to be freed from the cathode. The shape of the cathode is such that these electrons are focused on a small spot of the target. This gives nearly a point source of X-rays, but it does necessitate that the target be made of some high melting point material such as platinum or molybdenum. Since the penetrating power of the X-rays produced is determined by the potential difference across the tube, and since the potential required to maintain a gaseous discharge is determined largely by the pressure of the residual gas, the only way to change the hardness of the X-rays produced is to change the pressure of the gas in the tube. Most gas tubes are therefore equipped with a small side tube containing means for adjusting the gas pressure. The Coolidge tube utilizes a hot cathode which furnishes electrons. The tube is exhausted as thoroughly as possible. The vacuum must be good, for otherwise the heated filament is damaged by positive ion bombardment. The potential across

[2] A. H. Compton and S. K. Allison, *X-rays in Theory and Experiment* (2nd ed.; New York: D. Van Nostrand, 1935).

the tube can be made anything desired, for it is in no way dependent upon the residual gas pressure. The Coolidge tube therefore possesses the great advantage that the intensity and the hardness of the X-rays can be controlled independently. The intensity is controlled by varying the temperature of the filament, and hence the number of electrons striking the target per unit of time; the hardness is controlled by varying the potential difference across the tube. This independent control is not possible with a gas tube. Both types of tube are used extensively.

### Velocity

Only a few years after Roentgen's discovery of X-rays it was shown[3,4] that this new radiation travels through space at a velocity at least closely that of light. This was done by comparing the velocity with which the X-ray traveled with the velocity of an electric wave along a wire. An X-ray tube and a spark gap were connected, some distance apart, between two long wires. The straight line distance between the gap and the tube, and the length of the wire connecting these, could be varied independently. An electrical potential, a pulse of very short duration, was applied to the X-ray tube. This excited X-rays immediately, and these X-rays traveled through the air to the spark gap. The potential wave, after arriving at the X-ray tube, traveled along the wire to the gap. Now the gap would break down most readily if this potential wave arrived just as the X-rays were producing ionization in the gap. From the relative distances traveled by the potential wave and the X-ray in arriving at the gap simultaneously, it was found that the X-ray travels through air at a speed not far different from the speed of the electric wave on the wire. Since it was already known that an electric wave travels along a small straight wire far removed from the ground and other objects at a speed approaching that of light, it was evident that X-rays also travel with a velocity at least closely that of light. Some years later[5,6] a photoelectric cell was substituted for the spark gap. A maximum photoelectric current indicated that the potential wave and X-ray were arriving at the photoelectric cell simultaneously. Again the X-ray velocity was found to be equal to the velocity of light within the probable error of the rather crude method.

### Diffraction and Interference

*Diffraction by Slits.*—Early studies of diffraction and interference of X-rays were only moderately successful. It is now possible, however, to

[3] B. Brunhes, *Comptes Rendus*, **130**, 127 (1900).

[4] R. Blondlot, *Comptes Rendus*, **134**, 1559 (1902); **135**, 666, 721, 763, 766 (1902).

[5] E. Marx, *Ann. d. Physik*, **20**, 677 (1906); **28**, 37, 163 (1909); **33**, 1305 (1910); **35**, 397 (1911); *Verh. Deutsch. Phys. Gesell.*, **10**, 157, 598 (1908).

[6] J. Franck and R. Pohl, *Verh. Deutsch. Phys. Gesell.*, **10**, 489 (1908); *Ann. d. Physik*, **34**, 936 (1911).

produce these effects in three distinct ways, by narrow slits, by crystals, and by ruled gratings. These diffraction and interference phenomena show that the X-ray is a wave motion in every sense that ordinary light is a wave. Diffraction by narrow slits was first accomplished by Haga and Wind[7] in 1899. Having no real knowledge of the wave length of X-rays, in fact not knowing for certain that X-rays were even of wave character, early workers had little idea as to the width of slit that might show these effects. X-rays were therefore directed through a very narrow V-shaped slit a few thousandths of a millimeter wide at its wider end. In effect this served to try slits of various widths all at the same time. Exposure on a photographic plate placed beyond the slit showed a broadening of the X-ray beam after passing through the narrow parts of a slit. The shadow cast was not one sharply defined by the geometry of the apparatus. This broadening was attributed to diffraction. It was calculated that the observed broadening was such as to indicate a wave length of the order of $10^{-8}$ cm. Some years later Walter and Pohl[8] performed a similar experiment, presumably with several refinements, and reported little if any evidence for diffraction. They concluded that if any diffraction effects were present they were certainly far smaller than those previously reported. These latter data were later recalculated by Sommerfeld,[9] however, using accurate photometric measurements of the blackening of the photographic plates. Sommerfeld regarded the evidence as strongly in favor of diffraction, and calculated that the hard X-rays used to produce the observed diffraction pattern must have had a wave length of $4 \times 10^{-9}$ cm. He also found that the wave length of the softer more easily absorbed X-rays was somewhat greater, probably near the value reported by Haga and Wind.

In more recent years several workers have obtained exceedingly clear-cut photographs of diffraction effects produced by X-rays coming through slits. The improvement has come mainly through use of monochromatic X-rays. In the intervening years it had been shown definitely by other methods that X-rays had a wave length approximately that indicated by early diffraction experiments; and workers had learned how to obtain monochromatic X-rays, radiation of a single wave length. Just as in the case of light, the use of a single wave length leads to a much more striking diffraction pattern. Excellent diffraction photographs have now been obtained from slits using X-rays of several different wave lengths, 1.54 A°[10] and 0.71 A°[11] in particular. These wave lengths represent quite ordinary

[7] H. Haga and C. H. Wind, *Wied. Ann.*, **68**, 884 (1899).

[8] B. Walter and R. Pohl, *Ann. d. Physik*, **29**, 331 (1909).

[9] A. Sommerfeld, *Ann. d. Physik*, **38**, 473 (1912).

[10] B. Walter, *Ann. d. Physik*, **74**, 661 (1924); **75**, 189 (1924).

[11] I. I. Rabinov, *Proc. Nat. Acad. Sci.*, **11**, 222 (1925).

X-rays. Even more striking are the results which have been obtained[12,13] by using rather soft X-rays in vacuum. Fig. 1 reproduces a diffraction photograph taken by Larsson[12] of X-rays of wave length 8.3 A° passing

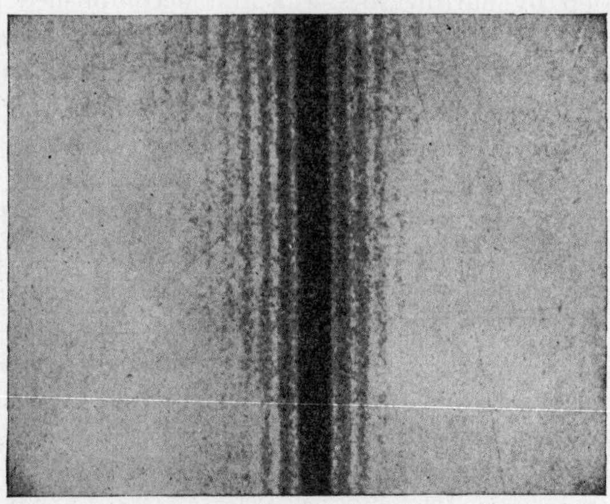

**Fig. 1.—Showing the diffraction of X-rays of 8.3 A° wave length in passing through a slit 0.0055 mm. wide.**

**Fig 2.—Showing the diffraction of X-rays of 8.3 A° wave length as they pass a wire 0.038 mm. in diameter.**

through a slit 0.0055 mm. wide. Fig. 2 reproduces a remarkable photograph by Kellström[13] of the diffraction pattern formed by these same X-rays in passing a piece of wire 0.038 mm. in diameter. These photographs are entirely analogous to those formed under similar circumstances by light;

[12] A. Larsson, *Uppsala Univ. Arsskrift*, No. 1, p. 97 (1929).

[13] G. Kellström, *Nov. Act. Reg. Soc. Sci. Uppsaliensis*, 8, No. 5 (1932).

and they are fully as definite as those obtained with light. The theory developed for the diffraction and interference of light holds equally well for these results obtained with X-rays. There can be no doubt that the behavior is entirely analogous. The only difference is that X-rays, being of much shorter wave length, require much narrower slits to show these effects clearly.

It is interesting that the similarity in behavior of X-rays and light has been illustrated even further by other experiments. Recall that interference fringes of light can be obtained through use of a Fresnel double mirror, the two mirrors being inclined at a very small angle with one another. Kellström[13] has obtained clear cut Fresnel interference fringes in exactly the same way using soft X-rays.

*Diffraction by Crystals.*—Long before any great success had been obtained in studies of the diffraction and interference of X-rays coming through narrow slits, in fact before there existed any conclusive proof of the wave character of X-rays, it occurred to Laue[14] that a crystal might act toward X-rays much as does a ruled grating toward light. Early slit diffraction experiments had indicated that X-rays had a wave length of the order of $10^{-8}$ or $10^{-9}$ cm. Although these early experiments were not accepted as particularly convincing at the time, the results have since been shown to be surprisingly accurate. At any rate, they no doubt played a big part in Laue's remarkable discovery, for Laue recognized that the regular spacing between atoms in a crystal was only a few times the estimated wave length of X-rays. But light passing through a grating having lines ruled a few wave lengths apart produces the well known interference spectra. Laue therefore argued that, since the atom planes in a crystal are separated by a few wave lengths of X-ray, the crystal might produce interference effects when traversed by X-rays.

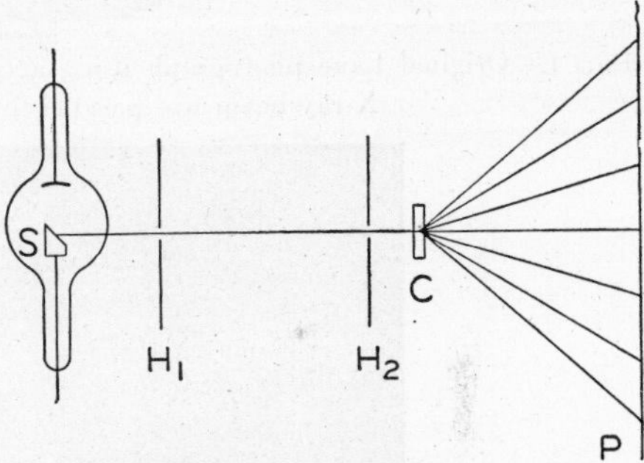

FIG. 3.—Illustrating the essential arrangement of apparatus for obtaining Laue photographs.

The original experiments were carried out by Friedrich, Knipping and Laue,[14] using an arrangement of apparatus illustrated in Fig. 3. A narrow beam of X-rays was collimated by passing through two circular holes $H_1$ and $H_2$. A thin crystal $C$ of zinc blende, zinc sulfide, was placed as shown. After passing through the crystal the X-rays fell on a photographic plate

[14] W. Friedrich, P. Knipping, and M. Laue, *Ber. bayer. Akad. Wiss.*, 303 (1912); *Ann. d. Physik*, **41**, 971 (1913).

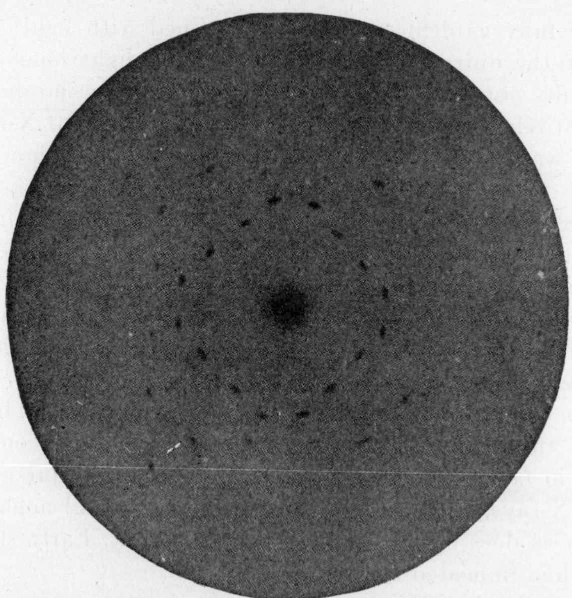

Fig. 4.—Original Laue photograph using a crystal of zinc sulphide. The direction of the X-ray beam was parallel to one of the three cubic axes.

Fig. 5.—A Laue photograph of an iron crystal.

placed perpendicular to the original direction of the X-rays. It was found that, in addition to a strong central spot, the X-rays produced intense and sharply defined spots considerably removed from this center and located symmetrically about it. Fig. 4 reproduces[14] a typical Laue diffraction photograph, one taken with a single crystal of zinc sulphide. Fig. 5 reproduces a similar photograph[15] taken with a single crystal of iron. It should be borne in mind that results such as these are obtained only when the crystal used is a single large crystal. As will be pointed out later, quite different appearing photographs result when a powdered crystalline material is used.

A logical interpretation of these Laue spots was offered immediately by W. L. Bragg.[16] It was shown that each of the spots surrounding the central spot could be interpreted as the reflection of the incident beam of

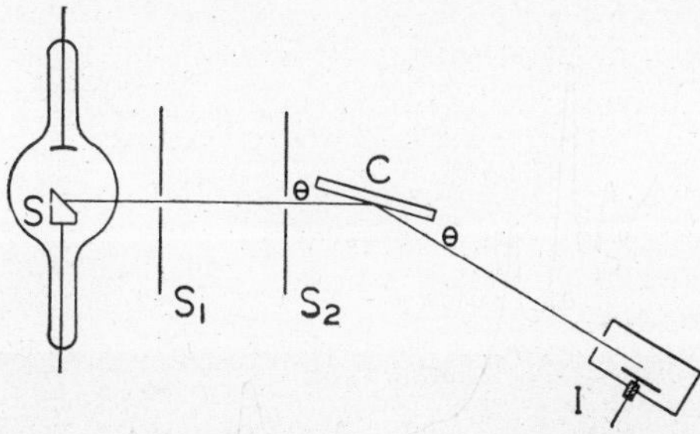


Fig. 6.—Showing the essential arrangement of apparatus in the Bragg method. This arrangement is frequently called a single crystal X-ray spectrometer. The ionization chamber is often replaced by a photographic film.

X-rays from some series of parallel atomic planes within the crystal. Let us imagine the innumerable planes which might be drawn through the regularly spaced atoms making up a crystal, say a crystal having a cubical array of atoms. The number of atoms in any particular plane depends upon the angle this plane makes with the principal planes of the atom array. It turns out that planes drawn at simple angles with the cubic axes of the crystal are relatively rich in atoms. And it is precisely these planes which produce the more intense Laue spots. The greater the number of atoms in a particular plane the more intense is the spot corresponding to reflection from this plane. It is clear, therefore, that considerable information regarding the crystalline structure of a material might be gained from Laue photographs taken in different directions through the crystal.

One would expect the natural cleavage face of a crystal to be one of that series of parallel planes which is richest in atoms. It was therefore natural

[15] G. L. Clark, *Applied X-rays* (2nd ed.; New York: McGraw-Hill, 1932), p. 186.
[16] W. L. Bragg, *Proc. Camb. Phil. Soc.*, **17,** 43 (1912).

that W. H. Bragg and W. L. Bragg,[17] father and son, attempted immediately to observe reflection from the cleavage face of a crystal. A narrow beam of X-rays was allowed to fall at near grazing incidence upon the cleavage face of a crystal. A search was made for a reflected beam by means of an ionization chamber. The essential arrangement of apparatus is shown in Fig. 6. The Braggs found a reflected beam of considerable intensity at a position such that the reflected beam made the same grazing angle with the crystal face as did the incident beam. Then keeping the relative angular positions of the incident beam, the crystal, and the ionization chamber, such as to receive this reflected beam, that is, keeping the two angles $\theta$ of Fig. 6 equal, the distribution of reflected energy with changing angle of incidence was investigated. The results were striking indeed. Fig. 7

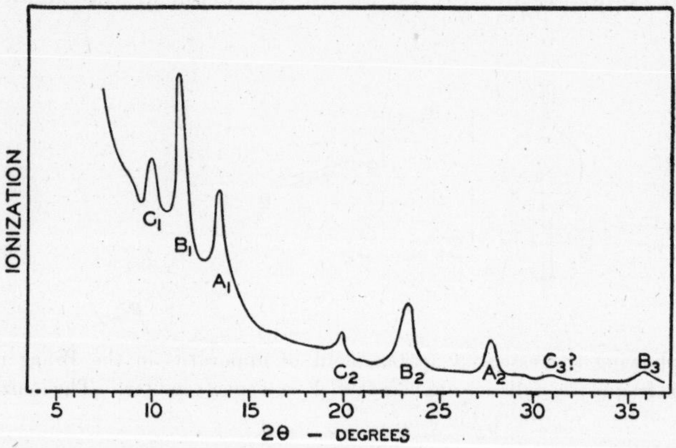


**Fig. 7.**—Showing the intensity of X-rays reflected for various angles of incidence on the (100) faces of rock salt.

reproduces those[17] obtained by reflecting from a NaCl crystal the X-rays given off by a tube having a platinum target. Although considerable energy is reflected at all angles, there are certain angles at which distinct maxima occur. These peaks occur in groups of three, first at $C_1$, $B_1$, and $A_1$, and then again at $C_2$, $B_2$, and $A_2$. It is natural to suppose that the general intensity represented by this curve is that due to the continuous radiation given off by the X-ray tube, radiation of all wave lengths. It is further supposed that the peaks $C_1$, $B_1$, and $A_1$ correspond to certain wave lengths characteristic of the target. If this interpretation is correct, it is possible that $C_2$, $B_2$ and $A_2$ represent the second order reflections of these same wave lengths. Although results are shown here for reflection from only one face of a NaCl crystal, the Braggs actually investigated reflections from various faces of a number of crystals. It was found that the same peaks

[17] W. H. Bragg and W. L. Bragg, *Proc. Roy. Soc.*, A, **88**, 428 (1913); **89**, 246 (1913).

always occur in the same relative positions regardless of the crystal face used, or even regardless of the crystal used, provided the same X-rays are used throughout. The actual angles at which these peaks occur depend upon the particular face used to reflect the X-rays and upon the crystal used. This fact was taken to indicate different spacings of atom planes in different directions within any one crystal, and different spacings between corresponding sets of planes in two different crystals.

Let us interpret the two groups of peaks in Fig. 7 as representing first and second order diffraction spectra, as did Bragg, and work out the connection between the wave length being reflected and the angular position of the reflected energy. The concept of a crystal, even previous to the work of the Braggs, was that of a regularly spaced set of atom planes. It is true that the spacing between planes was not known, nor was there any very

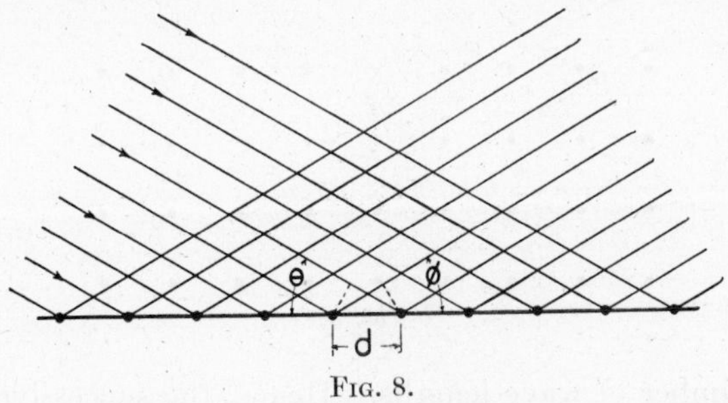


FIG. 8.

direct evidence regarding the arrangement of atoms. But the regularity of crystal faces, together with the pioneering work of Laue, had convinced scientists that a crystal does consist of some regular array of atoms. Let us think of a simple cubic crystal in which there is a rectangular array of atoms extending in three directions, and in which the distance between atoms is the same along the three rectangular axes. Let the points of Fig. 8 represent the atoms forming the facial plane of the crystal. Let a narrow beam of X-rays having a wave length $\lambda$ strike the crystal face at a grazing angle $\theta$. Since the distance between adjacent atoms is known to be of the order of $10^{-8}$ cm., even a very narrow incident X-ray beam will fall upon many atoms in this surface layer. X-rays will be diffracted in all directions from each atom. These diffracted waves will be in phase, and therefore reinforce, only when

$$n\lambda = d \cos \theta - d \cos \phi$$

where $\phi$ is the grazing angle of reflection and where $n$ is some whole number. It is thus obvious that waves diffracted by all atoms in any one plane will reinforce when $\phi = \theta$, that is when $n = 0$, and this regardless of wave length.

But an extremely small fraction of the incident X-ray energy is reflected by the single plane of atoms making up the surface; much that proceeds onward into the crystal will be reflected in a similar way from lower planes. For a maximum energy diffracted in any direction it is obvious that not only must waves diffracted by all atoms in any one plane reinforce, but waves diffracted from various planes of atoms must also reinforce. The first of these requirements is met for all wave lengths by keeping $\phi = \theta$. The condition under which waves reflected from successive planes will reinforce is easily obtained from Fig. 9. The difference in path traversed for waves reflected from successive planes is $(AB + BC)$, or $2AB$. Since $AB = d \sin \theta$, this difference in path is $2d \sin \theta$. For reinforcement this path difference must be

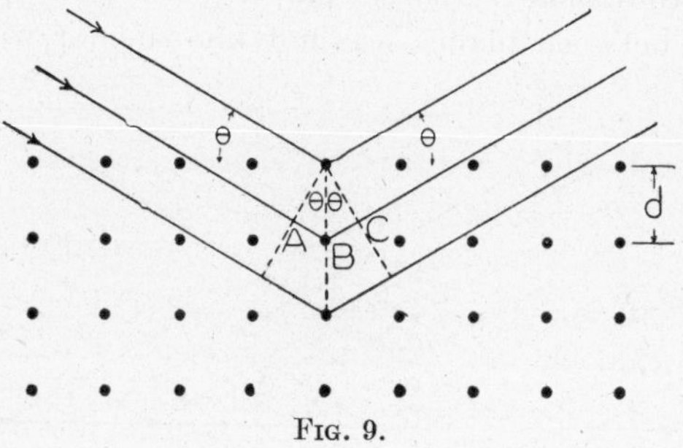


FIG. 9.

some whole number of wave lengths. Hence, the successive planes of the crystal will reinforce one another in their reflections when

$$n\lambda = 2d \sin \theta$$

This was deduced originally by Bragg and is known as Bragg's law.

A quantitative test can now be applied to the interpretation of Fig. 7. If $C_1$, $B_1$ and $A_1$ represent the first order reinforcements corresponding to three characteristic wave lengths, and if $C_2$, $B_2$ and $A_2$ represent the second order reinforcements for these same wave lengths, then the peak $C_2$ should occur at an angle whose sine is just twice the sine of the angle at which $C_1$ occurs. Similar statements could be made regarding the peaks $B_1$ and $B_2$, and $A_1$ and $A_2$. This actually turns out to be the case for each pair of peaks involved. Account must of course be taken of the fact that the angle shown in Fig. 7 is twice the angle which is here involved. There can be no doubt that the first group of these peaks represents first order reflections of three characteristic wave lengths, and that the second group of three peaks represents second order reflections of these same wave lengths. The small peaks $C_3$ and $B_3$ occur where the third order reflections should be found. Thus the Bragg law describes the observations quite fully.

*Diffraction by Ruled Gratings.*—While all early attempts of Roentgen and others to reflect X-rays failed, it is now known that the radiation is reflected from such polished surfaces as glass and metal under suitable conditions. There is no doubt some energy reflected under all conditions, but the fraction reflected from such surfaces is appreciable only when the radi-

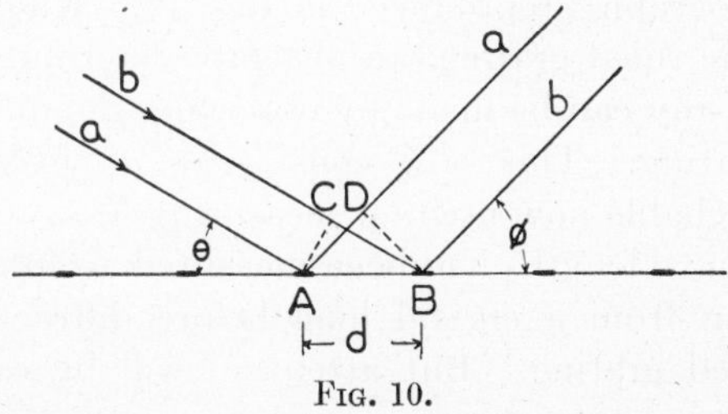


FIG. 10.

ation is incident at a very small grazing angle, an angle ordinarily less than half a degree. As will be shown later, when X-rays are incident at a grazing angle less than this on any polished surface such as glass or metal, that surface becomes an excellent reflector. It should therefore be possible, by ruling a series of parallel lines on a polished surface, to obtain a line grating spectrum for X-rays entirely analogous to the grating spectrum obtained with light.

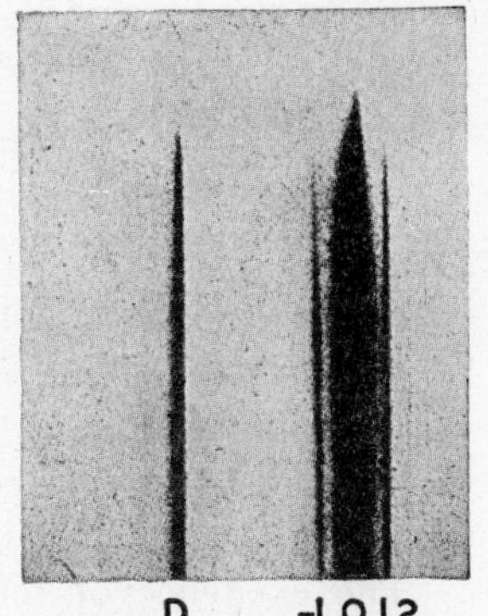


FIG. 11.—Spectrum of the $K\alpha_1$ line of Mo, $\lambda = 0.71$ A°, taken with a grating of 500 lines per cm. ruled on speculum metal.

It might be thought that the exceedingly short wave length of X-rays would necessitate ruling the lines so close together as to be impractical. The mere fact that the X-rays must be incident at such a small grazing angle, however, allows one to use a relatively coarse grating. Referring to Fig. 10, let $A$ and $B$ be two of the many reflecting regions left between the lines scratched on a grating. Let $aa$ and $bb$ be the paths of X-rays reflected from these. The difference in path length traveled by these two adjacent rays is $(CB - AD)$, or $(d \cos \theta - d \cos \phi)$. For reinforcement this path difference must be some whole number of wave lengths. Hence, reinforcement would be expected in a direction $\phi$ such that

$$n\lambda = d(\cos \theta - \cos \phi)$$

Various orders of spectra should be found, corresponding to $n = 0, \pm 1, \pm 2$, etc. Since $\theta$ and $\phi$ are each very close to 0, and therefore have cosines very close to unity, and since the cosine of a small angle changes very slowly with the angle, it follows that $\phi$ will be appreciably different for the different order spectra in spite of the fact that $d$ may be thousands of times larger than the wave length of the X-rays.

One of the first photographs taken with a ruled grating, one by Compton and Doan,[18] is reproduced in Fig. 11. The technique has now been improved so that the resulting lines are much more sharply defined as is shown by the photograph[19] reproduced in Fig. 12. Knowing the distance between lines on the ruled grating, an absolute determination of the wave length of a given X-ray can be made by observing the diffraction spectrum formed by the grating. This now constitutes an exceedingly accurate method, the most reliable now used, of measuring X-ray wave lengths. It is true that many wave lengths had been measured accurately by observing the Bragg reflection from a crystal long before diffraction spectra were produced by a ruled grating. But attention will be called later to the

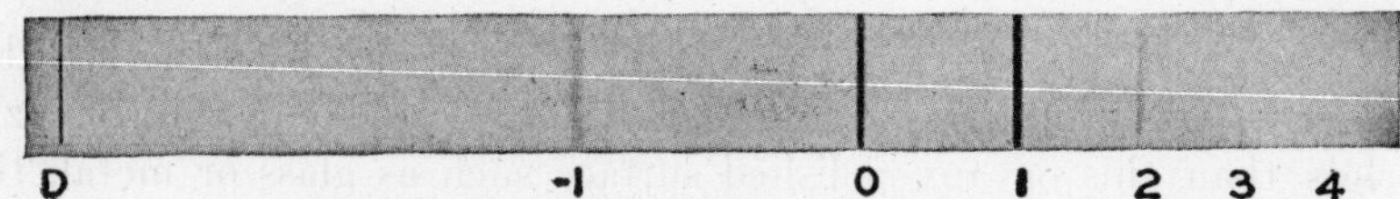


FIG. 12.—Spectrum of the $K\alpha$ line of C, $\lambda = 45$ A°, obtained with a ruled glass grating. Note the several orders of spectra.

fact that these crystal measurements have recently been modified by a fraction of 1% because they were found not to agree exactly with ruled grating measurements.

## Refraction

Early attempts by Roentgen and others to deviate a beam of X-rays by passing it through a prism failed. It was many years later that refraction was definitely proved. It can now be shown by three distinct methods[20] that X-rays are refracted; and each method yields a value for the index of refraction of the refracting material for the X-ray used.

The existence of refraction was first shown by Stenström[21] in 1919. In studying the reflection of X-rays from crystal faces, he found that the Bragg law did not give exactly the angles at which the several orders of reflection occurred for waves longer than about 3 A°. Stenström interpreted this as being due to refraction of the beam as it enters and leaves the crystal face. If this interpretation is correct, a similar, though smaller, effect should exist for shorter X-rays. Precision measurements[22,23] have since

[18] A. H. Compton and R. L. Doan, *Proc. Nat. Acad. Sci.*, **11**, 598 (1925).

[19] C. E. Howe, *Rev. Sci. Instr.*, **1**, 749 (1930).

[20] A. H. Compton and S. K. Allison, *X-rays in Theory and Experiment* (2nd ed.; New York: D. Van Nostrand, 1935), pp. 40–42, 279–285.

[21] W. Stenström, *Dissertation*, Lund (1919).

[22] W. Duane and R. A. Patterson, *Phys. Rev.*, **16**, 526 (1920).

[23] M. Siegbahn, *Comptes Rendus*, **173**, 1350 (1921); **174**, 745 (1922).

shown that the effect does exist for X-rays of any wave length. Results of this character show that the index of refraction is slightly less than 1. That is, the direction of the deviation from Bragg's law is such as to indicate that the X-ray entering the crystal is bent away from the normal to the surface. It is clear that this bending should have been taken into account in deducing the Bragg law. When it is taken into account it can be easily shown[24] that the modified form of Bragg's law becomes

$$n\lambda = 2d \sin\theta \left[1 + \frac{\mu^2 - 1}{\sin^2\theta}\right]^{1/2}$$

where $\mu$ is the index of refraction. This expression fits observations accurately when an appropriate index of refraction is assigned to the crystal. By observing the small deviation from the original Bragg law it is possible to evaluate this index for any particular crystal and for any given wave length. The indices found are so near unity that the quantity $(1 - \mu)$ is of the order of $10^{-5}$ or $10^{-6}$ for various materials.

A slight modification of this method of measuring the index has been used by numerous workers.[25–28] It has already been remarked that the observed deviations from the original Bragg law are extremely small. Now it is well known that the angle through which a ray is bent in the refraction process is considerably greater if either the incident or the refracted ray makes a very small grazing angle with the surface. But the grazing angle a beam must make with the atom planes in a crystal in order for the Bragg reflection to take place is determined by the wave length of the X-ray and the spacing of the crystal. Hence it is impossible, by using the normal face of a crystal, to have the incident or the refracted ray almost graze the surface. But if an artificial face is cut and polished on the crystal, a face making an angle with the atom planes almost, but not quite, equal to the Bragg grazing angle of incidence, then when a reflection takes place from the planes of the crystal, either the incident or the refracted ray will almost graze the surface. That this is the case is illus-

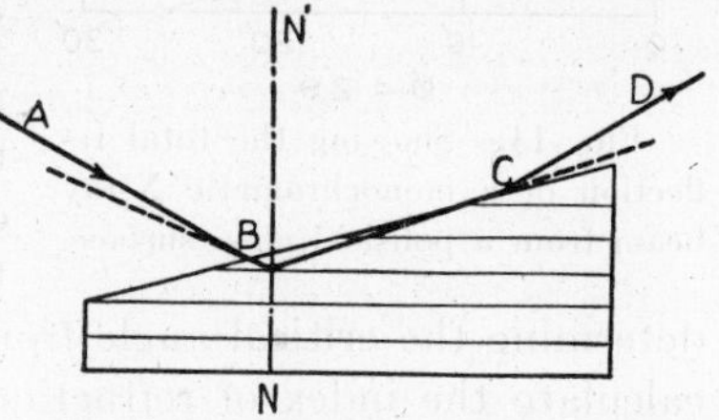

FIG. 13.—Illustrating the wedge method of magnifying deviations from Bragg's law, in order to obtain accurate values for indices of refraction.

[24] See, for example, H. Semat, *Introduction to Atomic Physics* (New York: Farrar & Rinehart, 1939), p. 110.

[25] C. C. Hatley and B. Davis, *Phys. Rev.*, **23,** 290 (1924).

[26] R. von Nardroff, *Phys. Rev.*, **24,** 143 (1924).

[27] C. C. Hatley, *Phys. Rev.*, **24,** 486 (1924).

[28] A. Larsson, *Dissertation*, Uppsala, (1929).

trated in Fig. 13. By this method, known as the wedge method, deviations from Bragg's law are greatly magnified. As a result, indices of refraction can be obtained with considerable precision.

Compton[29] realized that if a material had an index of refraction less than unity the phenomenon of total reflection should occur when X-rays are incident on that material at a very small grazing angle. Just as in light, the incident angle at which total reflection sets in should be that for which the refracted ray proceeds parallel to the surface. Total reflection should be observed at all grazing angles of incidence less than this. Since the index differs so little from unity, total reflection does not set in until the grazing angle of incidence becomes, for most materials, less than half a degree. The manner in which the observed intensity of reflected energy changes with the grazing angle of incidence in the vicinity of the critical angle for total reflection is shown[29] in Fig. 14. These data are for the reflection of a mono-chromatic X-ray beam, wave length 1.279 A°, from a polished glass surface. The marked and fairly abrupt increase in reflection at the critical angle is excellent confirmation of the theory of total reflection. It is possible to determine the critical angle from measurements such as these, and thence calculate the index of refraction. The fact that the phenomenon sets in gradually rather than abruptly for some materials is attributable to absorption. In many cases it is essential to take into account[20] the effect of this absorption in evaluating the index of refraction.

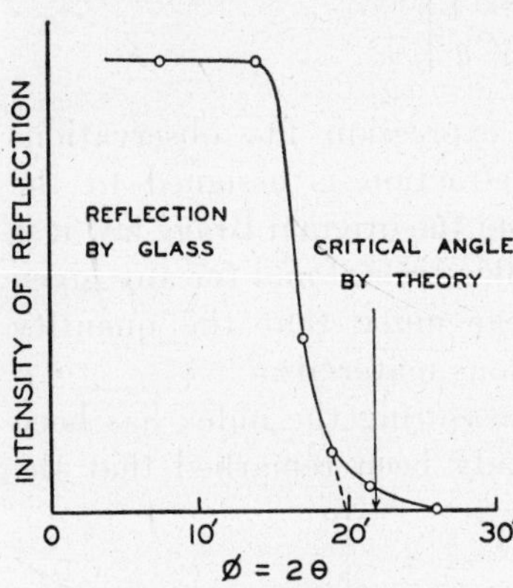


Fig. 14.—Showing the total reflection of a monochromatic X-ray beam from a polished glass surface.

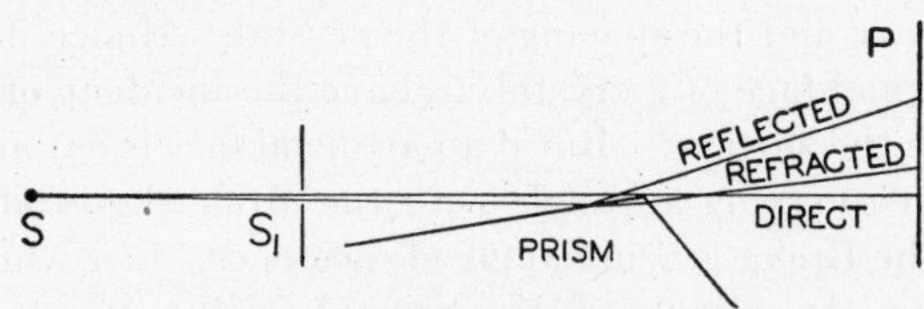


Fig. 15.—Showing the arrangement for refracting X-rays with a prism.

A third way of investigating the refraction of X-rays is through use of a prism. Although all early attempts to observe some bending of a beam in passing through a prism failed, it has since been shown definitely by this

[29] A. H. Compton, *Phil. Mag.*, **45**, 1121 (1923).

method that refraction does take place. Larsson, Siegbahn and Waller[30] were the first to succeed in this. The general arrangement of apparatus is illustrated in Fig. 15. They used a narrow beam of X-rays incident on the prism face at a very small grazing angle. This angle was just larger than that for which total reflection sets in. In this way the bending suffered by the ray was made much larger than it would have been had the incident ray struck the prism at a large grazing angle. A photograph obtained with this arrangement is reproduced in Fig. 16. The refracted ray is bent upward sufficiently that it strikes the photographic film above the place where the ray going directly over the top of the prism strikes it. The direction of bending shows clearly that the index of refraction is less than unity. From the positions at which the three rays fall on a photographic film, together with the angle of the prism, one can calculate the index of refraction of the material of which the prism is made.

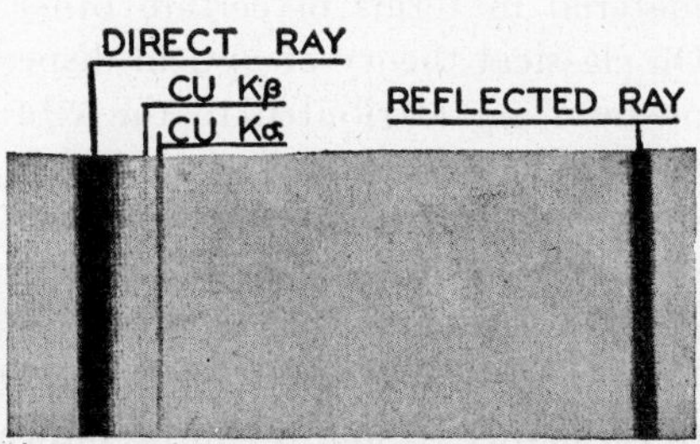


FIG. 16.—Photograph showing the refraction of X-rays by a prism.

Indices of refraction as determined by the three possible methods agree closely with one another. The fourth column of Table[31] I shows some

TABLE I

A comparison of observed and calculated indices of refraction of materials for X-rays

| λ | Substance | $(1-\mu)\times 10^6$ calculated | $(1-\mu)\times 10^6$ observed | Method |
|---|---|---|---|---|
| 0.52 A° | Glass | 0.9 | 0.9 | Reflection |
| 0.631 | Glass | 1.43 | 1.22 ± .15 | Prism |
| 1.279 | Glass | 5.2 | 4.2 | Reflection |
| 1.389 | Glass | 6.65 | 6.65 ± .05 | Prism |
| 1.537 | Glass | 8.14 | 8.12 ± .05 | Prism |
| 1.750 | Glass | 10.5 | 10.0 ± .4 | Prism |
| 1.933 | Glass | 12.8 | 12.4 ± .4 | Prism |
| 0.708 | Calcite | 1.84 | 2.03 ± .09 | Wedge |
| 0.708 | Calcite | 1.84 | 2.001 ± .009 | Prism |
| 1.279 | Silver | 19.8 | 21.5 | Reflection |
| 1.537 | Glycerine | 4.34 | 4.41 | Reflection |
| 1.537 | Water | 3.53 | 3.69 | Reflection |

[30] A. Larsson, M. Siegbahn, and T. Waller, *Naturwiss.*, **52**, 1212 (1924); *Phys. Rev.*, **25**, 235 (1925).

[31] A rearrangement of values quoted by A. H. Compton and S. K. Allison, *X-rays in Theory and Experiment* (2nd ed.; New York: D. Van Nostrand, 1935), p. 284.

of the indices observed for various materials at various wave lengths. Most indices differ from unity by only $10^{-5}$ or $10^{-6}$. The manner in which the index of a given material varies with wave length is interesting. Data in the table show this variation well for glass.

It is possible to calculate theoretically the index of refraction of a material in terms of certain other constants pertaining to the material. On classical theory of optical dispersion, the refractive characteristics of a medium are attributed to the vibrations of electrons within the medium under the influence of the incident electromagnetic wave. That is, one supposes that the incident wave sets electrons into vibration, and that these vibrating electrons affect the velocity of propagation of the wave. Development of the analytical theory of refraction has no place in this discussion. It is sufficient to state that if one extends the classical concept of dispersion to the X-ray region, it can be shown that

$$\mu = 1 + \frac{e^2}{2\pi m} \sum \frac{n_p}{(\nu_p{}^2 - \nu^2)}$$

where $\mu$ is the refractive index for the wave of frequency $\nu$, where $e$ and $m$ refer respectively to the charge and the mass of the electron, where $\nu_p$ is the so-called natural frequency associated with the electron, and where the summation is to be extended over all the various types of electrons ($K$, $L$, $M$, etc.) present. The quantity $n_p$ represents the number of electrons of the particular type $p$ which are present per cc. An expression entirely equivalent to this has been found quite satisfactory in the case of optical spectra. Now it is a fact that if one puts into the above expression values of $n_p$ consistent with the view that there are 2 $K$ electrons, 8 $L$ electrons, etc., and puts in for the values of $\nu_p$ the corresponding critical absorption limits, that is the frequency associated with an electron transfer from the orbit in question out to infinity, then the calculated values of refractive index agree quite satisfactorily with observed values. A number of values calculated in this way are shown in the third column of Table I. The small discrepancies between calculated and observed values are probably no larger than those which might reasonably be introduced experimentally.

It is apparent that in calculating the theoretical index it has been assumed that the number of planetary electrons within the atom is equal to the atomic number; and it has been assumed that they are arranged in definite groups at different discrete energy levels. The fact that the calculated index agrees accurately with the observed in most cases is strong indication of the correctness of these concepts. In fact Compton has stated that this provides one of the most accurate methods of showing that the number of planetary electrons per atom is equal to the atomic number; he believes that the calculations show this equality to within one percent.

A word should be said regarding the significance of an index of refraction less than unity. This indicates a wave velocity greater than the velocity of light in vacuum. Now it is a conclusion of the theory of relativity, and one in which great confidence is placed, that no particle or energy in any form can be transmitted with a velocity greater than the velocity of light. A refractive index less than unity may for this reason appear contradictory at first sight. However, the theory of relativity does not preclude the possibility of a wave velocity greater than the velocity of light. It can be shown that the energy associated with a wave motion is not necessarily propagated with a velocity equal to the wave velocity. There are really two velocities to consider, a so-called phase velocity and a so-called group velocity. The phase velocity is the velocity with which any particular phase of the disturbance is propagated outward from the source. The group velocity is the velocity with which the wave front moves forward. These are in general different for a dispersing medium, and the group velocity is the smaller. Energy is propagated from one place to another with the velocity with which the wave front moves, the group velocity. On the other hand, it is the phase velocity involved in the index of refraction. It is therefore clear that although an index less than unity indicates a phase velocity greater than the velocity of light, it in no way necessitates a group velocity as great as this. In no case is the group velocity greater than the velocity of light, even when the index is less than unity. An example of these two velocities is evident in watching water waves move over a quiet surface. If one watches a particular phase travel outward from the source he notices that it gradually catches up with the wave front, finally disappearing therein. Thus the phase velocity is greater than the velocity with which the wave front proceeds. Energy is of course propagated with the velocity possessed by the wave front.

## Reflection

The fact that X-rays can be reflected from polished surfaces has already been adequately presented in our discussion of diffraction and refraction. Although one is willing to accept the reflection observed from surfaces at angles less than the critical angle for total reflection as entirely analogous to the reflection of light from mirrors, one is perhaps hesitant to agree immediately that the reflection from crystals is entirely analogous. It is, however, except for the fact that X-rays are reflected not only from the surface plane of atoms, but also from many planes beneath the surface. The crystal is entirely equivalent to a series of equally spaced mirrors, each of which reflects only a small fraction of the incident energy. It is for this reason that the Bragg diffraction peaks occur for X-rays whereas one does not find the equivalent phenomenon for light.

**Polarization**

Polarization of primary X-rays, X-rays coming directly from the target of a tube, was first observed by Barkla[32] in 1905. The electromagnetic theory of radiation from an accelerated electron leads one to expect such polarization. Referring to Fig. 17, consider the X-rays traveling from the target $T$ out toward $S_1$. These were produced by the stoppage of high speed electrons which had traveled from $C$ to $T$. These electrons suffered large negative accelerations in stopping. This acceleration was parallel to a line joining $C$ and $T$. Now on electromagnetic theory an accelerated electron radiates energy in all directions perpendicular to which there is any component of acceleration. The electric field of the wave

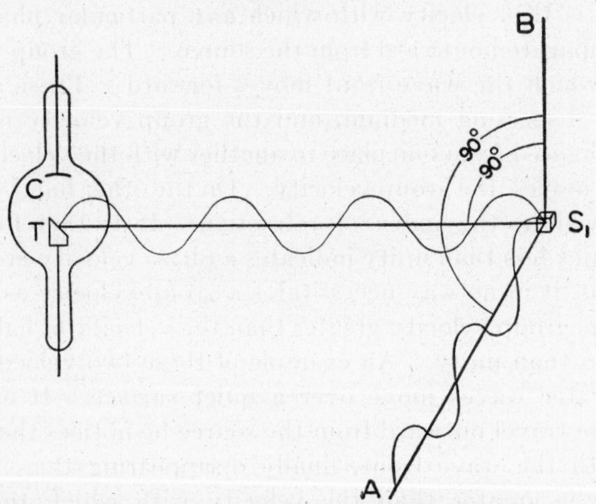


FIG. 17.—Illustrating the method of studying the polarization of X-rays.

radiated in any direction is parallel to that component of the acceleration perpendicular to this direction. One would therefore expect those X-rays radiated toward $S_1$ to be plane polarized with the electric field in the plane of the paper.

In order to investigate the possible polarization of these rays, Barkla scattered the primary X-rays by a small block of material such as carbon placed at $S_1$. He then proceeded to measure, with an ionization chamber, the intensity of X-rays scattered at right angles to the primary beam, particularly in the two directions $A$ and $B$. These early measurements showed a 10 to 20 percent greater intensity of X-rays scattered in direction $A$ than in direction $B$. This is precisely what one would expect if the primary X-rays had been partially plane polarized with the greater electric field parallel to $S_1B$, and hence to $CT$. Were the primary rays completely

[32] C. G. Barkla, *Phil. Trans. Roy. Soc.*, **204,** 467 (1905); *Proc. Roy. Soc.*, A, **77,** 247 (1906).

plane polarized with electric field parallel to $CT$, then one would expect to find no X-rays scattered in direction $B$. X-rays are supposedly scattered by electrons in the scattering material. Were the primary rays completely polarized a scattering electron would vibrate under the influence of the primary wave, parallel to $S_1B$, and its acceleration would be entirely in this line. Since this accelerated electron re-radiates most strongly in a direction perpendicular to its acceleration, the intensity of radiation scattered in direction $A$ should be large. Since the scattering electron would have no component of acceleration perpendicular to direction $B$, there would be no X-rays scattered in direction $B$. The fact that some radiation is scattered in this direction shows that the primary rays are only partially polarized.

Numerous later studies[33] have shown that filtering out the softer X-rays, those of lower frequency, increases the degree of polarization. Since the higher frequency radiation comes from electrons stopped at the very surface of a thick target, before they have been gradually slowed down by penetrating the material, it might be suspected that the total radiation from a very thin target would be more completely polarized than is that from a thick target. Such is found to be the case.[34,35] These facts suggest a plausible reason for the lack of complete polarization of a beam of primary X-rays. Those electrons which penetrate the target, gradually slowing down somewhat before producing the softer X-rays, would in all probability be deflected from their straight forward direction. When they do suffer their final large acceleration it is not parallel to the line $CT$. As a result the X-rays radiated would have a component of electric field parallel to direction $A$.

Barkla[32] was also the first to secure evidence regarding the polarization of X-rays which have been scattered. It is found that whenever X-rays are incident upon matter they are scattered diffusely in all directions, though not equally in all directions. The polarization of these scattered X-rays can be studied by rescattering this energy. Fig. 18 illustrates the method used originally by Barkla. Primary X-rays which are but partially polarized are scattered by $S_1$. The energy scattered at 90° by $S_1$ is rescattered by $S_2$. This rescattered radiation is examined, particularly in directions $D$ and $E$. It is found experimentally that but a very small amount of energy is scattered in direction $E$. This shows that the energy scattered by $S_1$ is strongly polarized with electric vector parallel to $S_2E$. Barkla's experiment indicated that the scattered radiation was 70% polarized. The

[33] A. H. Compton and S. K. Allison, *X-rays in Theory and Experiment* (2nd ed.; New York: D. Van Nostrand, 1935), pp. 18, 19, 93–95, 119–128.

[34] H. Kulenkampff, *Ann. d. Physik*, **87**, 597, (1928); *Phys. Zeits.*, **30**, 513 (1929).

[35] B. Dasannacharya, *Phys. Rev.*, **35**, 129 (1930).

apparent lack of complete polarization of the radiation scattered at 90° is attributed to the fact that, because of the finite size of the scattering block, not all energy is scattered at exactly 90°, and to the fact that appreciable multiple scattering probably occurs. More recent experiments[36] have shown that when multiple scattering is eliminated by using a very thin scattering block, and when the geometrical error arising from the finite size of the scattering block is allowed for, the polarization of the X-rays scattered at 90° is complete within an experimental error of 1 or 2 percent. This was found to be so regardless of whether the scattering material be paper, carbon, aluminum, or sulphur. X-rays scattered at other than 90° are but partially polarized, the degree and the direction of polarization depending upon the

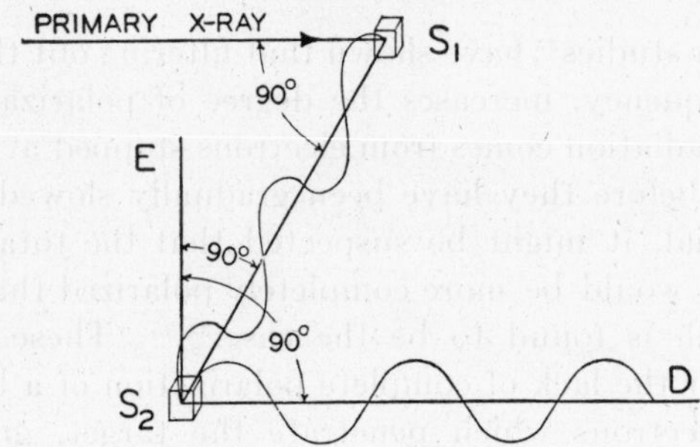


Fig. 18.—Illustrating the method of studying the polarization of scattered X-rays.

direction of scattering. Those X-rays scattered directly forward or directly backward are not polarized in the scattering process.

## Scattering

X-rays are diffusely scattered by matter in all directions, though not equally in all directions. On the classical theory of scattering, the electrons in the scattering material are set into vibration by the varying electric field of the incident electromagnetic wave. These vibrating, and hence accelerated, electrons then serve as radiators of energy. Scattering was therefore conceived of as equivalent to absorption and re-radiation. Obviously on this concept, since the frequency with which the electron is set into vibration is equal to the frequency of the incident X-rays, and since the frequency of the wave radiated is equal to that with which the electron vibrates, the scattered X-rays should have the same frequency, or the same wave length, as the incident X-rays.

The observed polarization of scattered X-rays has already been discussed and found to agree satisfactorily with that suggested by the classical concept. Let us now look briefly into the intensity of energy scattered

[36] A. H. Compton and C. F. Hagenow, *J.O.S.A.*, **8**, 487 (1924).

in various directions. Since the vibration of the scattering electron is perpendicular to the direction of propagation of the incident X-ray, and since the electric vector of the scattered wave must always be perpendicular to the direction of scattering, it follows that all scattering electrons will re-radiate most strongly in the forward and the backward directions. On the average only half of the electrons would scatter energy from an unpolarized primary beam at an angle of 90° with this beam. Hence, the intensity of energy scattered in either the forward or the backward direction should be twice that at 90°. For soft X-rays, radiation of long wave length, this is approximately the distribution observed. For harder X-rays, however, far more energy is scattered in the forward direction than in the backward direction, and far less in the backward direction than at 90°. This distribution cannot be reconciled with the classical concept.

On classical theory it was argued that the wave length of the scattered radiation should be the same as that of the incident radiation, and this regardless of the direction in which the scattered radiation is studied. It is observed that in the forward direction the wave length of the scattered radiation is always identical with that of the incident beam. And in all other directions some scattered radiation of this wave length is found. In all directions other than straight forward, however, there is considerable scattered radiation having a wave length measurably longer than that of the incident radiation. The difference between the wave lengths of the scattered and the incident radiations increases as the angle of scattering increases from 0 to 180°. The increase in wave length caused by scattering is independent of the wave length of the incident X-rays. This change of wave length upon scattering can in no way be reconciled with the classical concept.

A quantum theory of scattering was advanced by A. H. Compton[37] to interpret these facts found contrary to the classical theory. Compton conceived of the energy being scattered in quanta, each quantum being scattered by an individual free electron. One pictures a photon of energy $h\nu$ and momentum $h\nu/c$ striking a free electron at rest. The electron recoils in one direction and the photon goes off in some other direction. On the assumption that the laws of conservation of energy and conservation of momentum hold for the "collision" between the photon and the scattering electron, it has already been shown in the chapter on photons that the frequency of the scattered photon is less than that of the incident photon; the wave length of the X-rays is increased in the scattering process. It has been shown that this increase in wave length is given by

$$\Delta\lambda = \frac{2h}{mc}\sin^2\frac{1}{2}\phi$$

[37] A. H. Compton, *Bull. Nat. Res. Coun.*, **4**, 1–56 (1922); *Phys. Rev.*, **21**, 207, 483 (1923).

where $\phi$ is the angle between the direction taken by the scattered X-rays and that of the incident beam. If recent values[38] of the known constants are put into this expression, and if it is agreed to express the increase in wave length in A°, then

$$\Delta\lambda = 0.04853 \sin^2 \tfrac{1}{2}\phi$$

This theory of scattering predicts a definite value for the increase in wave length of X-rays scattered at any particular angle, and it predicts that this increase should be independent of the wave length of the X-rays being scattered.

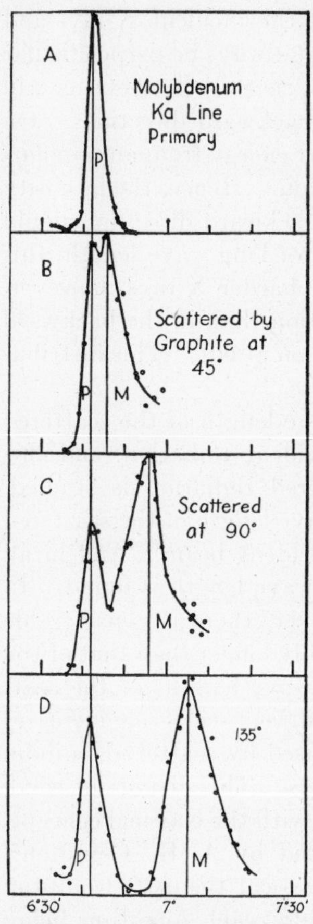


FIG. 19.—Showing the increase in wave length produced by scattering monochromatic X-rays, the Kα line of Mo, at various angles by graphite.

A wealth[39] of experimental work has shown that scattering does occur entirely in accord with this expression. The experimental curves[40] reproduced in Fig. 19 show definitely the relative wave lengths of the primary and the scattered radiation. Curve *A* represents the Bragg reflection of the primary X-rays from a crystal. Curve *B* represents the Bragg reflection of this same radiation after being scattered at an angle of 45°. Curves *C* and *D* are for scattering at larger angles. It is clear that the wave length of a portion of the scattered radiation is increased, while that of the remainder is not changed. These two components in the scattered radiation are referred to respectively as the modified and the unmodified beams. One can calculate the increase in wave length actually brought about by scattering from the Bragg angles at which the modified peak and the primary peak occur. It is found that the observed increase in wave length occasioned by scattering at any angle agrees accurately with that predicted by the quantum theory of scattering. The lines marked *M* in Fig. 19 were actually drawn at those angles at which the modified peak should fall

[38] R. T. Birge, A mimeographed, "*Consistent Set of Values of the General Physical Constants*," as of Aug. (1939).

[39] A. H. Compton and S. K. Allison, *X-rays in Theory and Experiment* (2nd ed.; New York: D. Van Nostrand, 1935), pp. 200–237.

[40] A. H. Compton, *Phys. Rev.*, **22**, 409 (1923); A. H. Compton and S. K. Allison, *X-rays in Theory and Experiment* (2nd ed.; New York: D. Van Nostrand, 1935), p. 203.

according to theory. It is seen that they coincide with the observed peaks. The wave length is increased during the scattering process, and it is increased in accord with the theoretical expression given by Compton. Only a few years ago what Compton[39] regarded as the best experimental observations[41] showed the increase in wave length to be

$$\Delta\lambda = (0.04848 \pm 0.00008) \sin^2 \tfrac{1}{2}\phi$$

an increase agreeing accurately with the numerical increase predicted by theory.

Although the quantum theory of scattering by free electrons accounts beautifully for the presence of the modified peak at a wave length slightly greater than that of the primary X-rays, scattering by these electrons can in no way account for the presence of the unmodified peak in the scattered radiation. This unmodified component is accounted for by the scattering by bound electrons, electrons held in the atom structure so firmly that the atom as a whole, rather than an isolated electron, recoils from the impact. Applying the same energy and momentum considerations to this interaction as were applied to the interaction between the photon and the free electron, one obtains an expression for the increase in wave length exactly similar to that already obtained except that the mass of the particle involved is now that of the entire atom instead of that of the electron. Since the mass of an atom of any scattering material is thousands of times that of the electron, the theoretical increase in wave length caused by scattering by bound electrons would be an entirely negligible and unmeasurable quantity. Qualitatively then, scattering by bound electrons might logically account for the unmodified beam. This might also account for the fact that one does not find the full equivalent of the modified beam in scattered light. Electrons which behave as free to energetic X-ray photons would probably behave as bound electrons to the low energy light photons. Rather convincing evidence of the correctness of this general view is furnished by measurements of the relative intensities of the two peaks when X-rays are scattered by materials of different atomic numbers. Experimental curves[42] showing these relative intensities for a number of scattering materials are shown in Fig. 20. Whereas practically all of the radiation scattered by Li and other materials of low atomic number is of the modified wave length, materials of higher atomic number have more and more of their scattered radiation in the unmodified peak. This is precisely what might be expected. Although there is some question as to just how firmly an electron may be attached to the atom and still behave as a free electron, it appears that even the *K* electron of Li might be classed as free for the

[41] N. S. Gingrich, *Phys. Rev.*, **36**, 1050 (1930).
[42] Y. H. Woo, *Phys. Rev.*, **27**, 119 (1926).

scattering of high energy X-ray photons, whereas the $K$ electrons, and probably also the $L$ electrons, of Cu would behave as bound electrons. The variations in the relative intensities of the two peaks shown in Fig. 20 are in agreement with this general view.

In this same connection it should be mentioned that Ross and Kirkpatrick[43] feel that the original Compton expression for the increase in wave length of the modified beam is not exactly correct, that a small term should be subtracted to take account of the fact that under no circumstances do the scattering electrons behave as if they were entirely free. This proposed correction is a function of wave length, increasing as the wave length increases. On this view the change of wave length upon scattering depends slightly upon the wave length of the X-ray being scattered. Ross and Kirkpatrick[43] present data which appear to bear out their contention. When no correction term is included in the Compton expression these experimenters find a value (0.04760 ± 0.00006) for the multiplier, a value appreciably lower than the theoretical 0.04853. It is only upon including their proposed correction term that they find a value (0.04836 ± 0.00008) for the multiplier $2h/mc$.

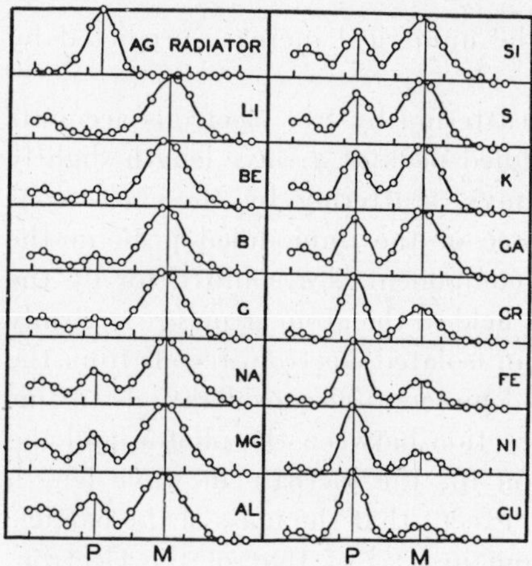

FIG. 20.—Showing the relative intensities of the modified and the unmodified scattered radiation.

It will be noticed from Fig. 20 that the modified peak of the scattered radiation has an appreciable width. This is not entirely due to lack of resolving power of the apparatus or to the lack of a truly monochromatic primary beam. The modified line is not sharp; it is broader than the primary beam, also broader than the unmodified beam. It was suggested by Jauncey[44] that the breadth of the modified line is due to the motion of the electron within the atom at the instant of scattering. The normal velocity of the electron may be in the direction of motion of the incident photon, in a direction opposite to this, or in a direction making any angle with it. Analytical treatment of the problem shows that this initial velocity produces a Doppler effect with a consequent broadening of the modified peak. The magnitude of the broadening has been investigated by DuMond and

[43] P. A. Ross and P. Kirkpatrick, *Phys. Rev.*, **45**, 223; **46**, 668 (1934).

[44] G. E. M. Jauncey, *Phys. Rev.*, **25**, 314, 723 (1925).

Kirkpatrick[45] and has been found to be that which one expects on the supposition that it is due to the initial velocities of the scattering electrons. Data of this character constitute rather direct evidence for the dynamical structure of the atom. These authors have also shown how the observed shape of the modified line can be analyzed to determine the distribution of electron velocities required to produce the observed effect. This procedure and the information it has yielded regarding the motions of electrons within atoms have been summarized by DuMond.[46]

There are many other aspects of the quantum theory of scattering which are subject to experimental test. As has already been stated in the chapter on photons, it is possible to photograph[47] this scattering process in the cloud chamber, and to determine from the photograph the angles at which the scattered photon and the recoil electron leave the point of scattering. Such photographs leave no doubt of the actual existence of recoil electrons; and they leave no doubt that the scattered photon proceeds in some definite direction until it is either rescattered or absorbed through the ejection of a photoelectron. The photon theory of scattering leads also to a definite correlation between the angles at which the recoil electron and the scattered photon leave the point of scattering, to a definite connection between the energy of the recoil electron and the angle at which the electron recoils, to the conclusion that there should appear one recoil electron for each quantum of energy scattered, and to the conclusion that the recoil electron and the scattered photon should appear simultaneously. All of these predictions are subject to experimental verification, and they are borne out[39] beautifully by many detailed observations. The scattering of $\gamma$-rays is entirely similar to that of X-rays, and many of the experimental tests have been made with $\gamma$-rays.[48] For example, it has been found that there is no time lag[48] greater than $10^{-4}$ seconds between the appearance of a scattered photon and that of a recoil electron. There can be no doubt that the Compton theory describes the scattering process correctly. It is true that an alternate theory leading to essentially the same results has been developed[49,39] on the modern wave theory of matter. There is little to choose between the two theories except for the fact that the Compton particle theory gives a simple and clear-cut picture of the process, whereas the wave theory is almost devoid of simple pictures.

[45] J. W. M. DuMond and H. A. Kirkpatrick, *Phys. Rev.*, **37**, 136 (1931); **38**, 1094 (1931); **52**, 419 (1937).

[46] J. W. M. DuMond, *Rev. Mod. Phys.*, **5**, 1 (1933).

[47] A. H. Compton and A. W. Simon, *Phys. Rev.*, **26**, 289 (1925).

[48] R. S. Shankland, *Phys. Rev.*, **52**, 414 (1937).

[49] E. Schrödinger, *Ann. d. Physik*, **82**, 257 (1927).

**Absorption**

X-rays are absorbed to some extent by all material through which they pass. The fraction of the incident energy absorbed by a given thickness of material depends upon both the nature of the absorber and the wave length of the X-ray. The decrease in intensity suffered by a beam in passing through a very thin element $dx$ of the absorbing material is assumed to be proportional both to the incident intensity and to the thickness of the absorber. That is,

$$dI = -\mu I dx$$

where $I$ represents the intensity at the front face of the element $dx$, and where $\mu$ is a constant. Integrating this expression, taking the antilogarithm of each side of the resulting equation, and calling the intensity at the initial face of the absorbing material $I_0$, one obtains

$$I = I_0 \epsilon^{-\mu x}$$

This gives the intensity $I$ after the beam has penetrated any finite thickness $x$ of the absorber. From the first equation written above the quantity $\mu$ is seen to represent the fraction of the energy removed from the beam per centimeter of path. It is called the linear coefficient of absorption. It is found experimentally that the intensity of an X-ray beam does fall off with distance in accord with the expression just deduced, provided the incident radiation be homogeneous, that is, monochromatic. If one applies this equation to the absorption of other than monochromatic radiation, one finds that the absorption coefficient $\mu$ decreases as the radiation proceeds through the absorbing medium. This should of course be expected, since the more easily absorbed radiation disappears more rapidly from the beam.

There are in frequent use two other ways of expressing the absorption coefficient of a material. Since by definition $I$ represents the energy falling per second on a square centimeter of the absorber, the quantity $\mu$ can also be regarded as the fraction of the energy removed per second from a beam one square centimeter in cross section by each cubic centimeter of the absorbing material through which the beam passes. In this sense it is referred to as the volume coefficient of absorption. If this coefficient be divided by the density of the absorbing material one obtains the energy removed from the beam per second per gram of absorbing material passed. This is known as the mass absorption coefficient. Or, if the coefficient $\mu$ is divided by the number of absorbing atoms per cubic centimeter one obtains the energy removed per second from the beam per atom of absorber it passes. This is known as the atomic absorption coefficient. Both the mass and the atomic absorption coefficients are independent of the physical and chemical state of an absorber, whereas the linear coefficient is not. For example, water has the same mass and the same atomic absorption coefficient regardless of whether it be in the form of ice, liquid or steam. It has quite different linear absorption coefficients in the liquid and the vapor state.

There are two distinct ways in which a material removes energy from an X-ray beam. One of these is by scattering the energy; the other is by true atomic absorption. The coefficient spoken of above refers to the total loss of energy from the beam. It is therefore called the total absorption coefficient and is often written as the sum of two coefficients, one the true absorption coefficient, the other the scattering coefficient. When true absorption takes place the energy given up by the X-ray is taken up by the absorbing atom. The atom absorbs this energy by having one of its electrons displaced from its normal level to some outer level, or by having this electron completely removed from the atom. Shortly thereafter this atom radiates energy in the form of its characteristic X-rays. In the case of gases one sees direct evidence in cloud chamber photographs that these electrons are ejected completely from the atoms as high speed photoelectrons. The additional energy possessed by the photoelectron after being torn from the atom is gradually dissipated through the formation of a multitude of low energy ions along its path. In fact it is almost altogether by this method that X-rays ionize a gas. The X-rays eject a few energetic photoelectrons. These photoelectrons in turn form a multitude of low speed ions which represent almost the entire ionization of the gas.

If the concept of scattering with the consequent appearance of recoil electrons is correct, and if the concept of absorption with the consequent ejection of photoelectrons is correct, then one should expect to find one recoil electron for each quantum of energy scattered and one photoelectron for each quantum of energy absorbed. The ratio of the number of photoelectrons to the number of recoil electrons should be equal to the ratio of the true absorption coefficient to the scattering coefficient. Many experiments[39] show that this is true within the rather large error associated with the measurements.

The magnitude of the mass absorption coefficient varies greatly with both the nature of the absorbing material and the wave length of the X-ray being absorbed. In general the coefficient increases rapidly with increases in wave length. There are certain regions, however, where a slight increase in wave length leads to a much lower absorption coefficient. This is illustrated by Fig. 21, which shows the absorption of argon over a considerable range of wave lengths.[50] X-rays of wave length 4.0 A° are absorbed far less rapidly than are those of 3.7 A°. All absorbers show sharp discontinuities of this character, though the wave length at which this discon-

[50] A. H. Compton and S. K. Allison, *X-rays in Theory and Experiment* (2nd ed.; New York: D. Van Nostrand, 1935), pp. 9–11, 511–542.

tinuity occurs becomes shorter for absorbers of high atomic number. For example, tables giving the positions[51] of such discontinuities show that the $K$ absorption jump occurs at 3.866 A° for A of atomic number 18, at 0.6185 A° for Mo of atomic number 42, and at 0.1577 for Pt of atomic number 78. Fig. 22 reproduces[52] a similar absorption curve for Pt. Still more discontinuities appear in this curve within the region of wave length for which

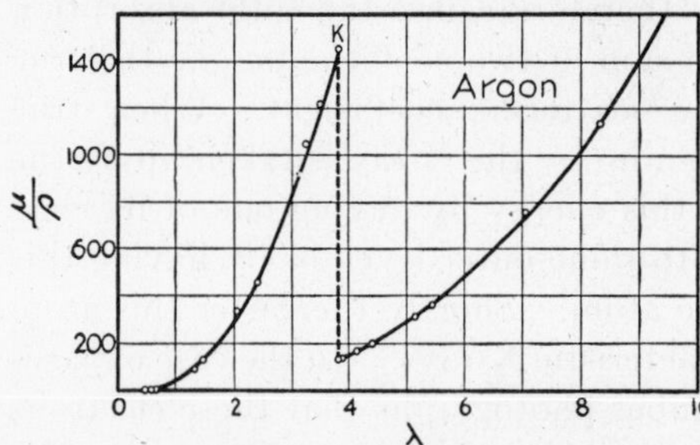


FIG. 21.—Showing the manner in which the mass absorption coefficient of argon varies with wave length.

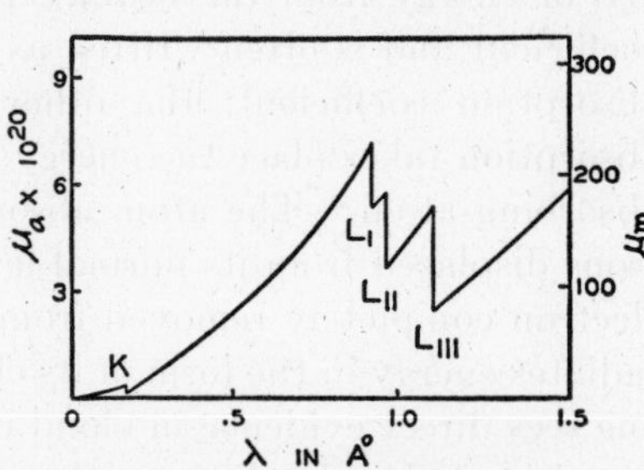


FIG. 22.—Showing the manner in which the absorption coefficient of platinum varies with wave length.

data are plotted. The wave lengths for which these abrupt discontinuities occur are known as critical absorption wave lengths. They are characteristic of the absorbing atom. Data for some materials have been extended over an appropriate range of wave length to show that there exists at a still higher wave length another group of 5 discontinuities. Tables[51] show that

TABLE II

Showing the critical absorption wave lengths of Pt and the energies corresponding to these

| Absorption discontinuity | Wave length in A° | Corresponding energy in volts |
|---|---|---|
| $K$ | 0.1577 | 78420 |
| $L_{I}$ | 0.8914 | 13870 |
| $L_{II}$ | 0.9321 | 13270 |
| $L_{III}$ | 1.0710 | 11550 |
| $M_{I}$ | 3.603 | 3432 |
| $M_{II}$ | 3.738 | 3308 |
| $M_{III}$ | 4.676 | 2645 |
| $M_{IV}$ | 5.544 | 2231 |
| $M_{V}$ | 5.746 | 2152 |

[51] A. H. Compton and S. K. Allison, *X-rays in Theory and Experiment* (2nd ed.; New York: D. Van Nostrand, 1935), pp. 792–794.

[52] A. H. Compton, *X-rays and Electrons* (New York: D. Van Nostrand, 1926), p. 187.

for Pt these discontinuities, some of which are shown in Fig. 22, occur at the wave lengths shown in Table II.

The quantum theory of radiation and absorption provides a simple interpretation of these discontinuities. If electrons within the atom exist only in well defined energy levels, and if absorption takes place when an X-ray photon ejects an electron from some inner level to some outer level, then whether or not a *K* electron contributes to the absorption depends upon whether the X-ray photon is sufficiently energetic to eject this electron. In the case of argon illustrated in Fig. 21, a photon of wave length 4.0 A° does not possess sufficient energy to eject the *K* electron; a photon of wave length 3.7 A° is sufficiently energetic to eject this electron. Hence there is an abrupt increase in absorption coefficient between these two wave lengths. All materials show just the one discontinuity in that group of discontinuities occurring at the shortest wave length. It would therefore appear that the two *K* electrons possessed by a given atom are in exactly the same energy level. There appear to be no sublevels in the *K* shell, and this is consistent with all other data. On the other hand, all materials show three discontinuities in the *L* region, corresponding to the three sublevels supposed to exist in the *L* shell. The three discontinuities occur at slightly different wave lengths, for the photon must possess slightly different energies to eject an electron from the three sublevels. In a similar way the five discontinuities shown to exist in the *M* region are due to the five sublevels in the *M* shell. Whereas a great many accurate measurements[50] have been made in the *K* and *L* regions, only isolated observations have been made in the *M* region. For all except the highest atomic number elements the *M* region corresponds to very soft X-rays.

Although these absorption discontinuities appear perfectly sharp in the figures reproduced here, they have fairly recently been shown not to be absolutely abrupt. And one would suspect a fine structure from the concept of atomic structure and absorption phenomena. Let us think in particular of the *K* critical absorption line, and let us take Pt as a specific example. Pt, having atomic number 78, has 2 *K*, 8 *L*, 18 *M*, 32 *N*, 16 *O* and 1 *P* electron. The *K*, *L*, *M*, and *N* shells are full. The *O* and outer shells continue to build up as one goes to elements of higher atomic number. If a *K* electron of Pt is to be displaced it must be taken at least to the *O* shell; the *L*, *M*, and *N* shells are already full. It would be possible, however, to transfer this electron to the *O* shell, the *P* shell, the *Q* shell, etc. In any case absorption would take place, but the energy involved in the absorption would depend slightly upon the final level in which the electron is left. This difference in energy could never amount to more than that required to transfer an *O* electron on out to infinity. This is less than 100 volts. Hence one might expect to find in the *K* absorption discontinuity involving an energy absorption of 78,420 electron volts, a fine structure extending over a width of something less than 100 volts. Using apparatus of extremely high resolving power, several observers[53,54] have found for a goodly number of materials a definite fine structure extending over a region of approximately 100 volts. This fine structure appears as narrow bands of slightly decreased absorption appearing on the high frequency side of the discontinuity. This is in general agreement with the picture formed above.

The absorption coefficient for X-rays of a given wave length varies rapidly also with the atomic number of the absorbing material. In general the materials of high atomic number are much the best absorbers. Again, however, there appear abrupt discontinuities, situations where a material of a given atomic number is a much better absorber than one of somewhat higher atomic number. This is illustrated by Fig. 23 which shows the absorption of X-rays of 1 A° wave length by various materials.[52] The interpretation of these discontinuities follows immediately from the discussion above. An X-ray photon of wave length 1 A° has a definite energy. This is not enough to eject a *K* electron from selenium, atomic number 34, but it is sufficient to eject this electron from arsenic, atomic number 33. Since the energy required to eject a *K* electron increases with the atomic number, the position of the *K* discontinuity moves toward higher atomic numbers as one decreases the wave length used for the measurement. The three *L* discontinuities arise because of the existence of three sublevels in the *L* shell, and because the energy corresponding to any one of these increases with the atomic number of the atom.

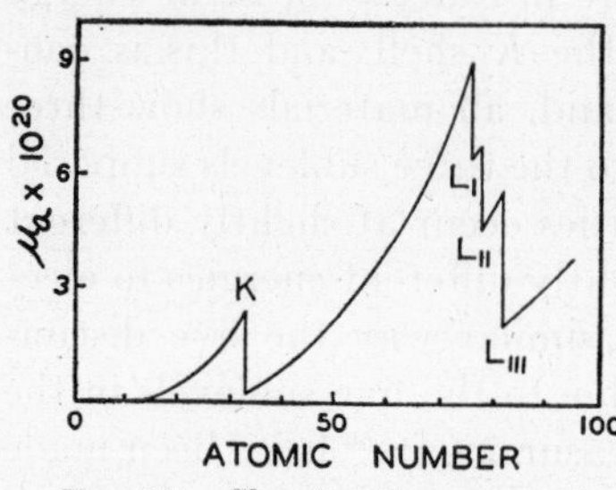


FIG. 23.—Showing the manner in which the absorption coefficient for X-rays 1 A° long varies with the atomic number of the absorber.

## 2. X-RAY SPECTRA

When high speed electrons are stopped abruptly by a target there are in general two types of X-rays given off. A part of the radiation is of a continuous distribution of wave lengths, the intensity and extent of which is determined mainly by the potential difference through which the electron fell before striking the target. This is called the continuous spectrum. The energy is distributed at all wave lengths down to a definite lower limit which is determined entirely by the potential difference through which the electron falls. Another part of the X-ray energy is radiated at certain definite wave

[53] P. A. Ross, *Phys. Rev.*, **44**, 977 (1933).
[54] W. H. Zinn, *Phys. Rev.*, **46**, 659 (1934).

lengths which are characteristic of the target. Although the potential difference across the tube must be at least a certain value in order to excite these characteristic lines, the wave lengths are entirely independent of this potential difference. This part of the radiation is called the line spectrum, or the characteristic radiation. A typical distribution of the energy in the

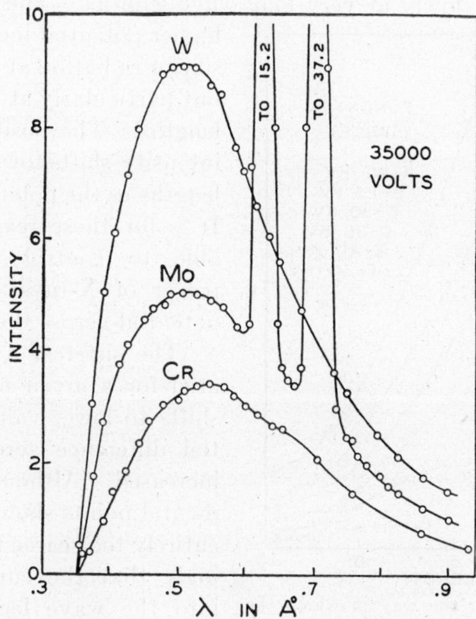


Fig. 24.—Typical X-ray spectra of W, Mo, and Cr with 35,000 volts across the tube. Note the intense characteristic spectra of Mo at approximately 0.63 and 0.71 A°. Similar characteristic spectra occur for Cr at wave lengths longer than those included in the figure, while equivalent spectra for W are excited only by application of a higher potential.

continuous spectrum, along with the characteristic line spectrum superimposed, is reproduced[55] in Fig. 24.

## Continuous Radiation

The continuous X-ray spectrum contains far the greater part of the total radiation, and shows several points of interest. Fig. 25 reproduces[56] the continuous spectrum from a *W* target when this target is bombarded by electrons which have fallen through various potential differences. *W* is a material of such high atomic number that the characteristic radiation of the target is not excited by potentials as low as those used here. Although the intensity of this continuous spectrum is considerably greater for targets of

[55] C. T. Ulrey, *Phys. Rev.*, **11**, 405 (1918).
[56] C. T. Ulrey, *Phys. Rev.*, **11**, 401 (1918).

high atomic number, the general features of the spectrum of $W$ are typical of that from any target. For a given potential across the tube there is no radiation at very short wave lengths. At a particular wave length, which depends upon the potential applied, the radiation starts abruptly and rises rapidly to a maximum. Its intensity then falls off more gradually, approaching zero slowly at very long wave lengths. The application of a higher potential increases the intensity of radiation at all wave lengths, but particularly at the shorter wave lengths. The position of the peak intensity shifts toward shorter wave lengths as the potential is increased. It is for these reasons that one is able to control the penetrating power of X-rays by varying the potential across the tube.

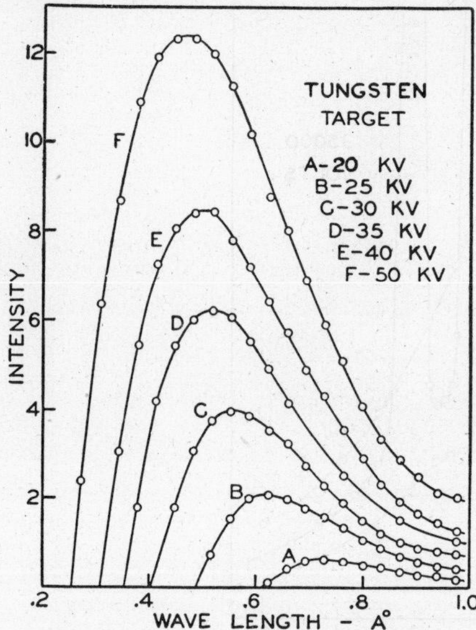


FIG. 25.—Showing the way in which the continuous spectrum from a W target depends upon the potential difference across the tube.

The shortest wave length radiated for a given potential likewise shifts to lower values as the potential difference across the tube is increased. Although the experimental points shown in Fig. 25 are entirely too scarce to show convincingly that the curves cut sharply into the wave length axis, other observations have shown definitely that they do. Furthermore, Duane and Hunt[57] have shown that this short wave limit is inversely proportional to the potential applied across the tube. It turns out that

$$Ve = h\nu_{max} = \frac{hc}{\lambda_{min}}$$

in which $V$ is the potential difference across the tube and in which $\nu_{max}$ and $\lambda_{min}$ refer respectively to the frequency and the wave length of the shortest X-ray radiated. It appears that the most energetic X-ray photon radiated is one possessing an energy which is equal to that of the electron striking the target. This relationship is known as the Duane and Hunt law. Its relationship to the Einstein photoelectric equation is obvious. Whereas the Einstein equation says that all the energy of an incident photon is spent in removing an electron from the material and giving it kinetic energy, the Duane and Hunt law says that the maximum energy a photon can receive

[57] W. Duane and F. L. Hunt, *Phys. Rev.*, **6**, 166 (1915).

is equal to the kinetic energy of the electron incident on the target. The production of X-rays according to this relationship is frequently referred to as the inverse photoelectric effect.

Since both potential differences and X-ray wave lengths can be measured with considerable accuracy, the Duane and Hunt law forms a basis for a precision determination of the ratio $h/e$. Many observers[57–62] have determined the ratio $h/e$ by this method. One of the most thorough sets of observations is one by DuMond and Bollman.[61] These observers find $h/e = (1.376 \pm 0.0003) \times 10^{-17}$ erg sec. per e.s.u. Quite recently Bearden and Schwarz[62] have found $1.3772 \times 10^{-17}$ and $1.3777 \times 10^{-17}$ for a gold and a copper target, respectively, the probable error being about 2 in the last place. These and other precise measurements by a different method have led Bearden to feel that the value obtained depends slightly upon the target used. If this is the case then some small factor has been neglected in the theory underlying the method. Most other results by the Duane-Hunt method are in close agreement with the values just given. Likewise, these agree rather well with the typical values[63,64] $1.372 \times 10^{-17}$ and $1.371 \times 10^{-17}$ obtained from studies of the photoelectric effect, although the photoelectric values are not as accurately determined as are the X-ray values.

There is still another method of evaluating the ratio $h/e$, however, which yields a value appreciably larger than any directly measured value. It will be recalled that the Rydberg constant in the Bohr expression for the frequencies of the characteristic spectral lines emitted by atomic hydrogen involves the quantities $e$, $e/m$, and $h/e$. If $e$ and $e/m$ are assumed to be known rather accurately from direct experiment, a supposedly accurate value of $h/e$ can be calculated from the observed value of the Rydberg constant. Unfortunately this value is slightly higher than any obtained by direct measurement. Birge[65] gives $(1.3793 \pm 0.0004) \times 10^{-17}$ as the most probable value obtained from the Rydberg constant. Although the discrepancy between this and the directly measured value is not large it is many times the probable error associated with the methods of determination. As a result the value of $h/e$ is at present somewhat in question.[38,66–68] Since $h$

58 A. H. Compton and S. K. Allison, *X-rays in Theory and Experiment* (2nd ed.; New York: D. Van Nostrand, 1935), p. 705.

59 P. Kirkpatrick and P. A. Ross, *Phys. Rev.*, **45**, 454 (1934).

60 G. Schaitberger, *Ann. d. Physik*, **24**, 84 (1935).

61 J. DuMond and V. Bollman, *Phys. Rev.*, **51**, 400 (1937).

62 J. A. Bearden and G. Schwarz, *Phys. Rev.*, **59**, 934 (1941).

63 P. Lukirsky and S. Prilezaev, *Zeits. f. Physik*, **49**, 236 (1928).

64 A. R. Olpin, *Phys. Rev.*, **36**, 251 (1930).

65 R. T. Birge, *Phys. Rev.*, **58**, 658 (1940).

66 J. W. M. DuMond, *Phys. Rev.*, **56**, 153 (1939).

67 F. G. Dunnington, *Rev. Mod. Phys.*, **11**, 65 (1939).

68 H. T. Wensel, *Jour. Res. Nat. Bur. Stds.*, **22**, 375, 392 (1939).

is obtained most accurately by combining the recent accurate value of $e$ with the value of $h/e$, then the quantity $h$ is also in question. If the directly measured[61] ratio $h/e$ is used one obtains a value

$$h = \left(\frac{h}{e}\right) e = 1.3762 \times 10^{-17} \times 4.803 \times 10^{-10} = 6.610 \times 10^{-27} \text{ erg sec.}$$

One recent survey[67] of physical constants suggests an arbitrarily accepted value $6.610 \times 10^{-27}$. This is equivalent to accepting the ratio $h/e$ observed directly in preference to the value calculated from the Rydberg constant. On the other hand, another recent survey[38] accepts the spectroscopic value of $h/e$ as the more probable, and this leads to a value $(6.6236 \pm 0.0024) \times 10^{-27}$ for $h$. Although there appears to be rather strong justification for accepting the value of $h/e$ calculated from the Rydberg constant in preference to that observed directly, it is disconcerting that not a single direct determination of $h/e$ by any method gives a value as high as the spectroscopic value. Very recently Bearden and Schwarz[62] have obtained a value $1.3793 \times 10^{-17}$, exactly equal to the spectroscopic value, by observing the excitation potential for the $K_{\alpha_1}$ line of nickel, but similar observations on targets of copper, zinc, gallium and tungsten all lead to lower values. That for copper is only slightly lower but for the other materials the value is essentially that obtained by the Duane-Hunt method. The fact that the directly measured value is always lower than the spectroscopic is particularly disconcerting when it is recalled that this ratio can be determined from the photoelectric effect with near visible light, from the limit of the continuous X-ray spectrum, from the excitation potentials of characteristic X-ray lines, from the energies of photoelectrons ejected by X-rays, from ionization and resonance potentials, from the Compton effect in the scattering of X-rays and from electron diffraction experiments. Only further work will show the real cause of this small but important discrepancy.

The origin of the continuous X-ray spectrum is open to considerable question.[69,70] The classical theory attempted to account for this electromagnetic radiation distributed continuously over a wide range of wave lengths in terms of the negative linear accelerations suffered by the electrons as they strike the target. Several features of this spectrum, together with some of the details of the angular distribution of radiation in various directions from the target, appear quite reasonable on this concept. Thinking in terms of radiation from an accelerated electron, the energy making up the continuous spectrum is often referred to as impulse radiation. Although

[69] A. H. Compton and S. K. Allison, *X-rays in Theory and Experiment* (2nd ed.; New York: D. Van Nostrand, 1935), pp. 56–115.

[70] F. K. Richtmyer, *Introduction to Atomic Physics* (New York: McGraw-Hill, 1928), pp. 483–497.

this general view of the continuous spectrum is based upon the rather basic concept that an accelerated electron should radiate energy, it is in serious disagreement with the observed energy distribution in the continuous spectrum in at least one respect. On the classical theory of radiation from an accelerated electron it can be shown that the energy distribution should approach zero asymptotically at short wave lengths. The existence of the sharp Duane-Hunt short wave length limit is quite inconsistent with the classical view.

The quantum theory offers a simple and convincing interpretation of this short wave limit. If the entire energy $Ve$ of the electron striking the target should be converted into a single photon of radiation, the frequency of this radiation should be given by

$$Ve = h\nu$$

Since this is the maximum energy that could be converted into a single photon, the frequency of the photon would be a maximum, or the wave length a minimum of those radiated. Thus the Duane-Hunt law becomes obvious. Only a few of the electrons striking the target would be expected to give up their total energy in the formation of a single photon. Most of them penetrate the target somewhat, giving up some of their energy to one atom and some to another. Such energy interchanges would result in the radiation of lower frequency, or longer wave length, photons. Hence a continuous distribution of energy at wave lengths greater than the Duane-Hunt limit would be expected. Calculation of the distribution of energy at various wave lengths expected on this view is also moderately successful. It is found, however, that some features of the continuous radiation are not so simply explained even on this view.

### Characteristic Radiation

The origin of the characteristic radiation appears much more certain. The characteristic radiation of a material can be excited by electron bombardment, by alpha particle bombardment,[71] by proton bombardment,[72,73] or by irradiating the material with sufficiently short X-rays. Whereas excitation by electron bombardment produces both the continuous and the characteristic radiation, bombardment with alpha particles or protons excites only the characteristic radiation. The X-rays given off by a material irradiated with other X-rays are in part those scattered from the primary beam and in part those characteristic of the material irradiated. The characteristic X-rays are often called fluorescent radiation. Barkla and

[71] W. Bothe and H. Fränz, *Zeits. f. Physik*, **52**, 466 (1928).

[72] C. Gerthsen and W. Reusse, *Phys. Zeits.*, **34**, 478 (1933).

[73] M. S. Livingston, F. Genevese, and E. J. Konopinski, *Phys. Rev.*, **51**, 835 (1937).

Sadler[74,75] were the first to study this fluorescent radiation seriously, and to classify it in different types. From a long series of measurements of the absorption coefficient of the characteristic radiation they concluded that the radiation characteristic of a given material could be divided into two types. One type was much more penetrating than the other, now known to be of shorter wave length, and this they called the *K* radiation. A more easily absorbed type they called the *L* radiation. The hardness of either type was

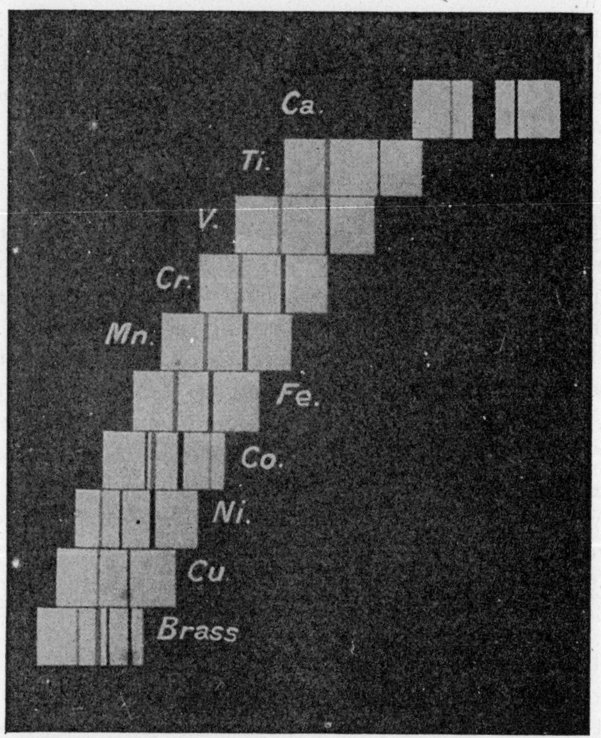


Fig. 26.—The original Moseley photograph of the K series lines from different elements.

found to increase with the atomic number of the material emitting the radiation. Barkla apparently recognized that these two types of radiation were probably composed of lines or groups of lines characteristic of the material.

Accurate analysis of these characteristic radiations had to await development of the X-ray crystal spectrometer. Moseley[76] was the first to attempt a systematic study of the line spectra making up the *K* and *L* characteristic radiation given off by the different elements. Using a Bragg crystal spec-

[74] C. G. Barkla and C. A. Sadler, *Phil. Mag.*, **16**, 550 (1908).
[75] C. G. Barkla, *Phil. Mag.*, **22**, 396 (1911).
[76] H. G. J. Moseley, *Phil. Mag.*, **26**, 1024 (1913); **27**, 703 (1914).

trometer in which a photographic film replaced the ionization chamber, Moseley examined the characteristic lines emitted by 38 different elements and found that these lines belonged to two distinct series which he identified with the *K* and *L* fluorescent radiation found by Barkla and Sadler. Moseley's original photograph of the *K* series spectra of a number of the elements is reproduced in Fig. 26. The record for any individual element is so placed in the figure that the distance of a given line from the left side of the figure can be taken roughly as a measure of the wave length of the line. The elements are arranged in the order of atomic number, the lowest being at the top of the figure. There is only one element between Ca of atomic number 20 and Zn, as a component of brass, of atomic number 30, which is missing from the figure.

The regular manner in which the frequency of the characteristic *K* radiation increases with the atomic number is remarkable. The lines characteristic of both Cu and Zn are present for brass, showing that an alloy gives the characteristic radiations of its component elements. Notice also the Fe and Ni impurities in Co. The photograph shows definitely that there is one element missing from the group, Sc of atomic number 21. X-ray data of this character would locate immediately any missing element for which a place should be left in the periodic table. They show definitely that all elements that exist between *H* and *U* have either been found or had blank spaces left for them in the periodic table. In early years there was considerable doubt as to whether Co of atomic weight 58.94 or Ni of atomic weight 58.69 should come first in the periodic table. The lower atomic weight of Ni provided a great incentive to place this element before Co. A glance at Moseley's results shows conclusively that Co falls between Fe and Ni. There are only three examples of reversal of atomic weight in the periodic table. These are A and K, Co and Ni, and Te and I. X-ray data show beyond all question that these elements have been placed in their proper order in the periodic table; the material of higher atomic weight has in each of these cases the lower atomic number.

The wave lengths of the lines comprising the characteristic *L* radiation vary regularly with atomic number in much the same manner as do those of the *K* lines. This is shown by the photograph[77] reproduced in Fig. 27. The atomic numbers of these four elements are 79, 81, 82, and 83 respectively, starting with Au. It is at once evident that one element, Hg of atomic number 80, is missing from the photograph. Similar regularity has been found for the lines of the *M* and *N* series. The wave lengths of a multitude of the characteristic lines for the different elements have been measured and can be found in tables.

[77] M. Siegbahn and E. Friman, *Ann. d. Physik*, **49**, 616 (1916); M. Siegbahn, *Spektroskopie der Röntgenstrahlen* (2nd ed.; Berlin: J. Springer, 1931), p. 92.

Moseley found from his experimental data that if the square root of the frequency of any particular line of the $K$ series of an element be plotted against the atomic number of this element, the points for the various ele-

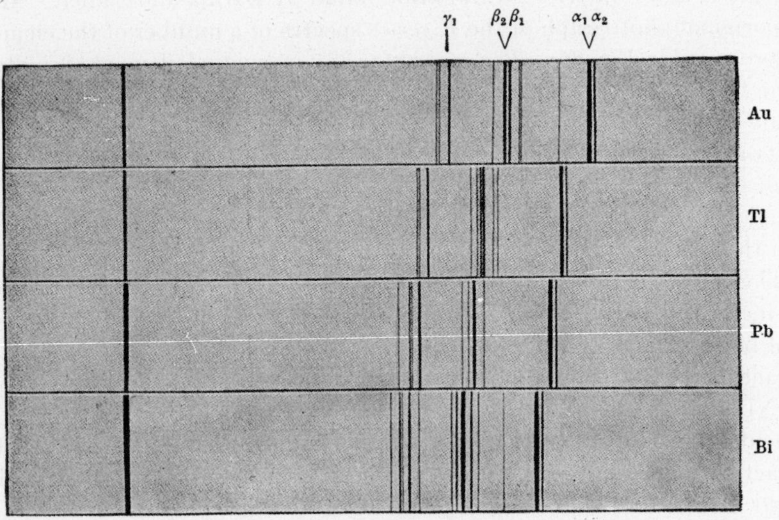


Fig. 27.—Typical $L$ series spectra of four elements nearly adjacent in the periodic table Hg, between Au and Tl, is missing from the photograph.

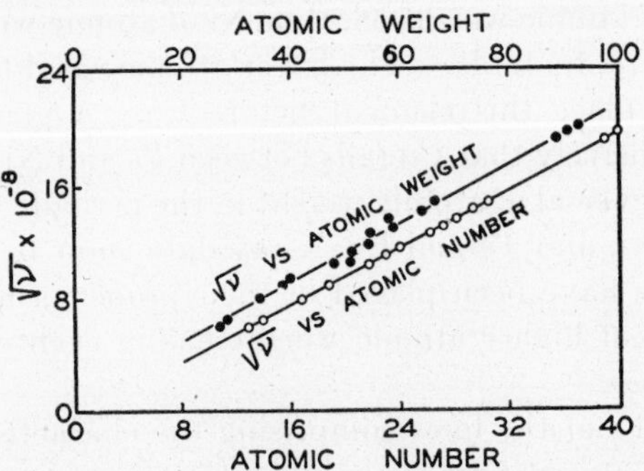


Fig. 28.—Moseley's curve showing the relation between the frequencies of characteristic X-ray lines and atomic number.

ments fall on a smooth curve which is very nearly a straight line. Expressed analytically this means that the frequency of a line is given by

$$\sqrt{\nu} = K(Z - k)$$

where $K$ and $k$ are universal constants for all the elements and where $Z$ is the atomic number of the element. This is known as Moseley's law. The essential correctness of this linear expression is evident from Fig. 28 in which

Moseley's original data have been plotted. The accuracy with which the points fall on a smooth curve shows that the atomic number is a much more fundamental quantity than the atomic weight in determining the frequency of the characteristic X-ray emitted by an element. A similar linear expression, with other constants instead of $K$ and $k$, holds for lines of the $L$ radiation.

Precise measurements have shown that these lines are not exactly straight, that the above linear relationship is not exact. But it is very close

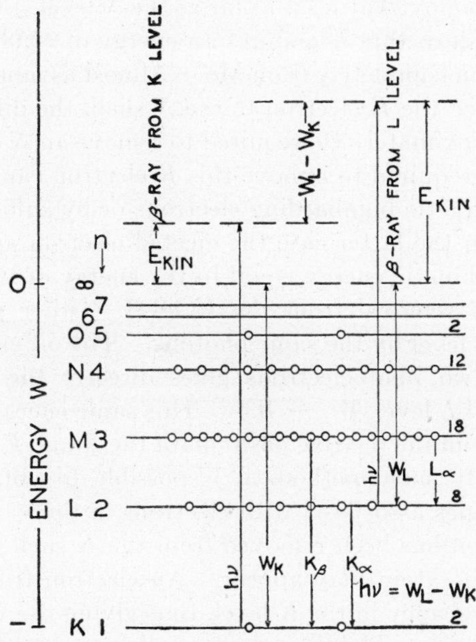


Fig. 29.—Illustrating the energy levels, and the distribution of electrons in these levels, for the Mo atom. (*Modeled after a diagram by Compton and Allison, X-Rays in Theory and Experiment*, p. 34, 1935.)

to the truth and, as a method of correlating the characteristic X-ray frequencies with atomic number, it led immediately to strong inferences regarding atomic structure and the process by which an atom emits an X-ray. The success that Bohr had just had in interpreting the several series of optical spectra of atomic $H$ in terms of discrete energy levels within the atom, led Moseley to attempt a similar interpretation for characteristic X-rays. Let us consider, as a specific example, the atom of Mo. Although in Moseley's day there existed little evidence regarding the distribution of electrons among the several supposed shells, let us think in terms of the distribution now known to be correct. Fig. 29 depicts[78] the several energy

[78] A. H. Compton and S. K. Allison, *X-rays in Theory and Experiment* (2nd ed.; New York: D. Van Nostrand, 1935), pp. 31–38.

levels and the number of electrons normally existing in each of these. Whereas optical line spectra result from a transition of one of the valence electrons from one level to another, X-ray spectra are associated with transitions of the deeper electrons. Obviously the normal atom is in no condition to radiate an energetic X-ray photon by having an electron fall into one of the lower levels; these lower levels are all full. The atom can absorb a large amount of energy, however, by having one of its electrons ejected. A large amount of energy would be required to eject a $K$ electron, for this electron must be removed at least as far as the $N$ level. Critical absorption wave length data show that it requires an energy of 20,000 electron volts to remove a $K$ electron completely from Mo. Almost as much energy would be required to displace the $K$ electron to the $N$ shell, the difference being only the few volts, approximately 20, required to remove an $N$ electron. The large amount of energy required to remove this $K$ electron can be supplied either by sufficiently energetic bombarding electrons or by sufficiently short wave length X-rays. In the latter case the ejected electron appears as a photoelectron having a kinetic energy equal to the energy of the incident photon less the energy of removal from the $K$ level. Other photoelectrons are ejected from the $L$ level by the same photons. The difference in the kinetic energy of these two photoelectrons gives directly the energy difference between the $K$ and $L$ level, $W_L - W_K$. This same energy difference might also be obtained from the relative positions of the $K$ and $L$ critical absorption discontinuities. By such methods it is possible to obtain the numerical values of the energies associated with electrons in the various shells.

Once an electron has been removed from the $K$ shell all the X-ray lines characteristic of the atom may appear. An electron from any outer shell may fall into the vacancy in the $K$ level, thus giving the various lines of the characteristic $K$ series. The line corresponding to a transition from the $L$ to the $K$ shell is called the $K_\alpha$ line. It is now obvious why the $K_\alpha$ line cannot be excited without the simultaneous appearance of higher frequency lines of the $K$ series, and why the energy required for excitation of the $K_\alpha$ line corresponds to that of a photon having the limiting high frequency of the $K$ series rather than to that of the $K_\alpha$ line itself. This $K_\alpha$ line should have a frequency given by

$$h\nu = W_L - W_K$$

where the energy difference is that determined by above mentioned methods. It is found that the longest wave length line of the $K$ series does have just this frequency. The frequency of the $K_\beta$ line agrees with the interpretation that this line arises because of a transition from the $M$ to the $K$ level. Similar statements can be made for other lines of the $K$ series. Furthermore, once an electron drops from the $L$ to the $K$ level there is a vacancy in the $L$ level. Electrons falling from outer levels into this vacant $L$ level give rise to the characteristic $L$ series of X-rays. In a similar way an $M$ series and an $N$ series arise for the heavier elements. One cannot excite the $K$ series without exciting also these other series. One can excite the $M$ series without exciting the $L$ or the $K$, or can excite the $L$ series without exciting the $K$.

Again, as was the case in optical spectra, close investigation shows that the characteristic lines are not actually as simple as has so far been inferred. The $K_\alpha$ line of Mo, for example, is a close doublet rather than a single line. The wave lengths of the two components of this doublet are 0.7121 A° and 0.7078 A°. Lines of the $L$ and $M$ series are still more complex multiplets. This suggests immediately the existence of sublevels within the main energy levels. The numerical energies associated with these sublevels are just those required to interpret quantitatively the one $K$, the three $L$ and the five $M$ critical absorption discontinuities. If there are three $L$ sublevels it would at first appear that the $K_\alpha$ line should be a triplet rather than a doublet. But again as in the case of optical spectra, transitions from certain sublevels of one shell to certain sublevels of another shell are apparently forbidden. A rather simple selection rule can be formed to cover all of the permitted transitions. Thus, although absorption can occur by the ejection of an electron from any one of the three $L$ sublevels, emission can occur only by transitions from two of these into the single $K$ level. Hence the resulting line is a doublet. Since the combined sublevel pattern of the $M$ and $L$ shells is more complex than that of the $L$ and $K$ shells, one should expect the line $L_\alpha$ and all other lines of the $L$ series to be more complex multiplets than are the lines of the $K$ series. Comparison of photographs[77] of the type shown in Fig. 27 of the $K$ and $L$ series respectively show that lines of the $L$ series have the more complex structure. Although the essential features of X-ray spectra are in entire accord with the simple picture here set forth, consideration of the many details of emission and absorption is a subject in itself. Such details must therefore be left to more specialized works.[79]

With these more recent and detailed views in mind, let us return to Moseley's interpretation of the observed manner in which the frequencies of characteristic lines vary with the atomic number. Following the general method which had been used by Bohr to calculate the energies associated with the various levels, and thence the frequencies of the emitted lines, of atomic $H$, Moseley attempted to calculate the frequencies of the characteristic X-rays. For an atom with net nuclear charge $Ze$ and but one planetary electron, Bohr obtained for the frequency of emission

[79] M. Siegbahn, *The Spectroscopy of X-rays* (London: Oxford University Press, 1925); *Spektroskopie der Röntgenstrahlen* (2nd ed.; Berlin: J. Springer, 1931).

$$\nu = \frac{2\pi^2 m Z^2 e^4}{\left(1 + \frac{m}{M}\right) h^3} \left(\frac{1}{n_f^2} - \frac{1}{n_i^2}\right) = RZ^2 \left(\frac{1}{n_f^2} - \frac{1}{n_i^2}\right)$$

where $R$ is known as the Rydberg constant. Now the many-body problem presented by a heavy atom prevents any rigorous calculation of an equivalent expression for X-rays. Not only the positive nuclear charge but all of the other planetary electrons as well would exert forces on any particular electron one might consider. While electrons in the outer shells would probably not affect a $K$ electron seriously, because they are on all sides of it, the second $K$ electron would no doubt decrease appreciably the net attraction between the nucleus and the first $K$ electron. Perhaps the net attraction, everything considered, might be represented as that due to an effective nuclear charge $(Z - k)e$, where $k$ is some small constant often called the screening constant. On this basis the expression for the frequency of emission becomes

$$\nu = \frac{2\pi^2 m (Z - k)^2 e^4}{\left(1 + \frac{m}{M}\right) h^3} \left(\frac{1}{n_f^2} - \frac{1}{n_i^2}\right) = R(Z - k)^2 \left(\frac{1}{n_f^2} - \frac{1}{n_i^2}\right)$$

Now for any particular line such as $K_\alpha$, the entire right side of this, except for the factor $(Z - k)^2$, is a constant for all the elements. If this constant factor be written $K^2$, one has

$$\nu = K^2(Z - k)^2 \qquad \text{or} \qquad \sqrt{\nu} = K(Z - k)$$

wherein, let it be remembered, $Z$ represents the net nuclear charge measured in electron units. But Moseley found experimentally that

$$\sqrt{\nu} = K(Z - k)$$

wherein $Z$ represents the atomic number. As Moseley pointed out, it is therefore almost impossible to escape the conclusion that the atomic number of an atom is equal to the net positive charge on the nucleus of that atom. This was the first convincing evidence obtained regarding the nuclear charge of an atom, and because of this Moseley's work took on still added importance. There had previously been two strong indications of this equality, one[80] from the intensity of X-rays scattered by light elements, the other [81] from the scattering of $\alpha$ and $\beta$ rays by thin films of metal. Although the latter of these has since provided convincing evidence of this equality, neither of these two other lines of evidence was entirely convincing at Moseley's time.

[80] C. G. Barkla, *Phil. Mag.*, **21**, 648 (1911).
[81] E. Rutherford, *Phil. Mag.*, **21**, 669 (1911).

Not only was the Moseley expression of the correct form, but it was shown to give essentially the correct numerical value for the frequency of the X-ray. The theoretical Moseley constant $K$ can be evaluated directly from the Rydberg constant and the initial and final quantum numbers $n_i$ and $n_f$ pertaining to the electron transition giving the line being considered. While the value of the screening constant $k$ cannot be deduced rigorously from theory, it can be calculated approximately. There is reason[78] to believe it to be 0.5. One can then calculate the theoretical frequency, or the theoretical wave length, of the Mo $K_\alpha$ line from the expression

$$\nu = R(Z - k)^2 \left(\frac{1}{n_f^2} - \frac{1}{n_i^2}\right)$$

where $Z = 42$, where $k = 0.5$, and where $n_f = 1$ and $n_i = 2$. This yields[78] a calculated wave length of 0.70 A°, which compares favorably indeed with the values 0.7121 A° and 0.7078 A° observed for the two components of the doublet of which the $K_\alpha$ line is actually composed. Carrying out a similar calculation[78] for the $L_\alpha$ line of $W$ of atomic number 74, using a screening constant of 5.5, one obtains a theoretical wave length of 1.40 A°. In view of the much larger screening effect of other electrons in this case, this figure agrees as well as we could expect with the observed wave length of 1.47 A°.

## 3. DIFFRACTION BY CRYSTALS AND CRYSTAL STRUCTURE

Considerable evidence concerning the diffraction of X-rays by crystals, and the interference and consequent reinforcement of the radiation in certain directions has already been presented. And it has been shown, following Bragg, just how such reinforcement is brought about through diffraction by the atoms or the molecules making up the regular lattice of the crystal. It is to be expected, therefore, that considerable information might be obtained regarding the details of crystal structure from the directions in which the beams diffracted by the different atom planes in a crystal reinforce. There are three distinct methods of studying crystal structure in this way, the Laue method, the Bragg method, and the powder crystal method. A fourth method, known as the oscillating crystal method, has also been used, but it involves no new features of crystal behavior. Detailed discussions of these methods can be found in many places.[82–84]

### The Laue Method

The first of the three methods to be developed, that of Laue,[14] consisted of sending a continuous spectrum of X-rays through a pinhole and thence

[82] W. H. Bragg and W. L. Bragg, *X-rays and Crystal Structure* (London: G. Bell & Sons, 1915).

[83] F. C. Blake, *Rev. Mod. Phys.*, **5**, 169 (1933).

[84] A. H. Compton and S. K. Allison, *X-rays in Theory and Experiment* (2nd ed.; New York: D. Van Nostrand, 1935), pp. 316–364.

through a single crystal of the material being studied, and of recording on a photographic plate placed beyond the crystal the spots of reinforcement. The essential arrangement has already been shown in Fig. 3, and typical photographs have been reproduced in Figs. 4 and 5. The complete analytical theory of the formation of these Laue spots has been developed. It turns out that each spot is due to a Bragg reflection from a series of parallel planes of atoms within the crystal.

The formation of these Laue spots is made more evident by the sketch reproduced[85] in Fig. 30. It will be shown shortly that some crystals such as

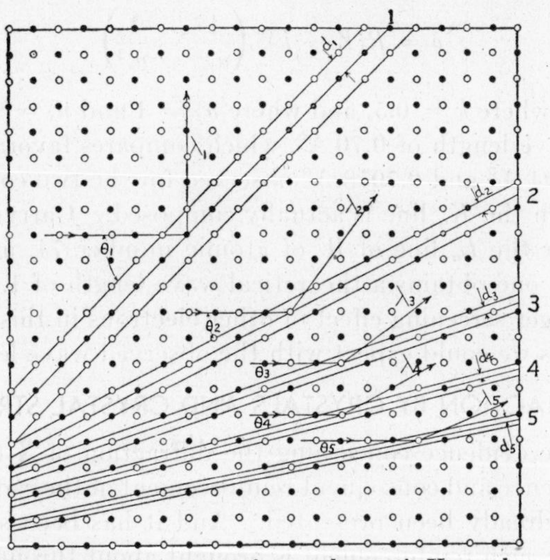


FIG. 30.—Illustrating the reinforcement of monochromatic X-rays by a cubic crystal made up of two kinds of atoms, when an X-ray beam containing all wave lengths is shown on the crystal horizontally from the left. (*Modeled after a diagram by Richtmyer, Introduction to Modern Physics, p.* 477, 1928.)

NaCl are made up of a simple cubic array of atoms, the two types of atoms alternating in position along the three axes of the cube. Fig. 30 reproduces one plane of such a crystal, the full circles representing one kind of atom and the open circles the other. A series of parallel planes, identical except for the alternation of atoms, can be imagined out in front of and behind the plane shown. There exist in the crystal numerous sets of parallel planes such as those represented by the lines 1, 2, 3, 4, and 5. The spacing between the planes is different for each different set of parallel planes. Let these spacings be represented by $d_1$, $d_2$, $d_3$, etc. Now imagine a pinhole beam of X-rays containing a continuous distribution of wave lengths incident horizontally on the left face of the crystal. Even the narrowest of beams would more

[85] F. K. Richtmyer, *Introduction to Modern Physics* (New York: McGraw-Hill, 1928), p. 477.

than cover the entire section of the crystal shown. Now the angles $\theta_1$, $\theta_2$, $\theta_3$, etc. are fixed by the orientation of the crystal with respect to the incident beam. Consequently, according to the Bragg law $n\lambda = 2d \sin \theta$, any particular set of planes will pick out from the continuous X-ray spectrum only one wave length for reflection. The planes of group 2 will pick out that wave length $\lambda_2$ for which

$$n\lambda_2 = 2d_2 \sin \theta_2$$

Since these are reflected in such a way that the incident and reflection grazing angles are equal, the reinforcement spot due to these planes will occur at an angle of $2\theta_2$ with respect to the incident beam. Other sets of planes will pick out other wave lengths from the continuous spectrum and produce reinforcements in other directions. In this way the many Laue spots are formed. We have of course considered reflections from only those planes drawn perpendicular to the plane of the paper in Fig. 30. If the entire cubic array of atoms is considered, it is clear that many other similar sets of planes would provide reflections which are not in the plane of the paper. Thus there results a symmetrical distribution of spots about a central spot. The degree of symmetry will depend upon the structure of the crystal and upon the orientation of the crystal with respect to the incident X-ray beam. With the beam incident on a cubic crystal as shown in Fig. 30 there should result a twofold symmetry of spots. The photograph reproduced in Fig. 4 shows this twofold symmetry.

Having a clear understanding of the formation of these Laue spots, it should be possible to determine the essential features of the structure of a given crystal from the angular positions of the spots for this crystal. The complete analytical considerations become rather involved, however. In view of this complexity, and in view of the much simpler experimental method developed immediately by the Braggs, we shall not discuss further the details of crystal analysis by this method.

## The Bragg Method

The general method of studying the reflection of X-rays from a crystal, as developed by the Braggs,[17,82] has already been outlined. The general arrangement of apparatus was shown in Fig. 6 and typical results were shown in Fig. 7. The manner in which the various atomic planes within the crystal operate to produce reinforcement of the reflected beam in certain directions has already been discussed. Let us now look briefly into how data of this character can be made to furnish information regarding the essential structure of a crystal. This will necessitate digressing for a moment to make clear the nomenclature used in referring to the various sets of planes within a crystal.

Let us confine our attention to a simple cubic array of diffracting centers forming a so-called cubic crystal. Let the small circles of Fig. 31 represent these diffracting centers spaced regularly and equally along the three cubic axes. Let us use as a unit of measure along the axes the spacing between successive diffraction centers along this axis. Let any plane parallel to the $yz$ plane be drawn through a group of atoms, say a plane containing the atom as coordinate (1, 0, 0). This plane intersects the $x$-axis at 1, the $y$-axis at $\infty$ and the $z$-axis at $\infty$. Let this plane be specified by stating the reciprocals of these three intercepts. Thus the plane is referred to as a (100) plane. Any parallel plane, regardless of whether it cuts the $x$-axis at 1, 2, 3, 4, etc., is called a (100) plane. An entirely similar group of planes might be drawn parallel to the $xz$ plane, and these might be called the (010) planes. Another similar set drawn parallel to the $xy$ plane might be called the (001) plane. It is clear, however, that these three sets of planes are entirely equivalent;

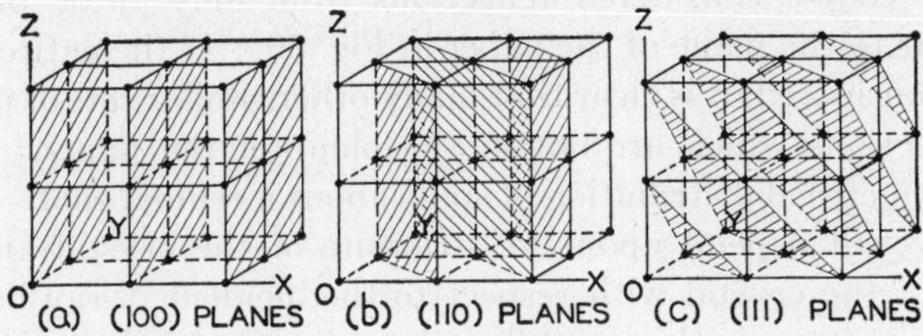


FIG. 31.—Showing the (100), the (110), and the (111) planes of a cubic crystal.

whether a set be called (100), (010), or (001) planes depends entirely upon the choice of axes in the crystal. Hence all three sets of planes are referred to as (100) planes. There are, however, other types of planes. Think of that plane intersecting the $x$-axis at 1, the $y$-axis at 1 and the $z$-axis at $\infty$. The reciprocals of these intercepts are respectively 1, 1, and 0. This plane, as well as any one parallel to it, is called a (110) plane. It is clear that one could draw two other sets of similar planes, one set parallel to the $x$-axis, the other parallel to the $y$-axis. These might be called respectively the (011) and (101) planes. But again these three sets of planes are exactly alike, their only distinction being due to the choice of axes. They are all called (110) planes. A third set of planes consists of those drawn parallel to that plane which intersects each of the three axes at 1. This is called a (111) plane, as is any other plane which intersects the three axes at equal distances out along the axes. A great many other types of planes might be drawn through the diffraction centers making up the crystal, and these are specified in an exactly similar way. It is clear that the simple planes, the (100), the (110) and the (111), are much richer in diffracting centers than are the more complex sets of planes. For this reason one is particularly interested in these three simple sets.

Let us think now of three different possible cubic arrays of diffracting centers. These are shown in Fig. 32. Configuration (*a*), drawn to half the scale used for the others for a reason which will soon become apparent, is known as a simple cube. Configuration (*b*) is known as a face centered cube; an additional lattice point is placed in the center of each face. Configuration (*c*) is known as a body centered cube; an additional lattice point is placed in the center of the cube. Now geometrical considerations show that the relative spacings of the (100), the (110), and the (111) planes are different for these three different cubic structures. If $d_{100}$ represents the spacing between

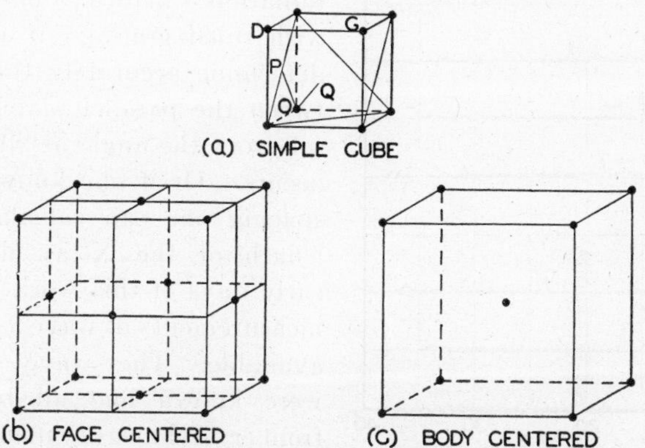


FIG. 32.—Illustrating the simple cubic lattice (*a*), the face centered cubic lattice (*b*), and the body centered cubic lattice (*c*).

the (100) planes in Fig. 32(*a*), it is seen that *OP* represents the distance between (110) planes, and that this is $\frac{\sqrt{2}}{2} d_{100}$. The distance between (111) planes represented by *OQ*, which is ⅓ of *OG*, is likewise seen to be $\frac{\sqrt{3}}{3} d_{100}$. If the same geometrical considerations are applied to the face centered and the body centered cubes, one finds that

| | |
|---|---|
| For simple cube | $d_{100}:d_{110}:d_{111}::1:1/\sqrt{2}:1/\sqrt{3}$ |
| For face centered cube | $d_{100}:d_{110}:d_{111}::1:1/\sqrt{2}:2/\sqrt{3}$ |
| For body centered cube | $d_{100}:d_{110}:d_{111}::1:2/\sqrt{2}:1/\sqrt{3}$ |

Thus the relative interplanar distances are different for these three cubic structures.

Consider now a typical crystal study, that of the crystals KCl and NaCl. Fig. 33 reproduces[82] Bragg's experimental curves for reflection from the several faces of these crystals. X-rays from a Pd target were used in obtaining these curves. The two peaks which consistently repeat themselves always in approximately the same relative intensity are due to two characteristic wave lengths of Pd. Evaluation of the angles at which a particular peak repeats itself for any one set of planes shows that the repetitions are the various orders of Bragg reflections occurring in accord with the Bragg law

$n\lambda = 2d \sin \theta$. The fact that a particular peak occurs at different angles for reflection from the several sets of planes of a given crystal, shows that the spacing is different for the different planes. And the fact that a given peak for reflection from the (100) planes occurs at a slightly different angle for the two crystals, shows that the spacing of the (100) is slightly different for KCl and NaCl. Since today the absolute wave length of a given characteristic radiation is known from measurements with ruled gratings, it is possible to determine accurately the spacing between the parallel planes of a given set from the angle at which the peak occurs. Or if one knows the crystal spacing one can calculate the wave length of the X-ray used. In the early days of this work ruled grating measurements of wave length were not available. The wave lengths that were known had all been obtained from crystal measurements, and evaluation of these necessitated knowing the crystal spacing. This crystal spacing could be calculated from the molecular weight and the density of the crystal if one could be certain of the arrangement of the atoms within the crystal. Thus it was important for more than one reason to learn all that was possible regarding the structure of these crystals.

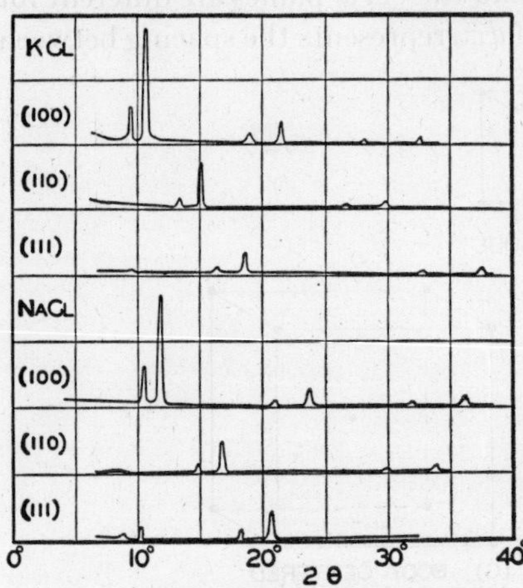


FIG. 33.—Showing the intensity of reflection for various grazing angles of incidence $\theta$ on the several faces of the crystals KCl and NaCl. The intensity of reflection is plotted as ordinate against $2\theta$ as abscissa.

The Braggs[82] were able to arrive definitely at the structure of these crystals from the curves of Fig. 33. Consider first the crystal of KCl. For the sake of brevity consider only the data furnished by the X-ray giving always the more intense of the two peaks. For the (100), the (110), and the (111) planes this peak occurs at angles $2\theta$ of 10.43°, 15.00° and 18.10°, respectively, or at angles $\theta$ of 5.22°, 7.50° and 9.05°. Since from the Bragg law the spacing of planes is inversely proportional to the sine of the angle $\theta$, it follows that

$$d_{100} : d_{110} : d_{111} :: \frac{1}{\sin 5.22^\circ} : \frac{1}{\sin 7.50^\circ} : \frac{1}{\sin 9.05^\circ}$$

$$:: \frac{1}{.0910} : \frac{1}{.1305} : \frac{1}{.1573}$$

$$:: 1 : 1/1.43 : 1/1.73$$

$$:: 1 : 1/\sqrt{2} : 1/\sqrt{3}$$

This ratio of spacings indicates a simple cubic structure rather than that of a face or a body centered cube.

Looking next at the curves for NaCl one sees immediately a peculiarity in the reflection from the (111) planes. Whereas for all other curves the intensity falls off continuously as one goes to higher orders of reflection, the second order for the (111) planes of NaCl appears much stronger than the first order. Bragg further remarks that these planes give a very weak third order and a definitely observable fourth. Were one to ignore the weak reflection at approximately 10° and judge solely by the strong peak at approximately 20° one would assign to NaCl a simple cubic structure similar to KCl. On the other hand, its structure as judged from the position of the first peak is that of a face centered cube. But this ignores entirely the peculiar changes in intensity as one proceeds to higher orders. Furthermore, there is reason to believe that the general structure of the NaCl crystal is the same as that of KCl, and for that matter the same as that of KBr and KI.

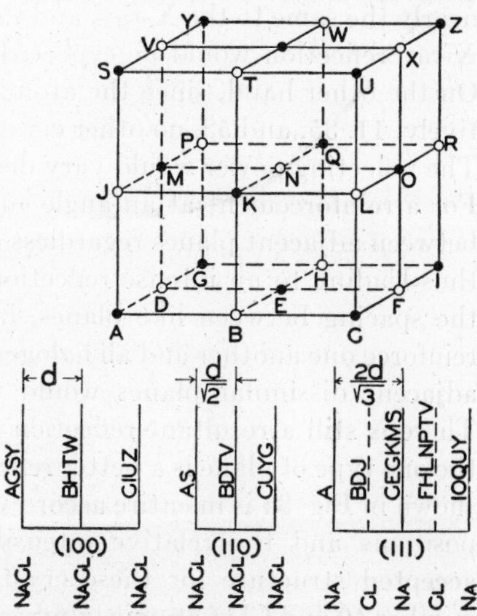


FIG. 34.—Illustrating the structure of an alkali metal halogen crystal, say NaCl. The full circles represent Na atoms and the open circles Cl atoms.

Similar Bragg curves for KBr and KI show that of all these KCl is the only one which does not show the peculiar alternation of intensity in the reflection from the (111) planes. This suggested immediately that the diffraction centers in all of these crystals were not molecules at all but single atoms of K or Na and single atoms of Cl, Br, or I. Let us therefore look into the possibility of a structure such as indicated in Fig. 34. In a crystal such as this, where the two kinds of atoms alternate in filling the lattice points along any one line, all (100) planes contain equal numbers of alkaline metal and halogen atoms. Likewise all (110) planes contain equal numbers of these. But the (111) planes do not. One of these planes is made up entirely of alkaline metal atoms, the next entirely of halogen atoms, the next of alkaline atoms, etc. Although the spacing between adjacent (111) planes is $d/\sqrt{3}$, the spacing between planes containing the same kind of atoms is $2d/\sqrt{3}$. The question of the relative reflecting powers of the planes made up entirely of the two different kinds of atoms must therefore be considered.

Now in a rough way at least, the reflecting power of an atom is proportional to its atomic number, or proportional to the number of planetary electrons. K of atomic number 19 and Cl of atomic number 17 would therefore have closely the same reflecting power. They would therefore act nearly the same to the X-ray, and the spacing of (111) planes calculated from X-ray reflection would be expected to come out $d/\sqrt{3}$, as it does for KCl. On the other hand, since the atomic numbers of Na, Br, and I are, respectively, 11, 35, and 53, no other crystal of this type would behave in this way. The reflecting power would vary decidedly from one (111) plane to the next. For a reinforcement at an angle corresponding to a spacing of $d/\sqrt{3}$, that between adjacent planes regardless of type, all of the planes would reinforce, thus leading to an intense reflection. At a smaller angle corresponding to the spacing between like planes, however, all alkaline atom planes would reinforce one another and all halogen planes would reinforce one another, but adjacent dissimilar planes would work pair by pair in exact opposition. There is still a resultant reflection for all crystals except KCl only because the one type of plane is a better reflector than the other. Thus the structure shown in Fig. 34 is in entire accord with the Bragg curves both as regards the positions and the relative intensities of the reflection peaks. It is the accepted structure for these crystals. One might ask how K of atomic number 19 and Cl of atomic number 17 have so nearly equal reflecting powers as to cause almost complete destruction of the first peak in the (111) reflection. If ions rather than atoms are at these lattice points, both the positive K ion and the negative Cl ion would have 18 planetary electrons. If the reflecting power is exactly proportional to the number of these electrons, then this structure would cause complete disappearance of this (111) peak for KCl. The fact that the peak is practically absent has been considered as some evidence that ions rather than atoms are at the lattice points of these crystals.

It is to be noted that the conclusions drawn regarding the arrangement of atoms in the NaCl and similar crystals have been possible without knowing the wave length of the incident X-ray. If one knew the distance between the characteristic planes of this crystal one could calculate the wave length of the X-ray from the observed angular position of the Bragg reflection peak. It is therefore of great importance that knowledge of the arrangement of atoms in the crystal allows one to calculate this spacing with certainty. Consider a cube of NaCl 1 cm. on a side. If $d$ be the distance between (100) planes, the number of atoms along one edge of the cube is $1/d$. The number of atoms in the centimeter cube is then $1/d^3$. But the number of molecules in this centimeter cube is $N\rho/M$ where $N$ is Avogadro's number, $M$ the molecular weight and $\rho$ the density of the crystal. Since there are two atoms, and hence two lattice points, for each molecule of NaCl, the number of atoms in the centimeter cube is $2N\rho/M$. Hence

$$\frac{1}{d^3} = \frac{2N\rho}{M}, \quad \text{from which} \quad d = \sqrt[3]{\frac{M}{2N\rho}}$$

Using $N = 6.064 \times 10^{23}$ as obtained from the Faraday and the Millikan oil drop value of $e$, and using $M = 58.46$ and $\rho = 2.167$ gms/cc., one finds that the spacing of (100) planes in the NaCl crystal is

$$d = 2.814 \times 10^{-8} \text{ cms.} = 2.814 \text{ A}^\circ$$

Knowing the spacing of planes in this crystal the wave length of any X-ray reflected from the face of the crystal can be calculated accurately from the angular position of the peak. It is from such crystal measurements that all early values of X-ray wave lengths were determined. Although there are now available more accurate values of the molecular weight and density of NaCl, from which a more accurate value of the lattice spacing could be calculated, this crystal is not used extensively for precision measurements of wave length. It turns out that calcite has many practical advantages over NaCl as a crystal to be used for precision measurements. The spacing of the calcite planes determined in a way analogous to that employed above, has been given[86] as

$$d = (3.02816 \pm 0.001) \text{ A}^\circ$$

for a temperature of 20.00° C. The probable error in this value is due almost entirely to that associated with the value of Avogadro's number. It will be recalled that at the time of this work the best value of Avogadro's number was obtained from the Faraday and the Millikan oil drop value of $e$. In the hands of Siegbahn[79] and others the crystal spectrometer has been developed to such a degree that the accuracy attained in the measurement of X-ray wave lengths is comparable to that attained in the measurement of the wave lengths of optical lines. Relative wave lengths could of course be measured much more accurately than absolute wave lengths, for the former does not involve the probable error in the crystal spacing. For the purpose of standardization Siegbahn[79] had already adopted an arbitrary value for the spacing of calcite approximately 1 part in 3,000 higher than the experimental value later reported by Bearden.[86] Until relatively few years ago all accurate X-ray wave lengths were specified on this Siegbahn scale.

It has since become possible to obtain X-ray spectra from ruled gratings and to calculate the wave length of the X-ray from the known distance between lines on the grating. It was found,[87,88] that wave lengths measured

[86] J. A. Bearden, *Phys. Rev.*, **38**, 2089 (1931).
[87] E. Bäcklin, *Dissertation*, Uppsala (1928).
[88] J. A. Bearden, *Phys. Rev.*, **48**, 385 (1935).

by this method did not agree exactly with those from crystal measurements; they were $(0.248 \pm 0.002)$ % larger. Although this is a relatively small error it was important, for it brought to light an appreciable error in another important fundamental physical quantity. After a careful search for any possible unrecognized error in either method of wave length measurement, it was concluded[88] that the ruled grating method gives the correct value and that the crystal measurements were slightly in error. Now the crystal measurements involved the calculated spacing of crystal planes and this calculation involves in Avogadro's number the Millikan oil drop value of the electronic charge. Since X-ray wave lengths are determined precisely by ruled grating measurements, one can now determine the crystal spacing directly, and thence calculate Avogadro's number with accuracy. This gives[88]

$$N = (6.0221 \pm 0.0005) \times 10^{23}$$

Then using this value of $N$ and the accurately known value of the Faraday, one obtains[88] for the electronic charge

$$e = (4.8036 \pm 0.0005) \times 10^{-10} \text{ e.s.u.}$$

This value is now accepted as essentially correct and, as brought out in a previous chapter, it has since been shown that the primary error in the original Millikan oil drop value was due to the use of a slightly incorrect value for the viscosity of air.

This new value of Avogadro's number made it necessary to revise slightly all previously calculated spacings for the various crystals. In fact it was from direct measurement of this spacing in terms of the ruled grating wave length that the new value for Avogadro's number was obtained. The spacings of all crystals are slightly higher than those previously calculated. For example, the accepted spacing for calcite at 20° C is[88] now

$$d = (3.03560 \pm 0.00005) \text{ A}^\circ$$

This is 0.246% higher than the value obtained[86] through use of the old value for Avogadro's number. It is also interesting that the probable error associated with this new spacing for calcite is very much smaller than the former.

### The Powder Crystal Method

A third method of studying crystal structure, one rather widely used today, was developed[89,90] shortly after the Bragg method. Whereas both the Laue and the Bragg methods required the use of a single crystal, and in

[89] P. Debye and P. Scherrer, *Gött. Nachr.*, (1916); *Phys. Zeits.*, **17**, 277 (1916).
[90] A. W. Hull, *Phys. Rev.*, **9**, 84 (1916); **10**, 661 (1917).

the Bragg method a fairly large one, this new method used the crystalline material in the form of a finely ground powder. It is therefore known as the

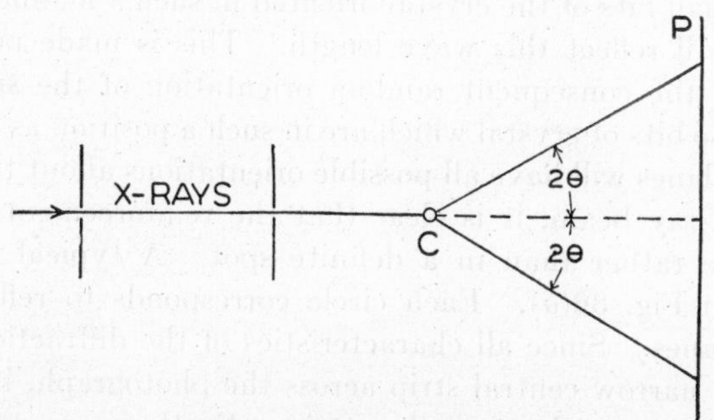


FIG. 35.—Illustrating the method of obtaining an X-ray diffraction pattern by using a powdered crystal.

powder crystal method. The principle of the method is illustrated in Fig. 35. Although the arrangement is essentially that used by Laue, a mono-

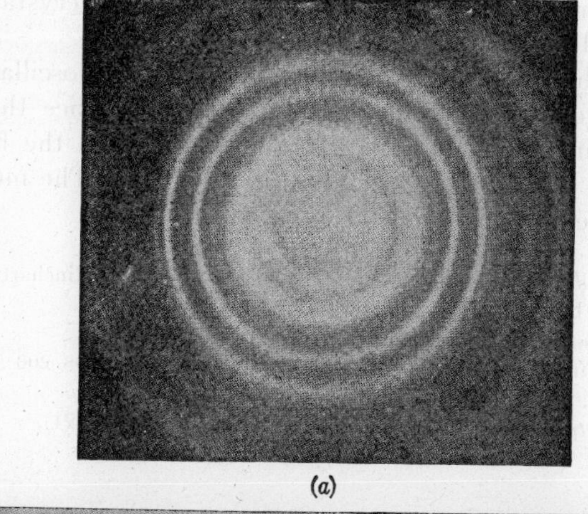

(a)

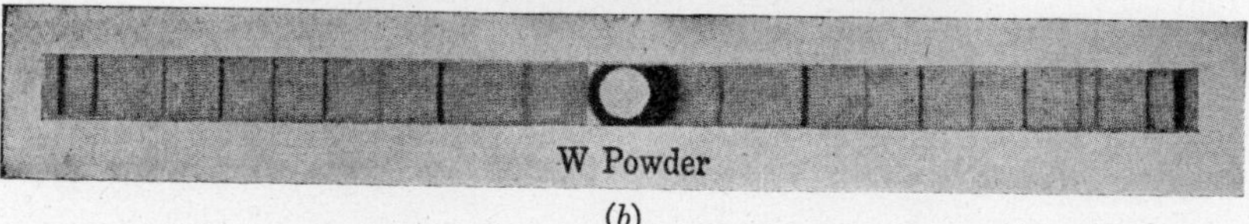


(b)

FIG. 36.—(a) X-ray powder diffraction pattern of Al. (b) X-ray powder diffraction pattern of W, obtained with a narrow strip of film bent in the arc of a circle.

chromatic beam of X-rays is used in this method whereas a continuous band of wave lengths was used in the Laue method. Whereas in the Laue method a given set of crystal planes was fixed in position and therefore had to pick out from the continuous band of wave lengths that particular wave length which it was in a position to reflect, in this method the single wave length finds certain small bits of the crystal oriented in such a manner that a given set of planes will reflect this wave length. This is made possible by the powdering and the consequent random orientation of the small particles. Since even those bits of crystal which are in such a position as to reflect from a given set of planes will have all possible orientations about the direction of the incident X-ray beam, it is clear that the reinforcement will occur all around a circle rather than in a definite spot. A typical photograph is reproduced[91] in Fig. 36(*a*). Each circle corresponds to reflection from a given set of planes. Since all characteristics of the diffraction pattern are contained on a narrow central strip across the photograph, it is customary to record the pattern only on such a strip. Furthermore, to facilitate the evaluation of angles, this strip is usually bent in the arc of a circle whose center is at the powdered crystal. A typical photograph obtained in this way is reproduced[91] in Fig. 36(*b*). The ease with which such photographs can be taken, together with the fact that the crystalline material need not be obtained in the form of a large crystal, makes the powder crystal method an exceedingly useful one for the analysis of crystals.

A fourth method of crystal analysis, known as the oscillating crystal method, was developed[92–94] still a few years later. Since the method is somewhat more involved, and since it adds nothing to the fundamental concepts we wish to convey, no details will be given. The method is not widely used in the practical analysis of crystals.

[91] H. Semat, *Introduction to Atomic Physics* (New York: Farrar & Rinehart, 1939), p. 109. Original photographs by A. W. Hull and coworkers.

[92] H. Seemann, *Phys. Zeits.*, **20**, 169 (1919).

[93] E. Schiebold, *Einführung i.d. Krist. Formenlehre*, 3rd ed., pp. 198–200 (1919); *Zeits. f. Physik*, **9**, 180 (1922); **23**, 337 (1924).

[94] M. Polanyi, *Naturwiss.*, **9**, 337 (1921); *Zeits. f. Physik*, **7**, 149 (1921).

## Chapter 8

# $\alpha$, $\beta$ AND $\gamma$-RAYS—NATURAL RADIOACTIVITY

## I. GENERAL PHENOMENA OF RADIOACTIVITY

### The Discovery

The discovery of radioactivity was brought about more or less directly by Roentgen's discovery of X-rays in 1895. For some time immediately following Roentgen's discovery it was suspected that the emission of X-rays might be connected in some way with the fluorescence of the glass walls of the X-ray tube. It was therefore natural that other observers searched for a penetrating radiation that might be given out by the more common fluorescent and phosphorescent materials. Among those substances investigated by Henri Becquerel[1] was a certain salt of uranium which, as he had shown some years earlier, phosphoresced brilliantly under the action of ultraviolet light. A bit of this salt, after exposure to light, was wrapped in black paper and placed near a photographic plate. A sheet of silver was placed between the salt and the photographic plate. After a few hours a distinct photographic effect was observed. The uranium salt gave off some radiation sufficiently penetrating to pass through the silver plate and affect the photographic emulsion. It was soon found that the emission came from the uranium component of the salt; all uranium compounds containing the same amount of uranium, or an equivalent amount of uranium itself, gave the same intensity of radiation. The emission of this penetrating radiation proved to be entirely independent of any property of fluorescence or phosphorescence. It has also turned out to be independent of the physical or chemical state of the substance.

Many investigations followed Becquerel's discovery in 1896. Such names as Rutherford, Soddy, and Curie are associated with these early studies. It was soon found that thorium,[2,3] polonium,[4] radium,[5] and actinium[6] also gave off penetrating radiation. In fact a great many substances were found to be radioactive, but practically all of these appeared to

[1] H. Becquerel, *Comptes Rendus*, **122**, 420, 501, 559, 689, 762, 1086 (1896).

[2] G. C. Schmidt, *Ann. d. Physik*, **65**, 141 (1898).

[3] Mme. S. Curie, *Comptes Rendus*, **126**, 1101 (1898).

[4] P. Curie and Mme. S. Curie, *Comptes Rendus*, **127**, 175 (1898).

[5] P. Curie, Mme. P. Curie and G. Bémont, *Comptes Rendus*, **127**, 1215 (1898).

[6] A. Debierne, *Comptes Rendus*, **129**, 593 (1899); **130**, 906 (1900).

come originally from either uranium or thorium. It soon became apparent that atoms of these radioactive materials are not stable. Sooner or later they disintegrate, giving off a penetrating radiation, and become a new material. This material in turn is radioactive and the procedure is repeated until the new atom formed in the disintegration process is one of stable structure. Thus it may be said that either uranium or thorium is the ancestor of at least nearly all the natural radioactive atoms. Most of these radioactive materials are heavy atoms, atoms having atomic weights greater than that of lead. The ancestry of all of these heavy radioactive atoms is almost completely known. There are four much lighter materials which have also been found to be naturally radioactive. These are $K^{40}$, $Rb^{87}$, $Sm^{148}$, and $Lu^{176}$. The activities of K and Rb were discovered[7–9] many years ago, while those of Sm[10–12] and Lu[13,14] have been found in relatively recent years. The atomic numbers of these materials are respectively 19, 37, 62, and 71, whereas the atomic numbers of all of the heavier radioactive atoms lie between 81 and 92. Innumerable investigations have been carried out in the field of natural radioactivity since its original discovery. Many summaries of the field, together with extensive tables of radioactive constants, can be found in the literature.[15–21]

### The Half Life Period

The average time a radioactive material exists before it disintegrates into some other material varies greatly from one substance to another. Only one half of a sample of UI disappears by disintegration in $4.5 \times 10^9$ years. Only thorium disappears less rapidly than this; one half of a sample of thorium disintegrates in $1.34 \times 10^{10}$ years. At the other extreme, one half of a

[7] J. J. Thomson, *Phil. Mag.*, **10**, 584 (1905).

[8] N. R. Campbell and A. Wood, *Proc. Camb. Phil. Soc.*, **14**, 15 (1907).

[9] N. Campbell, *Proc. Camb. Phil. Soc.*, **14**, 211 (1907).

[10] G. Hevesy, M. Pahl and R. Hosemann, *Zeits. f. Physik*, **83**, 43 (1933).

[11] R. Hosemann, *Zeits. f. Physik*, **99**, 405 (1936).

[12] T. R. Wilkins and A. J. Dempster, *Phys. Rev.*, **54**, 315 (1938).

[13] M. Heyden and W. Wefelmeier, *Naturwiss.*, **26**, 612 (1938).

[14] W. F. Libby, *Phys. Rev.*, **56**, 21 (1939).

[15] A. F. Kovarik and L. W. McKeehan, *Bull. Nat. Res. Coun.*, **10**, 1–203 (1925). Reprinted and revised in 1929.

[16] E. Rutherford, J. Chadwick and C. D. Ellis, *Radiations from Radioactive Substances* (London: Cambridge University Press, 1930).

[17] Mme. P. Curie, *Radioactivité* (Paris: Hermann & Co., 1935).

[18] G. Hevesy and F. A. Paneth (translated by R. W. Lawson), *A Manual of Radioactivity* (2nd ed.; London: Oxford University Press, 1938).

[19] K. K. Darrow, *Bell System Tech. Jour.*, **17**, 292–337 (1938).

[20] J. B. Hoag, *Electron and Nuclear Physics* (2nd ed.; New York: D. Van Nostrand, 1938), pp. 240–291, 462–464, 471.

[21] F. Rasetti, *Elements of Nuclear Physics* (New York: Prentice-Hall, 1936).

sample of RaC′ disappears in $10^{-6}$ seconds; one half of a sample of ThC′ probably disintegrates in approximately $10^{-11}$ seconds, although this figure is not so reliably known. The time required for one half of a sample to disintegrate is called the "half life" of the material. Approximately forty different natural radioactive materials are known, and the half lives of these are distributed widely between the limits just quoted. There is nothing one can do to change in any way the rate at which a given material disintegrates. The half life is entirely independent of pressure, temperature, and other conditions under our control. The radioactive atoms insist upon disintegrating, and at a rate which is no doubt determined somehow by the degree of instability of their structure.

### Nature of the Emissions

Investigations of the nature of the radioactive emissions of these materials have shown that there are three types of radiation. These are called $\alpha$, $\beta$ and $\gamma$-rays. The $\alpha$ and $\beta$-rays can be bent in an electric or magnetic field, though a relatively strong field is required to deflect $\alpha$-rays; these are definitely charged particles. The $\gamma$-rays cannot be deflected in either magnetic or electric fields; they are not charged particles. It has been shown that the $\alpha$ particles are He nuclei; they bear a positive charge equal to two electrons; they are He atoms which have lost their two planetary electrons. The $\beta$ particles are simply high speed electrons, negatively charged particles exactly like those leaving the cathode of a discharge tube. Both the $\alpha$ and the $\beta$ particles are ejected with energies of the order of a few million electron volts. The $\gamma$-rays have been shown to be very short electromagnetic waves; the wave length of these is in general shorter than that of X-rays, although many of the softer $\gamma$-rays are longer than the more penetrating X-rays.

### The Transformation Series

We now know something over forty natural radioactive substances, know the type of radiation each emits, and have in nearly all cases a reliable value for the half life. Most of these substances were identified within a decade after the discovery of radioactivity, although a few have been found in more recent years. All of the heavy substances fall within three series of chain transformations. These chains are referred to as the uranium, the actinium and the thorium series. The members of the three series are shown in Table I. The successive transformations proceed from the top toward the bottom in each series shown. UI, AcU and Th are the ancestors of the three families. RaG, AcD and ThD are the respective end products of the three chains. Table I gives also the half life associated with each transformation and the type of radiation emitted. The half lives given for UI, UII and AcU are those found recently by Nier,[22] while those given for $UX_1$, AcB and AcC″

[22] A. O. Nier, *Phys. Rev.*, **55**, 150 (1939).

TABLE I

Natural radioactive elements. The atomic number $Z$, the atomic weight $A$, the half life $T$, and the type of radiation is given for each. Beta radiations inclosed in parentheses are not of nuclear origin. The letters $y$, $d$, $h$, $m$ and $s$ used in expressing the half lives stand for year, day, hour, minute and second, respectively. The alpha particle ranges are those in air at 760 mm. of Hg and 15° C. * The series branches here, part of this element disintegrating into C′ and part into C″. ** The two branches reunite here

| Substance | $Z$ | $A$ | $T$ | Particle emitted | Extrapolated range of $\alpha$ particle |
|---|---|---|---|---|---|
| URANIUM SERIES | | | | | |
| Uranium I | 92 | 238 | $4.56 \times 10^9 y$ | $\alpha$ | 2.67 |
| Uranium X$_1$ | 90 | 234 | $24.1d$ | $\beta$ | |
| Uranium X$_2$ | 91 | 234 | $1.14m$ | $\beta, \gamma$ | |
| Uranium II | 92 | 234 | $2.7 \times 10^5 y$ | $\alpha$ | 3.23 |
| Ionium | 90 | 230 | $8.3 \times 10^4 y$ | $\alpha$ | 3.2 |
| Radium | 88 | 226 | $1590y$ | $\alpha, (\beta), \gamma$ | 3.39 |
| Radon | 86 | 222 | $3.825d$ | $\alpha$ | 4.08 |
| Radium A | 84 | 218 | $3.05m$ | $\alpha$ | 4.69 |
| Radium B | 82 | 214 | $26.8m$ | $\beta, \gamma$ | |
| Radium C* | 83 | 214 | $19.7m$ | $\alpha, \beta, \gamma$ | 4.1 |
| Radium C′ (99.96%) | 84 | 214 | $10^{-6}s$ | $\alpha$ | 6.95 |
| Radium C″ (0.04%) | 81 | 210 | $1.32m$ | $\beta$ | |
| Radium D** | 82 | 210 | $22y$ | $\beta, \gamma$ | |
| Radium E | 83 | 210 | $5.0d$ | $\beta, \gamma$ | |
| Radium F | 84 | 210 | $140d$ | $\alpha$ | 3.87 |
| Radium G | 82 | 206 | Stable—lead of atomic weight 206 | | |
| ACTINIUM SERIES | | | | | |
| Actinouranium | 92 | 235 | $7.13 \times 10^8 y$ | $\alpha$ | 3.2 |
| Actinium Y | 90 | 231 | $24.6h$ | $\beta$ | |
| Protoactinium | 91 | 231 | $3.2 \times 10^4 y$ | $\alpha$ | 3.67 |
| Actinium | 89 | 227 | $13y$ ? | $\beta$ | |
| Radioactinium | 90 | 227 | $18.9d$ | $\alpha, (\beta), \gamma$ | 4.68 |
| Actinium X | 88 | 223 | $11.2d$ | $\alpha$ | 4.37 |
| Actinon | 86 | 219 | $3.92s$ | $\alpha$ | 5.73 |
| Actinium A | 84 | 215 | $2 \times 10^{-3}s$ | $\alpha$ | 6.50 |
| Actinium B | 82 | 211 | $36.1m$ | $\beta, \gamma$ | |
| Actinium C* | 83 | 211 | $2.16m$ | $\alpha, \beta$ | 5.46 |
| Actinium C′ (0.16%) | 84 | 211 | $5 \times 10^{-3}s$ | $\alpha$ | 6.60 |
| Actinium C″ (99.84%) | 81 | 207 | $4.76m$ | $\beta, \gamma$ | |
| Actinium D** | 82 | 207 | Stable—lead of atomic weight 207 | | |
| THORIUM SERIES | | | | | |
| Thorium | 90 | 232 | $1.34 \times 10^{10} y$ | $\alpha$ | 2.59 |
| Mesothorium 1 | 88 | 228 | $6.7y$ | $\beta$ | |
| Mesothorium 2 | 89 | 228 | $6.13h$ | $\beta, \gamma$ | |
| Radiothorium | 90 | 228 | $1.90y$ | $\alpha, (\beta)$ | 4.02 |
| Thorium X | 88 | 224 | $3.64d$ | $\alpha$ | 4.35 |
| Thoron | 86 | 220 | $54.5s$ | $\alpha$ | 5.03 |
| Thorium A | 84 | 216 | $0.14s$ | $\alpha$ | 5.67 |
| Thorium B | 82 | 212 | $10.6h$ | $\beta, \gamma$ | |
| Thorium C* | 83 | 212 | $60.5m$ | $\alpha, \beta$ | 4.78 |
| Thorium C′ (65%) | 84 | 212 | $10^{-11}s$ ? | $\alpha$ | 8.62 |
| Thorium C″ (35%) | 81 | 208 | $3.1m$ | $\beta, \gamma$ | |
| Thorium D** | 82 | 208 | Stable—lead of atomic weight 208 | | |

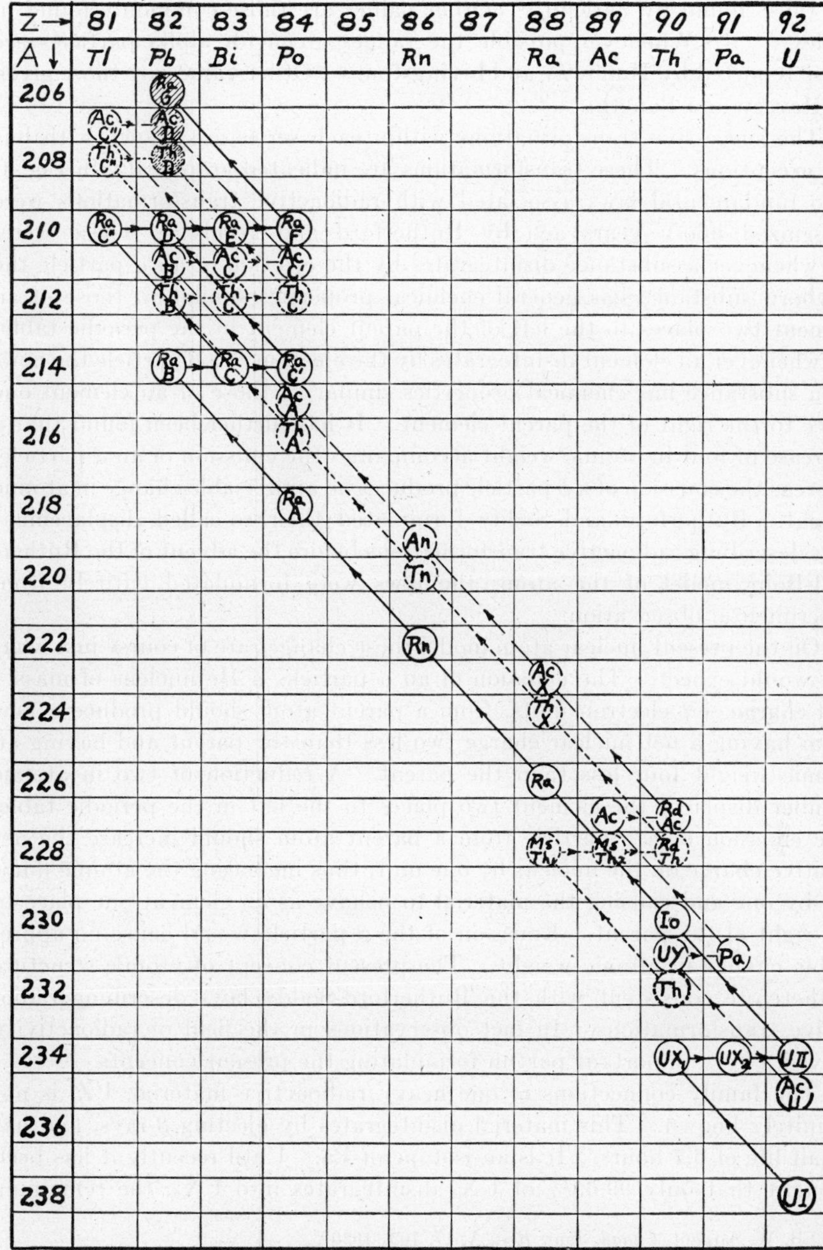


Fig. 1.—Illustrating the successive transformations within the uranium, the actinium, and the thorium series.

are those found by Sargent.[23] Other values are those commonly found in tables.[17,18,20] Whenever possible the ranges given for alpha particles are those reported by Holloway and Livingston.[24] Other values are those given by Hevesy and Paneth.[18]

The successive transformations within each series are known with but few exceptions. These transformations are indicated graphically in Fig. 1. Two fundamental laws associated with radioactive transformations were recognized many years ago by Rutherford and Soddy.[25] These were: (1) whenever a substance disintegrates by the ejection of an $\alpha$ particle the newborn substance has general chemical properties similar to those of an element two places to the left of the parent element in the periodic table; (2) whenever an element disintegrates by the ejection of a $\beta$ particle the newborn substance has chemical properties similar to those of an element one place to the right of the parent element. It has further been found that a decrease of four in atomic weight accompanies the emission of an $\alpha$ particle, whereas the emission of a $\beta$ particle produces no appreciable change in atomic weight. Rutherford and Soddy formulated their so-called displacement laws describing radioactive transformations before the advent of the Rutherford-Bohr model of the atom; the laws were formulated entirely from experimental observation.

On the present nuclear atom model these changes are of course just what one would expect. The emission of an $\alpha$ particle, a He nucleus of mass 4 and charge +2 electron units, from a parent atom should produce a new atom having a net nuclear charge two less than the parent and having an atomic weight four less than the parent. A reduction of two in atomic number displaces the element two places to the left in the periodic table. The emission of a $\beta$ particle from a parent atom should increase the net positive charge on the nucleus by one unit, thus increasing the atomic number by one and causing the material to behave as an element one place to the right of the parent. Emission of the $\beta$ particle would cause no appreciable change in atomic weight. The present concept of atomic structure is therefore consistent with the Rutherford-Soddy laws describing radioactive transformations. In fact observations in the field of radioactivity played a very important part in formulating the present concepts.

The family connections of one heavy radioactive material, UZ, is not definitely known. This material disintegrates by ejecting $\beta$-rays, and has a half life of 6.7 hours. It is an isotope of Pa. Until recently it has been thought that only 99.65% of $UX_1$ disintegrates into $UX_2$, the remaining

[23] B. W. Sargent, *Canad. Jour. Res.*, A, **17**, 103 (1939).

[24] M. G. Holloway and M. S. Livingston, *Phys. Rev.*, **54**, 18 (1938).

[25] E. Rutherford and F. Soddy, *Trans. Chem. Soc.*, **81**, 321, 837 (1902); *Phil. Mag.*, **4**, 370 569 (1902); **5**, 441, 445, 576 (1903).

0.35% forming UZ. Both $UX_2$ and UZ were then supposed to disintegrate into UII. Recent work indicates that it is more probable, however, that UZ is not the offspring of $UX_1$; it is probably a product of the disintegration of $U^{235}$. It is known that uranium has three isotopes, $U^{238}$, $U^{235}$ and $U^{234}$. These have all been observed with a mass spectrograph. Aston[26] found $U^{238}$ and estimated that this isotope constitutes at least 97% of all uranium. Dempster[27] detected the $U^{235}$ isotope in 1935, and Nier[22] found $U^{234}$ in 1938. According to Nier[22] the relative abundance of these isotopes is $U^{238}/U^{235} = 139$ and $U^{238}/U^{234} = 17{,}000$. $U^{238}$ is the ancestor of the uranium series. $U^{234}$ is UII, a member of this series. $U^{235}$ is now thought to be the ancestor of the actinium series. It disintegrates with a half life of $7.13 \times 10^8$ years,[22] forming AcY. It is thought that UZ may be a product of this disintegration series.

The atomic weights shown in Table I for the various members of the uranium and thorium series are without much doubt correct. Although a majority of these atomic weights have not been measured directly, those of certain members within these series have been measured. For example, the atomic weight of UI is known to be 238, that of Ra 226, and that of Rn 222. The latter two of these are the values one expects from the known series of transformations which UI undergoes to become first one and then the other of these materials. UI is changed to Ra after three α particle and two β particle transformations. The atomic weight of Ra should therefore be 12 less than that of UI, as is observed. Ra changes into Rn after one α particle transformation. One would therefore expect Rn to have an atomic weight 4 less than that of Ra, as is observed. Thus there is a considerable degree of certainty of the atomic weights assigned to the various members of the U series. In a similar way the atomic weight of Th is known and one can thus deduce rather certainly the weights of those members of the thorium series for which there are no directly measured values. The same certainty is not attached to the atomic weights shown for the actinium series. In fact only a few years ago it seemed that this entire series might be a branch of the uranium series. UY, a member of the actinium series and now frequently called AcY, was thought to come from UII. Part of UII was supposed to form ionium and thence the remainder of the uranium chain. Another part was supposed to form UY, which in turn formed protoactinium and the remainder of the actinium chain. On this supposed origin of UY the atomic weights assigned to members of the actinium chain were each one less than those shown in Table I. Recent observations indicate,[18] however, that the atomic weights are probably those shown in the table, and that UY is not a branch product of the uranium chain starting

[26] F. W. Aston, *Nature*, **128**, 725 (1931).

[27] A. J. Dempster, *Nature*, **136**, 180 (1935); *Proc. Amer. Phil. Soc.*, **75**, 755 (1935).

with $U^{238}$. Rather recently an U isotope of atomic weight 235, called actino-uranium, has been discovered. It seems probable that UY results from this U isotope through an $\alpha$ particle transformation. This view, consistent with the atomic weights shown in Table I, is now rather generally accepted. If this view is correct the actinium series is not a branch of the uranium series; it is an independent chain starting with $U^{235}$. Considerable progress has been made in recent years on the separation of isotopes. If several members of this series can be isolated so that their atomic weights can be obtained directly, then it will be known whether the atomic weights now assigned are correct.

It is both interesting and important to note that each of the three series of transformations ends with Pb, an atom of atomic number 82. Seven isotopes of Pb are shown in Fig. 1. The four heavier of these are radioactive; the three lighter ones are stable. The uranium series ends with $Pb^{206}$, the actinium series with $Pb^{207}$, and the thorium series with $Pb^{208}$. Now it was discovered quite early that the measured atomic weight of Pb depends upon the origin of Pb. The chemical atomic weight of Pb as it is ordinarily found is[28] 207.21. This is no doubt the mean of a number of isotopes normally present. There has been found[29] on numerous occasions, however, natural Pb which has an appreciably different atomic weight. The atomic weight of Pb present in the mineral thorite has been found to be unusually high, 207.9 for example. This is excellent evidence that most of this Pb has been formed through disintegration of Th; it is composed mainly of the $Pb^{208}$ isotope. On the other hand the atomic weight of Pb found in U minerals is unusually low, 206.03 for example. This is apparently composed almost entirely of the $Pb^{206}$ isotope, the end product of the disintegration of $U^{238}$. No one has yet found Pb composed mainly of the isotope $Pb^{207}$, the end product of the actinium series. This is probably because the supposed ancestor of the actinium series is a relatively rare U isotope, $U^{235}$. Since $U^{238}$ is 139 times as abundant in nature as $U^{235}$, and since both would be expected in U minerals, the presence of the end product $Pb^{207}$ would be masked by that of the end product $Pb^{206}$. For no other element does the isotopic composition vary as greatly as it does in Pb. It has been found[30] that the percentage of heavy hydrogen is slightly less and that of $O^{18}$ slightly greater in snow than in normal river water. Similarly the ratio of the carbon isotopes $C^{12}/C^{13}$ has been found[31] to differ in carbon

[28] *International Atomic Weights*, *Jour. Amer. Chem. Soc.*, **60**, 744 (1938).

[29] G. Hevesy and F. A. Paneth (translated by R. W. Lawson), *A Manual of Radioactivity* (2nd ed.; London: Oxford University Press, 1938), pp. 149–151.

[30] A. E. Brodsky, O. C. Scarre, E. I. Donzowa and M. M. Sluckaia, *Acta Physicochimica*, **7**, 611 (1937).

[31] A. O. Nier and Others, *Jour. Amer. Chem. Soc.*, **61**, 697 (1939); *Phys. Rev.*, **59**, 771 (1941).

obtained from various natural sources. But these variations are small, not even comparable with those observed for Pb associated with radioactive minerals. It is interesting that even common Pb, apparently not contaminated with radioactive minerals, shows[32] significant variations in isotopic constitution. This is probably because it has been contaminated with these minerals in the past.

It has been remarked that there are four relatively light natural elements which are radioactive. These are shown in Table II. Three of these emit

TABLE II
Natural radioactive light elements

| Substance | $Z$ | $A$ | $T$ | Particle emitted | Range of $\alpha$ particle |
|---|---|---|---|---|---|
| Potassium | 19 | 40 | $1.9 \times 10^9 y$ | $\beta, \gamma$ | |
| Rubidium | 37 | 87 | $5 \times 10^{10} y$ | $\beta$ | |
| Samarium | 62 | 148 | $1.4 \times 10^{11} y$ | $\alpha$ | 1.15 |
| Lutecium | 71 | 176 | $7 \times 10^{10} y$ | $\beta$ | |

$\beta$ particles. Samarium is the only natural light element known to emit $\alpha$ particles. Although it has been recognized for many years that K and Rb are radioactive, it is only recently that it has been known for certain which isotope of each is the active one. Since knowledge of both the particular isotope which is active and the relative abundance of this isotope is necessary before one can evaluate the half period, it is only recently that reliable values of these periods have been obtained. The $K^{40}$ isotope was discovered by Nier[33,34] in 1935 and found to make up $1/8300$ of the element. Two years later Smythe and Hemmendinger[35] succeeded in separating the isotopes of K with a mass spectrograph. Sufficient quantities of the several isotopes were isolated to show definitely that the radioactivity was associated with the $K^{40}$ component. Knowing the active isotope and its relative abundance it was then possible to obtain[36] a reliable value for the half period. Through use of the mass spectrograph and other methods the active isotope of Rb has been found to be that of atomic weight 87, the active isotope of Sm to be[12] that of atomic weight 148, and the active isotope of Lu to be[14] that of atomic weight 176. Nothing is known regarding any chain transformations among these lighter elements. There is no evidence that the four shown are connected in any way. It is interesting that the $\gamma$ radiation from K is

[32] A. O. Nier, *Jour. Amer. Chem. Soc.*, **60**, 1571 (1938).

[33] A. O. Nier, *Phys. Rev.*, **48**, 283 (1935).

[34] A. K. Brewer, *Phys. Rev.*, **48**, 640 (1935).

[35] W. R. Smythe and A. Hemmendinger, *Phys. Rev.*, **51**, 178 (1937).

[36] A. Bramley and A. K. Brewer, *Phys. Rev.*, **53**, 502 (1938).

almost as penetrating as that from RaC. The radiation from RaC is some $10^{10}$ times as intense, however. The intensity of radiation from all of these lighter elements is low, so low that it is difficult to study the radioactive properties reliably.

## 2. THE THEORY OF RADIOACTIVE TRANSFORMATIONS

### General Considerations

It was Rutherford and Soddy[25] who first proposed a general theory of radioactive transformations. It was supposed that radioactive atoms are unstable and that they disintegrate according to the laws of chance. They assumed that the disintegration of a single atom is accompanied by the ejection of a single $\alpha$ or a single $\beta$ particle. That this is the case at least statistically has now been shown by experiment. If $\alpha$ particles are allowed to strike a fluorescent screen a tiny flash of light called a scintillation is produced by each particle striking the screen. By counting the scintillations produced in a known time by $\alpha$ particles ejected within the known solid angle subtended by the screen at the source, one can evaluate the total number of $\alpha$ particles ejected per unit time. This number is always found equal to the number of atoms disintegrating per unit time, the number of disintegrating atoms being calculated from the observed rate of change of the parent substance into the new material. It has also been proved experimentally that the number of $\beta$ particles ejected per unit time from the nuclei of a substance undergoing a $\beta$-ray transformation is statistically equal to the number of atoms disintegrating per unit time. More $\beta$ particles are actually ejected but these additional particles are not of nuclear origin; they come from the planetary structure of the atom. While these observations really prove only statistically that one nuclear particle is ejected for each atom that disintegrates, it is logical to assume that the relationship holds for individual atoms and that the one ejected particle actually comes from the one disintegrating atom.

Analytically the problem of radioactive disintegration can be treated only statistically, that is, according to the laws of probability. That the disintegrations do occur at random is shown by the random distribution of observed $\alpha$ particles. These $\alpha$ particles are ejected at random as regards both direction and time. Let us suppose that at time $t$ there are $N$ radioactive atoms of a given parent element present. Let $\lambda$ be the fraction of these that disintegrate per unit time. Then the increase $dN$ in the number of atoms present occurring in the time interval $dt$ is

$$dN = -\lambda N dt$$

The negative sign appears because of the general agreement that the differential $dN$ represents an increase in $N$ and because the quantity $\lambda N dt$ itself represents a decrease in $N$. Integrating, and designating the number of parent atoms present at the time $t = 0$ by $N_0$, one obtains

$$N = N_0 \epsilon^{-\lambda t}$$

Experimentally it is found that any radioactive parent substance does decay along an exponential of this form. A typical decay curve, that for $UX_1$, is shown in Fig. 2. From the observed rate of decay the constant $\lambda$, or the half life $T$, can be evaluated. Starting with any point on the decay curve of Fig. 2, an additional 23 or 24 days are required for half of the $UX_1$ then present to disappear. These early data[37] agree favorably with the present accepted value of 24.1 days for the half life period of $UX_1$. If one takes the natural logarithm of each side of the last equation and plots log $N$ against $t$ a straight line results, a line whose negative slope is $\lambda$. One can therefore

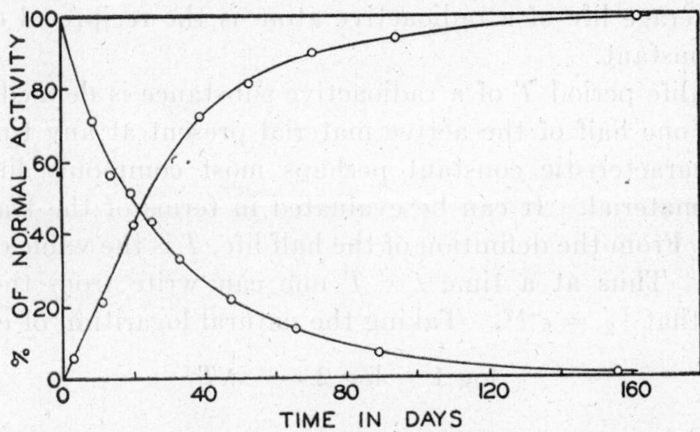


Fig. 2.—Illustrating typical decay and growth curves of radioactive materials.

test any particular transformation to see whether it conforms to the exponential decay just deduced by plotting experimental values of log $N$ against $t$. If this leads to a straight line then the disintegrations occur as supposed and the experimental value of $\lambda$ can be obtained from the slope of the experimental line. This constant $\lambda$ is characteristic of a particular transformation; it is called the transformation constant.

## Relationships among the Several Radioactive Constants

The average life of a radioactive atom can be expressed in terms of the transformation constant $\lambda$. While the actual lives of individual atoms may be anything from 0 to $\infty$, the average life is quite definite. From the definition of $\lambda$ the number of atoms which break down between times $t$ and $(t + dt)$ is

$$dN = \lambda N dt$$

[37] E. Rutherford, *Radioactive Substances and Their Radiations* (London: Cambridge University Press, 1913), p. 335.

Substituting the value of $N$ found above for the number of atoms still existing at this time $t$, one obtains

$$dN = \lambda N_0 \epsilon^{-\lambda t} dt$$

Each of these atoms has a life $t$. Then the average life $T_a$, all atoms considered, is

$$T_a = \frac{\int_0^\infty \lambda t N_0 \epsilon^{-\lambda t} dt}{N_0} = \lambda \int_0^\infty t\epsilon^{-\lambda t} dt = \lambda \left[ \frac{\epsilon^{-\lambda t}(-\lambda t - 1)}{\lambda^2} \right]_0^\infty$$

or

$$T_a = \frac{1}{\lambda}$$

Thus the average life of a radioactive atom is the reciprocal of the transformation constant.

The half life period $T$ of a radioactive substance is defined as the time required for one half of the active material present at any time to decay. It is the characteristic constant perhaps most commonly linked with a radioactive material. It can be evaluated in terms of the transformation constant $\lambda$. From the definition of the half life, $T$ is the value of $t$ for which $N/N_0 = \frac{1}{2}$. Thus at a time $t = T$ one can write from the expression $N = N_0 \epsilon^{-\lambda t}$ that $\frac{1}{2} = \epsilon^{-\lambda T}$. Taking the natural logarithm of each side,

$$\log 1 - \log 2 = -\lambda T$$

from which

$$T = \frac{\log 2}{\lambda} = \frac{0.693}{\lambda}$$

The half lives $T$ for the various radioactive substances, ranging from $10^{-11}$ seconds up to billions of years, are shown in Table I. It is clear that the rapidity with which a radioactive material disintegrates could be expressed by stating any one of three characteristic constants, the transformation constant $\lambda$, the average life $T_a$, or the half life period $T$. Having any one of these, either of the others can be found.

**The Manner in Which a New Substance Builds Up**

The quantitative manner in which a parent element decays has already been discussed; it decays along a decreasing exponential the equation of which is $N = N_0 \epsilon^{-\lambda t}$. Let us inquire into the manner in which the newborn substance builds up. The problem is complicated by the fact that during the rise of the new substance the amount of parent substance present continually decreases; also, the substance formed by decay of the parent begins itself to decay. Let us therefore consider the problem under two conditions: (1) that when the rate of decay of the parent substance is negligible; (2) that when the rate of decay of the parent is not negligible. The first condition is really a special case of the general situation represented by the second condition.

If the parent substance decays at a negligible rate the number of parent atoms $N_{01}$ remains essentially constant during the time required for the new substance to build up. Let $N_2$ be the number of newborn atoms actually present at any time $t$. There are being formed continually more new atoms by disintegration of the parent. The number of new atoms formed per second from the parent is $N_{01}\lambda_1$, where $\lambda_1$ is the transformation constant of the parent. At the same time some of these new atoms are themselves disintegrating. The number disintegrating per second is $N_2\lambda_2$ where $\lambda_2$ is the transformation constant of the new substance. If $dN_2$ represents the increase in the number of new atoms present which occurs in time $dt$, then

$$dN_2 = (N_{01}\lambda_1 - N_2\lambda_2)dt$$

Integrating this, and using the fact that $N_2 = 0$ when $t = 0$, one finds that the number of new atoms present at time $t$ is

$$N_2 = N_{01}\frac{\lambda_1}{\lambda_2}(1 - \epsilon^{-\lambda_2 t})$$

It is found experimentally that the rise of a radioactive product from a slowly decaying parent is in accord with this expression. Fig. 2 illustrates the manner in which the newborn substance builds up to an equilibrium value. It is obvious from the last equation that the number $N_2$ reaches a steady value, theoretically for $t = \infty$, given by

$$N_2 = N_{01}\frac{\lambda_1}{\lambda_2}$$

Under this condition the new substance, represented by the subscript 2, is decaying at the same rate as that at which it is being formed from the parent substance 1. The two are said to be in radioactive equilibrium. The proportions of the two substances present remain fixed.

In many instances there may be more than two radioactive materials in equilibrium. Each substance present is then disintegrating at exactly the same rate as that at which it is being formed. It is evident from the definition of the transformation constant $\lambda$ that when any number of substances are in radioactive equilibrium the product of the number of atoms of a particular kind present and the transformation constant for this atom is the same for each substance present. That is, for a number of substances in radioactive equilibrium $N_1\lambda_1 = N_2\lambda_2 = N_3\lambda_3 = N_4\lambda_4$. . . . This relationship has often been found useful in determining the transformation constant of a substance. If the transformation constant of one of two materials in equilibrium is known, and if the relative numbers of atoms of the two materials present can be determined by quantitative analysis, then the unknown transformation constant can be calculated.

In the above treatment it has been assumed that the parent substance decays at an inappreciable rate. If this parent substance disintegrates at a rate comparable with that of its product the treatment is somewhat more complex. The number of parent atoms present is no longer constant; let it be $N_1$ at time $t$. Then there will be $N_1\lambda_1$ new atoms formed per second from the parent; and $N_2\lambda_2$ of these newly formed atoms decay per second.

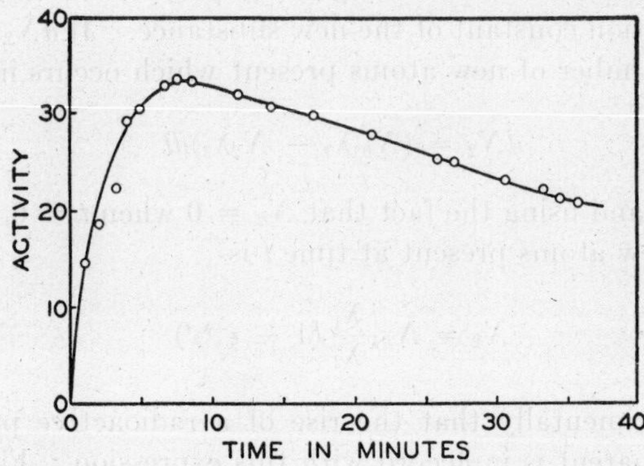


FIG. 3.—The rise and fall of AcC being formed from a fairly rapidly decaying parent AcB.

The increase in the number of new atoms in a small interval of time $dt$ is therefore

$$dN_2 = (N_1\lambda_1 - N_2\lambda_2)dt$$

But the number of parent atoms $N_1$ existing at time $t$ is given by

$$N_1 = N_{01}\epsilon^{-\lambda_1 t}$$

where $N_{01}$ represents the number of these atoms originally present. Putting this value of $N_1$ into the above equation,

$$dN_2 = (\lambda_1 N_{01}\epsilon^{-\lambda_1 t} - N_2\lambda_2)dt$$

Integrating this, and using the fact that $N_2 = 0$ when $t = 0$,

$$N_2 = N_{01}\frac{\lambda_1}{\lambda_2 - \lambda_1}(\epsilon^{-\lambda_1 t} - \epsilon^{-\lambda_2 t})$$

The manner in which $N_2$ actually varies with $t$ is illustrated by the experimental data of Fig. 3. Investigations[38–41] of the activities of various sources have shown that Fig. 3 is typical of the initial rise and subsequent fall of a product formed from a rapidly decaying parent. The behavior conforms to an expression of the type just deduced. $N_2$ reaches a true maximum at a time depending only upon $\lambda_1$ and $\lambda_2$. The time at which this maximum occurs could of course be obtained by differentiation of the above expression. At this maximum true equilibrium exists for the moment and $N_1\lambda_1 = N_2\lambda_2$.

## 3. ALPHA PARTICLES, THEIR ORIGIN AND PROPERTIES

### The Nature of the Particles

Alpha particles are He nuclei, atoms of He less the two planetary electrons. They are known to be He nuclei from a variety of experiments. It is possible to determine the total number of alpha particles ejected in a given time by counting the rate at which these particles strike a fluorescent screen which subtends a known solid angle at the $\alpha$-ray source. Then by allowing all of the particles ejected to strike a conductor connected to an electroscope it is possible to determine the charge carried by a known number of particles. In this way it has been shown[42–45] that each $\alpha$ particle carries a positive charge equal to two electrons. Streams of these particles can be bent in either electric or magnetic fields, though a relatively strong field is required to produce an appreciable bending. The ratio charge/mass can be obtained from the observed bending in known fields. Knowing both the charge and the ratio charge/mass, the mass of the $\alpha$ particle can be obtained. This mass comes out essentially that of the He atom. Such measurements are not sufficiently precise to distinguish between the mass of the atom and that of the nucleus. It has further been shown[46] that if particles are shot through a very thin glass wall into an evacuated vessel which has been carefully freed from He, gaseous He gradually accumulates in this vessel. Whereas the original contents of the vessel do not give out the spectrum characteristic of He, the region does give out this spectrum after $\alpha$ particles

[38] E. Rutherford, *Phil. Mag.*, **5**, 95 (1903).
[39] H. Brooks, *Phil. Mag.*, **8**, 373 (1904).
[40] H. L. Bronson, *Amer. Jour. Sci.*, **19**, 185 (1905).
[41] O. Hahn and L. Meitner, *Phys. Zeits.*, **9**, 321, 649 (1908).
[42] E. Rutherford and H. Geiger, *Proc. Roy. Soc.*, A, **81**, 141, 162 (1908).
[43] E. Regener, *Ber. Preuss. Akad. Wiss.*, **38**, 948 (1909).
[44] J. E. Shrader, *Phys. Rev.*, **19**, 422 (1922).
[45] E. Schopper, *Zeits. f. Physik*, **93**, 1 (1934); **94**, 649 (1935).
[46] E. Rutherford and T. Royds, *Manchester Lit. and Phil. Soc., Mem.*, **53**, 1 (1908); *Chem. News*, **99**, 49 (1909); *Phil. Mag.*, **17**, 281 (1909).

have been shot into it. There can be no doubt that $\alpha$ particles are truly He nuclei; they become ordinary He atoms after taking up two planetary electrons. The $\alpha$ particles emitted spontaneously by many radioactive substances must all be ejected from the nucleus, for it is only the small central nucleus of an atom that contains any positive charge.

### Velocity and Range

Alpha particles are ejected with velocities of the order of $\frac{1}{20}$ that of light, the actual velocity depending upon the radioactive material ejecting them. The velocity of ejection is characteristic of the radioactive substance, and tables giving the velocities characteristic of various $\alpha$ particle emitters are available.[16,17,20] These range from $1.420 \times 10^9$ cm/sec. for the $\alpha$ particles for UI to $2.054 \times 10^9$ cm/sec. for those ejected by ThC′. The energies of these $\alpha$ particles are respectively 4.19 and 8.78 MEV. $\alpha$-rays are thus extremely energetic particles. It appeared for many years that all the $\alpha$ particles ejected by a given substance had exactly the same energy. Only a decade ago Rosenblum[47] found that certain of the $\alpha$-ray emitters give off particles of a number of definite velocities. Many of these velocities have now been measured[47–50] and they can be found arranged in tabular form.[21] Most of these lie very close to that velocity characteristic of the main group, though a few have been found with much higher speeds. The very existence of this so-called fine structure in the energy of $\alpha$-rays, as well as the observation of occasional particles which have a very much greater energy, has been of utmost importance in forming the present concepts of nuclear structure. Attention will be called shortly to the nature of this influence.

For a majority of purposes one can still regard all $\alpha$ particles emitted by a given material as having a common velocity, since it is only by careful experiment that one can distinguish among them or find those few particles which have unusually high velocities. Since all particles have essentially a common velocity they all travel the same distance through a material before losing their energy and coming to rest. Although $\alpha$ particles possess large energies they are not very penetrating. An ordinary sheet of paper will stop all of them. Since it is only in a gas that they travel an appreciable distance, it is customary to specify the penetrating power of a given group by stating the distance these particles will travel through air at

[47] S. Rosenblum, *Jour. de Physique et le Radium,* 1, 438 (1930); *Comptes Rendus,* **190,** 1124 (1930); **194,** 1919 (1932).

[48] Mme. P. Curie and S. Rosenblum, *Comptes Rendus,* **196,** 1598 (1933).

[49] E. Rutherford, C. E. Wynn-Williams, W. B. Lewis and B. V. Bowden, *Proc. Roy. Soc.,* A, **139,** 617 (1933).

[50] W. B. Lewis and B. V. Bowden, *Proc. Roy. Soc.,* A, **145,** 235 (1934).

760 mm. of Hg pressure and 15° C temperature. This distance is called the range of the particle. That all particles from a given source travel essentially the same distance before stopping is evident from Fig. 4, a typical curve[51] showing the relative numbers of particles that proceed out various distances from the source before being stopped. It is true that some particles fail to go quite as far as others; there is a gradual falling off in number as they near the end of their range. This falling off is not due necessarily to any variation in the original energy of ejection. The cloud chamber photograph reproduced[16] in Fig. 5 shows also that all $\alpha$ particles do not go exactly the same distance, although the variation is quite small. Some of these particles suffer abrupt changes in direction just before reaching the end of the range. These abrupt deflections will account for some of the straggling of the ranges of individual particles, but experiment shows that this is by no means the only cause of straggling. Some variation is observed among those particles which do not suffer appreciable deflections.

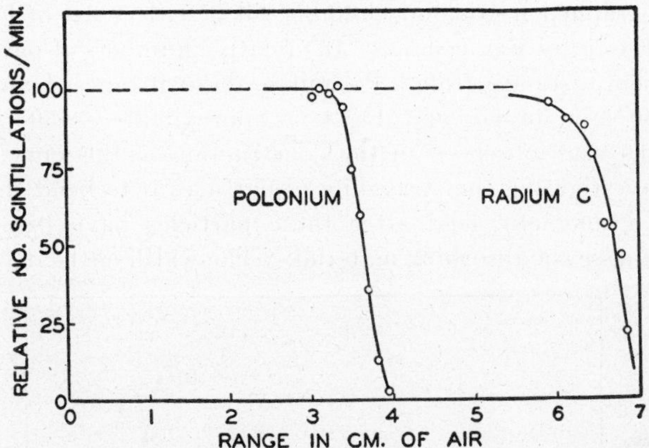


FIG. 4.—Showing that all alpha particles from a given source have approximately the same range.

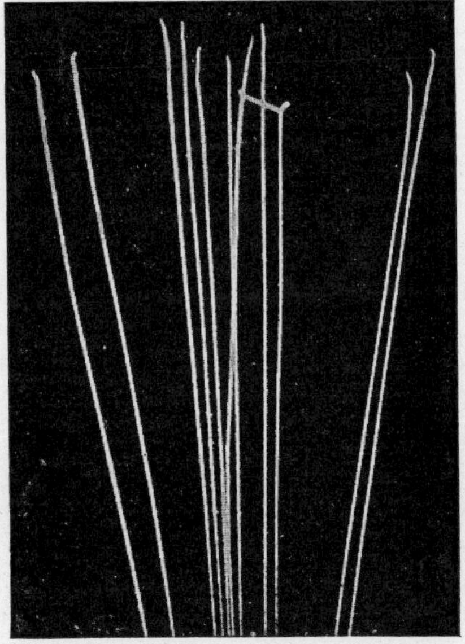

FIG. 5.—Illustrating the straggling of alpha particles.

[51] H. Geiger, *Proc. Roy. Soc.*, A, **83**, 505 (1910).

In relatively recent years the magnitude of this straggling effect has been investigated[52–56] accurately by measuring the ranges of many individual tracks photographed in a cloud chamber filled with a gas of low stopping power. Curve (*a*) of Fig. 6 shows[55] the relative numbers of particles which stop at different distances from a Po source, these distances being converted to air at 760 mm. of Hg and 15° C. Approximately 450 individual $\alpha$ particle tracks were observed in the construction of this curve. Another method of investigating the straggling of particles is to bend the stream of particles in a magnetic field after these particles have passed through various thicknesses of absorbing material. The width of the deflected beam

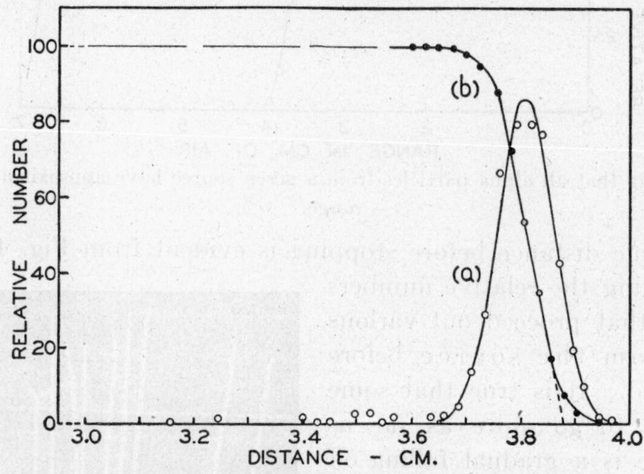


Fig. 6.—Showing the straggling of alpha particles from Po.

is a measure of the variation in velocity among the particles. Any variation in velocity introduced by passage through matter can thus be measured. Accurate measurements of this character by Briggs[57] show that a definite straggling is introduced by even a thin sheet of mica equivalent to only a few mm. of air. Observations by this method are consistent with those illustrated by curve (*a*) of Fig. 6.

The shape of the straggling distribution curve is just that which one would expect from a purely accidental distribution about a mean. The straggling is a chance proposition. In their travel through matter various particles give up slightly different energies in the collisions which they happen to make. Some particles make a few more collisions than other

[52] I. Curie, *Ann. de Physique*, **3**, 299 (1925).
[53] L. Meitner and K. Freitag, *Zeits. f. Physik*, **37**, 481 (1926).
[54] I. Curie and M. P. Mercier, *Jour. de Physique et le Radium*, **7**, 289 (1926).
[55] W. M. Rayton and T. R. Wilkins, *Phys. Rev.*. **51**, 818 (1937).
[56] A. King and W. M. Rayton, *Phys. Rev.*, **51**, 826 (1937).
[57] G. H. Briggs, *Proc. Roy. Soc.*, A, **114**, 313 (1927).

particles in traveling the same distance; thus the ranges are slightly different. Curve (*b*) of Fig. 6, which can be obtained from (*a*), shows[56] the fraction of the total number of $\alpha$ particles which proceed a given distance before stopping. This curve, obtained from ranges measured in a cloud chamber, is essentially the same as that obtained by the scintillation method and shown in Fig. 4. The straggling of particles near the end of the range brings up the question of just how one is going to specify the range for a given group of particles. Since curve (*a*) of Fig. 6 is essentially symmetrical, the position of the peak represents the average range of the particles. This so-called mean range is often specified. On the other hand, other methods of measuring the range lead more directly to a slightly different value. Other possible ways of specifying the range will be considered after looking into methods of measuring.

There are several ways[20] of determining the range experimentally. Two methods have already been suggested. It can be obtained by counting the visual scintillations produced on a fluorescent screen as this screen is placed farther and farther from the source; and it can be obtained by measuring the lengths of tracks photographed in a cloud expansion chamber. The range can also be found by using a shallow ionization chamber to measure the ionization produced by the particles at various distances from the source, or by using apparatus which counts the number of particles which proceed various distances before stopping. It can be measured electrically[58,59] by placing the source of particles at the center of a hollow conducting sphere and using an electroscope to measure the total ionization produced by the $\alpha$ particles for various air pressures within the sphere. If the radius of the sphere is greater than the range the total ionization will remain constant as the pressure is reduced, for the $\alpha$ particles produce always the same number of ions in being brought to rest. Since the range increases as the pressure is decreased, there exists a pressure at which the $\alpha$ particles just reach the inside surface of the sphere. As the pressure is further reduced the total ionization falls off, for the particles have not been completely stopped in the air. Typical results by this method are reproduced[58] in Fig. 7. From that pressure for which the total ionization starts to fall off, along with the radius of the sphere, the range under normal conditions can be calculated.

Let us now consider in more detail the several ways in which the range of a given group of alpha particles can be expressed. As has already been pointed out, the position of the peak of a curve similar to (*a*) in Fig. 6 gives the mean range. As many particles have ranges longer than this as have shorter ranges. Instead of this mean range one can specify a so-called

[58] H. Geiger and J. M. Nuttall, *Phil. Mag.*, **22**, 613 (1911); **23**, 439 (1912).

[59] H. Geiger, *Zeits. f. Physik*, **8**, 45 (1921).

extrapolated range. Curves similar to (*b*) of Fig. 6 are fairly straight over a considerable distance during the rapid fall near the end of the range. There is actually a point of inflection, corresponding to the position of the peak of curve (*a*), at the center of this approximately straight section. The extrapolated range is obtained by projecting this nearly straight line until it cuts the axis, and taking the intercept as the range. This extrapolated range is always larger than the mean range. Both the mean and the extrapolated ranges of alpha particles are frequently given in tables.[17,20]

Some recent work by Holloway and Livingston shows that there are really two extrapolated ranges, the value obtained depending upon the nature of the curve extrapolated. Many range determinations have been made by using a shallow ionization chamber to determine the ionizing power of alpha particles which have traveled different distances. It will be shown later that the ionizing power increases as the velocity of the particle decreases, reaches a maximum just short of the end of the range, and then drops rapidly to zero. The curve representing the final rapid fall is fairly straight. The range is obtained by projecting this line until it cuts the axis. This procedure yields an extrapolated range intermediate between the mean range and that obtained by extrapolating a curve similar to (*b*) of Fig. 6. Thus there are really three ranges in use, the mean range, an extrapolated range obtained from a curve representing the ionizing power of a group of particles after these particles have traveled a given distance, and an extrapolated range obtained from a curve representing the number of particles which go a given distance before stopping. Holloway and Livingston[24] have discussed the theoretical connections among these three ranges. These connections involve the observed straggling coefficient of the particles and the manner in which the ionizing power varies with velocity. These authors have given in tabular form all three ranges for those alpha particles for which accurate data are available. Differences among the three ranges are not large, but they are significant. For example, for alpha particles from Po in air at 760 mm. of Hg pressure and 15° C tem-

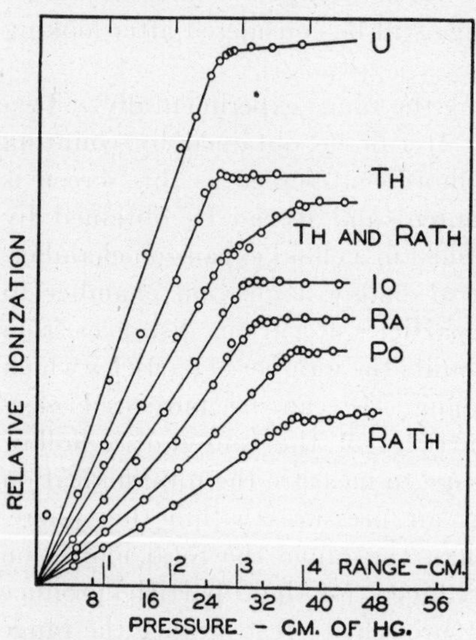


FIG. 7.—The range corresponds to the position at which the curve changes slope abruptly.

perature the mean range is (3.842 ± 0.006) cm., the extrapolated range from the ionization curve is 3.870, and the extrapolated range from the number-distance curve is 3.897. Differences among ranges for other alpha particles are of the same order. Although the theoretical connections among these ranges are rather involved, there exists[60] a rather accurate simple relationship. The ionization extrapolated range is 0.61% greater than the mean range, and the number extrapolated range is 1.33% larger than the mean range.

The ranges observed for normal alpha particles in air at 760 mm. of Hg and 15° C vary from 2.59 cm. for those from Th, to 8.62 for those from ThC′. The ranges characteristic of the various alpha ray emitters are given in Table I. These are ionization extrapolated ranges. The range in air is found to be inversely proportional to the concentration of molecules; it is inversely proportional to pressure and directly proportional to the absolute temperature. Ranges in other gases differ from those in air, sometimes being different by a factor of 5. Ranges in liquids and solids are of course much smaller than those in gases. The ranges of $\alpha$ particles in a number of gases, liquids and solids are known.[17,20,21]

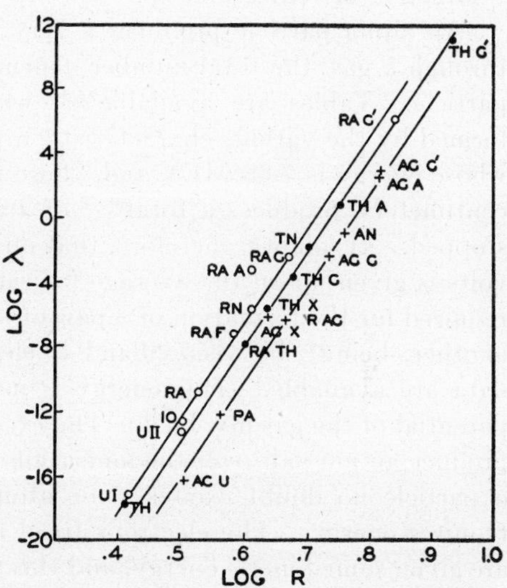


FIG. 8.—The Geiger-Nuttall relationship between the ranges of alpha particles and the rates at which the substances ejecting these particles decay.

It will be noticed from Table I that in general those materials which decay slowly emit $\alpha$ particles of short range while those which disintegrate rapidly emit more energetic particles. A relationship between the transformation constant $\lambda$ and the range $R$ was discovered empirically by Geiger and Nuttall[58] in 1911. These constants are connected by the equation

$$\log \lambda = A + B \log R$$

This relationship, known as the Geiger-Nuttall law, is only approximate. The constant $B$ is approximately the same for the three radioactive series, while the constant A takes on a different value for each of the series. Fig. 8

[60] Author's calculations from the data by M. G. Holloway and M. S. Livingston, *Phys. Rev.*, **54**, 18 (1938).

shows the degree of accuracy with which the Geiger-Nuttall law does relate the range to the transformation constant. Although the law is only approximate it has been of considerable aid in evaluating the approximate transformation constant of newly discovered $\alpha$-ray emitters.

**Production of Ionization**

An alpha particle produces a very large number of ions along its path through a gas, the total number depending upon the original energy of the particle. Tables are available[17,20] which give the total number of ions formed by the various characteristic $\alpha$ particles. An $\alpha$ particle from RaC′, whose energy is 7.68 MEV and whose ionization extrapolated range is 6.95 centimeters, produces a total[61,62] of $2.2 \times 10^5$ ion pairs in air before being stopped. It follows, therefore, that an energy of approximately 35 electron volts is given up on the average for each pair of ions formed. The energy required for the formation of a pair of ions varies somewhat from one gas to another, being[63] between 20 and 40 electron volts for those gases for which data are available. This energy is invariably higher than the ionization potential of the gas involved. The excess of the average energy required to produce an ion pair over the ionization potential is due to two things. The $\alpha$ particle no doubt excites some atoms without ionizing them, and this requires energy. The electrons freed from those atoms which are ionized are given some kinetic energy, and this as well as the ionization energy must be furnished by the $\alpha$ particle.

It can be calculated from the numerical values given above that if the ionization produced were uniform throughout the entire range of the $\alpha$ particle, there would be $3.2 \times 10^3$ ion pairs formed per millimeter along the the path of the particle. That the ionization is intense is evident from the cloud chamber tracks of such particles. The water droplets which have condensed upon the ions formed are so close together that the individual droplets are not distinguishable; they form what appears to be a continuous line. These many ions are produced as the $\alpha$ particle passes through or near the planetary electron system of the atoms in the air. Planetary electrons are freed from the atoms by the electrical forces exerted on them by the $\alpha$ particle passing nearby. Although this is undoubtedly the primary process in ionization, an appreciable number of the ions are formed indirectly. If one examines closely the $\alpha$ particle track in a gas, say helium, at considerably less than atmospheric pressure, one sees very short branches leading off from the main track. These are due to the

[61] H. Fonovits-Smereker, *Wien Ber.*, **131**, 355 (1922).

[62] I. Curie and F. Joliot, *Comptes Rendus*, **187**, 43 (1928).

[63] E. Rutherford, J. Chadwick and C. D. Ellis, *Radiations from Radioactive Substances* (London: Cambridge University Press, 1930), pp. 67–82.

fact that certain of the primary electrons produced directly by the particle have been given sufficient energy that they themselves can produce a number of ions. These electrons are often called "delta rays." Although they are not particularly obvious in ordinary photographs, they nevertheless sometimes produce an appreciable part of the total ionization. In some cases they may account for more than half of the ions formed.

The ionization along an α particle track is not actually uniform. The ionizing power of the particle grows continually larger as the particle slows down, reaches a maximum very near the end of the range, and then falls rapidly to zero. Many workers have determined the manner in which the ionizing power varies with the distance the α particle has traveled. The essential method of making such measurements is illustrated by the apparatus of Fig. 9. A narrow beam of particles is allowed to enter a shallow

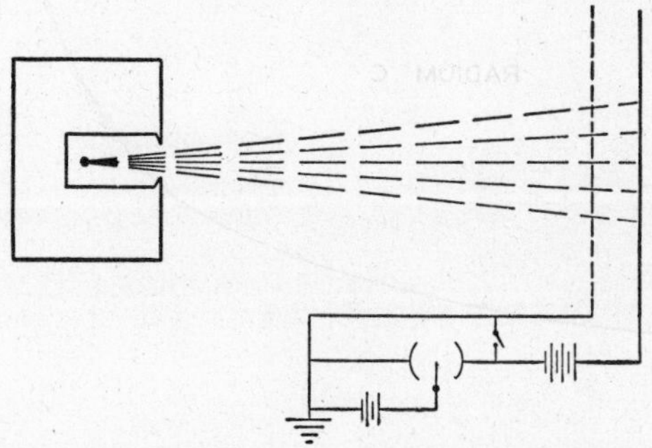

FIG. 9.—Illustrating the method of determining the specific ionization of alpha particles.

ionization chamber through a gauze which serves as one electrode. An attempt is made to have the depth of the chamber small as compared to the range of the particle. In order to approximate this condition the range is often increased by carrying out the measurements at reduced pressures. Many such measurements[63] have shown that the specific ionization, the number of ions formed per millimeter of path, varies with the distance the particle has traveled in the manner shown[64] in Fig. 10. Much the same type of curve is obtained for any gas and for any group of α particles, though the magnitude of the ionization and that of the range vary considerably. A very fast α particle, say one still able to go 7.0 centimeters through air at 760 mm. of Hg and 15° C, will produce[63,65] about 2150 ion pairs per mm. The ionizing power increases very slowly at first as the α-ray loses energy, being only 2700 ions per mm. 3.0 cms. from the end of the range. It then increases more and more rapidly, reaching a maximum of about 7000 ions

[64] G. H. Henderson, *Phil. Mag.*, **42**, 538 (1921).
[65] G. Stetter and W. Jentschke, *Phys. Zeits.*, **36**, 441 (1935).

per mm. when the particle is still 4 or 5 mm. from the end of its range. Beyond this the specific ionization falls off very rapidly.

The curve of Fig. 10 represents the average ionization produced by a large number of alpha particles. The shape of the curve is therefore influenced somewhat by the straggling of the particles. In recent years it has become possible to obtain the specific ionization curve for a single alpha particle. This was first done by Feather and Nimmo[66] through a study of the photographic density of tracks in a cloud chamber. Similar data have since been obtained by others[24,65,67] using different methods. All these data lead to a rather well defined curve[24] which has the same general shape as that of Fig. 10.

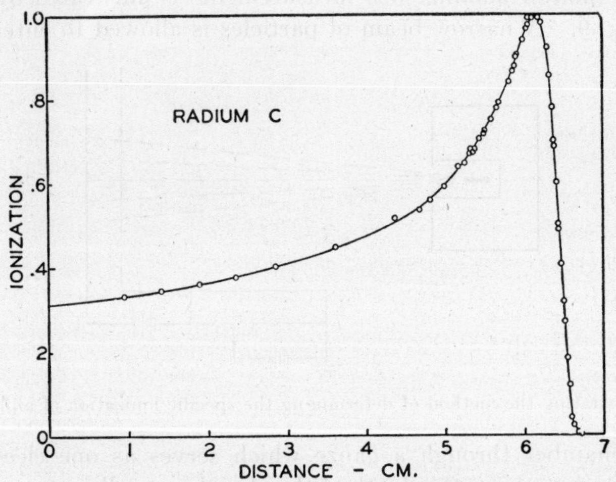


FIG. 10.—The manner in which the ionizing power of the alpha particles from RaC varies with the distance the particles have gone.

One might wonder why the ionizing power of an $\alpha$ particle should vary at all with velocity; the charged particle exerts the same force on a given planetary electron regardless of the particle's velocity. But the length of time for which this force is exerted is also important in determining whether or not the electron is to be freed from the atom. One might suspect that as a first approximation the probability of freeing an electron would be proportional to the product of the force and the time. Since the force is independent of the velocity, and since the time for which this force acts is inversely proportional to the velocity, the ionizing power of the $\alpha$ particle should be inversely proportional to its velocity. It is observed that the

[66] N. Feather and R. R. Nimmo, *Proc. Camb. Phil. Soc.*, **24**, 139 (1928).
[67] H. Schulze, *Zeits. f. Physik*, **94**, 104 (1935).

ionizing power does vary approximately as $1/v$ as long as the particle still has an energy many times that required for ionization.

This variation of ionizing power is entirely consistent with the fact that the range of an $\alpha$ particle is approximately proportional to the cube of its velocity. Suppose that a particle of range $R$ has already gone a distance $x$, and that it still retains a velocity $v$. Then

$$v^3 = A(R - x)$$

Now one would certainly expect the number of ions formed per unit distance to be proportional to the rate of energy loss. Except for the small change of mass with velocity, the energy of the particle is proportional to $v^2$. Solving for $v^2$ and differentiating this with respect to $x$,

$$v^2 = A_1(R - x)^{2/3} \qquad \text{and} \qquad \frac{d(v^2)}{dx} = \frac{A_2}{(R - x)^{1/3}} = \frac{A_3}{v}$$

where $A_1$, $A_2$ and $A_3$ are constants. Thus, if the range is proportional to the cube of the velocity then the rate of energy loss is inversely proportional to the velocity. One would therefore expect the ionizing power to be inversely proportional to $v$. The fact that the specific ionization does vary approximately as $1/v$ is thus consistent with the observed range-velocity relationship.

**Long Range Particles and Fine Structure**

*Long Range Particles.*—It is commonly stated that all $\alpha$ particles from a given source are ejected with one and the same velocity, and this statement is sufficiently near the truth for many purposes. Careful measurements show, however, that a given source often emits particles of a number of velocities. Some sources emit a few particles having ranges very much greater than that of the main group. These $\alpha$ particles are frequently referred to as long range particles. Again, some sources emit particles of a number of different but well defined velocities all relatively close together. These velocities differ so little that the ranges of the individual components of the group are indistinguishable by ordinary methods; they all occur within the region of straggling. The existence of these discrete and closely spaced components within an $\alpha$-ray group is referred to as the fine structure of the rays.

The existence of a few particles of unusually long range has been known for years; the early history[68] of these is interesting. They were first observed by Rutherford and Wood.[69] Using a preparation of ThC, which

[68] E. Rutherford, J. Chadwick and C. D. Ellis, *Radiations from Radioactive Substances* (London: Cambridge University Press, 1930), pp. 87–95.

[69] E. Rutherford and A. B. Wood, *Phil. Mag.*, **31**, 379 (1916).

of course contained ThC′ whose $\alpha$ particles have an extrapolated range of 8.62 cms., these investigators found that a few particles were able to penetrate an absorbing screen which was sufficiently thick to stop all particles of normal range. These few particles continued to produce scintillations on a zinc sulfide screen after penetrating the absorber. By inserting more absorbing material these particles were found to have a range of about 11.3 cms. in air. There are very few of these particles, the original estimate being about 100 per million normal particles ejected. There was some indication at the time that some of these long range particles had a range of only

FIG. 11.—Showing a single long range particle, of range 10.3 cm., among a multitude of normal particles from RaC′.

FIG. 12.—Showing a long range particle from ThC′.

10 cms., whereas a majority had a range of 11.3 cms. A few years later[70] similar long range particles were observed to come from a RaC preparation, no doubt from the RaC′ as is now known. Here again the number of long range particles is very small, an early estimate being 22 per million particles of normal range.

In more recent years these long range particles have been studied by three other methods, each of which gives definite information[68,71] regarding the number of particles involved and their ranges. One of these methods[72,73] involves the measurement of a large number of tracks photographed in a cloud chamber. The photograph reproduced[72] in Fig. 11 shows the track

[70] E. Rutherford, *Phil. Mag.*, **37**, 537 (1919).

[71] G. Hevesy and F. A. Paneth (translated by R. W. Lawson), *A Manual of Radioactivity* (2nd ed.; London: Oxford University Press, 1938), pp. 26, 27, 98–101.

[72] K. Philipp and K. Donat, *Zeits. f. Physik*, **52**, 759 (1929).

[73] R. R. Nimmo and N. Feather, *Proc. Roy. Soc.*, A, **122**, 668 (1928).

of a single long range particle among an enormous number of normal particles from RaC′. In some cases[73] several of these long range particles have been observed in a single photograph. Fig. 12 is interesting in that it shows[73] two relatively rare phenomena on the same photograph in spite of the fact that the total number of tracks recorded is very small. One of these is a long range particle from ThC′, a particle having a range of 11.49 cms. The other relatively rare phenomenon is the forking of one of the normal tracks. The second branch of the fork is produced by a nucleus recoiling from a close collision with the α particle.

A second method of studying these long range particles[74–77] involves the use of a very shallow ionization chamber coupled with an extremely sensitive current amplifier. By designing the amplifier so that its response is proportional to the ionization produced, it is possible to study quantitatively the number of particles of various ranges longer than the normal.

Fig. 13.—Showing the several characteristic velocities of alpha rays from ThC.

A third method[47–50,78–81] of studying these long range particles, as well as of investigating the fine structure of the normal particles, has been made possible through the development of sufficiently strong and extensive magnetic fields to deflect the energetic α particles in semicircles. In this way one can determine accurately their velocities. The first important investigation[47] of this character used a magnet having poles 6 cms. apart and 75 cms. in diameter, capable of producing an essentially uniform field of 24,000 oersteds over a region some 35 cms. in diameter. After passing through collimating slits the α particles were deflected through 180° by the magnetic field. Particles of a given velocity formed an exceedingly sharp trace on a photographic plate, the sharpness being enhanced by the geometrical focusing associated with the 180° deflection. That the normal α particles from ThC are ejected with several discrete velocities, and not with various velocities varying continuously over a narrow range, is shown[47] clearly by Fig. 13. From the position of a given line it is possible to evaluate accurately the velocity of the particle. Relative velocities can be measured

[74] E. Rutherford, F. A. B. Ward and C. E. Wynn-Williams, *Proc. Roy. Soc.*, A, **129**, 211 (1930).

[75] E. Rutherford, F. A. B. Ward and W. B. Lewis, *Proc. Roy. Soc.*, A, **131**, 684 (1931).

[76] E. Rutherford, C. E. Wynn-Williams and W. B. Lewis, *Proc. Roy. Soc.*, A, **133**, 351 (1931).

[77] W. B. Lewis and C. E. Wynn-Williams, *Proc. Roy. Soc.*, A, **136**, 349 (1932).

[78] E. Rutherford, W. B. Lewis and B. V. Bowden, *Proc. Roy. Soc.*, A, **142**, 347 (1933).

[79] G. H. Briggs, *Proc. Roy. Soc.*, A, **139**, 638 (1933); **143**, 604 (1934).

[80] G. H. Briggs, *Proc. Roy. Soc.*, A, **157**, 183 (1936).

[81] R. Ringo, *Phys. Rev.*, **58**, 942 (1940).

to an accuracy[50,80] of a few parts in $10^5$; the absolute velocity is probably accurate[80] to 1 part in $10^4$. Photographs such as Fig. 13, obtained with $\alpha$ particles in vacuum, show that the usual straggling of particles is introduced entirely by the absorber. All particles of a given subgroup are ejected with exactly the same velocity. There is some indication[81] that there may be a few particles having relatively low velocities distributed over a wide range, but the existence of these is far from definite.

Studies by the three methods outlined have yielded reliable information[71,82] regarding these long range particles. It appears that of all the $\alpha$-ray emitters it is only RaC′ and ThC′ that eject long range particles. One might suspect that AcC′ would also eject them, but they have not yet been observed. The long range particles ejected by ThC′ fall into two groups, one having a mean range of approximately 9.8 cms., the other a range of 11.6 cms. These two groups are shown by Fig. 14 which incorporates measurements[73] of over 550 cloud chamber tracks of long range particles. The distribution about a mean in each group is due to straggling. Analysis of these results shows that the straggling distribution is essentially of random character, and that the mean ranges of the two groups of particles are 9.82 and 11.62 cms. The results shown in Fig. 14 leave no doubt of the two distinct groups of long range particles. There were observed about 65 particles of 9.8 cm. range and 180 particles of 11.6 cm. range for every million particles of normal range. The fact that the distribution about the mean range in each group is essentially random, and therefore probably due to straggling, indicates that no other long range particles are present. It is true that Nimmo and Feather[73] actually observed a few isolated particles with ranges of from 13 to more than 17 cms. Actual ranges greater than 17 cms. could not be measured, for these particles passed outside the cloud chamber. These isolated particles with ranges still much greater than the 11.6 cms. do not come from ThC′; they may result from the disintegration of

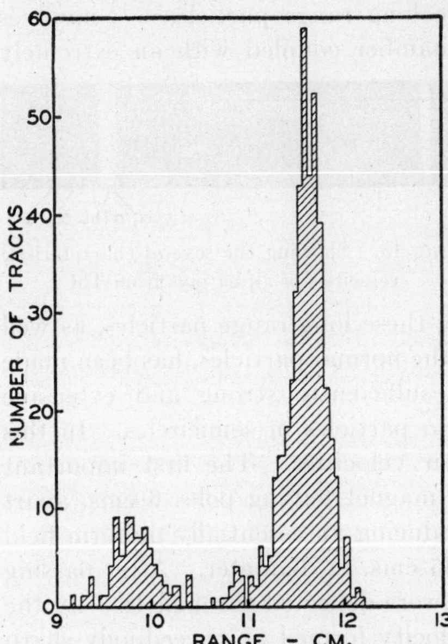

Fig. 14.—Showing the distribution of long range particles from ThC′.

[82] F. Rasetti, *Elements of Nuclear Physics* (New York: Prentice-Hall, 1936), pp. 114–120.

other matter produced either by the radiation from the preparation used or by cosmic rays.

These general findings regarding long range particles have been confirmed by both the shallow ionization chamber and the magnetic deflection method. In the latter case the results are of a high order of accuracy. Lewis and Bowden[50] find two long range groups, one of mean range 9.69 and the other 11.54 cms. Magnetic deflection measurements show only 34 particles in the first group and 190 particles in the second group per million normal particles. It is gratifying that measurements by the cloud chamber method and by the magnetic deflection method agree so well, particularly as regards the ranges of the particles. One recent table[24] gives for the mean ranges of these two groups (9.724 ± 0.008) and (11.580 ± 0.008) cms.

Whereas ThC′ ejects only two groups of long range particles, RaC′ has been found to eject many groups. These groups are so close together that they cannot be distinguished with certainty from cloud chamber observations.[73] Measurements of the magnetic deflections suffered by these particles in vacuum show, however, that the particles do fall into definite groups. Table III lists the long range particles emitted by RaC′ as given by Lewis and Bowden.[50] There are 12 groups of long range particles from RaC′, the mean range of the longest being 11.47 cms. The total number of long range particles is again very small, approximately 30 per million of normal range. The ejection of a long range particle is indeed a rare occurrence. It is interesting that the longest range particles from RaC′ have a mean range of 11.47 cms., corresponding to an energy of 10.51 MEV, whereas those from ThC′ have a range of 11.54 cms., corresponding to an energy of 10.54 MEV. These represent the most energetic particles ever ejected by any natural radioactive material.

It is desirable to call attention at this time to the last two columns in Table III. The actual energy released during the disintegration of an atom by $\alpha$ particle ejection is slightly greater than the energy of the $\alpha$ particle itself. The same nuclear force which projects the $\alpha$ particle with a high velocity in one direction also causes the remainder of the atom to recoil in the opposite direction. From the conservation of momentum one could calculate, in a given case, the velocity, and thence the energy, with which the newborn nucleus recoils. These recoil energies are from 0.1 to 0.2 MEV for those heavy atoms which emit rather energetic $\alpha$ particles. The actual energy furnished by a disintegrating atom is of course the sum of the energy of the particle and the recoil energy. The energies of disintegration corresponding to the various groups of long range $\alpha$ particles from RaC′ are given in next to the last column of Table III. We shall inquire shortly into the origin of the long range particles, and in this inquiry we shall be interested in the excess energies these particles have over that of the normal particles. This excess energy is given in the last column of the table.

TABLE III

**Long range α particles from RaC′. There are 12 groups of particles with ranges longer than 6.870, the range of the normal particles. There are emitted approximately 30 long range particles per million of normal range. A table of ranges by Holloway and Livingston[24] gives ranges about 0.4% larger than those given here**

| Velocity × $10^{-9}$ in cm/sec. | Mean range in cm. | Energy in MEV | Relative No. of particles | Energy of disintegration in MEV | Difference of energy of disintegration from that of main group |
|---|---|---|---|---|---|
| 1.9220 | 6.870 | 7.683 | $10^6$ | 7.829 | 0 |
| 1.9950 | 7.755 | 8.280 | 0.43 | 8.437 | 0.608 |
| 2.0729 | ...... | 8.941 | (0.45) | 9.112 | 1.283 |
| 2.0876 | 9.00 | 9.069 | 22 | 9.242 | 1.412 |
| 2.1157 | ...... | 9.315 | 0.38 | 9.493 | 1.663 |
| 2.1356 | ...... | 9.492 | 1.35 | 9.673 | 1.844 |
| 2.1543 | ...... | 9.660 | 0.35 | 9.844 | 2.015 |
| 2.1678 | ...... | 9.781 | 1.06 | 9.968 | 2.138 |
| 2.1817 | ...... | 9.908 | 0.36 | 10.097 | 2.268 |
| 2.2001 | ...... | 10.077 | 1.67 | 10.269 | 2.439 |
| 2.2079 | ...... | 10.149 | 0.38 | 10.342 | 2.513 |
| 2.2274 | ...... | 10.329 | 1.12 | 10.526 | 2.697 |
| 2.2466 | 11.47 | 10.509 | 0.23 | 10.709 | 2.880 |

*Fine Structure of Alpha Rays.*—Except for the few long range particles emitted by only ThC′ and RaC′, it was thought until 1930 that all α particles from a given substance were ejected with accurately the same velocity. In that year it was shown by Rosenblum[47] that this was not true. Upon carefully collimating a beam of α particles and bending it in a semicircular path with a strong and extensive magnetic field, he found that the normal α particles ejected by any one of a number of materials fall into several very closely spaced velocity groups. The photograph reproduced in Fig. 13 represents typical findings. The previously supposed homogeneous α-rays emitted from ThC actually fall into five distinct groups. The rays are said to have a fine structure. These general findings have been verified both by shallow ionization chamber studies[49,50] and by many other magnetic deflection experiments, many of these by Rosenblum. References to these works are available elsewhere.[48,50] The distribution of α particles making up the fine structure of ThC, as given by Lewis and Bowden,[50] is shown in Table IV.

TABLE IV

The fine structure of the $\alpha$ particles from ThC. The ranges of the individual groups have been calculated relative to the average range of the two most prominent groups

| Group | Velocity $\times 10^{-9}$ in cm/sec. | Mean range in cm. | Energy in MEV | Relative No. of particles | Energy of disintegration in MEV | Difference of energy of disintegration from that of $\alpha_1$ group |
|---|---|---|---|---|---|---|
| $\alpha_1$ | 1.7108 | 4.73 | 6.084 | 27.2 | 6.201 | 0 |
| $\alpha_2$ | 1.7053 | 4.68 | 6.044 | 69.8 | 6.161 | 0.040 |
| $\alpha_3$ | 1.6651 | 4.36 | 5.762 | 1.80 | 5.873 | 0.328 |
| $\alpha_4$ | 1.6445 | 4.20 | 5.620 | 0.16 | 5.728 | 0.473 |
| $\alpha_5$ | 1.6418 | 4.18 | 5.601 | 1.10 | 5.709 | 0.492 |
| Average of $\alpha_1$ and $\alpha_2$ | ...... | 4.693 | | | | |

The extreme energy difference among the components of this fine structure is only 0.492 MEV. The difference in range of adjacent groups is often only a few tenths of a millimeter, and never more than a few millimeters. It is apparent that the entire fine structure occurs within the region of straggling, and it is this fact that delayed so long the discovery of the structure. Table IV gives also the number of particles associated with each component, the energy of disintegration of each component, and the apparent deficiency in disintegration energy of the shorter range particles below that of the highest energy group.

Entirely similar findings have been made for many other $\alpha$-ray emitters. A number of materials show a fine structure consisting of only two groups. Some have three components, one five components, and one eleven components. It is RdAc which shows a fine structure consisting of eleven components. On the other hand a goodly number of substances appear to have no fine structure; they emit all of their $\alpha$ particles with exactly the same velocity. Some of these may later be found to have a structure which has not yet been detected. Careful but still unsuccessful searches for a possible structure have been made for some of these, and it seems very doubtful that even a structure of weak lines exists. Perhaps the most extensive measurements have been on the $\alpha$ particles from Po, and these have failed without exception to show more than a single sharp line. The fine structures of the rays from a great majority of the twenty-five heavy elements which emit $\alpha$ particles are now known. Rather complete tables of these structures, including both fine structure and long range particles, are available in the literature.[50,82] These give the velocity and the energy of the $\alpha$ particles, the energy of disintegration, and the number of particles associated with each group comprising the fine structure.

*The Origin of Long Range and Fine Structure Particles.*—Accurate knowledge of the fine structure of $\alpha$-rays, together with knowledge of the long range particles emitted by ThC′ and RaC′, has been of inestimable value in arriving at a clear-cut concept of the origin of these particles. All $\alpha$ particles must of course come from the nucleus, but just why should they be ejected from a given nucleus with a variety of discrete energies? In view of the success already attained in the interpretation of spectroscopic phenomena in terms of discrete energy levels in the planetary system of an atom, it was natural to attempt an interpretation of these phenomena in terms of discrete energy levels within the nucleus. In fact considerable quantitative evidence for the existence of these nuclear energy levels had already been obtained from studies of the $\beta$ and $\gamma$-rays emitted by radioactive materials.

Suppose that there do exist in the nucleus a number of discrete energy levels. Although these nuclei would normally exist in their lowest energy state, they might exist for short times in excited states. The mere existence of nuclear energy levels provides the possibility of excited states, configurations having more than the normal amount of energy. Definite evidence that the fine structure of $\alpha$-rays can be interpreted simply and logically in terms of these supposed energy levels was first given by Gamow.[83] As a specific example, consider the fine structure particles emitted by ThC. The characteristics of the five components of this structure are given in Table IV. It is supposed that a ThC atom always releases an energy of 6.201 MEV when it disintegrates by $\alpha$-ray ejection to form ThC″. This, according to Table IV, is the energy of disintegration associated with the most energetic component in the fine structure. When ThC ejects one of these most energetic $\alpha$-rays the resulting ThC″ nucleus would be in its lowest energy state; all of the disintegration energy has gone into ejecting the $\alpha$ particle and causing the recoil of the newly formed atom. Suppose, however, that a ThC atom ejects an $\alpha$ particle of the second group, one for which the apparent energy of disintegration is only 6.161 MEV. The resulting ThC″ nucleus should possess more than its normal amount of energy. It should be in an excited state, and the energy associated with the excitation should be 0.040 MEV, the difference between 6.201 and 6.161 MEV. One would expect this excited nucleus to release this excess energy almost immediately, probably through the radiation of a $\gamma$-ray. Now there is found in the $\gamma$-ray line spectrum of ThC″ a line of such frequency that the photon energy is exactly 0.040 MEV. If ThC disintegrates instead by ejecting an $\alpha$ particle of the third group the energy of excitation of the resulting ThC″ nucleus should be $(6.201 - 5.873) = 0.328$ MEV. Again, there is found in the line spectrum of ThC″ a $\gamma$-ray having an energy 0.327 MEV. On

[83] G. Gamow, *Nature*, **126**, 396 (1930).

occasion this excited ThC″ nucleus might not pass directly to its lowest energy state, but to some intermediate state instead. If it should pass from the third to the second state then one would expect a γ-ray having an energy of $(6.161 - 5.873) = 0.288$ MEV. There is found a γ-ray of energy 0.287 MEV.

Other theoretically possible transitions should give rise to other γ-rays. The second column of Table V[50] shows the energies which should be released by each of the theoretically possible nuclear transitions. These are calculated from the fine structure of the α-rays from ThC. The third column

TABLE V

A comparison of the energies of observed γ-rays from ThC″ and the differences of apparent disintegration energies for the various α-ray groups emitted by ThC. All energies are given in MEV

| Transitions between levels | Apparent difference of disintegration energy of α-ray groups of ThC | Energy of observed γ-ray from ThC″ |
|---|---|---|
| $L_2 - L_1$ | 0.040 | 0.040 |
| $L_3 - L_1$ | .328 | .327 |
| $L_4 - L_1$ | .473 | .471 |
| $L_5 - L_1$ | .492 | |
| $L_3 - L_2$ | .288 | .287 |
| $L_4 - L_2$ | .433 | .432 |
| $L_5 - L_2$ | .452 | .451 |
| $L_4 - L_3$ | .145 | |
| $L_5 - L_3$ | .164 | |
| $L_5 - L_4$ | 019 | |

shows the energies of actually observed γ-rays from ThC″. The agreement is excellent. It is true that not all of the theoretically possible γ-rays have yet been observed, but this may be due to either their feeble intensity or some nuclear selection principle which precludes certain transitions. Similar quantitative results have been obtained for other radioactive materials whose α-rays show a fine structure. The evidence for the actual existence of discrete nuclear energy levels is quite convincing.

The origin of the long range particles emitted by RaC′ and ThC′ can also be interpreted in terms of nuclear energy levels. We shall discuss shortly the emission of β and γ-rays from radioactive atoms and shall then see that the emission of a nuclear β-ray sometimes leaves the newly formed nucleus in an excited state. This excited nucleus passes almost immediately to its normal state through the emission of a γ-ray photon of the proper energy. Evidence substantiating this concept will be quoted later. In only two cases do the newly formed atoms appear to get rid of this excess energy in any way other than through emission of a $\gamma$-ray. These are the cases of ThC′ and RaC′, the two materials which eject long range $\alpha$ particles. These are the two shortest lived radioactive atoms; they have half lives of $10^{-11}$ and $10^{-6}$ seconds, respectively. As a specific example, suppose that a RaC atom ejects a $\beta$-ray of such an energy that the newly formed RaC′ nucleus is left in an excited state. The average length of time for which a nucleus remains in an excited state is none too reliably known, but it is very small, probably of the order of $10^{-13}$ seconds. Thus most atoms emit a $\gamma$-ray photon and pass to their normal energy states long before they undergo a subsequent nuclear disintegration. But the half life of RaC′ is so short that a few of these atoms may well undergo their next transformation, ejecting an $\alpha$ particle and becoming RaD, before the excited RaC′ nucleus has ejected its $\gamma$-ray and passed to its normal state. The same general argument would lead one to expect also that some of the exceedingly short lived ThC′ atoms would disintegrate, ejecting an $\alpha$ particle and becoming ThD, while the ThC′ nucleus is still in an excited state. The particle might well be given not only its normal energy but the excitation energy as well. This is the supposed origin of the long range particles of RaC′ and ThC′. Another short lived atom is AcC′, which has a half life of about $10^{-3}$ seconds. This is so large as compared to the average life of an excited nucleus that the chance of a disintegration occurring from an excited nucleus becomes increasingly remote. Hence it is only ThC′ and RaC′ which eject long range particles, and even these eject only 224 and 30, respectively, per million normal particles.

If the general concept of the origin of long range particles is correct then one would expect ThC′ to emit $\gamma$-ray photons having energies equal to the differences of energy levels required to interpret properly the excess energies of the long range particles. The energies of disintegration corresponding to the normal and the two long range groups of particles from ThC′ are 8.948, 9.674 and 10.745 MEV, respectively. These require three energy levels, the normal and 0.726 and 1.797 MEV above the normal. One might therefore expect to find three nuclear $\gamma$-rays having energies of 0.726, 1.797 and 1.071 MEV, the last being the difference between the two excited states. $\gamma$-ray photons of energies 0.726 and 1.802 MEV are found. These agree closely with those expected from transitions from the two excited states into the normal state. A $\gamma$-ray corresponding to the transition between the two excited states has not been observed.

In the case of RaC′ it is possible to make a much better test, for the 12 groups of long range $\alpha$ particles it emits require at least 12 energy levels above the normal state. The excess energies represented by these states are shown in the last column of Table III. One might expect a nuclear $\gamma$-ray corresponding to transitions from each of these levels into the normal state. There are observed $\gamma$-rays having energies which agree with 7 of these transitions.[78] In order to interpret completely the nuclear $\gamma$-ray lines emitted by RaC′ it is necessary to assign a total of 16 energy levels above the normal instead of the 12 indicated by long range $\alpha$ particles. These include those states indicated by the energies of the long range particles and 4 others in addition. Now one might expect $\gamma$-rays corresponding not only to transitions from each excited state into the normal, but also others which correspond to transitions between various pairs of excited states. Calculation will show that the total of 17 energy levels in the RaC′ nucleus might theoretically give rise to 136 $\gamma$-rays. A tabular arrangement of these energy levels and the energies associated with the various possible transitions can be found in the literature.[78] Now $\gamma$-rays which correspond in energy, within 0.007 MEV, to 65 of those theoretically possible on this energy level scheme have actually been found. While some of these correspondences may be accidental, it is inconceivable that all of them could be. The quantitative evidence on nuclear $\gamma$-rays supports strongly the nuclear level picture assigned largely from data on long range $\alpha$ particles. It therefore supports the interpretation of the origin of these long range particles. It seems certain that this interpretation is correct as regards its essential features.

## 4. $\beta$ AND $\gamma$-RAYS, THEIR ORIGIN AND PROPERTIES

### Nature of the Radiations

The $\beta$-rays ejected by radioactive substances during the process of disintegration are high speed electrons. They charge bodies on which they impinge negatively; they can be bent by either an electric or a magnetic field; they bear the same ratio $e/m$ as do electrons emitted from a hot filament; the ratio $e/m$ varies with velocity in exactly the same manner as it does for electrons obtained from hot filaments. They are certainly electrons, electrons which have been given a high energy by the disintegrating nucleus which ejects them. Energies of $\beta$-rays range from nearly zero up to several million electron volts, the distribution and upper energy limit depending upon the radioactive source. There is considerable evidence[84,85] that some materials may emit a few $\beta$-rays with energies as great as 8 or possibly even 11 MEV. Energies above 2 or 3 MEV are, however, rare. A great majority of the $\beta$-rays have energies still much smaller than this.

In general the energies of the $\beta$-rays are somewhat less than those of $\alpha$ particles. Practically all of the $\beta$-rays have energies less than 3 MEV,

[84] D. K. Yovanovitch and J. d'Espine, *Jour. de Physique et le Radium*, **8**, 276 (1927).

[85] E. Rutherford, J. Chadwick and C. D. Ellis, *Radiations from Radioactive Substances* (London: Cambridge University Press, 1930), pp. 337–450.

whereas all of the normal $\alpha$ particles have energies between 4 and 9 MEV. Even though the energy is somewhat smaller the $\beta$ particle, because of its much smaller mass, travels with much the greater speed. Like the $\alpha$ particle, the $\beta$-ray gives up its energy gradually by forming many low energy ions along its path as it proceeds through an absorber. But the $\beta$ particle forms far fewer ions per mm. of travel. Whereas a 3 MEV $\alpha$ particle has a velocity $1/25$ that of light and produces some 4,000 ion pairs per mm. of travel through air at 760 mm. of Hg and 15° C, a 3 MEV $\beta$ particle has a velocity nearly 0.99 that of light and produces only about 4 ion pairs per mm. of travel through air. Because of the much smaller specific ionization the $\beta$ particle has much the greater range. Whereas a 3 MEV $\alpha$ particle has an air range of approximately 1.7 cm., a $\beta$ particle of this energy travels some 13 meters through air before being stopped. A $\beta$ particle having an energy of only 0.5 MEV has a range of approximately 1 meter. Thus the average $\beta$-ray is hundreds of times more penetrating than the average $\alpha$ particle. Even the most energetic normal $\alpha$ particles are stopped by an ordinary sheet of paper or by a sheet of aluminum having a thickness of the order of 0.06 mm. This thickness of absorber makes only a bare beginning in slowing down the $\beta$-rays. Some of these are able to pass through more than a mm. of aluminum. Whereas an $\alpha$ particle usually proceeds through air in nearly a straight line path, cloud chamber photographs of $\beta$ particle tracks show that these particles suffer many gradual deflections. The $\beta$ particle track is far from a straight line. As a consequence the range of $\beta$ particles is of less definite meaning than is the range of $\alpha$ particles. The real range of a $\beta$ particle could be evaluated properly only by observing the total distance traveled along the irregularly curved track.

The $\gamma$-rays accompanying radioactive disintegration are of the same character as X-rays. They cannot be bent in electric or magnetic fields; they travel with the velocity of light; they can be diffracted and made to interfere just as can X-rays; they eject photoelectrons from materials in the same manner as do X-rays. These $\gamma$-rays are short electromagnetic waves, still shorter and more penetrating than the X-rays. The wave length of $\gamma$-rays depends upon the material emitting the rays and is characteristic of this material. Some of the longest $\gamma$-rays emitted are those from RdAc and those from ThC″. These have wave lengths of 3.9 and 3.0 A°, respectively. The equivalent photon energies are respectively 0.032 and 0.041 MEV. The shortest and most penetrating $\gamma$-rays observed are those from ThC″ and RaC. These have wave lengths of 0.0466 and 0.0557 A°, respectively; the equivalent photon energies are respectively 2.65 and 2.22 MEV. The lower energy $\gamma$-rays have wave lengths much longer than many of the X-rays. The more energetic $\gamma$-rays have wave lengths considerably shorter than any X-rays normally produced, though X-ray tubes have been designed recently to operate at potentials which yield some X-rays whose wave length approaches closely that of the shortest $\gamma$ radiation.

The wave lengths of $\gamma$-rays can be determined by two methods. Upon allowing $\gamma$-rays to fall on a crystal one observes interference phenomena entirely analogous to that obtained with X-rays. It is therefore possible to obtain the wave length from observations on the interference produced by a crystal of known spacing. While this method is rather satisfactory for the longer $\gamma$-rays it is inaccurate for the shorter ones. Difficulties arise mainly because the crystal reflects such a small fraction of the penetrating $\gamma$ radiation falling upon it; and because the $\gamma$-ray wave length is so much smaller than the crystal spacing that the spread of the interference pattern is greatly reduced.

A much more widely applicable and more reliable method of evaluating $\gamma$-ray wave lengths makes use of the fact that these rays eject high speed photoelectrons from materials on which they fall. It has been found that photoelectric ejection by $\gamma$-rays conforms accurately to the Einstein photoelectric equation. As in the case of X-rays, the study is complicated somewhat by the fact that the $\gamma$-rays are sufficiently energetic to eject photoelectrons from many levels within the atom. By observing the discrete energies possessed by the various photoelectrons ejected from one or more materials by a given $\gamma$-ray, and by knowing the different energy levels from which these electrons may have come, it is possible to determine the energy of the $\gamma$-ray photon which ejected them.

The ionization by $\gamma$-rays is quite different from that produced by the $\alpha$ or the $\beta$ particle. Whereas a charged particle produces a more or less continuous succession of ions along its path, giving up its energy gradually, a $\gamma$-ray photon produces directly no ions along its path. Any particular photon retains all of its energy, except for the relatively small amount lost in the scattering process, until it ejects a high speed photoelectron from some atom in the absorber. It gives up its entire energy to this photoelectron and ceases to exist thereafter. The photoelectron then proceeds to lose its energy by ionizing directly just as would any other high speed electron. On the average a $\gamma$-ray photon proceeds a considerable distance through a material before it is absorbed through the ejection of a photoelectron; it is very penetrating. Whereas energetic $\alpha$ particles are absorbed by a sheet of paper and energetic $\beta$ particles by a few millimeters of aluminum, many of the $\gamma$-rays penetrate a block of lead a number of inches thick. Gamma rays are thus many times more penetrating than are $\beta$-rays. The intensity of gamma radiation of a single wave length falls off exponentially as the radiation proceeds through an absorbing medium. The absorption is entirely analogous to that for X-rays except that it is somewhat less rapid on the average.

## Beta and Gamma Ray Spectra

*The Continuous Beta Ray Spectrum.*—The $\beta$-rays[85,86] emitted by a given radioactive substance have energies distributed continuously from nearly 0 up to several MEV, the upper limit depending upon the substance emitting the radiation. The velocities of the $\beta$-rays given off by a particular substance can be determined experimentally by bending the rays in a magnetic field as shown in Fig. 15. Electrons of different velocities fall at different places on the photographic plate. The distribution of velocities can therefore be evaluated roughly from the variation in the intensity of exposure along the plate. When an accurate count of the $\beta$-rays of a given velocity is desired, it is preferable to substitute for the photographic plate either an electroscope or a Geiger counter tube. By allowing first one and then

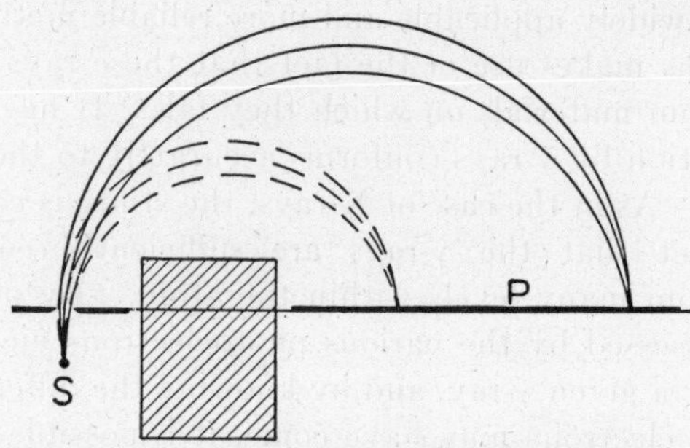


FIG. 15.—Illustrating the method of determining the velocities of the line $\beta$-rays.

another velocity of particle to fall upon this the relative distribution of particles can be determined reliably. Such experiments show that the general distribution of $\beta$ particles, except for one feature to which attention will be called shortly, is as illustrated[87] by Fig. 16. Other substances such as RaB, RaC, ThB, ThC, and ThC″ have been shown[85,88,89] to have similar energy distributions of their disintegration electrons. The energies are distributed continuously over a wide range. These $\beta$-rays are therefore said to form a continuous energy or a continuous velocity spectrum.

Data are somewhat inconsistent as to the exact shape of the continuous spectrum curve at the lower energies. It is rather generally supposed that the curve continues through the origin as indicated by the broken line in Fig. 16, but this is by no means certain. It is certain that all such curves have a definite maximum, the height and position of which depend upon the substance emitting the $\beta$-rays. It is also certain that there exists a

[86] G. Hevesy and F. A. Paneth (translated by R. W. Lawson), *A Manual of Radioactivity* (2nd ed.; London: Oxford University Press, 1938), pp. 101–107.

[87] J. S. O'Conor, *Phys. Rev.*, **52**, 303 (1937).

[88] R. W. Gurney, *Proc. Roy. Soc.*, A, **112**, 380 (1926).

[89] E. Madgwick, *Proc. Camb. Phil. Soc.*, **23**, 982 (1927).

definite upper limit of energy for the β particles ejected by any particular material. This upper limit, or end point, of the continuous spectrum is quite different for different substances; expressed in MEV it is[86] 0.36 for ThB, 0.65 for RaB, 1.23 for RaE, 1.80 for ThC″, 2.20 for ThC, 2.25 for $MsTh_2$, 2.32 for $UX_2$, and 3.15 for RaC. The average energy of the β-rays is roughly 1/3 or 1/4 that of the high energy limit.

Experiment has shown that the total number of β-rays going to make up this continuous spectrum ejected in a given time is equal to the number of atoms which disintegrate in this same time, the number of electrons being measured electrically and the number of atoms disintegrating being calculated from the known transformation constant. Thus the continuous

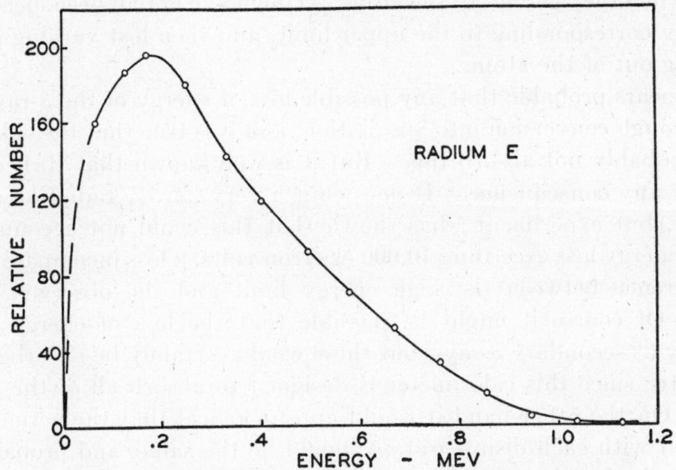

FIG. 16.—Showing the energy distribution of the β-rays from RaE.

β-rays are certainly the disintegration electrons ejected from the nucleus. Just why they should be ejected with a continuous distribution of velocities is a question of considerable importance, and one which will be discussed later. It appears certain, however, that they are actually ejected from the nucleus with this continuous distribution of velocities. It might appear possible that all β particles are ejected with the same energy, that corresponding to the high energy limit, and that the continuous velocity spectrum results from various losses of energy suffered by the different electrons in getting out of the atom. Such a possibility has been considered seriously. Experiments now to be described show,[85] however, that such cannot be the case.

Having the experimental curve representing the continuous β-ray spectrum of a substance, say RaE, it is possible to calculate the average energy of the β-rays. For RaE, which has a high energy limit of 1.2 MEV, this average energy turns out to be 0.34 MEV. Now it is possible to determine the average energy associated with a disintegration by placing the disintegrating substance within a calorimeter designed to absorb all the known products of disintegration, and by measuring the total heat energy produced by a known number of disintegrations. Such an experiment has been carried out carefully, one observer[90] finding for RaE an average energy of disintegration of (0.35 ± 0.04) MEV, another[91] obtaining a value (0.337 ± 0.020). This is in excellent agreement with the value 0.34 MEV for the average energy of the $\beta$-rays, and far below the upper energy limit 1.2 MEV. Thus it appears certain that the original energy given the $\beta$-ray is, on the average, just that which one finds these particles possess when they get out of the atom. They have not all been ejected with an energy corresponding to the upper limit, and then lost varying amounts in getting out of the atom.

It appears probable that any possible loss of energy of the $\beta$-rays would come through conversion into $\gamma$ radiation, and it is true that the calorimeter would probably not absorb this. But it is well known that RaE emits no $\gamma$-rays of any consequence. It does emit a very hard $\gamma$ radiation of feeble intensity, but experiment[92] has shown that this could not account for an average energy loss exceeding 10,000 electron volts, a loss incomparable with the difference between the high energy limit and the observed average energy. Of course it might be possible that the loss of energy appears indirectly as secondary $\beta$-rays, but these would certainly be absorbed in the calorimeter since this calorimeter is designed to absorb all of the primary $\beta$-rays. On the other hand it would appear logical that the actual energy associated with each disintegration should be the same, and probably that corresponding to the upper energy limit of the continuous $\beta$-ray spectrum. But if this is true a great deal of the energy must be given to some unobserved particle which is not absorbed in the calorimeter. It is felt that in all probability there is such a particle, called the neutrino, which shares this energy of disintegration. If such a particle exists it bears no electrical charge, for it does not produce ionization; and it must be extremely small, and probably of very small mass, for it is very penetrating. There is no direct evidence for the existence of such a particle, but the indirect evidence is becoming more and more convincing.

*Beta Ray Line Spectra.*—It has been stated that except for one important feature the energy distribution of $\beta$-rays is similar to that shown in Fig. 16. For a great many materials there is superimposed upon the continuous distribution curve a number of distinct peaks. These are very narrow and

[90] C. D. Ellis and W. A. Wooster, *Proc. Roy. Soc.*, A, **117**, 109 (1927).

[91] L. Meitner and W. Orthmann, *Zeits. f. Physik*, **60**, 143 (1930).

[92] G. H. Aston, *Proc. Camb. Phil. Soc.*, **22**, 935 (1927).

often quite high. Thus many $\beta$-ray sources give off in addition to the continuous spectrum a number of particles of well defined energies or velocities. These are said to constitute a line $\beta$-ray velocity spectrum. These line $\beta$-rays are characteristic of the radioactive substance giving them off. The number of line $\beta$ particles going to make up the line spectrum is for some materials inappreciable as compared to the number going into the continuous spectrum. Other materials, however, emit more $\beta$-rays in their line spectra than they do in their continuous spectra.

The velocities of the line $\beta$-rays given off by a particular substance can be determined experimentally by bending the rays in a magnetic field as shown in Fig. 15. Whereas those electrons making up the continuous spectrum expose the photographic plate somewhat over an extended region, those making up the line spectrum cause an excessive darkening at a relatively few sharply defined positions. From these positions and the known magnetic field the velocities of the particles can be calculated. Many careful measurements of this character have been carried out. The energies of the line $\beta$-rays are accurately known for a good number of those substances which eject such particles, and can be found tabulated in the literature.[85,93]

*Gamma Ray Line Spectra.*—The $\gamma$-rays emitted by all radioactive substances are of definite wave lengths characteristic of the material. They are line $\gamma$-rays, quite similar to the characteristic bright line optical spectra and the characteristic X-ray spectra. The lines are extremely sharp. The emission of $\gamma$-rays was thought for years to be associated with $\beta$ disintegration only. It is now certain, however, that a number of those substances which disintegrate with the ejection of an $\alpha$ particle also emit $\gamma$-rays. On the other hand, some of those materials which disintegrate with the ejection of a $\beta$ particle do not emit any appreciable $\gamma$ radiation. It is true that a great majority of the $\gamma$-rays are associated with $\beta$ rather than $\alpha$ transformations, and these $\gamma$-rays are in general much the more intense and penetrating. In the early years of the knowledge of radioactivity it was frequently stated that all radioactive radiations were of nuclear origin. It is now known definitely that this is not the case. Evidence will now be presented to show that some of the $\gamma$-rays are emitted from the nucleus while many others are emitted from the planetary structure of the atom.

*The Origin of Beta and Gamma Rays.*—The early view that all radioactive radiations came from the nucleus of the atom grew largely from the fact that these radiations are entirely independent of any physical or chemical change to which one can subject the atom. In more recent years it has been recognized clearly that certain parts of this radiation are of extranuclear origin; they arise in the planetary electron structure. The

[93] C. D. Ellis, *Proc. Roy. Soc.*, A, **138**, 318 (1932); **143**, 350 (1934).

purpose of this section will be to present the modern concept regarding the origins of the radiations and to call attention to typical evidence which has given rise to this concept.

The continuous beta rays[94] certainly come from the nucleus. Every material which disintegrates through the emission of $\beta$ particles emits a continuous $\beta$-ray spectrum; it may or may not emit a line $\beta$-ray spectrum. Furthermore, in all cases where reliable measurements have been made, the number of continuous $\beta$ particles ejected per unit time is closely equal to the number of atoms disintegrating per unit time. The particles making up the continuous $\beta$-ray spectrum are definitely the disintegration electrons. They are, therefore, of nuclear origin. The logical and almost inescapable inference is that each disintegrating atom ejects one disintegration electron; in fact the ejection of this electron from the nucleus must constitute the actual disintegration.

It is conceived that these electrons are ejected spontaneously from the nucleus with an energy equal to or less than that corresponding to the end point of the $\beta$-ray spectrum. The total energy of the disintegration is shared by the $\beta$ particle and a supposed neutrino which is assumed to be ejected simultaneously with the electron. These two particles supposedly share the energy and the momentum in such a way that both of these quantities are conserved.

Almost the entire evidence for the existence of the neutrino is theoretical; no satisfactory general concept of the continuous distribution of $\beta$-rays that does not involve the assumed neutrino has yet been suggested. No direct effects attributable to the particle have been observed; the particle does not ionize and hence possesses no electrical charge; it must be of very small mass for it produces no directly observed effects attributable to collision. Perhaps the most direct experimental evidence for the existence of this particle is a recent cloud chamber study[95] of individual atoms ejecting $\beta$-rays. As a $\beta$-ray is ejected the atom recoils. Unfortunately this recoiling atom produces a track entirely too short to measure even in a cloud chamber operated at the lowest practical pressure. It has therefore been impossible to evaluate the energy and the momentum of recoil from the length of this track. This recoil energy goes into forming new ions, and a rough count of the number of ions formed can be made by delaying the expansion a sufficient time after the disintegration that the droplets form after the ions diffuse considerably. The recoil energy can then be estimated from an actual count of the number of ions formed and the known average energy required for the formation of a pair. Thus the energy and the momentum

[94] E. Rutherford, J. Chadwick and C. D. Ellis, *Radiations from Radioactive Substances* (London: Cambridge University Press, 1930), pp. 385–410.

[95] H. R. Crane and J. Halpern, *Phys. Rev.*, **53**, 789 (1938).

of the recoiling nucleus can be obtained. The energy and the momentum of the $\beta$ particle ejected is easily obtained from the length of the track or from the curvature of the track in a known magnetic field. It should then be possible to determine whether energy and momentum are conserved in a $\beta$ particle disintegration involving just the particle and the recoiling nucleus. Experiments[95] of this character, although still rather rough, indicate strongly that neither momentum nor energy is conserved in the individual disintegrations if only these two particles are involved. Thus a third particle, the neutrino, is definitely indicated.

Not all $\beta$-ray emitters give out $\gamma$ radiation, RaE for example. On the other hand $\gamma$-rays do accompany most disintegrations of the $\beta$-ray type. It has already been seen that both the fine structure of the normal $\alpha$ particles from many substances and the existence of long range particles from RaC′ and ThC′, provide strong evidence for the existence of discrete energy levels within the nucleus. It might therefore be possible that $\beta$-rays could be ejected from more than one energy level. If after ejection of a $\beta$ particle the nucleus is left in its lowest energy state, one would expect no further radiation. On the other hand, the ejection of a $\beta$ particle might leave the new nucleus in an excited state. In this case one would expect the disintegration to be followed by the radiation of a $\gamma$-ray photon having an energy equal to the excitation energy. Or, if the nucleus should return to its normal state by steps, there should appear two or more line $\gamma$-rays of smaller frequencies. This is the supposed origin of some of the line $\gamma$ radiation, and if the concept is correct these $\gamma$-rays are of nuclear origin. The observed frequencies of these $\gamma$-rays therefore provide further evidence concerning the differences of energy levels within the nucleus. It has already been pointed out that most of these nuclear $\gamma$-ray photons observed are just those which one should expect from transitions between the nuclear levels assigned from data on the fine structure of $\alpha$-rays and on long range particles. A few other $\gamma$-rays seem also to be of nuclear origin, and in order to include these in the interpretation one is forced to amplify slightly the energy level picture formed on the basis of $\alpha$-ray evidence alone. There remains no doubt but that those gamma rays emitted from the nucleus have energies, and hence frequencies, determined by the differences between pairs of energy levels within the nucleus.

There are emitted, however, many line gamma rays which do not fit into any reasonable nuclear energy level scheme. These are in general of longer wave length than the shorter ones emitted from the nucleus, but they are often of shorter wave length than other nuclear gamma rays. There is ample evidence that these gamma rays have their origin in the planetary system of the atom. In considering this evidence it will be convenient to discuss at the same time the origin of those beta particles making up the line beta ray spectrum. Both the line gamma rays of extranuclear origin and the line beta rays, which will be shown also to be of extranuclear origin, are characteristic of the atom emitting them; they are just as characteristic as are the nuclear gamma rays. In arriving at a proper concept of the origin of these, it is important to note first of all that those materials emitting a well-defined beta ray line spectrum invariably emit also a strong line spectrum of gamma rays, while those materials emitting only a continuous beta ray spectrum emit exceedingly weak if any gamma radiation. Recall that RaB is an isotope of Pb, atomic number 82, and that RaC is an isotope of Bi, atomic number 83. Recall also that the characteristic $K$ and $L$ series X-rays of the various isotopes of a given element are almost identical. That is, two or more isotopes have almost identical systems of energy levels in the planetary electron structure.

Now it has been found[96] that many of the line gamma rays emitted when RaB disintegrates to form RaC are identical in wave length with, and similar in relative intensities to, the $K$ and $L$ characteristic X-rays of Bi. This means that they are identical with the characteristic X-rays of RaC, since RaC is an isotope of Bi. These gamma rays which appear really to be X-rays are just those which cannot be assigned a nuclear origin on any simple picture of nuclear energy levels. There can be no doubt that a part of the electromagnetic radiation accompanying the disintegration of RaB into RaC, a part of the gamma ray line spectrum, is truly the characteristic X-rays of RaC. These lines clearly have their origin in the planetary system, for all characteristic X-rays arise there.

These findings would appear quite reasonable if the RaB atom has already disintegrated, ejecting a beta particle, before the nuclear gamma rays are emitted. In this case the atom would already have become RaC before emission of these gamma rays. In this case the process could be interpreted as follows: Because of its inherent instability the RaB nucleus ejects a beta particle, becoming immediately an atom of RaC. If the ejection of this beta ray should leave the nucleus in its lowest energy state, no gamma ray would be emitted. This is apparently the case for some materials, such as RaE, which eject only a continuous beta ray spectrum; these materials emit no gamma rays and no line beta rays. If, however, the nucleus is left in an excited state it proceeds to eject gamma radiation. Those atoms which pass immediately to their lowest state eject a single gamma ray, an energetic one. Other nuclei may proceed to the lowest state by a series of changes, and these eject a number of lower energy gamma rays. In any case, regardless of how the nucleus does return to its ground state, nuclear line gamma rays are emitted. Now this nuclear gamma ray

[96] E. Rutherford, J. Chadwick and C. D. Ellis, *Radiations from Radioactive Substances* (London: Cambridge University Press, 1930), pp. 356–381.

falls directly upon the planetary electron structure of the atom which emitted it. It will eject from this atom photoelectrons. If a photoelectron is ejected from the $K$ level, leaving a vacancy therein, other electrons fall into this level and give rise to the entire $K$ series of characteristic X-rays. Vacancies arising in other shells, say the $L$, either because of the ejection of a photoelectron directly from this shell or because electrons from this shell have fallen into a vacancy created in the $K$ shell, give rise to other series of characteristic X-rays. And since it has been supposed that the ejection of the disintegration electron was the first step in this process, these X-rays should be those of RaC, an isotope of Bi, rather than those of RaB. This is in entire agreement with observations. It is clear, however, that this interpretation is proper only if the assumption that the ejection of the disintegration electron is the first step in the process is correct. We shall soon cite evidence showing conclusively the correctness of this assumption.

Think next of the line beta rays.[96] The velocity, and thence the energy, of these can be determined accurately by bending the particles in semicircles in a magnetic field. Now it turns out that the energies of these line beta rays are identical, as nearly as one can measure, with those with which photoelectrons are ejected from Bi when the gamma rays from disintegrating RaB are allowed to fall on Bi. All of the line beta rays are apparently photoelectrons ejected from the planetary system by the so-called internal conversion of nuclear gamma rays. The energy of a given line beta ray is equal to the energy of the nuclear gamma ray photon less the energy required to extract the planetary electron from the level from which it came. Now the energy associated with a given planetary electron level of RaC is somewhat higher than that of the corresponding level of RaB. The observed energies of the line beta rays indicate that these are photoelectrons from RaC rather than from RaB. Here again then the interpretation is quite simple and direct if one assumes that the RaB atom has already disintegrated into RaC, by ejection of a beta particle, before the emission of the nuclear gamma ray.

It is seen that the order in which these emissions take place is of considerable importance. As a consequence there have been a number of experiments designed to test the correctness of the assumption that the emission of the nuclear beta particle is the first step in the process. The early history of these efforts has been well summarized elsewhere.[97] One of the most direct and most convincing experiments was that performed by Ellis and Wooster[98] in 1925. These workers placed a thin-walled glass tube containing radon inside a small Pt cylinder. Radon disintegrates rather

[97] E. Rutherford, J. Chadwick and C. D. Ellis, *Radiations from Radioactive Substances* (London: Cambridge University Press, 1930), pp. 352–356.

[98] C. D. Ellis and W. A. Wooster, *Proc. Camb. Phil. Soc.*, **22**, 844 (1925).

rapidly into RaA, RaB and RaC successively. The walls of the Pt cylinder were sufficiently thick to stop all of the alpha rays from Rn and RaC and all of the natural beta rays from RaB and RaC. The gamma rays from RaB and RaC were only partially absorbed. These gamma rays eject photoelectrons from the Pt. Some of these photoelectrons are ejected from the outermost surface of the cylinder, and it is only these in which we are interested. On the outside surface of the Pt there was deposited a very thin layer of RaB and RaC. This layer served as a source of the natural line beta rays characteristic of RaB and RaC. Thus the experimenters had essentially a common source, as far as position goes, giving off the natural line beta rays of RaB and RaC, and in addition the photoelectrons from Pt ejected by the same gamma rays as are responsible for the production of the natural beta rays.

Ignore for the moment the original presence of RaC and think only of the radiation associated with the transformation of the original RaB atoms into RaC. Now the energy $E_1$ of a given photoelectron from Pt is given by

$$E_1 = h\nu - W_{78}$$

where $h\nu$ is the energy of the gamma ray photon responsible for the ejection and where $W_{78}$ is the energy corresponding to the level in Pt from which the photoelectron comes. In a similar way the energy $E_2$ of the line beta ray given out during the disintegration of RaB should be either

$$E_2 = h\nu - W_{83} \qquad \text{or} \qquad E_2 = h\nu - W_{82}$$

depending upon whether the RaB atom has or has not already ejected its disintegration electron. It follows, therefore, that the difference between the measured energies, $(E_1 - E_2)$, of the photoelectron and of the beta ray from corresponding levels should be either $(W_{83} - W_{78})$ or $(W_{82} - W_{78})$, depending upon whether the nuclear beta ray has or has not been ejected. The energy difference $(E_1 - E_2)$ was measured directly by bending the paths of the particles in a semicircle by means of a magnetic field. The choice of Pt, a material of atomic number rather close to that of the radioactive atom being studied, allows a direct and rather accurate measurement of this energy difference. It was found that this energy difference is definitely $(W_{83} - W_{78})$ rather than $(W_{82} - W_{78})$. This shows conclusively that the first step in the disintegration of RaB is the ejection of a nuclear beta particle, for the RaB atom has already changed into RaC, atomic number 83, before the nuclear gamma ray ejects the natural line beta rays. In a similar way it was found that the natural beta rays coming from the disintegration of the RaC present come from an atom of atomic number 84 rather than 83, showing that the ejection of the nuclear electron is the first step in this process also.

Somewhat similar evidence has been obtained on several other materials, some of which disintegrate by ejecting beta particles and others of which disintegrate by ejecting alpha particles. As early as 1930 Rutherford[97] remarked as follows: "It is extremely satisfactory that this important problem has been settled so conclusively. Five bodies have been investigated, of which two showed the alpha ray type of disintegration, and three the beta ray type. In every case the gamma rays were found to be emitted after the disintegration, and we can safely extend this conclusion to all radioactive bodies." All evidence which has been obtained since has served only to bear out this conclusion. Whereas a great share of the early accurate work was done on RaB and RaC, there are now available[93] data of comparable accuracy on the gamma rays and the line beta rays emitted by ThB and ThC.

## Chapter 9

# THE POSITRON

## 1. DISCOVERY OF THE POSITRON

Previous to 1932 there was every reason to believe that the nuclei of all atoms were constructed of various combinations of just two fundamental building stones, electrons and protons. It is true of course that the existence of the photon was recognized; but this quantum of radiant energy had scarcely those characteristics which would lead one to call it a particle in the usual sense of the word. There were recognized just two fundamental particles, the very light and negatively charged electron, and the relatively massive and positively charged proton. Workers had frequently considered the possible existence of a positive electron, a particle having the same mass and magnitude of charge as the Millikan electron, but one bearing a positive rather than a negative charge. But there was no evidence whatever that such a particle existed. The proton was the lightest positively charged particle known; no one thought seriously that a still lighter one would soon be discovered.

The way in which this discovery came about is interesting. It illustrates beautifully how some of the most important discoveries grow out of studies undertaken for quite a different purpose. About 1930 there was an intense interest in cosmic rays. It was recognized at that time that these rays were exceedingly penetrating. But there was no general agreement as to the nature of the radiation; neither was there any convincing evidence as to the energy associated with the radiation. It was known that when a cosmic ray is absorbed it often ejects one or more very energetic charged particles from an atom of the absorbing material. It appeared, therefore, that one might gain some knowledge regarding the energy of the incident cosmic ray by measuring the energies of the particles ejected during absorption. The natural way to undertake such measurements was to photograph the tracks of ejected particles as they passed through a Wilson cloud expansion chamber placed between the poles of an electromagnet. There was a difficulty, however. The charged particles were usually ejected with such high energies that they could not be bent appreciably by any magnetic field then in use. The highest energies that had so far been measured by such a method were of the order of 15 MEV. The problem then presenting itself required the measurement of energies far greater than this. The natural solution was to build a large cloud chamber and an unusually large and powerful magnet. This was undertaken by Anderson and Millikan of the California Institute of Technology.

The resulting magnet, with its associated cloud chamber, was a distinct improvement over previous similar pieces. The general design and the enormous size of the magnet are illustrated[1] by Fig. 1. The vertical cloud chamber was 17 cm. in diameter and 4 cm. thick. The magnetic field between the poles of the magnet was nearly uniform over this region. A current of 2000 amperes was sent through the winding of this magnet. A

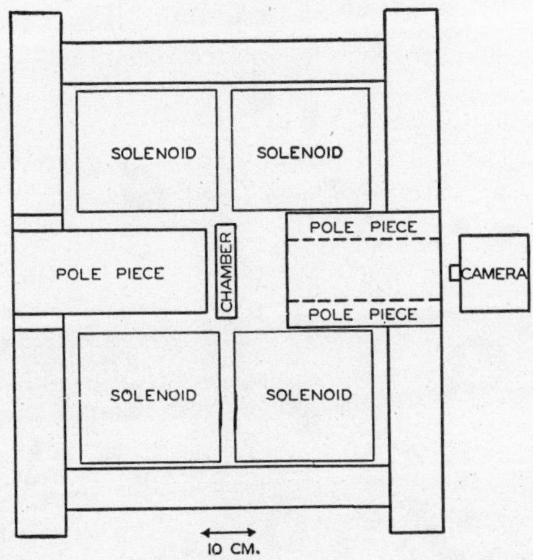


FIG. 1.—A diagram of the original cloud chamber and magnet built at the California Institute of Technology for the purpose of measuring directly the energies of cosmic ray particles.

generator of nearly 1000 horsepower was required to furnish it. The resulting magnetic field was 24,000 oersteds. This was a much larger field, existing over an extended region, than had previously been used. The apparatus was capable of producing a measurable bending of particles having energies as great as 6000 MEV. This made possible the measurement of energies some 400 times as great as those previously measured. Figs. 2 and 3 illustrate the ability of this apparatus to bend energetic electrons. Fig. 2 is a photograph,[2] taken with a magnetic field of 12,000 oersteds, showing tracks of electrons ejected by some of the most penetrating gamma rays. The magnetic field is sufficiently strong to cause these electrons to describe very small circles. The paths are really spirals about the magnetic lines of force, for most of the electrons are not traveling

[1] C. D. Anderson, *Phys. Rev.*, **44**, 406 (1933).
[2] C. D. Anderson, *Phys. Rev.*, **41**, 405 (1932).

perpendicular to these lines. This spiraling effect can be seen in some instances for, although the camera is pointed parallel to the magnetic field, the light from some parts of the field of view comes into the camera at a slight angle with the magnetic field. Fig. 3 shows[2] the path described by a cosmic ray electron in the same magnetic field. Although the energy of this electron is more than three times as great as that of any electron ever ejected by a natural gamma ray, the magnetic field is nevertheless capable

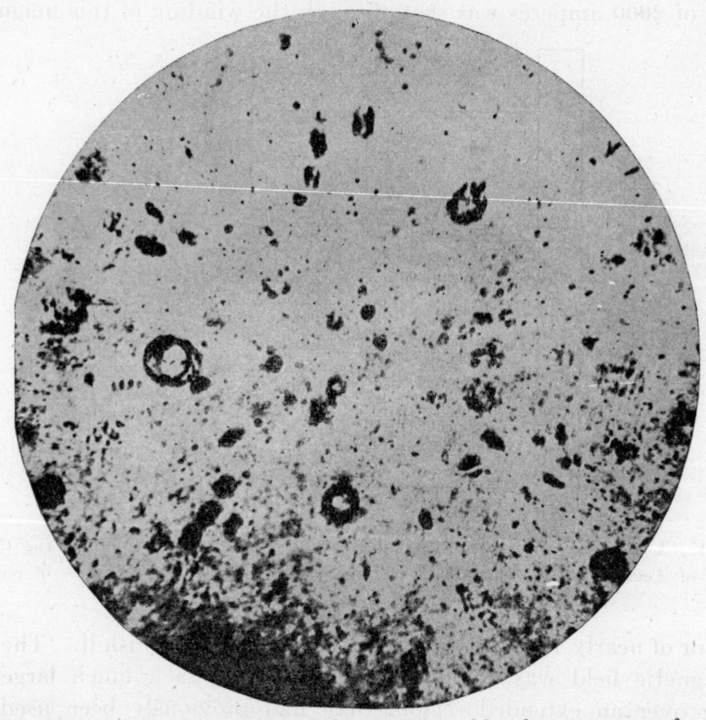

Fig. 2.—A photograph of the tracks of electrons ejected by the gamma rays from radium after these had been filtered through 2.5 cm. of steel. Some of the electrons have energies of 1 MEV. The photograph was taken with a magnetic field of 12,000 oersteds.

of causing the particle to describe a circle so small as to be completed within the chamber. It will be seen later, however, that this electron possesses a very low energy for a cosmic ray particle. Some are so energetic that they are not bent perceptibly by the strongest fields even now available.

Studies with this powerful magnet produced results of far-reaching consequences. One of the early photographs taken is reproduced[2] in Fig. 4. Here are shown two tracks left by particles apparently arising simultaneously at a common point. Both tracks show an appreciable curvature in the magnetic field. Other experimenters[3] had previously observed such paired tracks, but the magnetic field which had been used was too small to produce any certain curvature of the tracks. Here the curvature is quite apparent, and the two particles clearly have opposite signs. It is barely possible that the two particles did not arise at a common point, that they are of like charge and traveling in essentially opposite directions across the chamber. Such a possibility is extremely improbable, and the frequency

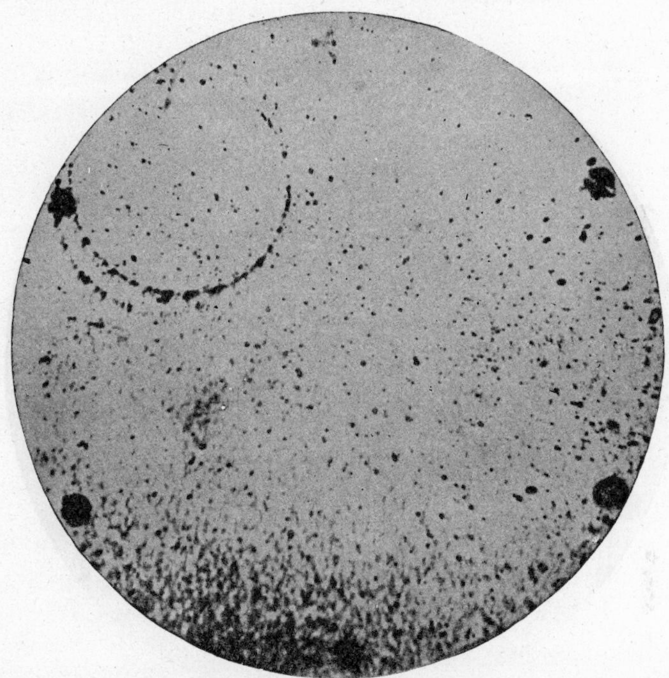

FIG. 3.—Showing a track left by a cosmic ray electron in a magnetic field of 12,000 oersteds. The energy of this electron is 8 MEV, very low for a cosmic ray, but much higher than that of any electron ever ejected by a gamma ray from a natural radioactive substance.

with which such paired tracks are obtained rules out such an interpretation. The thinner of the two tracks is undoubtedly due to an electron, one possessing an energy of 120 MEV. The more dense, straighter track appears to be that of a proton of 130 MEV energy. A proton of this energy should ionize several times as heavily as an electron, and this track shows evidence of this greater ionization. Since it had long been recognized that all positive particles contained in the structure of an atom were contained within the small central nucleus, and since here a cosmic ray has ejected from an atom

[3] D. Skobelzyn, *Zeits. f. Physik*, **54**, 686 (1929).

a positive particle, this photograph constituted the first direct experimental proof that the nucleus of an atom plays an important role in the absorption of cosmic rays.

It has often been said that this photograph showing the electron and proton paired tracks actually delayed the discovery of the positron by several months. As it has turned out, proton tracks of this character are relatively rare. Of several thousand photographs studied by Anderson and

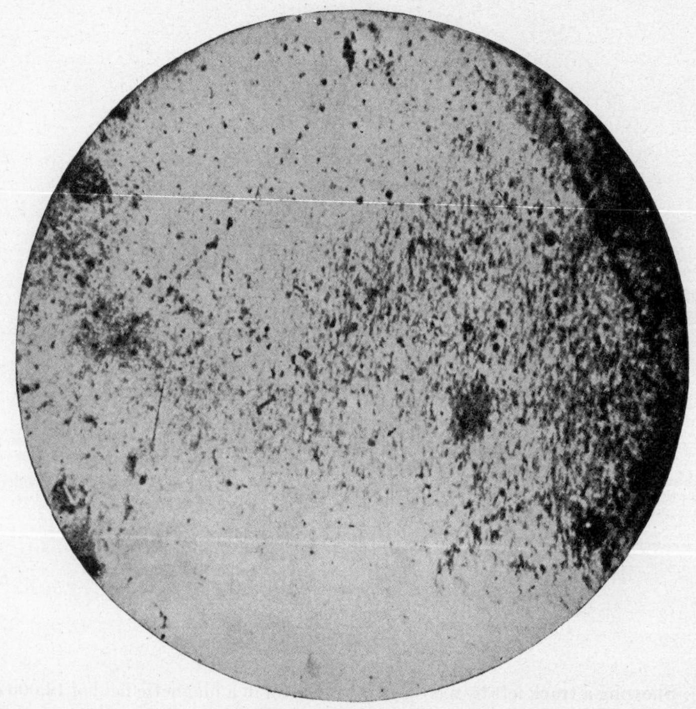

FIG. 4.—A pair of tracks apparently arising simultaneously from a common point outside the field of view. The particles responsible for these tracks have been ejected when a cosmic ray was absorbed. The thinner track is that of a 120 MEV electron. The more dense track is that of a 130 MEV proton. This photograph was taken with a field of 17,000 oersteds.

his associates at this time, that reproduced in Fig. 4 shows the only track that seemed certainly to demand a proton as the particle responsible for the track. A great majority of the photographs showing paired tracks were more as illustrated[2] in Fig. 5. Here again the two particles are clearly of opposite sign; but they appear to produce equal ionizations. The particle producing the track of greater curvature is a 27 MEV electron. If the two particles arose at a common point, and there is an extremely small chance of obtaining two such tracks under any other circumstance, then the particle producing the straighter of the two tracks must have been positively charged. But a proton of this curvature should produce an ionization several times as heavy as that produced by an electron; and this particle does not do so. There seemed to be no reasonable escape from the conclusion that this was a new particle, a positively charged electron, a particle having the same mass and magnitude of charge as the ordinary electron but

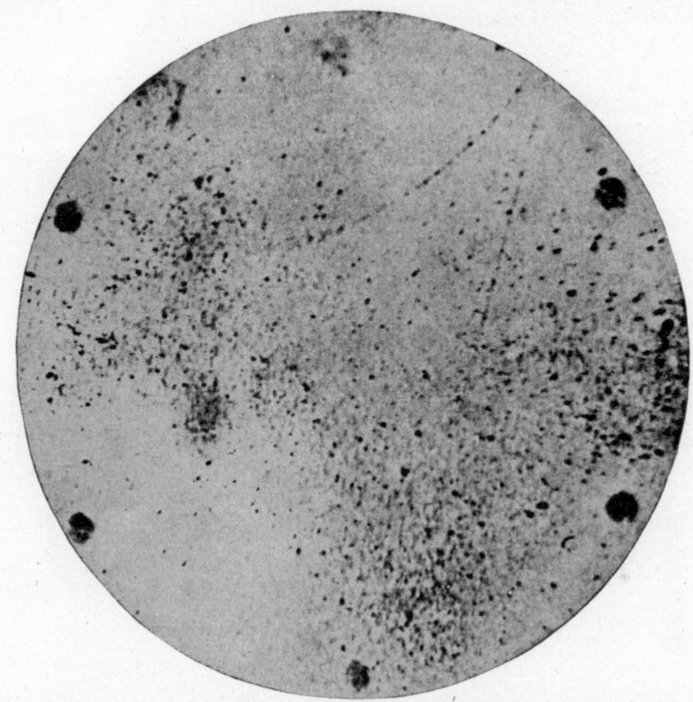

FIG. 5.—Another pair of tracks arising simultaneously from a common point. The two particles responsible for these tracks produce equal specific ionizations. The one leaving the track of greater curvature is an electron of 27 MEV energy. The one leaving the track of smaller curvature was apparently left by a particle not then known to exist, a particle identical with the electron except that it carries a positive charge. It is a 450 MEV positron.

bearing a positive rather than a negative charge. This particle has been called the positron. The original announcement[4] of evidence indicating its existence was made by Anderson in 1932.

Far more convincing evidence for the existence of such a particle was obtained shortly. The method of paired tracks seemed quite safe, but when a question of this importance is to be settled ample evidence is necessary. More paired tracks were obtained, but the process was tedious. In the

[4] C. D. Anderson, *Science*, **76**, 238 (1932).

procedure originally used by Anderson[2] the cloud chamber was expanded and the photograph taken at random. One trusted to luck as to whether a high energy particle had passed through the chamber just before the expansion. As a result, only about one photograph in 50 showed a usable track of a high energy particle; and only a small fraction of these showed the clearly defined pairs. Single tracks were not sufficient for identification of

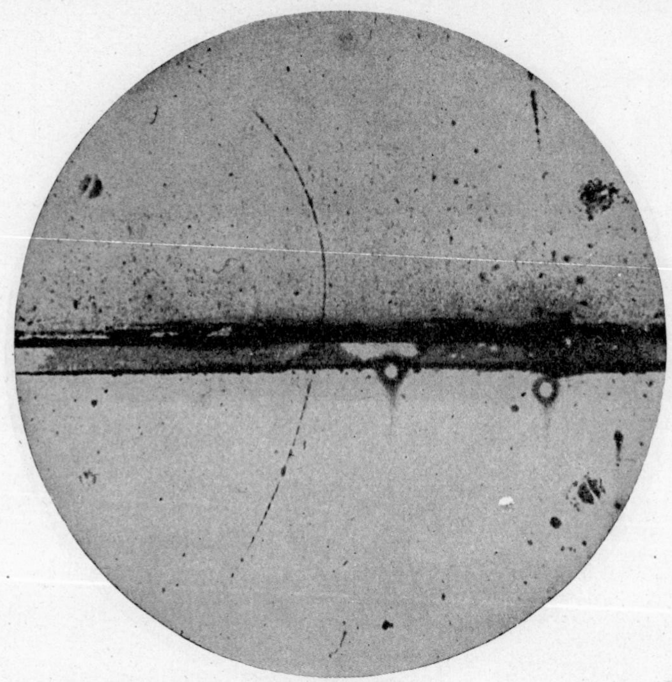

Fig. 6.—A photograph of great historical interest. The track is one left by a positron. This positron possessed an energy of 63 MEV before entering the lead plate from below; after penetrating the 6 mm. lead plate it proceeded with an energy of 23 MEV. This change of energy shows definitely the direction of motion of the particle and, therefore, allows one to conclude that it is positively charged.

the new positive particle, for one never knew for certain in which direction the particle was moving through the chamber.

This question was settled by Anderson[5] in a simple manner. A sheet of lead 6 mm. thick was placed within the cloud chamber and in such a position that the track of a particle passing through the lead might be photographed. Fig. 6 reproduces[5] the highly important photograph obtained by Anderson in August, 1932. The curvature of this track is much greater above the lead plate than below it. The track below the plate

[5] C. D. Anderson, *Phys. Rev.*, **43**, 491 (1933).

is that of a 63 MEV electron; this particle might be either positive or negative, depending upon the direction of motion across the chamber. Above the lead plate the track is that of a 23 MEV electron, again either positive or negative, depending upon the direction of motion. Now one would scarcely wish to argue that the particle gained 40 MEV of energy in penetrating the 6 mm. lead plate; actually this is approximately the amount of energy one would expect such a particle to lose. The particle must have been moving upward across the chamber. But if it was moving upward, then the known direction of the magnetic field shows definitely that it is a positive particle. One would scarcely wish to consider the highly improbable possibility that the two tracks on the two sides of the lead were made by two entirely different negative electrons each moving downward. The sign of the particle is definitely established as positive. The next question is—could it be a proton? The answer is again quite definite. A proton leaving a track having a curvature of that above the plate would possess an energy of only 300,000 electron volts. A proton of this low energy is known to ionize many times more heavily than does an electron; and this track does not indicate an ionization at all comparable with what one should expect of such a proton. In the second place, the range of a proton of this energy is known to be only about 5 mm. in air. But this particle has a range of more than 5 cm., more than 10 times that which it would have were it a proton. The only answer seemed to be that the particle responsible for the entire track was a positron, a newly discovered particle. This evidence was so convincing that Anderson was later awarded the Nobel Prize in physics for his discovery.

Shortly after Anderson's discovery other workers reported similar tracks of positive particles. Ability to obtain tracks of high energy particles was greatly enhanced by development of the automatically controlled cloud chamber. About this time Blackett and Occhialini[6] arranged two Geiger tubes, one above and one below the cloud chamber, in such a way that the chamber was automatically expanded whenever a particle passed through both Geiger tubes simultaneously. A few expansions were set off by two different particles passing through the two tubes at essentially the same time, neither of these particles passing through the cloud chamber. Experiment showed, however, that the expansion control was tripped in a great majority of cases by a single particle passing through the upper Geiger tube, through the cloud chamber, and thence through the lower Geiger tube. High energy particles were thus caused to take photographs of their own tracks. Using such apparatus, these observers found that 80 percent of their exposures showed tracks of high energy particles. This represented

[6] P. M. S. Blackett and G. P. S. Occhialini, *Proc. Roy. Soc.*, A, **139**, 699 (1933).

a marked increase over the 10 percent[7] and the 2 percent[2] found by previous observers taking photographs at random. The use of such counter controlled expansion chambers is common today in all such work. The photographs obtained by Blackett and Occhialini[6] recorded numerous tracks showing clearly the existence of the positron, and thus confirming Anderson's discovery of the new particle. Other confirmatory evidence[7–9] appeared about the same time. Several historical summaries of these early developments are available in the literature.[10–12]

In more recent years many workers have photographed the tracks of such particles, and have observed the particles under a variety of conditions. The positron is on a firm experimental foundation; there can be no doubt of its existence. As far as is known, the mass of this particle is identical with that of the negative electron; its charge is also probably exactly equal in magnitude to that of the electron, although here again there is no accurate information. All estimates of the charge of the positron have come from studies of the tracks left by the particles. These studies also furnish estimates of the mass, although the mass of the particle can be obtained indirectly through other studies as well. Such methods yield far from precise values for either the charge or the mass, but they do furnish rough values for each. Anderson[5] concluded from his original work that the charge cannot be as great as twice that of the electron. He also concluded that the mass could not be greater than 20 times that of the electron. There was at that time, and there has since appeared, no evidence to suggest that either the charge or the mass is actually any different from that associated with the ordinary negative electron. More recent evidence has lowered considerably the probable limits by which either might differ. Anderson[1] found that the specific ionization produced by the positron does not differ from that of the electron by more than 20 percent; measurements were not sufficiently precise to detect a difference smaller than this. Since the specific ionization produced by a charged particle is proportional to the square of the charge, other things being constant, it follows that the positron charge cannot differ from that of the electron by more than 10 percent. Millikan[13] states that these studies show also that the two masses cannot differ by more than 20 percent. Experiments of a different type, to be discussed later, show that the masses cannot differ by as much as this.

[7] D. Skobelzyn, *Comptes Rendus*, **195**, 315 (1932).

[8] P. M. S. Blackett, *Nature*, **132**, 917 (1933).

[9] P. Kunze, *Zeits. f. Physik*, **80**, 559 (1933); **83**, 1 (1933).

[10] P. Kunze, *Phys. Zeits.*, **34**, 849 (1933).

[11] W. Bothe, *Naturwiss.*, **21**, 825 (1933).

[12] C. D. Anderson, *Nature*, **133**, 313 (1934); *Naturwiss.*, **22**, 293 (1934).

[13] R. A. Millikan, *Electrons (+ and −), Protons, Photons, Neutrons, and Cosmic Rays* (Chicago: University of Chicago Press, 1935), p. 335.

It is interesting that two attempts have been made to determine the ratio $e/m$ for the positron through use of magnetic and electric deflecting fields. The first of these,[14] utilizing a rather unusual arrangement of deflecting fields, gave results which showed that the numerical value of this ratio does not differ by more than 15% from that for the negative electron. The results did not indicate that the ratio was any different. A more recent experiment by Spees and Zahn[15] has shown the equality of the ratio $e/m$ for positrons and electrons to a much greater degree of accuracy. Recall that these workers had measured $e/m$ for the electron using a modification of the original Bucherer method, a modification in which the positions of the source and the detecting device were interchanged, and in which a counter tube replaced the photographic film used by Bucherer. Exactly the same method was employed for positrons. The source of positrons used was an artificially radioactive material, $Cu^{64}$, which emits both positrons and electrons. By using this common source of electrons and positrons it was possible to compare directly, through reversal of the electric and magnetic deflecting fields, the ratio $e/m$ for the two particles. Results showed that the ratio $e/m$ for positrons is the same as that for electrons within a probable error of approximately 2%.

While no attempt to measure directly the charge on the positron has yet been reported, there is one method which has been used recently by Ladenburg and Beers[16] to measure the charge on the beta particle that is equally applicable to the measurement of the positron charge. The method consists essentially of measuring the charge deposited per second on a collector of beta rays from RaE, and of determining the number of beta particles arriving per second by means of a Geiger counter. The ratio of these two quantities gives the charge carried by the beta particle. This experiment led to a charge $(4.84 \pm 0.03) \times 10^{-10}$ e.s.u., a value agreeing closely with the accepted electronic charge. If an artificial radioactive source emitting positrons were to be substituted for the RaE, the method could be used to measure the specific charge of the positron.

## 2. ARE POSITRONS ABUNDANT IN NATURE?

In view of the recent discovery of the positron, one might suspect that these particles are extremely rare in nature. Such is by no means the case. They appear to be about as numerous in cosmic ray studies[1,6] as are the common negative electrons. What part they play in the cosmic radiation itself need not concern us at this time. Suffice it to say that certainly most of those observed near sea level are of secondary origin; they have been

[14] J. Thibaud, *Ann. Soc. Sci. de Bruxelles*, **54**, 36 (1934); *Phys. Rev.*, **45**, 781 (1934).

[15] A. H. Spees and C. T. Zahn, *Phys. Rev.*, **57**, 72 (1940); **58**, 861 (1940).

[16] R. Ladenburg and Y. Beers, *Phys. Rev.*, **58**, 757 (1940).

ejected from the nuclei of atoms making up the atmosphere and the material about us as a result of absorption of the primary cosmic radiation.

If these newly formed particles are really numerous, then why were they not found earlier? There are two main reasons for the delay. In the first place these particles do not exist for long as free positrons; this is particularly true of the lower energy ones. As might be suspected, the positively charged positron has a great tendency to combine with the negatively charged electron; and there is an abundance of electrons, some free and many but lightly attached to the planetary structures of atoms, with which it may combine. As a result the normal life of a free positron is an extremely small fraction of a second. One might suspect that positrons which had lost most of their energy would combine more readily with electrons than would those of high energy. Such is no doubt the case. And one might well ask the interesting question—Just what is formed when a positron does combine with, and electrically neutralize, an electron? We shall see in a moment whether experimental evidence can help answer this question. First, however, another reason for not recognizing earlier the existence of the positron should be mentioned. Recall that it has been only a decade since investigators enlarged the Wilson cloud expansion chamber, and increased the magnetic field applied thereto, sufficiently to produce observable curvature of the track left by a truly high energy particle. Many tracks of energetic positrons had no doubt been photographed before the existence of the particle was recognized, but these had been attributed to electrons. Even when it became possible to produce observable curvature of these tracks it was still necessary to use some auxiliary criterion, such as paired tracks or the penetration of the particle through a lead sheet, before one could be certain of the direction of motion of the particle, and hence of the sign of its charge. In view of this situation, and in view of the very short time for which free positrons exist, it is no wonder that discovery of the particle was delayed until a relatively late date.

There are several further developments that should be mentioned before taking up the question of what happens when an electron and a positron neutralize one another. These have to do with other sources of positrons that were developed within a year after the original discovery of the particle. All of the works so far discussed utilized positrons produced by cosmic rays. It was soon discovered[17–19] that if the element beryllium were bombarded with alpha rays given off by the natural radioactive material polonium, this bombardment resulted in the production of positrons. The evidence[19] indicated that these positrons might be formed indirectly, formed by the

[17] J. Chadwick, P. M. S. Blackett and G. P. S. Occhialini, *Nature*, **131**, 473 (1933).

[18] I. Curie and F. Joliot, *Comptes Rendus*, **196**, 1105 (1933).

[19] L. Meitner and K. Philipp, *Naturwiss.*, **21**, 286 (1933).

gamma rays resulting from the bombardment. Regardless of how they were formed, positrons were certainly produced. Further evidence[19–22] was soon forth-coming that positrons can be produced directly by allowing gamma rays of sufficiently short wave length to fall upon any of the heavier elements. Many electrons are also ejected. Frequently one obtains cloud chamber photographs showing paired tracks entirely similar to those found in cosmic ray studies. The two tracks are those of an electron-positron pair, the two particles having arisen at a common point, the point of impingement of the gamma ray photon. This constitutes direct evidence that sufficiently energetic photons are capable of producing electron-positron pairs. We shall shortly return to a more detailed discussion of the manner of such production and of the energies involved in the production. For the time being it is sufficient to recognize that hard gamma rays do produce positrons when they impinge upon matter. The number of positrons emitted increases rapidly both with the atomic number of the material irradiated and with the frequency of the gamma ray. The production of positrons lasts only as long as the gamma radiation continues to fall upon the material.

In 1934 Curie and Joliot[23] announced the discovery of artificial radioactivity, and this phenomenon has provided excellent sources of positrons. These observers, who have won the Nobel Prize Award for their outstanding contributions to science, found that if boron, magnesium, or aluminum is bombarded with the alpha particles given off by polonium, the bombarded material begins to emit positrons. It is certain that the emitted particles are positrons, for the nature of the charged particles has been studied by both ionization and magnetic deflection experiments. The emission of these particles continues even after the source of alpha particles has been removed. Curie and Joliot showed that the rate of positron emission decreases exponentially after the alpha ray source is removed; it decreases in the same manner as does the emission of any natural radioactive substance. The half life of positron emission from that artificial radioactive substance made by bombarding aluminum with alpha particles was found to be 3 minutes and 15 seconds. The average energy of the positrons ejected was found from absorption measurements to be approximately 2.2 MEV. We shall defer until later any attempt to formulate working concepts connected with the phenomenon of artificial radioactivity. It is interesting to know, however, that these original experimenters formed a

[20] C. D. Anderson, *Science*, **77**, 432 (1933).

[21] I. Curie and F. Joliot, *Comptes Rendus*, **196**, 1581 (1933).

[22] J. Chadwick, P. M. S. Blackett and G. P. S. Occhialini, *Proc. Roy. Soc.*, A, **144**, 235 (1934).

[23] I. Curie and F. Joliot, *Comptes Rendus*, **198**, 254 (1934).

sufficiently concise view to allow them to predict that if carbon were to be bombarded with energetic deuterons, nuclei of heavy hydrogen, the same radioactive end product would result as that which they had observed when boron was bombarded with alpha particles. It has since become possible to produce in the laboratory very high energy particles of one kind and another, particularly protons, deuterons, and alpha particles. It was almost immediately verified[24] that bombardment of carbon by deuterons does produce the radioactivity that had been predicted. Since these original works on artificial radioactivity the field has been expanded tremendously. Today it is possible to make a radioactive isotope of practically any element desired. There are[25] well over 60 of these radioactive isotopes that emit positrons; some of these have quite long half lives. Thus there are available in the laboratory today, as a by-product of artificial radioactivity, convenient and intense sources of positrons.

## 3. CREATION AND ANNIHILATION OF ELECTRON-POSITRON PAIRS

Let us return now to the question of just what is produced when a positron and an electron combine. Fortunately there is sufficient experimental evidence to answer this question definitely. Although sufficient quantitative evidence has already been presented, in connection with the accurate determination of the masses of isotopes by the nuclear disintegration method, to convince one of the interchangeability of mass and energy, it is nevertheless somewhat of a shock to learn that when an electron and a positron combine the two masses disappear and there appears simultaneously a definite amount of radiant energy. It is equally surprising that a photon of radiant energy often disappears, and in its place arises simultaneously an electron-positron pair. Nevertheless, it is quite certain that this is just what happens. In the main, evidence concerning nuclear disintegrations has to do with the conversion of mass into kinetic energy, and vice versa. The present problem has to do with the conversion of mass into radiant energy, and vice versa. There is ample evidence to show convincingly that this latter conversion also takes place.

Let us speculate for a moment on what might happen when a free positron and electron combine. According to the mass-energy equivalence concept, the rest mass of an electron represents an energy

$$V = \frac{m_0c^2}{e} = \frac{(2.99776 \times 10^{10})^2}{1.7584 \times 10^7 \times 10^8} = 0.511 \times 10^6 \text{ EV}.$$

That is, if the mass of an electron could be changed into energy there should be exactly this amount of energy formed. If the mass of the positron

[24] H. R. Crane and C. C. Lauritsen, *Phys. Rev.*, **45**, 430 (1934).

[25] R. Grégoire, *Jour. de Physique et le Radium*, **9**, 419 (1938).

is identical with that of the electron, and there is every reason to believe that it is, then an equal energy would result from the conversion of this mass into energy. Hence, if an electron and a positron combine and their rest masses disappear as a result of such combination, there should be released an energy of 1.022 MEV. If this mass were to be transformed into a single photon having this energy, the wave length of the radiation should be

$$\lambda = \frac{c}{\nu} = \frac{c}{Ve/h} = \frac{2.99776 \times 10^{10} \times 6.608 \times 10^{-27}}{(1.022 \times 10^{6}/299.776) \times 4.803 \times 10^{-10}}$$
$$= 0.01210 \times 10^{-8} \text{ cm.}$$

This wave length, 0.012 A°, is in the region of the hard gamma rays. If for some reason this energy should be split equally between two photons, instead of all going into one, each would possess an energy of 0.511 MEV, and would represent radiation having a wave length of 0.024 A°.

Several experimenters have found radiation of these two wave lengths formed under conditions where there should be a number of free positrons combining with electrons. A number of investigations[26–28] had shown that very hard gamma rays were absorbed much more rapidly in the heavier elements than one would expect. As far as was previously known the so-called Klein-Nishina formula gave quite well the absorption of X-rays or gamma rays to be expected in the extranuclear electronic structure of an atom. And it was not then suspected that the nucleus itself played any appreciable role in this absorption. The actually measured absorption was, however, much greater for very penetrating gamma rays than this formula led one to expect. Particularly was this true for the heavier elements. It was obvious that either the Klein-Nishina formula did not hold for very short wave length gamma rays, or that there was some absorption mechanism other than that connected with the extranuclear electronic structure. Most workers referred to the additional absorption as nuclear absorption. The presence of an unexplained secondary gamma radiation given off during the absorption process was first shown by Chao.[29] It was recognized that the energy going into this secondary radiation probably accounted for the unexpectedly large absorption of the primary gamma rays. The secondary gamma radiation observed by Chao was of approximately 0.55 MEV, approximately 0.0225 A° wave length. This estimate of wave length, and hence of energy, was made through absorption measurements; hence, no great accuracy can be claimed.

[26] C. Y. Chao, *Proc. Nat. Acad. Sci.*, **16**, 431 (1930); *Proc. Roy. Soc.*, A, **135**, 206 (1932).
[27] L. Meitner and H. H. Hupfeld, *Zeits. f. Physik*, **67**, 147 (1930).
[28] G. T. P. Tarrant, *Proc. Roy. Soc.*, A, **128**, 345 (1930).
[29] C. Y. Chao, *Phys. Rev.*, **36**, 1519 (1930).

It is suggestive that this gamma ray agrees essentially in energy with one of those which, according to the calculations just carried out, might result from the annihilation of an electron-positron pair. The existence of this new secondary gamma radiation was confirmed immediately by Gray and Tarrant,[30] who found evidence also of a second and weaker component, a component of shorter wave length. The existence of this shorter wave length component was confirmed[31] immediately. Gray and Tarrant obtained for the two radiations, energies of 0.47 and 0.92 MEV, or wave lengths of 0.027 and 0.0135 A°. The first of these agrees, within the large probable error associated with these early measurements, with the finding of Chao. The second represents a gamma ray photon having twice the energy of the first.

These experiments also brought to light several other pertinent facts. The energy, or the wave length, of the secondary radiation did not depend upon the energy of the incident gamma rays. Neither did it depend upon the material used for absorbing the primary gamma rays. It could not be identified with any of the characteristic gamma rays given off by the absorber. Its wave length was independent of the angle, with respect to the incident beam, at which it was observed; hence, it could not be attributed to Compton scattering with the accompanying change of wave length with angle of scattering. There was considerable evidence that there existed some minimum energy which must be possessed by the incident gamma ray photon before the secondary radiation was excited. By rather indirect methods this minimum was placed[30] as probably between 1.5 and 2 MEV.

A connection between these unexplained secondary gamma rays and the annihilation of positrons was first suggested by Blackett and Occhialini[6] in 1932. All subsequent evidence has only emphasized the probable correctness of this suggested connection. It has already been stated that positrons are formed when sufficiently energetic gamma rays are allowed to fall on any absorber; they become more numerous the higher the atomic number of the absorber and the higher the energy of the gamma ray photons. It will be shown shortly that these high energy gamma ray photons actually form electron-positron pairs. It would appear from the calculation of the energy represented by the rest masses of this pair, that an energy of at least 1.02 MEV would be required to form the pair. If the incident photon had more energy than this, the remainder might logically go into kinetic energy of the two particles constituting the pair. Experimental evidence showing that this is the case will soon be presented. For the present purpose, however, one needs only recognize that when a material is irradiated by gamma rays of 2 or 3 MEV energy there are formed many positrons.

[30] L. H. Gray and G. T. P. Tarrant, *Proc. Roy. Soc.*, A, **136**, 662 (1932); **143**, 681 (1934).
[31] L. Meitner and H. H. Hupfeld, *Zeits. f. Physik*, **75**, 705 (1932).

While some of these probably have considerable kinetic energy at the instant of formation, they no doubt lose this rapidly in penetrating the absorber in which they are formed. As a result, most of the positrons combining with electrons probably have very little kinetic energy at the time they combine. If the energy of the rest masses of these two particles is converted into a single photon when they combine, then this photon should have an energy of 1.02 MEV, a wave length of 0.012 A°. This agrees essentially with the more penetrating component of the previously unexplained secondary gamma radiation just discussed. If the energy of the rest masses of the two particles of the combining pair should be radiated as two equal photons, then the energy of each of these should be 0.51 MEV; the wave length should be 0.024 A°. This agrees essentially with the softer component of the secondary gamma radiation found experimentally.

This annihilation radiation has also been observed coming from artificial radioactive bodies which emit positrons, and also from metals against which the positrons are allowed to strike. Both Joliot[32] and Thibaud[14] measured the absorption of gamma rays coming from metals against which a stream of positrons was directed. McMillan[33] measured the absorption of gamma rays given off by radioactive $N^{13}$, a material which emits positrons. In each case the energy of the gamma radiation was found to be approximately 0.5 MEV, corresponding to the annihilation radiation given off when the positron combines with an electron of the material in which it is absorbed. More recently Richardson and Kurie[34] and Richardson[35] have observed the gamma rays from a number of artificial radioactive materials. Each of those materials which emit positrons also give out gamma rays of 0.5 MEV energy; the negative electron emitters do not give out this gamma ray. Individual values obtained for the gamma ray energy were 0.51 MEV from $N^{13}$, 0.53 from $V^{48}$, and 0.47 from $Cu^{64}$. These agree well with the expected 0.51 MEV. No gamma radiation of 1.02 MEV is found except in the case of $V^{48}$. This material emits a strong gamma ray of 1.05 MEV energy. While this agrees quite well with the more penetrating annihilation radiation, it appears more likely that this particular radiation is one characteristic of the atom.

One might properly ask how it happens that the combining electron-positron pair sometimes gives rise to a single photon of approximately 1 MEV energy, while at other times it gives rise to two photons of essentially ½ MEV each. Consideration of the simple laws of conservation of energy and conservation of momentum will show that if the combination takes place in

[32] F. Joliot, *Jour. de Physique et le Radium*, **5**, 299 (1933).

[33] E. McMillan, *Phys. Rev.*, **46**, 868 (1934).

[34] J. R. Richardson and F. N. D. Kurie, *Phys. Rev.*, **50**, 999 (1936).

[35] J. R. Richardson, *Phys. Rev.*, **53**, 124, 610 (1938).

free space, removed from any third particle, it is impossible for the energy to be converted into a single photon. There is no way in which both energy and momentum can be conserved in such a process. On the other hand, these conditions can be met if two photons are radiated. These two need not be of equal energy, though a more involved theoretical treatment shows that the probability of the formation of two equal photons is far greater than that of any other distribution between the two. Thus one accounts for the formation of two ½ MEV photons instead of one having the entire energy. If, however, the combination of the electron-positron pair takes place near a third particle, say an atomic nucleus, then both energy and momentum can be conserved even though a single photon is formed. The third particle takes up some of the momentum and some of the energy, so that both are conserved. If the third particle be relatively massive, as would be the nucleus of any atom, the amount of energy taken by it is so small that it can be neglected entirely in calculating the energy of the resulting photon. Thus, when an electron-positron combination takes place near an atomic nucleus, the energy represented by the rest masses of the two particles may be radiated as a single photon of 1.02 MEV energy. Theoretically then, one would expect both types of photon, some of 1.02 and some of 0.51 MEV energy. As has already been pointed out, both are observed. A complete theory would predict the fraction of the energy going into each type of radiation, and present day theory attempts to do so. It will be necessary to await improvement in experiment, and probably in theory, before one can be certain how successful such predictions are. At present the possibility of both types of photon is recognized, and it is known that the relative number of the two types depends[30] upon the nature of the material in which the electron-position combination takes place.

Studies of the inverse process, the production of electron-positron pairs through the disappearance of an energetic photon, have been more satisfying from a quantitative point of view. One has the advantage here of studying in a cloud chamber the particles created, and of being able to measure fairly accurately their energies. As soon as it was discovered that the gamma rays from ThC″ eject positrons as well as electrons when they fall upon heavy elements such as lead, several workers[17,21,36,37] set about measuring the energies of the ejected particles. In one of these studies Anderson and Neddermeyer[36] obtained photographs of several thousand tracks of individual positrons, individual electrons, and electron-positron pairs. These particles were ejected from lead, aluminum or carbon irradiated by the hard gamma rays from ThC″. These gamma ray photons have an energy of 2.62 MEV. Measurements of the energies of the ejected particles yielded

[36] C. D. Anderson and S. H. Neddermeyer, *Phys. Rev.*, **43**, 1034 (1933).

[37] L. Meitner and K. Philipp, *Naturwiss.*, **24**, 468 (1933).

pertinent information concerning the production phenomenon. The energies of the single positrons were all less than approximately 1.6 MEV; the energy seemed to approach this as an upper limit. The energies of the single negatives were distributed over a wide range, approaching approximately 2.6 MEV as an upper limit. The sum of the energies of any electron-positron pair was usually from 1 to 1.6 MEV; there appeared to be an upper limit of about 1.6 MEV.

These results speak strongly in favor of the concept of creation of electron-positron pairs from photons. An energy of 1.02 MEV would be required to form the rest masses of the resulting electron and positron. Since the photons used in this investigation possessed an energy of 2.62 MEV, it follows that there should be left over an energy of 1.6 MEV which might go into kinetic energy of the pair particles. This is apparently just what happens. The energy is not necessarily divided equally between the two, so that the maximum energy of either individual particle constituting the pair, or the maximum combined energy of the pair, should be 1.6 MEV. Single electrons with energies much higher than this are observed, the maximum energy approaching 2.6 MEV. These electrons are not those resulting from the pair creation process. They are photoelectrons which have been ejected from the planetary electron system by the gamma rays. The energies of those photoelectrons coming from the outermost shells should of course approach the energy of the gamma ray photon. Hence the energetic single electrons observed are to be expected. One might also wonder why pair energies less than 1.6 MEV are observed. In general there are two reasons. Gamma rays sources give off gamma rays corresponding to a wide range of energies. Attempts are usually made to filter out the lower energy radiation, but an appreciable amount often remains. Pairs created by these lower energy photons would of course have correspondingly less kinetic energy. Secondly, it is to be remembered that these pairs are produced in some material, perhaps lead. The pair may lose an appreciable part of its original kinetic energy before emerging from the absorber, and hence before its energy is measured.

A survey[38] of the early literature shows that other experimental works of this character led to much the same conclusions as those just outlined. The general concept seemed to be already upon a rather firm foundation. A number of more precise measurements[39–44] of the energies of the particles

[38] P. M. S. Blackett, *Nature*, **132**, 917 (1933).
[39] J. Chadwick, P. M. S. Blackett and G. P. S. Occhialini, *Proc. Roy. Soc.*, A, **144**, 235 (1934).
[40] M. N. S. Immelman, *Naturwiss.*, **24**, 61 (1936).
[41] H. Klarmann and W. Bothe, *Zeits. f. Physik*, **101**, 489 (1936).
[42] L. Simons and K. Zuber, *Proc. Roy. Soc.*, A, **159**, 383 (1937).
[43] T. Takeuchi and T. Sugita, *Proc. Phys. Math. Soc.* Japan, **19**, 555 (1937).
[44] M. Miwa and S. Kozima, *Proc. Phys. Math. Soc.* Japan, **19**, 757 (1937).

followed. A relatively early series of observations[39] involving some 4000 photographs led to the conclusion that the highest energy positron ejected from lead by the 2.62 MEV photons from ThC″ was (1.55 ± 0.03) MEV, and that it could have this maximum energy only when the associated electron remained at rest when formed. It was further concluded that an electron was always created simultaneously with a positron, though only one of the particles is observed in a majority of cases. The other particle making up the pair frequently does not emerge from the absorber in which the pair is formed. Hence, the maximum energy found for the positron should also represent the kinetic energy of the pair at the instant of creation. The experimental value 1.55 is only 3 percent under that theoretically expected. These observations also led to a maximum energy of (2.49 ± 0.04) MEV for the ejected electrons, a value only 5 percent under that which would be possessed by a photoelectron ejected from the outermost planetary shell.

Several studies[40–42] have been made in which the electron-positron pairs were formed in the gas itself in the cloud chamber. This procedure has the disadvantage that the probability of forming a pair is much smaller in any of the gases than in lead. It has the advantage, however, that the observations are relatively free from the unknown energy losses suffered by the two particles of the pair before they emerge from the lead or other heavy absorber more commonly used. Photographs have been obtained of pairs formed in krypton,[40] in xenon and in krypton,[41] and in argon and in methyl iodide.[42] These gases range in atomic number from 18 for argon to 54 for xenon. The observations are concerned not only with the energies of the pairs but also with the angular distribution of the ejected particles with respect to the incident photon. One series[41] of measurements in xenon and krypton, utilizing the 2.62 MEV photons from ThC″, yielded an average of 1.66 MEV for the energy of the pair. Any possible difference between the average energies of the positive and negative components of the pair was smaller than the experimental error of measurement. The average observed angle between the pair particles formed in xenon was much larger than that for pairs formed in krypton. This led to the conclusion that the average angle between the pair particles increases with the atomic number of the element in which the pair is formed. The data of Simons and Zuber[42] are scarcely consistent, however, with this last conclusion. These observers took 1032 photographs using methyl iodide and 1380 using argon gas. These showed 75 paired tracks in methyl iodide and 52 in argon. This illustrates in a rough way how much more probable is the formation of pairs in a material of high atomic number. Most of those pairs formed in methyl iodide are no doubt formed near the iodine nucleus. This nucleus has an atomic number 53, as against 18 for argon.

These data of Simon and Zuber indicated no difference between the average angles of ejection of particles in the two cases. Fig. 7 reproduces[42] the angular distribution of all the particles observed, both positive and negative. The number of particles observed within a given angular region is shown by the rectangular curve. The full line smooth curve represents the theoretical distribution.[45] If $f$ represents the fraction of particles projected at angles between $\theta$ and $(\theta + d\theta)$ with the direction of the incident photon, it turns out theoretically that

$$f = \frac{\theta\, d\theta}{[(m_0c^2/E)^2 + \theta^2]^2}$$

where $E$ represents the total energy of the projected particle, the sum of its kinetic and rest energies. Since $E$ depends upon the energy of the photons,

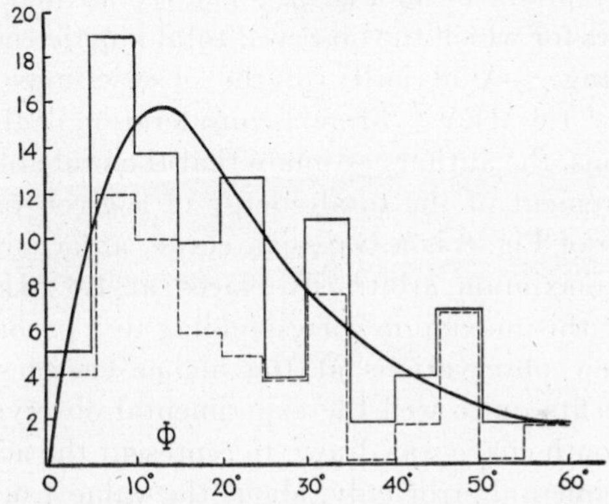


FIG. 7.—Showing the angular distribution of pair particles, both positrons and electrons, about the line representing the direction of the original photon. The solid rectangular curve is the observed distribution when measurements are made only on those tracks whose length exceeds 3.0 cm. The dashed rectangular curve is the observed distribution when measurements are further confined to only those tracks for which both partners of each pair are measured. The full line curve represents the theoretical distribution.

the angle at which the maximum of this curve occurs will depend upon the photons used. The higher the energy of the photon creating the pair, the greater the probability that the particles will be ejected in a nearly straight forward direction. For one member of a pair ejected by the 2.62 MEV photons from ThC″, the average value of $E$ will be $\left(\frac{1.6}{2} + 0.51\right)$, or approximately 1.3 MEV. Using this value of $E$ it can be calculated that the maximum number of particles should fall at angles near 13°. This prediction is illustrated by the theoretical curve. While the experimental data shown in

[45] H. Bethe and W. Heitler, *Proc. Roy. Soc.*, A, **146**, 83 (1934).

Fig. 7 are rather meager, and while the experimental errors are large, it is pleasing to see that the data fall as close as they do to the theoretical curve. Results of a study by Adams[46] are in agreement in that they yield an average angle of about 30° between the electron and the positron components of a pair. On the other hand, Grosev and Frank[47] found an average angle of 48° between these components. Furthermore, these observers found that the positrons are ejected in directions making smaller angles on the average with the original direction of the incident photon than do the directions of the corresponding electrons.

It has been remarked that one study[41] of pairs formed in a gas led to a value 1.66 MEV for the average total kinetic energy of the pair. This is quite close to the theoretical value $(2.62 - 1.02) = 1.60$. The kinetic energies of pairs formed in gases were also measured by Simons and Zuber.[42] Their results are reproduced in Fig. 8. The rectangular curve represents the number of pairs for which the observed total kinetic energy was within a certain energy range. A majority of the observations fall close to the theoretical value of 1.6 MEV. From a consideration of the errors involved in their observations, the authors estimate that the probable error associated with their measurement of the total energy of a given pair is 0.17 MEV. The smooth curve of Fig. 8 is a Gaussian curve, an accidental distribution curve having its maximum arbitrarily placed at 1.6 MEV and having a distribution about this maximum corresponding to a probable error of 0.17. Except for the few observations at the higher energies, this accidental distribution curve fits quite well the experimental observations. Now the breadth of the smooth curve was drawn to represent the accidental distribution, due to experimental error only, about the value 1.6. The agreement between the two curves therefore indicates that the apparent distribution is due entirely to experimental error, that the true total kinetic energy of each pair is 1.6 MEV. The authors felt that there were actually present a few pairs with total kinetic energies from 2.0 to 2.5 MEV. They attributed these to the probable presence of a few photons having energies considerably higher than 2.62 MEV. A weak but very penetrating gamma radiation from ThC″, a radiation of energy roughly 3.2 MEV, had already been reported.[48] If this estimate is taken as the actual energy of these few photons, then these should give rise to electron-positron pairs having total kinetic energies of 2.2 MEV. This agrees essentially with the few high energies recorded in Fig. 8.

[46] H. Adam, *Phys. Zeits.*, **38**, 824 (1937).

[47] L. V. Grosev and I. M. Frank, *Comptes Rendus* (Doklady) *de l'Acad. des Sciences*, U.R.S.S., **19**, 49 (1938).

[48] A. I. Alichanow, A. I. Alichanian and M. S. Kosodaew, *Jour. de Physique et le Radium*, **7**, 163 (1936).

Studies of the energies of electron-positron pairs formed in lead and other heavy materials have also supported the concept of the creation of pairs from photons. In one recent study Takeuchi and Sugita[43] photographed the energy spectrum of electrons and positrons produced by gamma rays from Ra filtered through 6 mm. of lead. These gamma rays, which consisted of a mixture of photons of several characteristic energies, were allowed to fall on Pb, Ag, Bi and Sn. The energies of the ejected electrons and positrons were determined by bending the particles in a magnetic field. The positrons showed 5 distinct bands corresponding to the energy limits of positrons ejected by gamma rays of the 5 different characteristic energies known to be present in the gamma ray spectrum of Ra. In a cloud chamber study by Miwa and Kozima,[44] a study of 151 pairs formed in lead by the 2.62 MEV

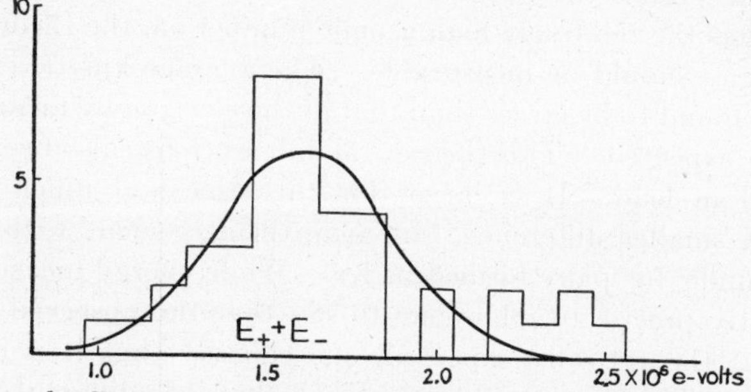


FIG. 8.—Showing the distribution of measured values of the total kinetic energy of electron-positron pairs formed by photons from ThC″.

gamma rays of ThC″, the kinetic energy of the pair was found to be (1.51 ± 0.02) MEV. By making a small correction necessary for the loss of the energy in the lead, the authors showed that the actual kinetic energy at the instant of creation was very close to the theoretical value of 1.60 MEV.

Another interesting aspect of the creation of electron-positron pairs has to do with the relative average kinetic energies of the electron and the positron constituting the pair. As has already been inferred, the formation of a pair almost always takes place near the nucleus of some atom. The probability of pair creation is increased enormously by the presence of the additional particle which can absorb a real but nearly negligible part of the momentum and energy. It has been pointed out that this probability increases rapidly with the atomic number of the nucleus near which the pair is created. Now if a pair is created close to a nucleus which bears a large net positive charge, it is logical to expect that on the average the positron would leave the point of creation with a somewhat greater kinetic energy than would the electron. The positron is repelled by the nucleus while the electron is somewhat attracted. The positron should therefore possess, on the average, slightly more kinetic energy than the electron. Theoretical calculations[49] show that while this difference is rather negligible for the elements of low atomic number, it is proportional to the atomic number, and amounts to 0.28 MEV for pairs formed near lead nuclei by photons of 2.62 MEV energy. This is sufficiently large to be detected.

No certain difference between the average kinetic energies of the positron and the electron was found in a study[41] of pairs ejected in xenon and krypton, though these data were not extensive; nor was the expected difference sufficiently large to make detection probable. In another study[42] no difference was found for pairs formed in argon, but the theoretical difference was smaller than the probable error associated with the measurements. This same study did show an apparently real difference for pairs formed in methyl iodide. Since these are formed mainly near the iodine nuclei, and since iodine has the relatively high atomic number 53, the theoretical difference of energies should be measurable. The average kinetic energy of the positron was found to be larger than that of the electron by an amount of the general order expected. This theoretical difference has also been found[44] for pairs formed in lead. It is larger for this case and much more easily detected. A smaller difference, but again in agreement with theory, has also been found[47] for pairs formed in Kr. While energy measurements are not sufficiently precise to allow one to say that the observed difference is equal to that theoretically expected, one can say that it is of about the expected size. There is no reason to think that it is different.

Experiments of the types discussed leave no doubt of the interchangeability of mass and radiant energy. The mass represented by an electron-positron pair often changes completely into either one or two photons of radiant energy. And a photon of radiant energy often disappears completely, changing into an electron-positron pair with a kinetic energy equal to the difference between the photon energy and the energy required to form the rest masses of the two particles. And in all cases energy is conserved; but it is necessary to consider mass as one form of energy. It is interesting that experiments on the creation of electron-positron pairs also show rather conclusively that the mass of the positron is essentially the same as that of the electron. In calculating the theoretical kinetic energy of the created pair, the energy to form the rest mass of the positron is taken as 0.51 MEV, the same as that for the electron. This figure would not be appropriate if the mass of the positron were much different from that of the electron. But use of this figure leads to a calculated kinetic energy essentially equal to that observed. Hence, the positron mass must be essentially equal to that of the electron. It is difficult to say how closely these measurements fix it as equal to that of the electron, but perhaps to within 5 or 10 percent. This con-

[49] J. C. Jaeger and H. R. Hulme, *Proc. Roy. Soc.*, A. **153**, 443 (1936).

stituted the best information available previous to Spees and Zahn's[15] direct measurement of the ratio $e/m$.

Electron-positron pairs have also been produced[50,51] by the bombardment of F with protons. It is known that gamma rays are produced in this process, and it first appeared[50] that the pairs resulted from the internal conversion of these gamma rays. A later study[51] showed, however, that there was little if any connection between the gamma ray emission and the pair creation. This work makes it appear more probable that the pairs are ejected from the nucleus as a result of the proton bombardment. There are numerous references in the literature[52] also to the creation of pairs, or at least positrons, by electron bombardment. In fact some observers have reported an unexpectedly high rate of production. In a recent careful study by Crane and Halpern,[52] however, no evidence whatever could be found for the creation of either pairs or positrons by electron bombardment.

50 J. Halpern and H. R. Crane, *Phys. Rev.*, **55**, 260 (1939).
51 W. A. Fowler and C. C. Lauritsen, *Phys. Rev.*, **56**, 840 (1939).
52 H. R. Crane and J. Halpern, *Phys. Rev.*, **55**, 838 (1939).

## Chapter 10

# THE NEUTRON

## I. DISCOVERY OF THE NEUTRON

Almost simultaneously with the identification of the positron there was discovered still another particle, the neutron. In fact, the first experimental evidence indicating the existence of the neutron actually preceded by a year or so that bearing on the positron; but final recognition of the nature of the particle did not come until 1932, the same year as that in which the positron was announced. Announcement of these two new particles, particles as fundamental as the electron and the proton, doubled the number of fundamental building stones of which matter might be constructed. Whereas before all nuclei had been conceived as being built from electrons and protons, it was now necessary to decide among a number of possibilities involving not only electrons and protons but positrons and neutrons as well. These various possibilities, and some evidence which bears upon the problem, will be discussed briefly in the next chapter.

The first convincing evidence of the existence of some unrecognized particle or radiation came from studies having to do with the artificial disintegration of the elements. Bothe and Becker[1] found that if the alpha rays from the natural radioactive material polonium were allowed to fall upon certain of the light elements, among which were beryllium, boron and lithium, there was emitted from these elements a very penetrating radiation. Similar bombardment of certain of the other light elements was soon found[2] to result in the same type of radiation. Early works[1–3] showed this radiation to be far more penetrating than the gamma rays from ThC″, the hardest gamma rays known. This new radiation was originally interpreted as gamma radiation of unusually short wave length. There were several reasons for which such an interpretation seemed natural. First, no particles as penetrating as the hard gamma rays were known. It appeared more logical to conceive of the new radiation as an extension to shorter wave lengths of the already known penetrating gamma rays, than to postulate a new and altogether different radiation. Second, this new radiation left no

[1] W. Bothe and H. Becker, *Zeits. f. Physik*, **66**, 289 (1930); *Naturwiss.*, **19**, 753 (1931).

[2] H. C. Webster, *Proc. Roy. Soc.*, A, **136**, 428 (1932).

[3] I. Curie, *Comptes Rendus*, **193**, 1412 (1932).

track in a cloud chamber; it could not be a charged particle, for all such particles leave continuous tracks.

Measurements of the absorption of this new radiation, made by using both Geiger tubes and ionization chambers to compare the intensities before and after passing through various absorbers, led to various estimates[2,3] of the order of 7 to 15 MEV for the energy of the most penetrating component of the radiation. This is several times the energy of the 2.62 MEV photons coming from ThC″. In order to account for such a high energy, early workers assumed that the bombarding alpha particle was captured by the beryllium nucleus, that this nucleus was thereby transformed into a nucleus of carbon, and that the energy represented by the excess mass of the beryllium plus the alpha particle over that of the final carbon, was radiated as a gamma ray photon. This process might be indicated by writing

$$_4Be^9 + {}_2He^4 \rightarrow {}_6C^{13} + h\nu$$

where the subscript preceding the symbol for the element represents the atomic number and where the superscript indicates the atomic weight of the isotope involved. That such a process might contribute an energy of the order of that believed to be possessed by the radiation can be shown by a simple calculation. If instead of the atomic masses available at that time one chooses the more recent values[4] 4.00389, 9.01504 and 13.00761 for $_2He^4$, $_4Be^9$ and $_6C^{13}$ respectively, it follows that there would be a mass decrease of 0.01132 grams for every gram atom of carbon so formed. This means a mass decrease of $(0.01132)/(6.023 \times 10^{23}) = 1.88 \times 10^{-26}$ grams for each atom transformed. Now from the expression Energy $= mc^2$ it can be calculated that a one gram mass represents an energy of $8.987 \times 10^{20}$ ergs, or $5.609 \times 10^{32}$ electron volts. A mass decrease of $1.88 \times 10^{-26}$ grams per atom of carbon formed would therefore release an energy of $(1.88 \times 10^{-26}) \times (5.609 \times 10^{32}) = 10.5 \times 10^6$ electron volts, or 10.5 MEV. This, increased by the energy of the incident alpha particle, and decreased by the recoil energy of the carbon atom formed, should represent the actual energy released per atom transformed. This is of the order of the energy the supposed gamma ray was thought to possess. One might object to using in this calculation the mass of the helium atom instead of that of the alpha particle. The two differ by the mass of two electrons, $2 \times 0.00055$, or 0.00110 atomic mass units. This represents approximately 1 MEV of energy, a negligible item for the present purpose. Moreover, failure to take account of this is exactly counterbalanced by similarly neglecting the fact that the carbon atom formed originally lacks two planetary electrons which it must pick up before it has the atomic weight used above.

[4] M. S. Livingston and H. A. Bethe, *Rev. Mod. Phys.*, **9**, 373 (1937).

The next important contribution along these lines was made by Curie and Joliot.[5] Whereas Bothe and Becker had used Geiger tubes, these workers used ionization chambers to measure the intensity of the new radiation. They found that this unknown radiation produced very much greater ionization in the chamber if, upon entering the chamber, it were made to pass through paraffin or some other material containing hydrogen. The ionization was increased sometimes by a factor of two. Allowing the radiation to pass through carbon, aluminum, copper, silver, or lead produced practically no change in the ionization. The presence of hydrogen as a component in the absorber was essential to the production of an increase in

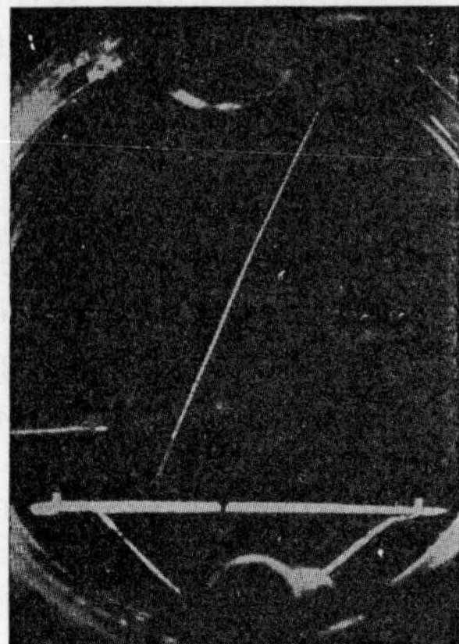

FIG. 1.—Showing the track of a proton ejected from paraffin by a penetrating radiation now recognized as a neutron. This track is more than 14 cm. long.

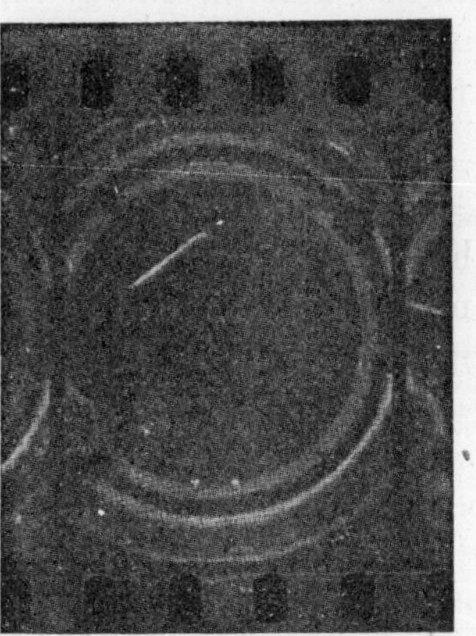

FIG. 2.—Showing the track of a helium nucleus projected by impact of a penetrating radiation now recognized as a neutron.

ionization within the chamber. These observers were able to show that the increase in ionization was due directly to protons which had been knocked out of the hydrogen compounds by this new radiation. The resulting protons are far more efficient ionizers than the original radiation. Cloud chamber studies[5] showed that some of these ejected protons had surprisingly long ranges, up to 26 cm. in air. The lengths of tracks showed that some of the protons were ejected with energies as high as 4.5 MEV. It was suggested that this energy was transferred from the photon to the proton by a process similar to the Compton effect with planetary electrons. Applying the laws of conservation of energy and conservation of momentum, it was calculated that if the energy was transferred in this manner, then the incident photon often had to possess an energy of some 50 MEV.

[5] I. Curie and F. Joliot, *Comptes Rendus*, **194**, 273, 708 (1932).

Fig. 1 reproduces[6] the track of such a proton ejected from paraffin. The incident radiation, which has since been shown to be a neutron, leaves no track as it approaches the paraffin; it produces a negligible number of ion pairs along its path, probably[7] about one pair in passing through 3 meters of air. Fig. 2 shows[6] the track of a helium nucleus projected forward by the impact of this new radiation. Again the incident radiation, then thought to be a photon but now recognized as a neutron, leaves no track. Other light nuclei such as carbon, nitrogen, oxygen and argon are similarly projected.[8] Still believing this new radiation to be an unusually penetrating gamma ray, early workers thought they had produced evidence showing that electromagnetic radiation could impart high energies directly to the nuclei of light elements. From the energies imparted to these nuclei, an attempt was made to calculate the energy of the incident radiation. Unfortunately the energy which had to be assigned to the hypothetical photon did not always come out the same. The energy calculated for a given photon seemed to depend upon the projected nucleus used in determining this energy.

It was recognized that if these supposed photons did communicate energy directly to the nuclei of light elements, projecting these nuclei in various directions, then it would be necessary to give up the laws of conservation of energy and conservation of momentum for the individual encounters. Physicists disliked very much to do this; too much respect had been gained for these laws to give them up so easily. It has often been thought in recent years that perhaps these laws hold only in a statistical sense, perhaps not for individual atomic or subatomic encounters. And perhaps we were destined to find that they held only statistically here. Investigators might have been reconciled to such a situation more readily were it not for the fact that on previous similar occasions some one had always succeeded in finding another solution of the difficulty, one showing clearly that these two laws hold even for individual encounters.

Fortunately Chadwick[8] soon solved this perplexing problem, and solved it so convincingly that he won the Nobel Prize. It has already been stated that if the recoil energies of various nuclei projected by impact of this radiation are observed, and if the laws of conservation of energy and conservation of momentum are used to calculate from this the energy of the incident radiation, then on the photon hypothesis the energy of the photon comes out quite different for different recoil nuclei. Chadwick first emphasized again this difficulty, bringing out that the energy of the incident assumed photon calculated from absorption measurements did not agree with that calculated from recoil measurements; and the energy calculated for a given supposed

[6] I. Curie and F. Joliot, *Comptes Rendus*, **194**, 876 (1932).

[7] P. I. Dee, *Proc. Roy. Soc.*, A, **136**, 727 (1932).

[8] J. Chadwick, *Proc. Roy. Soc.*, A, **136**, 692 (1932).

photon from recoil observations increased markedly as heavier nuclei were used for recoil. Using apparatus essentially that illustrated in Fig. 3, in which absorbing screens of aluminum were placed between the paraffin and the ionization chamber, Chadwick found that the beryllium radiation projected some protons from the paraffin with energies as great as 5.7 MEV. If one supposes that this maximum energy is communicated through a head-on collision of a photon with the proton, it turns out that the supposed photon must have possessed an energy of 55 MEV to have given the proton the observed recoil energy. When nitrogen was used it was found that the same beryllium radiation produced a maximum recoil energy of at least 1.2 MEV. It is natural that this recoil energy should be less than that observed for the proton, for the nitrogen nucleus is much the heavier and the photon would not be expected to communicate to it as large a portion of its energy.

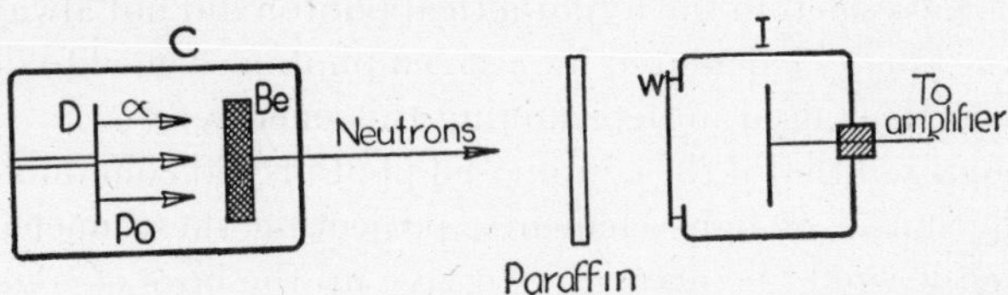


FIG. 3.—Illustrating the method used by Chadwick to measure the maximum range, and thence the energy, of the protons ejected from paraffin by the neutrons from beryllium. The maximum range was determined by placing various thicknesses of aluminum sheet between the paraffin and the ionization chamber.

In view of the 55 MEV energy assigned to the photon on the basis of observed hydrogen recoil, a nitrogen recoil of 1.2 MEV is much larger than one would expect. In fact a photon would have to possess an energy of 90 MEV to communicate the observed recoil energy to the nitrogen. Experiments involving the observed recoils of two different nuclei lead to quite different energies for the incident photon. The photon hypothesis was thus inconsistent with the laws of conservation of energy and conservation of momentum. Investigators were in a position of having to give up either the photon hypothesis or these laws.

Chadwick[8] went on to show that if this new and highly penetrating radiation were an uncharged particle having a mass essentially equal to that of the proton, all the difficulties disappeared. Such a particle is called the neutron. If one considers a head-on collision between a neutron and a proton, one can write from the law of conservation of energy, neglecting for the present purpose the change of mass with velocity,

$$\tfrac{1}{2}MV_1^2 = \tfrac{1}{2}MV_2^2 + \tfrac{1}{2}MV_r^2$$

where $M$ represents the mass of either particle, $V_1$ the original velocity of the neutron, $V_2$ the velocity of this same particle after collision, and $V_r$ the velocity of recoil of the proton. From the conservation of momentum one can write

$$MV_1 = MV_2 + MV_r$$

Solving the second of these equations for $V_2$ and substituting this value in the first, one finds that $V_r = V_1$. This in turn shows that $V_2 = 0$. That is, for a head-on collision between the two particles of equal mass, all the energy of the incident neutron is given over to the proton at collision. The proton proceeds forward with this energy while the neutron remains at rest. Now Chadwick found that beryllium radiation projected protons with a maximum energy of 5.7 MEV. If the incident radiation consisted of neutrons, then this figure also represents the energy possessed by the incident neutron.

If a head-on collision between a neutron and a nitrogen nucleus is considered in exactly the same way, it turns out that closely one fourth of the original energy of the incident neutron should be given over to the recoiling nitrogen nucleus. Now Chadwick observed a nitrogen recoil energy of 1.2 MEV. Hence, the incident neutron must have possessed an energy of 4.8 MEV. This figure agrees, within the rather large probable experimental error, with the value 5.7 obtained through use of the hydrogen recoil. That this difference is only one of experimental error is indicated by the fact that another observer[9] found from cloud chamber photographs of nitrogen recoil tracks that the recoil energy is 1.6 MEV. This yields a value 6.4 MEV for the energy of the neutrons used. This figure is nearly as much above that obtained from hydrogen recoil as Chadwick's value was below. Further experiment has shown that, on the neutron hypothesis, energies calculated from recoil observations on still other nuclei likewise come out consistent with these figures. This concept of a new particle, the neutron, removed not only those difficulties presented by Chadwick's own data, but it fit in equally well with all previous data gathered by other workers. The neutron was immediately upon a firm experimental foundation. A brief historical account of these early developments has been given by Bothe.[10] Since these pioneering works a mass of information involving the neutron has been gathered. And all of this only emphasizes the correctness of Chadwick's concept. The existence of the neutron, a particle bearing no net electrical charge, and one having essentially the same mass as the proton, can no longer be questioned.

The great penetrating power of the neutron, as well as failure of the particle to leave a visible track in a cloud chamber, is quite consistent with the supposed nature of the particle. Particles such as electrons, protons,

[9] N. Feather, *Proc. Roy. Soc.*, A, **136**, 709 (1932).
[10] W. Bothe, *Naturwiss.*, **21**, 825 (1933).

positrons, and alpha particles suffer most of their resistance in passing through matter due to the fact that they are charged. For all but the higher energy particles most of the resistance is due to interactions between the flying particle and the planetary electrons of the atoms of matter through which it passes. For the higher energy particles interactions between the particle and positively charged nuclei play an important role. One refers to interactions, whether they be with planetary electrons or with nuclei, as collisions. They are collisions, but no doubt of an electrical rather than a mechanical type. The mere fact that the particle is charged allows it, upon fairly close approach, to exert appreciable forces upon the other charged particles which make up the atom. In this way the flying particle gradually transfers its energy to the atoms of the absorber, the particle finally coming to rest.

Now the neutron possesses no net electrical charge; no electrical field extends an appreciable distance from it. It is very unlikely, therefore, that the particle would suffer many collisions in passing through matter. There may be electrical or magnetic fields exceedingly close to the neutron, perhaps due to a nonuniform distribution of charges which neutralize electrically at appreciably distant points, or due to some magnetic property of the particle. If such residual fields exist they must be confined to a very small region. The neutron itself is exceedingly small, perhaps of the order of size of the proton. It is far smaller than the hydrogen atom. It is essentially a hydrogen atom with the one planetary electron placed down in the nucleus instead of in the *K* shell. Since any possible residual electrical field is confined to an exceedingly small region, the neutron would have to come very close to a planetary electron or to a nucleus before it could communicate any appreciable energy to it. Hence, the neutron loses energy but slowly as it passes through matter; it has a great penetrating power.

It is known that there are forces exerted between neutrons and other particles, between neutrons and protons, or even between neutrons and neutrons. Experiments on the scattering of neutrons have shown the existence of such forces. The mere fact that neutrons are absorbed to some extent shows definitely that there are some retarding forces exerted between them and other particles. But these forces become appreciable only for very close approach of the particles involved. The lack of appreciable forces between the neutron and the planetary electrons of an atom accounts also for the failure of the particle to leave a visible track in a cloud chamber. The particle forms too few ions on which droplets can condense to make the track visible.

It is interesting that the possible existence of a particle having the properties of the neutron had been discussed as early as 1920. Rutherford,[11] in his Bakerian Lecture, had considered the possibility of a "neutron," a particle consisting of a proton and an electron in close combination. During the ensuing years there were many experiments[8] designed to detect the possible existence of such a particle. But it was not until 1932 that its existence was recognized, and this recognition came as a result of studies which certainly did not have as their primary purpose the finding of the neutron. This is another illustration that the by-products of research may often be of as great or greater importance than the direct results anticipated.

## 2. SOURCES OF NEUTRONS

It has been stated that neutrons are given off when beryllium or other light elements are bombarded with alpha rays. Let us look briefly into the the mechanism by which these particles are given off. This question is tied up intimately with another which will be discussed in some detail later, the artificial transmutation of the elements. We shall, therefore, content ourselves for the present with the bare essentials of the concept. Before recognition of the neutron, early workers regarded the penetrating radiation given off from beryllium when bombarded with alpha particles as high energy photons. It was suggested that the beryllium nucleus absorbed the alpha particle, becoming a carbon nucleus, and gave off a photon of radiant energy to compensate for the decrease of mass accompanying the change. Such a reaction might be indicated by writing

$$_4Be^9 + {}_2He^4 \rightarrow {}_6C^{13} + h\nu$$

where the subscripts preceding the symbol of the element represent the atomic number and where the superscripts refer to the atomic weight of the isotope involved. The difficulties encountered by such a concept have already been discussed. With Chadwick's recognition of the neutron, however, these difficulties disappeared. The reaction which had been pictured, the one written above, was not correct. Experiment showed that the beryllium nucleus did absorb the alpha particle and it did then become a nucleus of carbon, but it became a nucleus of $C^{12}$ rather than $C^{13}$. The actual reaction was found to be

$$_4Be^9 + {}_2He^4 \rightarrow {}_6C^{12} + {}_0n^1$$

where $_0n^1$ stands for the neutron, a particle of zero charge, and hence zero atomic number, and of atomic weight 1. Chadwick's work left no room to doubt the correctness of this concept. Experimentally determined energies, including mass as energy, were in full accord with the laws of conservation of energy and momentum. The mechanism of neutron ejection was no doubt as indicated by the last written reaction.

[11] E. Rutherford, *Proc. Roy. Soc.*, A, **97**, 374 (1920).

Since recognition of the neutron as a fundamental particle, many other similar reactions have been shown to occur. Many light nuclei other than ${}_4Be^9$, such as ${}_3Li^7$, ${}_5B^{11}$, ${}_7N^{14}$, ${}_9F^{19}$, ${}_{11}Na^{23}$, ${}_{12}Mg^{24}$, ${}_{13}Al^{27}$ and others, capture the bombarding alpha particle and eject a neutron in the same way as does beryllium. The nucleus capturing the alpha particle then becomes the nucleus of another atom. The total energy of the ejected neutron, including both mass and kinetic energy, can be calculated from the known kinetic energy of the incident alpha particle and the difference between the mass of the two combined original particles and the one newly formed nucleus. Bombardment with alpha particles is not essential to the production of neutrons. Bombardment with other high energy particles, protons, deuterons, and even photons, often results in the emission of neutrons. Any one of the disintegration reactions which leads to the ejection of a neutron might be used as a source of neutrons. Thus many sources are available. Some of these reactions are much easier to produce than others, some give a much greater yield of neutrons per bombarding particle than others, and the energy of the ejected neutron depends upon the reaction producing the particle. It is from these considerations that choice of an appropriate source is made.

The problem of collimating a beam of fast neutrons is difficult. A narrow beam of electrons, positrons or alpha particles can be obtained by placing in the path of the particles an absorbing screen having in it a small opening. Lead or similar metal screens a few millimeters thick will suffice for this purpose. A beam of hard X-rays or gamma rays can be collimated in the same way by using screens a few centimeters thick. Such screens are almost useless, however, in stopping fast neutrons. It can be shown that a particle making repeated collisions with other particles will give up its energy most rapidly if the particles being struck are of the same mass as the particle it is desired to stop. Consequently, the best neutron absorbers are those materials containing an abundance of hydrogen nuclei. Water and paraffin constitute the two most widely used neutron absorbers. It has been estimated[12] that an initially homogeneous beam of 10 MEV neutrons would be reduced in number by a factor of $10^5$ in passing through 5 feet of water.

Collimating arrangements[13,14] for fast neutrons consist of channels through large thicknesses of water or paraffin. Aebersold[13] has obtained a well-defined and intense beam by using a slightly tapering channel through a 50 cm. wall of paraffin or water. The large thickness of matter required to produce a well-defined beam introduces considerable difficulty due to the

[12] S. M. Dancoff, *Phys. Rev.*, **57**, 251 (1940).

[13] P. C. Aebersold, *Phys. Rev.*, **55**, 596 (1939); **56**, 714 (1939).

[14] R. F. Bacher and D. C. Swanson, *Phys. Rev.*, **56**, 483 (1939).

scattering of radiation by the sides of the channel and the production of secondary radiation in the absorber. In Aebersold's apparatus this difficulty was minimized by lining the channel with a 3 cm. thick lead wall and by surrounding the absorbing material with a 2.5 cm. lead wall. This lead absorbed a great part of the secondary gamma radiation.

It is interesting that there is evidence[15] indicating the existence of some neutrons in the atmosphere. Studies[16,17] have shown that these are associated with the cosmic radiation, probably constituting a part thereof. From the general knowledge that cosmic rays are very penetrating, together with the fact that neutrons themselves are very penetrating, one might be tempted to conclude that the cosmic rays consist largely of neutrons. But a mass of experimental evidence, some of which will be discussed later, shows that such is not the case. Certainly if neutrons are present in cosmic rays, they make up only a small part of the radiation.

## 3. THE MASS OF THE NEUTRON

It is clear from previous discussion that the mass of the neutron is essentially the same as that of the proton. It is both interesting and important to inquire, however, just how the mass of this particle can be obtained from experimental data, and just how accurately it is possible to determine the mass. Chadwick[8] originally assumed for the particle a mass equal to that of the proton, and proceeded to show that such a mass was entirely consistent with all known observational data. It is obvious, however, that the procedure might have been reversed; observational data might have been combined and the mass of the neutron solved for explicitly. This also was done by Chadwick. For a head-on collision between a neutron of mass $M$ and original velocity $V_1$ and a recoil atom of mass $M_r$ originally at rest, one has

$$\tfrac{1}{2}MV_1^2 = \tfrac{1}{2}MV_2^2 + \tfrac{1}{2}M_rV_r^2$$

and

$$MV_1 = MV_2 + M_rV_r$$

where $V_2$ is the velocity of the neutron after collision and $V_r$ the velocity of recoil of the atom struck. Solving the second equation for $V_2$ and substituting this value in the first, one finds that the recoil velocity is given by

$$V_r = \frac{2M}{M_r + M} V_1$$

[15] E. Fünfer, *Naturwiss.*, **25,** 235 (1937).

[16] E. Fünfer, *Zeits. f. Physik*, **111,** 351 (1938).

[17] D. K. Froman and J. C. Stearns, *Phys. Rev.*, **54,** 969 (1938).

Now if the recoil velocities are measured in hydrogen and in nitrogen, using the same neutrons,

$$V_{rH} = \frac{2M}{1 + M} V_1 \qquad \text{and} \qquad V_{rN} = \frac{2M}{14 + M} V_1$$

Dividing the first of these by the second,

$$\frac{V_{rH}}{V_{rN}} = \frac{14 + M}{1 + M}$$

At the time of Chadwick's work the best observations for the maximum recoil velocities were $3.3 \times 10^9$ cm/sec. for hydrogen,[8] and $4.7 \times 10^8$ for nitrogen.[9] Inserting these values and solving for $M$, Chadwick found a mass 1.15 for the neutron. In view of the probable errors involved in the measurement of recoil velocities, estimated as easily 10 percent, this did not indicate that the mass of the neutron differs from that of the proton. Neither did it show to any degree of accuracy that the two are equal; but it did show that they are essentially the same. Unfortunately there seems little hope of ever measuring recoil velocities with sufficient accuracy for this method to provide a precise value for the mass of the neutron. One could not hope for an accuracy better than a few percent.

In this same paper Chadwick[8] pointed out another method of evaluating this mass, a method which has since yielded the mass of the neutron to the same degree of accuracy as that to which the masses of the individual isotopes of the light elements are known. This method involves knowledge of the nuclear transformation giving the neutron, and accurate knowledge of the atomic weights of the nuclei involved. Since at that time the mass of the beryllium isotope involved was not at all well known, no attempt was made to apply the method rigorously to the beryllium reaction. But boron also gives off neutrons when bombarded with the alpha rays from polonium, and there were available accurate data on the atomic weights of the nuclei involved in this process. The reaction by which the neutrons are formed is no doubt as indicated by

$${}_5B^{11} + {}_2He^4 \rightarrow {}_7N^{14} + {}_0n^1$$

Now from the law of conservation of energy, considering mass as energy, one can write

$$\begin{aligned}\text{Mass of } {}_5B^{11} + \text{Mass of } {}_2He^4 + \text{K.E. of } {}_2He^4 = \text{Mass of } {}_7N^{14} \\ + \text{K.E. of } {}_7N^{14} + \text{Mass of } {}_0n^1 + \text{K.E. of } {}_0n^1\end{aligned}$$

The best values of atomic masses available at that time, and these were from Aston's mass spectograph work, were ($11.00825 \pm 0.0016$), ($4.00106 \pm 0.0006$) and ($14.0042 \pm 0.0028$) for boron, helium and nitrogen, respectively. The kinetic energy of the alpha particles from polonium was known to be 5.25 MEV, the equivalent of 0.00565 grams on the atomic mass scale of energy.

The kinetic energy of the neutron can be determined by allowing these particles to project protons and measuring the maximum energy of these projected hydrogen nuclei. This energy can be measured with fair accuracy, for these protons have long ranges. The kinetic energy of the neutrons formed, when converted to mass units, was found to be 0.0035. The recoiling nitrogen leaves a very short track; its energy can be obtained only roughly from such tracks. From the law of conservation of momentum, however, one can easily calculate the maximum velocity, and hence the maximum energy, with which the neutrons used could project a nitrogen nucleus. Such a calculation showed that this was 0.00061. One might object that the unknown mass of the neutron is involved both in the experimental determination of the kinetic energy of the neutron and in the calculation of the kinetic energy of the recoiling nitrogen. Both of these are relatively small quantities, however, and one is justified in using for their evaluation an approximate mass, say one equal to that of the proton; the error so introduced in the final result is quite negligible. Thus all quantities except the mass of the neutron appearing in the energy equation are known. Inserting these values in this equation, one has

$$11.00825 + 4.00106 + 0.00565 = 14.0042 + 0.00061 + \text{Mass of } {}_0n^1 + 0.0035$$

In this way Chadwick[8] obtained for the atomic mass of the neutron the value 1.0067. Allowing for the probable errors involved in the atomic weights and in the energy measurements, Chadwick felt that the mass of this new particle was probably between 1.005 and 1.008.

This general method of determining the mass of the neutron has since been used by many workers. The boron reaction is only one of many that might be employed for such purpose. Any reaction involving the neutron is suitable provided the atomic masses of the nuclei involved are known with sufficient accuracy, and provided the original and final kinetic energies of the particles can be determined accurately. One of the best reactions for this purpose is the photodisintegration of heavy hydrogen by gamma rays. It was found by Chadwick and Goldhaber[18] that irradiation of heavy hydrogen with gamma rays from ThC″ produces protons and neutrons. Thus

$${}_1H^2 + h\nu \rightarrow {}_1H^1 + {}_0n^1$$

[18] J. Chadwick and M. Goldhaber, *Nature*, **134**, 237 (1934).

These gamma rays have an energy of 2.62 MEV. Since the proton and the neutron have nearly equal masses these two particles will proceed from the disintegration with approximately equal energies. The energy of the proton can be measured readily. It is found[19] that the two particles together have a kinetic energy of 0.45 MEV. Recalling that 1 MEV is equivalent to 0.001074 atomic mass units, and taking the mass of ${}_1H^2$ = 2.01473 and that of ${}_1H^1$ = 1.00813, one has

$$2.01473 + 0.00281 = 1.00813 + \text{Mass of neutron} + 0.00048$$

This gives for the mass of the neutron 1.00893. By methods such as those illustrated the mass of the neutron has become known to a high degree of accuracy. Table I summarizes the values which have been obtained.

Experimental data having to do with many different types of reactions, some set off by alpha particles and some brought about by bombardment with other high energy particles, are incorporated in these values. The atomic mass of the neutron is accurately known, to about the same degree of precision as the atomic masses of most of the light elements. It is significant that in evaluating this mass one applies the laws of conservation of energy and conservation of momentum to individual interactions, and treats mass definitely as one form of energy. The fact that the neutron mass turns out so closely the same regardless of the reaction used in its evaluation, speaks convincingly in favor of both of these concepts. It is just as certain today that mass and energy are interchangeable as it is that heat is a form of energy.

It is interesting that the mass of the neutron is definitely larger than that of the proton. If one takes for the atomic weight of the lightest isotope of hydrogen the value[4] 1.00813, and subtracts the atomic weight of the planetary electron, 0.00055, one obtains for the proton the value 1.00758. This is less than the mass of the neutron[19] by 0.00135. This represents a considerable amount of energy, 1.27 MEV. One might therefore suspect the neutron to be unstable with respect to the proton, perhaps becoming a proton through the ejection of a negative electron. While this may occur, there is no direct experimental evidence for it. Had it not been for the almost simultaneous discovery of the positron, one would have been tempted to view the neutron as a close combination of a proton and an electron. In this case one would expect that

$$M_n = M_p + M_{e-} - \text{Binding Energy}$$

where $M$ represents the atomic weight and where the subscripts $n$, $p$, and $e-$ refer to the neutron, the proton and the negative electron, respectively.

[19] H. A. Bethe, *Phys. Rev.*, **53**, 313 (1938).

Substituting appropriate values,

$$1.00893 = 1.00758 + 0.00055 - \text{Binding Energy}.$$

From this one finds a binding energy of $-0.00080$ atomic weight units, or $-0.74$ MEV. Thus one would not expect a combination of this sort to take place. Although the existence of the proton has been recognized far

TABLE I

Determinations of the mass of the neutron arranged in approximately chronological order. The increase from about 1.0084 to approximately 1.0090 came about in 1936 as a result of recognition of an error in the atomic weights which had previously been used for the light elements. For example, although Chadwick and Goldhaber reported 1.0084 in 1935, they remarked that if the then apparent error in atomic weights should prove correct, this value would be raised to 1.0090. This error, mainly in the He/O ratio, did prove to be real

| Observer | Date | Reference | Mass |
|---|---|---|---|
| Chadwick | 1932 | 8 | 1.15 |
| Chadwick | 1932 | 8 | 1.0067 |
| Curie and Joliot | 1933 | 20 | 1.012 |
| Lauritsen and Crane | 1934 | 21, 22 | 1.0068 ± 0.0003 |
| Chadwick and Goldhaber | 1934 | 18 | 1.0080 ± 0.0005 |
| Oliphant, Kempton and Rutherford | 1935 | 23 | 1.0083 ± 0.0003 |
| Bethe | 1935 | 24 | 1.0085 ± 0.0005 |
| Chadwick and Goldhaber | 1935 | 25 | 1.0084 (1.0090) |
| Ising and Helde | 1936 | 26 | 1.0080 |
| Oliphant | 1936 | 27 | 1.0091 ± 0.0003 |
| Cockcroft and Lewis | 1936 | 28 | 1.0087 |
| Bonner and Brubraker | 1936 | 29 | 1.0090 ± 0.0001 |
| Chadwick, Feather and Bretscher | 1937 | 30 | 1.0090 |
| Mano | 1937 | 31 | 1.00904 ± 0.00006 |
| Livingston and Bethe | 1937 | 4 | 1.00897 ± 0.00006 |
| Stetter and Jentschke | 1938 | 32 | 1.00895 ± 0.00003 |
| Bethe | 1938 | 19 | 1.00893 ± 0.00005 |

[20] I. Curie and F. Joliot, *Jour. de Physique et le Radium*, **4**, 494 (1933).

[21] C. C. Lauritsen and H. R. Crane, *Phys. Rev.*, **45**, 550 (1934).

[22] R. A. Millikan, *Electrons (+ and −), Protons, Photons, Neutrons, and Cosmic Rays* (Chicago: University of Chicago Press, 1935), p. 395.

[23] M. L. E. Oliphant, A. E. Kempton and E. Rutherford, *Proc. Roy. Soc.*, A, **150, 241** (1935).

[24] H. Bethe, *Phys. Rev.*, **47**, 633 (1935).

[25] J. Chadwick and M. Goldhaber, *Proc. Roy. Soc.*, A, **151**, 479 (1935).

[26] G. Ising and M. Helde, *Nature*, **137**, 273 (1936).

[27] M. L. E. Oliphant, *Nature*, **137**, 396 (1936).

[28] J. D. Cockcroft and W. B. Lewis, *Proc. Roy. Soc.*, A, **154**, 261 (1936).

[29] T. W. Bonner and W. M. Brubaker, *Phys. Rev.*, **50**, 308 (1936).

[30] J. Chadwick, N. Feather and E. Bretscher, *Proc. Roy. Soc.*, A, **163**, 366 (1937).

[31] G. Mano, *Soc. Roumaine de Physique*, Bull. 38, **69**, 51 (1937).

[32] G. Stetter and W. Jentschke, *Zeits. f. Physik*, **110**, 214 (1938).

longer than that of the neutron, this is no reason to regard the proton as necessarily the more fundamental building stone, and to conceive of neutrons as necessarily being manufactured of protons and electrons. With the discovery of the positron it became equally possible to view the neutron as more fundamental than the proton, and to conceive of the proton as being a neutron and a positron in close combination. On such a concept one would expect that

$$M_p = M_n + M_{e+} - \text{Binding Energy}$$

where $M_{e+}$ represents the atomic weight of the positron. Substituting appropriate values,

$$1.00758 = 1.00893 + 0.00055 - \text{Binding Energy}.$$

From this one finds a binding energy of 0.00190 atomic weight units, or 1.77 MEV. This energy is of the proper sign, but the mass defect, or the binding energy, is larger than one would anticipate from knowledge of similar mass defects in various atomic nuclei. Perhaps one must regard both neutrons and protons as fundamental particles. The nuclei of atoms could be conceived as made up from protons and neutrons, without regard to electrons and positrons, just as well as they could from protons and electrons, or from neutrons and positrons. In fact the most successful theory of nuclear structure today does just this. The proton-neutron concept of nuclear structure possesses several distinct advantages over the other possible concepts.

## 4. THE MAGNETIC MOMENT OF THE NEUTRON

It has been remarked that in the interpretation of some of the details of the emission of the characteristic spectral lines of atoms it has been found necessary to introduce the concept of the spinning electron. More directly, it is necessary to attribute to the electron a definite magnetic moment. One pictures this magnetic moment as due to a spinning of the electron. This spin would give to the electron a certain amount of angular momentum and perhaps, due to the charge of the electron, a certain magnetic moment. Other details of characteristic line spectra, known as hyperfine structure, have made it necessary to assign also to the nuclei of atoms certain magnetic moments. Early evidence for the existence of these nuclear moments, along with early measured values of the moments, have been summarized elsewhere.[33]

In more recent years there have been developed several molecular beam methods of measuring nuclear moments fairly directly, and in some instances these give precise values. The fundamental experiments of this character

[33] N. Dallaporta, *N. Cimento*, **12**, 576 (1935).

were those of Stern[34] and his collaborators, in which the magnetic moments of the proton and the deuteron were determined by deflecting molecular beams of these in inhomogeneous magnetic fields. Still more recently Rabi[35] and his associates have developed a molecular beam resonance method which has been applied to determine accurately the magnetic moments of a number of nuclei. If a particle having angular momentum and a magnetic moment is placed in a magnetic field the particle will execute a precessional motion about the field. The frequency of precession increases as the strength of the magnetic field is increased. The resonance method of determining magnetic moments consists of increasing this magnetic field until the precession is in resonance with an auxiliary oscillating magnetic field. The magnetic moment can be calculated from the known frequency of the auxiliary oscillating magnetic field and the strength of the primary magnetic field required to produce resonance.

Because of certain theoretical considerations it has become customary to express nuclear magnetic moments in terms of a unit known as the nuclear magneton. The size of the nuclear magneton is given by $eh/4\pi Mc$, where $e$, $h$ and $c$ have their ordinary significance and where $M$ is the mass of the proton. Rabi[35] and his collaborators have found that the magnetic moment of the proton is $(2.785 \pm 0.02)$ nuclear magnetons, and that the magnetic moment of the deuteron is $(0.855 \pm 0.006)$. The molecular beam resonance method has been used to determine the magnetic moments of a number of other nuclei also.

It is not difficult to conceive of a particle such as an electron, a proton or a neutron as possessing a certain angular momentum. They have mass, and therefore a moment of inertia. If they should be spinning as a whole, or if they should have certain parts that are spinning, they would possess angular momentum. Neither is it difficult to conceive that a charged particle such as an electron, a proton, or any nucleus might possess a magnetic moment. On the other hand, one can not picture readily just what might give rise to a magnetic moment for the neutron. Nevertheless, it has been established definitely that the neutron has a magnetic moment of the same general order of magnitude as that of the proton or the deuteron. The magnetic moment of a neutron must be regarded as a fundamental property of the particle. It is a fundamental property just as much as is charge or mass. Since the deuteron is in all probability made by adding a neutron to a proton, and since the deuteron and the proton have magnetic moments 0.855 and 2.785 nuclear magnetons, respectively, it appeared likely that the neutron would have a magnetic moment approximately $-1.93$.

[34] O. Stern and Others, *Zeits. f. Physik*, **85**, 4, 17 (1933); **89**, 665 (1934); *Phys. Rev.*, **45**, 761 (1934).

[35] I. I. Rabi and Others, *Phys. Rev.*, **51**, 652 (1937); **55**, 526 (1939).

The negative sign indicates that the relative directions of the magnetic moment and the angular momentum of the neutron are opposite to that for the proton and for the deuteron.

Convincing proof that the neutron does possess a magnetic moment came from studies of the scattering of slow neutrons by magnetic materials. It turns out theoretically that an appreciable part of the scattering of slow neutrons should be due to interactions between the magnetic moments of the neutrons and those of the extranuclear electrons in the scattering atoms. Furthermore, magnetization of the scatterer should change slightly this part of the scattering. Dunning and his associates;[36,37] have shown that this small effect does exist for the scattering of neutrons by the strongly magnetic material iron. While studies of this character showed that the neutron does possess a magnetic moment, they did not allow an accurate determination of the moment.

A precise value for this moment has been obtained recently, however, by an adaptation of the resonance method to a beam of neutrons. In this way Alvarez and Bloch[38] find for the neutron a magnetic moment $-(1.935 \pm 0.02)$ nuclear magnetons. Actually these observers determined only the magnitude of the moment, but it had previously been shown by Powers[37] that the sign of the moment is negative. It is remarkable that this is exactly the magnetic moment that must be added to that of the proton in order to obtain that of the deuteron. In fact one would scarcely expect such close agreement, for as the neutron and the proton combine, the forces of interaction might well modify slightly the moments of the individual particles. If effects of this character are present, however, they must cancel out, for to the accuracy with which the moments are known the magnetic moment of the deuteron is equal to that of the proton plus that of the neutron.

[36] J. R. Dunning and Others, *Phys. Rev.*, **51**, 1112 (1937); **52**, 38 (1937).

[37] P. N. Powers, *Phys. Rev.*, **54**, 827 (1938).

[38] L. W. Alvarez and F. Bloch, *Phys. Rev.*, **57**, 111 (1940).

Chapter 11

# ATOMIC NUCLEI—ARTIFICIAL DISINTEGRATION

## I. EARLY EXPERIMENTS ON THE STRUCTURE OF THE NUCLEUS

Although the general concept of the atomic structure of matter was firmly entrenched long before the beginning of the present century, it was more than a decade after the start of the century that convincing evidence regarding the details of this structure began to accumulate. Before this there was no definite knowledge concerning even the general distribution of the positive and the negative parts of the atom. It was in 1913 that Bohr had such notable success in interpreting line spectra in terms of planetary electrons describing orbits about a massive and positively charged nucleus. It was about this same time that Rutherford and his coworkers initiated a series of experiments that were to yield later definite information regarding the effective size of, and the net positive charge on, the central nucleus. The Rutherford-Bohr atom model grew largely from these two lines of evidence.

### Rutherford's Work on the Scattering of Alpha Particles by Thin Films

Before 1911 there was no convincing evidence regarding the size of the positively charged nucleus. In fact many, following Thomson,[1] conceived of a jelly-like atom made up of positive and negative electricity, the positive charge being distributed throughout a sphere which was supposed to represent the atom. Evidence gathered from viscosity, diffusion, discrepancies from the perfect gas law, etc., had shown that the effective diameter of the atom is of the order of $10^{-8}$ cm. On the Thomson model the positive part of the atom was supposed to extend over this entire region. A strong suggestion that the positive parts of the atom must be more concentrated than this was contained in the observation that alpha particles are shot off from many natural radioactive elements with tremendous energies, energies of the order of 5 MEV. The large energy given the positively charged alpha particle suggests that this particle may have been repelled strongly in leaving the other positive charges in the atom. A repulsion which could account for these tremendous energies could come

[1] J. J. Thomson, *Camb. Lit. and Phil. Soc.*, **15** (1910).

about only if all the positive charge in an atom were concentrated in a very small region.

The first convincing evidence that the positive charge is concentrated in a very small region came from studies[2–7] of the scattering of alpha particles as these particles passed through a gold foil approximately 0.0004 cm. thick. It had been found[8] that, although most of the particles proceeded nearly straight through the foil, approximately one particle in 20,000 was deflected through an angle of the order of 90°. With this knowledge Rutherford and his associates undertook a long series of experiments on the scattering of alpha particles by thin films. The results of these studies

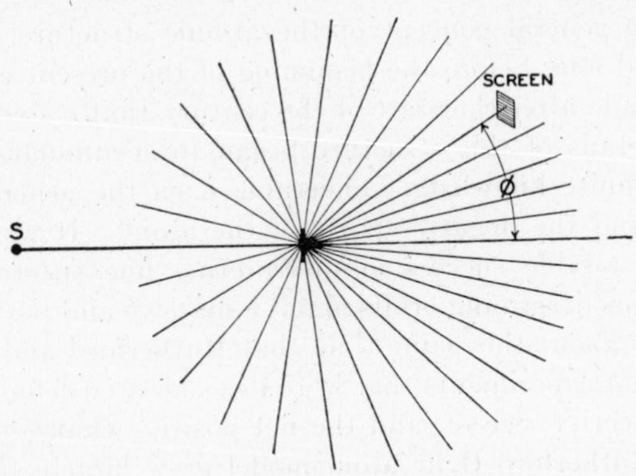


FIG. 1.—Illustrating the method of studying the scattering of alpha particles by thin films.

proved to be of utmost importance in the development of the modern concept of atomic structure.

The basic procedure followed in these experiments is indicated in Fig. 1. Alpha particles from a distant source were allowed to strike the surface of a thin film perpendicularly. Films of gold, platinum, silver and copper were used at various times. The distribution of scattered alpha particles was determined by counting the number of scintillations produced per second on a small fluorescent screen placed in first one and then another angular position. It was found that most of the positively charged alpha particles passed on through the film with but slight deflections. There were observed, however, a few particles which were deflected through very large angles; some were turned almost directly back on their paths.

[2] E. Rutherford, *Phil. Mag.*, **21,** 669 (1911).
[3] H. Geiger, *Proc. Roy. Soc.*, A, **86,** 235 (1912).
[4] H. Geiger and E. Marsden, *Phil. Mag.*, **25,** 604 (1913).
[5] J. Chadwick, *Phil. Mag.*, **40,** 734 (1920).
[6] E. Rutherford, *Proc. Roy. Soc.*, A, **97,** 374 (1920).
[7] E. Rutherford and J. Chadwick, *Phil. Mag.*, **50,** 889 (1925).
[8] H. Geiger and E. Marsden, *Proc. Roy. Soc.*, A, **82,** 495 (1909).

In attempting to form a proper concept of how the scattering of these particles takes place, the question arises immediately as to whether the deflection suffered by any given alpha particle is the resultant of a large number of small deflections brought about as the particle passes fairly close to atomic nuclei within the film (multiple scattering), or whether it is the result of a single deflection produced by a very close approach of the particle to some one particular nucleus (single scattering). The deflections suffered by the alpha particle because of close approaches to electrons would be insignificant; the mass of the electron is too small to cause the relatively heavy alpha particle to deviate appreciably from its path.

It is possible to work out[2,9–11] on the laws of probability the theoretical angular distribution of alpha particles scattered by either the single or the multiple scattering process. Theoretical conclusions regarding the details of the distribution resulting from the two types of scattering are somewhat different. On the theory of multiple scattering an entirely negligible number of particles should be scattered at large angles; on the theory of single scattering a much greater fraction of the particles should be deviated through large angles. On the theory of single scattering the number of particles scattered at a particular angle should be proportional to the thickness of the scattering film; on the theory of multiple scattering this number should be proportional to the square root of the film thickness. On the single scattering view, theory leads one to expect also that the number of particles scattered at any particular angle, per unit area of the fluorescent screen, should be proportional to $\operatorname{cosec}^4 \frac{1}{2}\phi$, should be proportional to the square of the net positive nuclear charge, and should be inversely proportional to the square of the kinetic energy of the incident alpha particle.

Many experiments[2–7] have shown that the scattering by sufficiently thin films at other than very small angles is definitely of the single scattering type. Brief summaries of these works can be found in the literature.[10,11] All experiments show an excess of large angle scattering over that which would be expected on the theory of multiple scattering. This excess of scattering at large angles led Rutherford to suggest that the deflections suffered by these particles were the result of single very close encounters with atomic nuclei, that is, the result of single scattering. In order that a single encounter can produce such a large deflection, however, it is necessary that the deflecting nucleus have its positive charge concentrated in a very

[9] C. G. Darwin, *Phil. Mag.*, **23**, 901 (1912); **27**, 499 (1914); **41**, 486 (1921).

[10] E. N. da C. Andrade, *The Structure of the Atom* (3rd ed.; New York: Harcourt, Brace and Co., 1926), pp. 19–39.

[11] K. K. Darrow, *Introduction to Contemporary Physics* (2nd ed.; New York: D. Van Nostrand, 1939), pp. 122–138.

small region, and that the deflected alpha particle come quite close to this. Rutherford therefore assumed that the atom is composed of a positively charged nucleus, extremely small as compared to the size of the atom, surrounded by planetary electrons. An alpha particle should be able to move among the planetary electrons without experiencing a measurable deflection; an appreciable deflection should occur only when the alpha particle approaches the central positive nucleus. It is quite apparent, therefore, that experimental evidence concerning the type of scattering produced by thin films allows one to judge with some certainty as to the correctness or incorrectness of Rutherford's concept of the nucleus.

Numerous experiments bear upon the nature of this scattering. Careful investigation of the way in which the number of particles scattered varies with the angle of scattering have shown[4] that the number of scattered particles is proportional to $\operatorname{cosec}^4 \frac{1}{2}\phi$, just as one expects on the concept of single scattering. These measurements extended over scattering angles ranging from 5 to 150°. Over this range the number of particles scattered per unit area varied by a factor of 250,000. This type of angular distribution has been confirmed[12,13] by measurements on the scattering of particles produced in a gas confined in a cloud chamber. Experiments have shown also that the number of particles scattered at any particular large angle by a thin film is proportional to the thickness of the film, provided this thickness be small. For greater thicknesses the number of scattered particles increases with thickness less rapidly than that indicated by direct proportionality. This observation is of considerable importance. While for single scattering the number should be proportional to the first power of the thickness, for multiple it should be proportional to the square root of this thickness. This is further strong evidence that for sufficiently thin films the large angle scattering is the result of single encounters and not of multiple scattering. The part played by multiple scattering would be expected to increase as one uses thicker films. It has been observed also that the number of particles scattered at any particular angle is inversely proportional to the square of the kinetic energy of the incident particles, just as one expects on the single scattering view. While it was impossible to determine directly whether the number of particles scattered at any given angle is proportional to the square of the net positive nuclear charge, for the nuclear charge was not yet known, it was found that the number is proportional to the square of the atomic number of the element. These many experiments confirmed in all respects the theory of single scattering for large angle scattering. It should not be inferred that multiple scattering does not take place. Both types of scattering are always present. At very

[12] P. M. S. Blackett, *Proc. Roy. Soc.*, A, **102**, 294 (1922).

[13] P. Auger and F. Perrin, *Comptes Rendus*, **175**, 340 (1922).

small scattering angles, or for relatively thick films, multiple scattering predominates. For large angle scattering, however, particularly for thin films, it is the single scattering that predominates.

Two highly important calculations can be made from the data on single scattering if one assumes that the electrical repulsion between the alpha particle and the nucleus follows the inverse square law. The analytical theory of single scattering was developed on the assumption that this inverse square law does hold, even for the close distances of approach between the alpha particle and the scattering nucleus. The fact that this theory is confirmed so beautifully by experiment gives one assurance that the law holds accurately even at these small distances. One observer[5] concluded that the power of the distance involved in the actual force law cannot be less than 1.97 nor more than 2.03. The inverse square law holds to at least this degree of accuracy even though the alpha particle often comes as close as $5 \times 10^{-12}$ cm. to the deflecting nucleus. Accepting the theory of single scattering, it is possible to calculate from data on the number of particles scattered at large angles both the closest distance of approach between the alpha particle and the deflecting nucleus, and the net positive charge on the nucleus. The closest distance of approach is that for those particles turned directly back on their paths. From the closest distance of approach one obtains an upper limit for the size of the nucleus, for the inverse square law still holds at these distances. Such calculations yield an upper limit for the diameter of the nucleus of the order of a few times $10^{-12}$ cm. This upper limit depends somewhat, though not greatly, upon the atom whose nucleus is being considered.

TABLE I

Values of the net positive nuclear charge as obtained from the scattering of alpha particles

| Element | Atomic No. $Z$ | Nuclear charge | Reference |
|---|---|---|---|
| Au | 79 | $79 \pm 2\%$ | 7 |
| Pt | 78 | $Z \pm 5\%$* | 4 |
| | | $77.4 \pm 1$ | 5 |
| Sn | 50 | $Z \pm 5\%$* | 4 |
| Ag | 47 | $Z \pm 5\%$* | 4 |
| | | $46.3 \pm 0.7$ | 5 |
| Cu | 29 | $Z \pm 5\%$* | 4 |
| | | $29.3 \pm 0.5$ | 5 |
| A | 18 | 19 | 13 |
| Al | 13 | $Z \pm 5\%$* | 4 |
| | | $13.0 \pm 0.5$ | 14 |
| Mg | 12 | $12.6 \pm 1.0$ | 14 |

* These values were calculated on the supposition that $Z = 79$ for Au.

[14] E. S. Bieler, *Proc. Roy. Soc.*, A, **105**, 434 (1924).

It is possible to calculate also the net positive nuclear charge. Experimental values obtained for various atoms are shown in Table I. Experiments of this type leave no doubt that the net positive nuclear charge on an atom is equal to the atomic number. It is true that these results do not show this equality with any degree of precision, but this is due to the difficulties inherent in such work. There are of course other lines of evidence which show this equality of net nuclear charge and atomic number. One convincing piece of evidence is the Moseley[15] law, which connects the frequency of characteristic X-rays with the atomic number of the target which emits them. This evidence became available shortly after the start of the work on the scattering of alpha particles.

It is well to call attention here to some further evidence in favor of the theory of single scattering. If the tracks of alpha particles are photographed in a cloud chamber one frequently observes an abrupt change in direction near the end of the particle's path. These abrupt deflections are obvious from the photograph reproduced[16] in Fig. 2. Since the chance of deflection through a given large angle is inversely proportional to the fourth power of the velocity of the particle, these abrupt deflections are far more probable near the end than near the beginning of the path. These changes in direction are quite inconsistent with multiple scattering, but they are in accord with the concept of single scattering. The phenomenon of multiple scattering no doubt accounts at least in part for the very gradual change in direction suffered by some of the particles.

FIG. 2.—Illustrating the abrupt bends which occur near the ends of alpha particle paths. The forked track represents a close collision between an alpha particle and an oxygen nucleus. (These alpha particles were passing through oxygen.)

Many times an abrupt change in direction is accompanied by a spur track. This spur is due to a recoiling nucleus which has been struck by the alpha particle. Such a spur is shown in Fig. 2, the longer branch of the forked track being due to the alpha particle and the shorter spur representing the recoiling nucleus. That this interpretation is correct can be shown by calculations based upon the measured angles through which these two particles are deflected. Obtaining these angles from stereoscopic views

[15] H. G. J. Moseley, *Phil. Mag.*, **26,** 1024 (1913); **27,** 703 (1914).

[16] P. M. S. Blackett, *Proc. Roy. Soc.*, A, **103,** 62 (1923).

such as shown in Fig. 2, Blackett[16] calculated the mass of the particle responsible for the spur track. This calculation involved only the assumption of the laws of conservation of energy and conservation of momentum, the measured angles of deflection, and the known mass of the alpha particle. It was calculated that the mass of the particle responsible for the spur track in Fig. 2 is 16.72 ± 0.42. This spur track was obtained when the cloud chamber was filled with oxygen. It seems quite certain, therefore, that the track is that of a recoiling oxygen nucleus. Similar calculations have been made[16] on spur tracks made in hydrogen and in helium. The calculated mass of the particle responsible for the spur track in hydrogen is 1.024 ± 0.022 while that leaving the track in helium is 4.032 ± 0.032.

FIG. 3.—A forked track formed by shooting alpha particles through helium.

These spurs are certainly due to recoiling atoms of hydrogen and helium respectively.

Another interesting forked track[17] is shown in Fig. 3. This was obtained by shooting alpha particles through helium gas. In this case the nucleus struck has the same mass as the oncoming alpha particle. By writing equations for the conservation of energy and the conservation of momentum for a collision between an oncoming particle and a second particle of equal mass which is originally at rest, it can be shown that the two particles should proceed in such directions that the angle between their paths is 90°. Really, this result is obtained only if one neglects the change of mass with velocity. If one considers this change for alpha particles, however, the theoretical angle is not appreciably different from 90°. The angle should have this value regardless of the way in which the collision takes place. Careful measurement of the angle between the two tracks of the fork shown in

[17] P. M. S. Blackett, *Proc. Roy. Soc.*, A, **107**, 349 (1925).

Fig. 3 shows that the angle between these is 89° 27′. This is very close to the theoretical 90°.

**Failure of the Inverse Square Law of Repulsion between Nuclei**

Experiments on the scattering of alpha particles as they pass through films composed of fairly heavy atoms have shown that the inverse square law of repulsion between the alpha particle and the nucleus holds to the closest distances of approach encountered in these studies. It would be important to know for just how much closer distances of approach this law might hold. There are two ways in which the alpha particle might be made to approach more closely the scattering nucleus. One of these is by using some atom of low atomic number for the scatterer. The nucleus of such an atom possesses a small positive charge and the alpha particle would, therefore, have to approach relatively close before the force becomes sufficient to stop its forward motion. Hydrogen would be the best material to choose for such purposes. Studies[18–21] of the scattering of alpha particles by hydrogen have given valuable information regarding the limiting distance of approach for which the inverse square law still holds.

In studying the scattering of alpha particles by heavy nuclei, it was permissible to neglect entirely the motion of the nucleus which had been struck. For light nuclei, however, this motion must be considered; in fact, for hydrogen the velocity with which the nucleus is projected is sometimes greater than the velocity of the incident alpha particle. Consider a head-on collision between an alpha particle of mass $M$ and velocity $V_1$ and a hydrogen nucleus of mass $m$ originally at rest. If $V_2$ represents the velocity with which the alpha particle continues forward after the collision, and if $v$ represents the velocity with which the hydrogen nucleus is projected forward, then one can write from the law of conservation of momentum,

$$MV_1 = MV_2 + mv$$

Assuming also the law of conservation of energy,

$$\tfrac{1}{2}MV_1^2 = \tfrac{1}{2}MV_2^2 + \tfrac{1}{2}mv^2$$

If one solves the first of these equations for $V_2$ and substitutes this into the second equation, and if one makes use of the fact that $M/m = 4$, it is found that $v = 1.6V_1$. Thus a hydrogen nucleus which is struck head-on proceeds forward with a velocity 1.6 times the velocity of the incident alpha particle. Now it can be argued[21] that a proton of a given velocity should

[18] E. Marsden, *Phil. Mag.*, **27**, 824 (1914).

[19] E. Rutherford, *Phil. Mag.*, **37**, 537, 562 (1919).

[20] J. Chadwick and E. S. Bieler, *Phil. Mag.*, **42**, 923 (1921).

[21] E. N. da C. Andrade, *The Structure of the Atom* (3rd ed.; New York: Harcourt, Brace, and Co., 1926), pp. 75–88.

have essentially the same range in a given gas as would an alpha particle of the same velocity. Furthermore, the range of a particle is closely proportional to the cube of its velocity. One therefore concludes that a hydrogen nucleus projected straight forward should have a range $(1.6)^3$ or 4.1 times the range of the alpha particle which struck it. Consideration of minor differences in the ranges of an alpha particle and a proton of the same velocity indicates that the range of the proton should be slightly less than this. For the present purpose we shall say that it should be approximately 4 times the range of the incident alpha particle.

It had been noticed by Marsden[18] that some protons of about this range are projected forward when alpha particles are passed through hydrogen. It is of course only those particles which are struck head-on that should have this range. The forward range of other particles would be smaller for two reasons. First, the velocity of a particle projected at an angle is less than that of one projected straight forward. Second, the forward range of a particle projected at an angle is only one component of its entire range.

It is possible to work out analytically[9] both the range distribution and the angular distribution of hydrogen nuclei projected by the impact of alpha particles. The calculation of this distribution involves the assumption that the inverse square law of repulsion holds. Rutherford[19] tested the theoretical distribution by observing the distribution of protons projected by alpha particle impact. The distribution was determined by observing the scintillations produced by the protons on a small fluorescent screen. The ranges of those particles projected straight forward agreed with expectations. It was certain, however, that far more particles had this maximum range than one would expect to be projected straight forward. In other words, a far greater fraction than one expects of the hydrogen nuclei struck behaved as if they had suffered head-on collisions. In one instance[20] the number of protons projected within 30° of the direction of the incident alpha rays was found to be 100 times as great as that theoretically expected.

Observations of this character have been made using alpha particles of various energies, ranges from 3.9 to 8.2 cm. For the slower alpha particles it is found that the distribution of projected hydrogen nuclei agrees more or less closely with that calculated theoretically. As alpha particles of higher velocity are used, the percentage of protons projected nearly straight forward increases rapidly. For example,[20] using alpha particles of 4.3 cm. range the number of protons projected within 30° of straight forward is 15 times the theoretical number, whereas for alpha rays of 8.2 cm. range the number projected within this angle is 100 times as great as expected.

Results of such experiments can be interpreted only on the basis of failure of the inverse square law. Deviations from theory set in when the alpha particles have an energy sufficient to cause the particle to approach to within about $3 \times 10^{-13}$ cm. of the hydrogen nucleus. The inverse square law appears to hold down to this distance. It is interesting that this closest distance of approach is approximately $\frac{1}{10}$ that encountered in the studies of the scattering of alpha particles by metallic films. The preference of projected hydrogen nuclei for the direction of the original alpha particles for these close distances of approach cannot be reconciled with a spherical nucleus. If the charged nucleus were spherical, and if it remained so even upon close approach to another nucleus, its charge would behave as if it were concentrated at a point, the center of the sphere. To account for the great number of particles projected forward it is necessary to suppose that one of the two nuclei is flattened. Since the alpha particle, which is a helium nucleus, is more complex than the hydrogen nucleus it is supposed that this is the one which is flattened. If this flattened nucleus proceeds with its flattened face forward, the electric field would be such as to project an abnormally large fraction of the hydrogen nuclei nearly straight forward. It is not necessary to assume that the helium nucleus is normally flattened; it probably becomes flattened as it approaches the proton. It has been calculated[20] that the shape of the helium nucleus which best fits experimental data for the closest distance of approach, is that of an elastic oblate spheroid of semiaxes $8 \times 10^{-13}$ and $4 \times 10^{-13}$ cm. Such a particle, moving in the direction of its minor axis, accounts most satisfactorily for the observed distribution of projected protons.

### The First Successful Experiments on Artificial Disintegration

Since the earliest days of chemistry it had been the dream of scientists that some day it might become possible to convert one element into another, to tear apart the structure of one atom and make it over into another. These dreams envisaged the turning of some cheap metal into gold, silver, or platinum to acquire huge profit. No success had been attained in this artificial disintegration of matter until 1919. At that time Rutherford, no doubt one of the greatest physicists ever to live, succeeded without question in disintegrating in the laboratory a number of materials. Since that time, physicists have learned how to disintegrate practically any element one might choose, and the new element produced in the process is now recognized. Today the artificial disintegration of matter has become an important division of physics, both because of the fundamental knowledge of atomic structure gained from such studies and because of certain possible important applications of this knowledge to so-called practical problems. It is of interest therefore to review briefly the early work on the subject.

It was in 1919 that Rutherford[22] first succeeded in demonstrating the artificial disintegration of matter. He had been studying[19–23] intensely the projection of nuclei of hydrogen, nitrogen, and oxygen as alpha particles were passed through these gases. In each case nuclei were projected forward with ranges essentially in agreement with those expected on the basis of a collision between the alpha particle and the projected nucleus, the laws of conservation of momentum and conservation of energy being assumed to hold. In studying nitrogen, however, Rutherford[22] observed an anomalous behavior. Using as a source RaC, containing no doubt some RaC′, alpha particles having a range of approximately 7 cm. in air were shot through various gases. Now it is true that whenever one uses such a source of alpha particles one observes a few very long range protons, particles having a

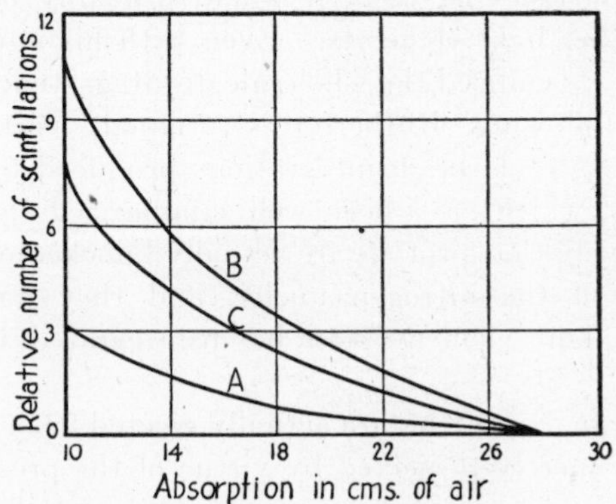


FIG. 4.—Showing the distribution of protons coming from nitrogen disintegration by bombardment with alpha particles.

maximum range approximately 4 times that of the alpha particle. While it is possible that these protons might be ejected during the radioactive disintegration, it seems far more likely that they are the result of a small amount of hydrogen impurity on the surface of the source. The maximum range is just that which one should expect from a hydrogen nucleus which has been struck and knocked straight forward.

Curve *A* of Fig. 4 shows[22] the range distribution of these natural long range particles from the source used by Rutherford. They are present even when the space around the source is evacuated; they come from the source or from the gas absorbed thereon. It was observed that there were, surprisingly, a far greater number of these long range protons when the space around the source was filled with air. Curve *B* of Fig. 4 shows the number and range distribution when air is used. Curve *C*, the difference between *B*

[22] E. Rutherford, *Phil. Mag.*, **37**, 581 (1919).
[23] E. Rutherford, *Phil. Mag.*, **37**, 571 (1919).

and $A$, gives the number arising because of the presence of the air. The hydrogen content in air is by no means sufficient to account for these additional particles. If oxygen or carbon dioxide be substituted for the air these long range particles disappear. It was demonstrated conclusively that these long range particles come from the nitrogen content of the air; they are proportionately more abundant when pure nitrogen is used. Detailed investigation,[24] which includes deflecting the particles in magnetic fields, has proved that these particles are actually protons. It was concluded by Rutherford that these were knocked out of the nitrogen nuclei when these were struck by alpha particles. Atoms of nitrogen were truly disintegrated by bombardment with alpha rays. Rutherford suggested then that if there were available alpha particles or other particles with more energy than the particles he used, it would probably be possible to disintegrate many other light elements. Even with his unusual foresight he could scarcely have visualized the wholesale disintegrations produced today.

Immediately following Rutherford's original work, many further studies[25–27] were made of the disintegrations produced by alpha particles. These early works, which have been well summarized elsewhere,[28] showed still more conclusively that protons are actually knocked out of the nitrogen by disintegration of the nitrogen nuclei; and they have demonstrated that many other light elements can be disintegrated by alpha particle bombardment.

That the long range particles are actually ejected from nuclei of nitrogen atoms rather than merely projected by virtue of the presence of hydrogen impurity, is evidenced by two other observations. If hydrogen nuclei as impurity in the nitrogen are struck and projected straight forward the range would be only 28 cm. when alpha particles having a range of 7 cm. are used. However, a few long range particles from nitrogen have a forward range as great as 40 cm. Furthermore, while hydrogen nuclei are projected predominately in the forward direction when coming from hydrogen atoms, the hydrogen nuclei arising from nitrogen are distributed almost uniformly at all angles. It is true that the range of those particles projected forward is considerably greater than that of those projected backward. These facts show clearly that the protons are shot off from the nitrogen nuclei. Under these circumstances, the exceptionally long forward range of the particles must be due to release of nuclear energy accompanying the disintegration.

[24] E. Rutherford and J. Chadwick, *Phil. Mag.*, **48**, 509 (1924).

[25] E. Rutherford, *Nature*, **109**, 614 (1922).

[26] E. Rutherford and J. Chadwick, *Phil. Mag.*, **42**, 809 (1920); **44**, 417 (1922); *Nature*, **113**, 457 (1924); *Proc. Phys. Soc.*, London, **36**, 417 (1924).

[27] G. Kirsch and H. Pettersson, *Phil. Mag.*, **47**, 500 (1924).

[28] E. N. da C. Andrade, *The Structure of the Atom* (3rd ed.; New York: Harcourt, Brace and Co., 1926), pp. 91–102.

The impact of the alpha particle seems only to trigger off the nuclear ejection of the proton.

It was not only nitrogen that was disintegrated in these early experiments. Long range particles with forward ranges greater than 28 cm. were also observed from B, F, Na, Al, and P. The fact that the protons resulting from disintegration are distributed almost equally at all angles while those resulting from hydrogen impurity are nearly all projected straight forward, has allowed the study of materials giving off slower protons during the disintegration process. These materials have been studied by observing the protons projected at right angles to the incident alpha rays. None of the 28 cm. natural long range particles are projected at right angles. Hence it is possible to make observations at this angle with the observing screen closer to the source. In this way, it is possible to search for the presence of much lower disintegration protons. By this method it was possible to show that Ne, Mg, Si, S, Cl, A, and K were also disintegrated. The ranges of the disintegration protons given out by these materials are shown in Table II.

Rutherford and his associates did not succeed in disintegrating Li, Be, C, or O. Kirsch and Pettersson[27] confirmed the disintegration of Mg and

TABLE II

The disintegration of light elements by alpha particle bombardment, as judged from the early work of Rutherford and his associates

| Element | Atomic number | Maximum range of protons in cm. of air | | |
|---|---|---|---|---|
| | | Forward | At 90° | Backward |
| Li | 3 | | | |
| Be | 4 | | | |
| B | 5 | 58 | ... | 38 |
| C | 6 | | | |
| N | 7 | 40 | ... | 18 |
| O | 8 | | | |
| F | 9 | 65 | ... | 48 |
| Ne | 10 | .. | 16 | .. |
| Na | 11 | 58 | ... | 36 |
| Mg | 12 | .. | 25* | .. |
| Al | 13 | 90 | ... | 67 |
| Si | 14 | .. | 25* | .. |
| P | 15 | 65 | ... | 49 |
| S | 16 | .. | 28* | .. |
| Cl | 17 | .. | 30* | .. |
| A | 18 | .. | 23* | .. |
| K | 19 | .. | 23* | .. |

* These ranges are approximate only.

Si and reported also the disintegration of Li, Be, and C. In regard to the last three materials, this work is contrary to the results of Rutherford and his associates. In any case, all of these and many other materials have been disintegrated by newer methods.

It has been remarked that the alpha particle serves only to trigger off the nuclear disintegration, and that a large part of the energy given to the projected particle comes from the release of nuclear energy. It has been shown that if an alpha particle of range 7 cm. strikes a hydrogen nucleus and projects it straight forward, this proton will have a range of approximately 28 cm. Although the alpha particle may originally have had more energy than it gave to this proton, there is no possible way in which it could communicate more of its energy to the hydrogen nucleus. The fact that some disintegration protons have ranges in excess of 28 cm. shows,

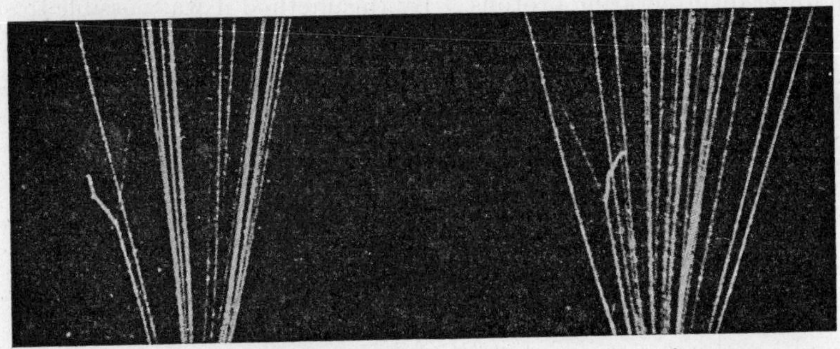

FIG. 5.—Showing a disintegration proton coming from nitrogen.

therefore, that the original alpha particle served merely to trigger off the nuclear disintegration. The case of aluminum is particularly interesting. For this material the forward range of the ejected proton is 90 cm. If one makes use of the facts that the range of a particle is proportional to the cube of its velocity, that the kinetic energy of a particle is proportional to the square of its velocity, and that the proton has a mass ¼ that of the alpha particle, it can be shown that the energy of a proton of 90 cm. range is greater than that of an alpha particle of 7 cm. range. It is approximately 40% greater. Thus the ejected proton actually possesses more energy than the incident alpha particle had before it struck the aluminum nucleus. What more certain evidence could one ask that the alpha particle serves merely to trigger off the nuclear disintegration and thus release a large store of nuclear energy?

Attention should be called here to some further beautiful evidence showing the disintegration of nitrogen with the accompanying ejection of a proton. By firing alpha particles through a cloud chamber filled with nitrogen, it has been possible[17] to photograph the track of the proton leaving the nitrogen nucleus. Figures 5 and 6 show this phenomenon. The thin track leaving the point of collision is that of the projected proton. In Fig. 6 it is clear that this proton is ejected nearly backward. Since there are only two tracks leaving the point of disintegration, it appears that the ruptured nitrogen nucleus must have absorbed in its structure the original alpha particle. If the original nitrogen nucleus $_7N^{14}$ absorbs an alpha particle and ejects a proton, its atomic number would be increased by 1 and its atomic weight increased by 3. The new nucleus would be one of atomic number 8 and atomic weight 17. If the disintegration takes place in this way, the new nucleus should be $_8O^{17}$. This is one of the relatively

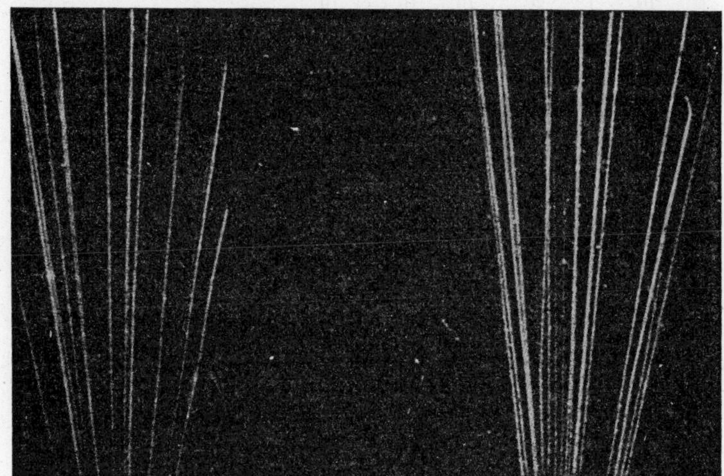

FIG. 6.—Showing a disintegration proton projected nearly backward.

rare oxygen isotopes. Whether or not these details of the disintegration are correct, the mere existence of the proton track leaving the point of collision in these photographs is about as direct evidence as one could desire for the disintegration of the nitrogen nucleus.

### The Present Concept of Atomic Structure

We are in a position to form a fairly definite concept of the general structure of the atom. There are a few basic requirements that this model must meet. First, the nucleus must be very small, not larger than $10^{-12}$ cm.; almost the entire mass of the atom must be concentrated in this nucleus. Second, this nucleus must bear a net positive charge equal to $Z$ electron units, where $Z$ is the atomic number of the element. Third, there must be $Z$ electrons not associated with the nucleus; these are the planetary electrons pictured by Bohr. Fourth, these planetary electrons

TABLE III

The structure of typical atoms on the proton-neutron concept of nuclear structure

| Element | Known nuclear charge | Known mass | Contents of the nucleus | | Known outer electrons | Distribution of electrons | | | | | | |
|---|---|---|---|---|---|---|---|---|---|---|---|---|
| | | | *p* | *n* | | *K* | *L* | *M* | *N* | *O* | *P* | *Q* |
| H | 1 | 1 | 1 | 0 | 1 | 1 | | | | | | |
| He | 2 | 4 | 2 | 2 | 2 | 2 | | | | | | |
| Li | 3 | 7 | 3 | 4 | 3 | 2 | 1 | | | | | |
| Be | 4 | 9 | 4 | 5 | 4 | 2 | 2 | | | | | |
| B | 5 | 11 | 5 | 6 | 5 | 2 | 3 | | | | | |
| Ne | 10 | 20 | 10 | 10 | 10 | 2 | 8 | | | | | |
| Na | 11 | 23 | 11 | 12 | 11 | 2 | 8 | 1 | | | | |
| A | 18 | 40 | 18 | 22 | 18 | 2 | 8 | 8 | | | | |
| K | 19 | 39 | 19 | 20 | 19 | 2 | 8 | 8 | 1 | | | |
| Ca | 20 | 40 | 20 | 20 | 20 | 2 | 8 | 8 | 2 | | | |
| Sc | 21 | 45 | 21 | 24 | 21 | 2 | 8 | 9 | 2 | | | |
| Ni | 28 | 59 | 28 | 31 | 28 | 2 | 8 | 16 | 2 | | | |
| Cu | 29 | 64 | 29 | 35 | 29 | 2 | 8 | 18 | 1 | | | |
| Kr | 36 | 83 | 36 | 47 | 36 | 2 | 8 | 18 | 8 | | | |
| Rb | 37 | 85 | 37 | 48 | 37 | 2 | 8 | 18 | 8 | 1 | | |
| Sr | 38 | 87 | 38 | 49 | 38 | 2 | 8 | 18 | 8 | 2 | | |
| Y | 39 | 89 | 39 | 50 | 39 | 2 | 8 | 18 | 9 | 2 | | |
| Pd | 46 | 107 | 46 | 61 | 46 | 2 | 8 | 18 | 16 | 2 | | |
| Ag | 47 | 108 | 47 | 61 | 47 | 2 | 8 | 18 | 18 | 1 | | |
| Xe | 54 | 130 | 54 | 76 | 54 | 2 | 8 | 18 | 18 | 8 | | |
| Cs | 55 | 133 | 55 | 78 | 55 | 2 | 8 | 18 | 18 | 8 | 1 | |
| Ba | 56 | 137 | 56 | 81 | 56 | 2 | 8 | 18 | 18 | 8 | 2 | |
| La | 57 | 139 | 57 | 82 | 57 | 2 | 8 | 18 | 18 | 9 | 2 | |
| Ce | 58 | 140 | 58 | 82 | 58 | 2 | 8 | 18 | 19 | 9 | 2 | |
| Lu | 71 | 175 | 71 | 104 | 71 | 2 | 8 | 18 | 32 | 9 | 2 | |
| Hf | 72 | 179 | 72 | 107 | 72 | 2 | 8 | 18 | 32 | 10 | 2 | |
| Pt | 78 | 195 | 78 | 117 | 78 | 2 | 8 | 18 | 32 | 16 | 2 | |
| Au | 79 | 197 | 79 | 118 | 79 | 2 | 8 | 18 | 32 | 18 | 1 | |
| Rn | 86 | 222 | 86 | 136 | 86 | 2 | 8 | 18 | 32 | 18 | 8 | |
| ... | 87 | ... | 87 | ... | 87 | 2 | 8 | 18 | 32 | 18 | 8 | 1 |
| Ra | 88 | 226 | 88 | 138 | 88 | 2 | 8 | 18 | 32 | 18 | 8 | 2 |
| Ac | 89 | ... | 89 | ... | 89 | 2 | 8 | 18 | 32 | 18 | 9 | 2 |
| U | 92 | 238 | 92 | 146 | 92 | 2 | 8 | 18 | 32 | 18 | 12 | 2 |

must be arranged in definite energy levels outside the nucleus. The actual arrangement of these electrons is obtained from chemical, magnetic, optical, and X-ray data.

The contents of the nucleus itself are open to some question. The particles which go into its structure must account for a net nuclear charge equal to the atomic number and for a mass essentially equal to that of the atom in question. These nuclei might be made up entirely from protons and electrons, the protons accounting for the mass and the difference between the number of protons and the number of electrons accounting for the net nuclear charge. This was the picture universally held before the almost simultaneous discoveries of the positron and the neutron. The discovery of these particles opened a large number of other possibilities of nuclear structure. Among these possibilities is that of constructing the nucleus entirely of protons and neutrons. On this view the number of protons going into the structure of any nucleus is equal to the atomic number; these provide the proper nuclear charge. In addition to these protons the nucleus contains a number of neutrons sufficient that the protons and neutrons together account for the proper mass of the nucleus. Evidence gathered from several sources points more and more strongly toward the correctness of the proton-neutron concept of nuclear structure. The general structures of typical atoms are indicated in Table III.

No account has been taken in this table of the existence of isotopes. These fit into the picture with no trouble. Consider, for example, the case of Ne. This element is composed of three isotopes, $Ne^{20}$, $Ne^{21}$, and $Ne^{22}$. Each isotope has the same atomic number 10. Each of the three nuclei therefore contain 10 protons. $Ne^{20}$ contains 10 neutrons, $Ne^{21}$ contains 11 neutrons, and $Ne^{22}$ contains 12 neutrons. The arrangement of planetary electrons is of course the same for each of the three isotopes. Isotopes of other elements can be built up in a similar manner.

One might object to the proton-neutron model on the grounds that the nucleus contains no electrons. One might raise the question as to whether the ejection of beta rays from the nuclei of natural radioactive materials does not necessitate that the nucleus contain electrons. The present day answer to this question is that it does not. Convincing evidence that electron-positron pairs can be manufactured out of radiant energy has already been presented. A certain amount of radiant energy can be caused to disappear and one finds in its place an electron-positron pair. Perhaps the electrons which are ejected from the nuclei of atoms are actually manufactured in this way; perhaps they are not present as electrons in the nuclear structure. It is the present belief that they are not; the nucleus is made up entirely of protons and neutrons.

## 2. RECENT PRODUCTION OF EXTREMELY HIGH ENERGY PARTICLES

All of the early artificial disintegrations were produced by bombarding materials with alpha particles given off from natural radioactive materials. Disintegration studies could be carried out, therefore, only in those laboratories having a good supply of the proper radioactive substances. No other type of high energy particle was available in those years. It was recognized early that many other disintegrations might be produced if more energetic alpha particles were available, or if there were other particles with comparable energies. In fact some other particle, such as a proton, might cause certain disintegrations even though this particle have a somewhat lower energy. It was important, therefore, to develop laboratory methods of obtaining high energy particles if the study of artificial disintegration was to be pushed far.

### Early Types of Apparatus

Several early methods of producing high energy charged particles were developed about 1930. These are of various types. One method used a group of high voltage transformer windings in series to obtain the high potential. Another utilized a series arrangement of vacuum tube rectifiers. A third method is based upon the principle of the electrostatic machine, while in still another the equivalent of a high voltage is obtained by repeatedly accelerating ions through the same relatively low potential. The first successful effort[29] to develop a high voltage utilized several transformer windings in series. By this method a potential of 750 kv. was developed and applied across an X-ray tube.

Cockcroft and Walton[30] were the first to succeed completely in producing high energy ions in the laboratory, and to show that these artificially produced particles actually cause disintegration. They used a number of special vacuum tube rectifiers, having their outputs in series, to generate the high d.c. potential. The full potential developed was then applied across an accelerating tube into which positive ions had been urged. The positive ions were produced by ionization of a gas in an auxiliary tube and then allowed to pass through a small opening into the main accelerating tube. In the original experiments of Cockcroft and Walton, the positive ions were those of hydrogen. Potentials slightly over 700 kv. were obtained, and these were steady to within a few percent. Proton currents of 10 microamperes were produced. Other high energy particles could, of course, be produced in a similar way. Particles having an energy of approximately one MEV have been obtained through use of vacuum tube rectifier arrange-

[29] C. C. Lauritsen and R. D. Bennett, *Phys. Rev.*, **32**, 850 (1928).

[30] J. D. Cockcroft and E. T. S. Walton, *Proc. Roy. Soc.*, A, **129**, 477 (1930); **136**, 619 (1932).

ments, though the protons with which Cockcroft and Walton originally succeeded in disintegrating Li had an energy of only 150,000 electron volts.

Another method [31–33] which has been used consists of arranging coaxially a series of cylinders of ever increasing length, and of applying an alternating potential of the proper phase between successive cylinders. The general arrangement is shown in Fig. 7. Positive ions produced in an auxiliary tube are urged into region $S$, from which they continue to move along the tube through the series of cylinders. Alternate cylinders are connected together and a high frequency potential is applied between the two groups. During the proper half cycle ions are accelerated toward the first cylinder. After entering this cylinder they continue at a fixed velocity along its axis, entirely unaffected by any applied potential. Now if the length of this cylinder is

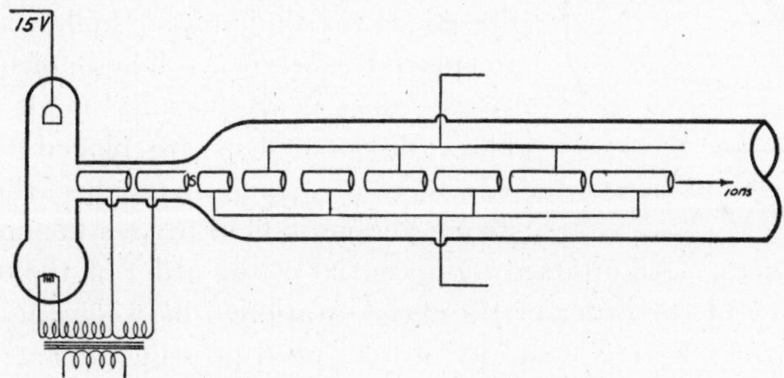


Fig. 7.—Illustrating the Sloan and Lawrence method of producing high energy particles.

properly proportioned to the speed of the ion traveling through it, the phase of the alternating potential will have reversed by the time the ion arrives at the space between this and the next cylinder. It is clear that if the lengths of the cylinders are such that the more and more rapidly moving particle spends one-half period in going from one gap to the next, this particle will be given additional energy at each gap. Thus the final energy of the particle may correspond to a potential difference many times that used for the acceleration. In one of the early pieces of apparatus[31] employing 30 accelerating cylinders and an accelerating potential of 42,000 volts, Hg ions having an energy of 1.26 MEV were produced; the ion current was $10^{-7}$ amperes. The concentration of these ions into a narrow stream is effected largely by the focusing action at each gap. Consideration of the electric field distribution at the gap shows that there is a net impulse urging the ion always toward the axis of the cylinder. With a later apparatus[33] utilizing

[31] D. H. Sloan and E. O. Lawrence, *Phys. Rev.*, **38**, 2021 (1931); *Proc. Nat. Acad. Sci.*, **17**, 64 (1931).

[32] R. L. Thornton and B. B. Kinsey, *Phys. Rev.*, **46**, 324 (1934).

[33] D. H. Sloan and W. M. Coates, *Phys. Rev.*, **46**, 539 (1934).

36 cylinders and an accelerating potential of 79,000 volts, singly charged Hg ions were given an energy of 2.85 MEV; the ion current in this case was $10^{-8}$ amperes. The overall length of the accelerating system was 185 cm; the spacing between cylinders was about 20% of the length of the cylinders.

### The Cyclotron

One of the two most important methods of developing high speed ions today is that of the cyclotron.[34–39] This is another method by which the ion is made to pass repeatedly through the same accelerating potential difference, the ion finally acquiring an energy corresponding to a potential difference many times that actually used for the acceleration. The principle of the cyclotron is illustrated in Fig. 8. Two semicircular hollow metal boxes are placed as shown. These pieces, referred to as "dees," are usually made of copper. These disc-like dees are placed between the pole faces of a huge magnet so that there is a strong magnetic field perpendicular to the flat faces of the dees. An alternating potential of the order of 10,000 volts and of a frequency of the order of $10^7$ cycles is applied between the dees at *a-b*.

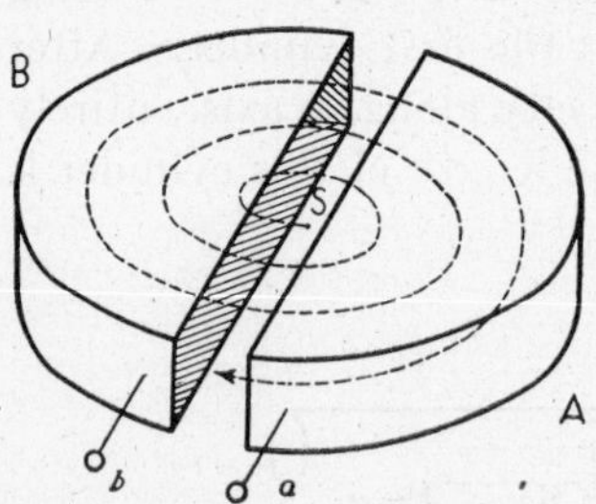

Fig. 8.—The dees of a cyclotron.

Suppose that there is a supply of low speed positive ions at *S*. During the proper half cycle these will be accelerated toward one of the dees, say *b*. Once these ions enter the hollow space within the metallic dee they will no longer be accelerated; they will move with a constant speed. However, since they are traveling perpendicular to a magnetic field they describe a semicircular path, finally coming back to the gap between dees. Now if the frequency of the a.c. potential applied should be such that the time required to describe this semicircle corresponds to one-half cycle, then the ion will arrive at the gap at just the proper time to be further accelerated by the now reversed electric field. The ion is moving much faster after it enters the second dee and will, therefore, describe a circle of greater radius. The radius *r* of the circular arc described in any case can be obtained from the relationship

$$Hev = \frac{mv^2}{r}, \qquad \text{or} \qquad r = \frac{mv}{He}$$

[34] E. O. Lawrence and N. E. Edlefson, *Science*, **72**, 376 (1930).

[35] E. O. Lawrence and M. S. Livingston, *Phys. Rev.*, **37**, 1707 (1931); **38**, 834 (1931); **40**, 19 (1932).

[36] M. S. Livingston, *Phys. Rev.*, **42**, 441 (1932).

[37] M. S. Livingston and E. O. Lawrence, *Phys. Rev.*, **43**, 212 (1933); **45**, 608 (1934).

[38] M. S. Livingston, *Rev. Sci. Instr.*, **7**, 55 (1936).

[39] E. O. Lawrence and D. Cooksey, *Phys. Rev.*, **50**, 1131 (1936).

where $v$ is the velocity with which the ion is traveling at the time considered.

Now the time $t$ required for the ion to describe a semicircle and come back again to the gap between dees is

$$t = \frac{\pi r}{v}$$

If the value of $r$ be substituted into this, one finds that

$$t = \frac{\pi m}{He}$$

Thus, neglecting the change of mass with velocity, the ion describes all semicircles, regardless of radius, in exactly the same time. The larger velocity of the ion when it describes the circle of larger radius is just sufficient to allow it to complete the longer path in the same time. Thus it is clear that the ion will arrive each time at the gap between dees at just the proper instant that the a.c. potential will accelerate it further. The ion therefore describes a series of semicircles of ever increasing radius, gradually spiraling outward and finally emerging at the outer edge of the dee. For each complete turn of the spiral the ion gains an energy equal to twice the voltage applied between dees. It emerges, therefore, with an energy equivalent to a potential very much higher than that used in the accelerating process.

One might wonder that the ion beam could be kept at all well-defined as the ions execute the irregular spiral toward the outer edge of the dees. Fortunately, it turns out that both the magnetic field perpendicular to the dees and the electric field across the gap between the dees, produce a focusing action which tends to keep the beam well-defined. One might also wonder whether the ions might not have various energies as they arrive at the outer edge of the dees, the energy perhaps depending upon what part of the half cycle the ion was accelerated across the gap. It turns out that, although those ions which cross the gap before or after the peak of the a.c. potential wave are given less energy each time they cross the gap, these ions make more revolutions before reaching the outer edge of the dees and in so doing acquire the same total amount of energy as do those ions which cross the gap at the peak of the wave. The ions arriving at the edge of the dees are, therefore, rather homogeneous in energy.

The positive ions to be accelerated by the cyclotron are obtained by ionization of a gas. The entire vessel housing the dees is evacuated thoroughly. It is then filled with the gas whose positive ion it is desired to use at a pressure of the order of one micron. A stream of electrons given off from a hot filament is shot, perpendicular to the faces of the dees, through the gap at the center of the dees. These electrons ionize the gas, and the resulting positive ions are accelerated toward the negative dee. If it were desired to produce high-speed protons one would fill the cyclotron with hydrogen; if one desired energetic helium ions one would use helium gas in the cyclotron. Recently a low voltage arc[40,41] has been used for formation of the positive ions in the gas. This results in a more copious supply than is obtained through the use of a hot filament.

These cyclotrons, together with associated magnet and other auxiliary apparatus, become extremely large and massive. There are approximately

FIG. 9.—General view of Lawrence's 37″ cyclotron at Berkeley.

twenty-five cyclotrons either in use or well under construction. A great majority of these are at laboratories[42] in this country. Among those institutions having installations are California,[34–39,43] Illinois,[44] Chicago,[45] Massachusetts Institute of Technology,[46] Purdue,[41] Harvard,[47] Cornell,[38] Michigan, Princeton, Yale, Ohio State, Indiana, and Washington. Many descriptions of the general design and technique of the cyclotron,[42,48] as well as that of other apparatus[49,50] for obtaining high energy particles, are available in the literature.

Lawrence, to whom the Nobel Prize was awarded for his outstanding contributions in this field of physics, has supervised the building of several

[40] M. S. Livingston, M. G. Holloway and C. P. Baker, *Rev. Sci. Instr.*, **10**, 63 (1939).
[41] W. J. Henderson, L. D. P. King and J. R. Risser, *Phys. Rev.*, **55**, 1110 (1939).
[42] N. D. Kurie, *Jour. App. Phys.*, **9**, 691 (1938).
[43] E. O. Lawrence and Others, *Phys. Rev.*, **56**, 124 (1939).
[44] P. G. Kruger and G. K. Green, *Phys. Rev.*, **51**, 699 (1937).
[45] W. D. Harkins and Others, *Phys. Rev.*, **55**, 1110 (1939).
[46] M. S. Livingston, J. H. Buck and R. D. Evans, *Phys. Rev.*, **55**, 1110 (1939).
[47] *Science Suppl.*, **87**, 8 (1938).
[48] W. B. Mann, *Nature*, **143**, 583 (1939).
[49] W. H. Wells, *Jour. App. Phys.*, **9**, 677 (1938).
[50] M. Pauthenier, *Soc. Franc. Elect., Bull.*, **8**, 687 (1938).

cyclotrons at California. The first of these[35] was one having pole faces 11″ in diameter. This apparatus was capable of producing 1.2 MEV protons. It was soon superseded by a much larger apparatus having originally 27½″ diameter pole faces, and later poles of 37″ diameter. This apparatus, the general features of which are shown in Fig. 9, was very large and massive. The magnet weighed some 85 tons; there were 9 tons of copper wire used to wind the magnet. A magnetic field of approximately 15,000 oersteds was produced[36] between the poles whose faces were 3½″ apart. A vacuum tube oscillator capable of furnishing 20 kilowatts of power supplied a high frequency potential of the order of 15,000 volts to the dees. The frequency of this alternating potential was approximately $10^7$ cycles per second. With this apparatus, using the 27½″ pole faces, molecular ions of hydrogen were given[36] an energy of 3.6 MEV. Later, using the 37″ pole faces, alpha particles of 16 MEV were produced. This energy is higher than that of any of the alpha particles given off by radioactive substances. In most respects the 37″ California cyclotron is typical of numerous other installations.

But Lawrence and his coworkers did not stop there. They soon constructed a still larger instrument, one having pole faces 60″ in diameter. This unit, weighing 200 tons, is the largest in use today. The high frequency oscillator supplying voltage to the dees delivers 60 kilowatts. With this apparatus Lawrence has produced[43] 8 MEV protons, 16 MEV deuterons, and 38 MEV alpha particles. A 25 microampere current of 8 MEV protons is available at the edge of the dees; 100 microamperes circulates within the dees. Those using this 60″ instrument foresee no difficulty in adjusting it so as to produce 25 MEV deuterons and 50 MEV alpha particles. Lawrence has already started construction of a still much larger cyclotron.[51] The magnet of this instrument will have pole faces 184″ in diameter. This is three times the diameter of the poles of the largest cyclotron now in use. It is planned that this new instrument will produce deuterons of 100 MEV energy.

On numerous occasions various science writers have discussed for the layman the practical significance of continued efforts to produce higher energy particles. Very large amounts of energy are liberated when certain atoms are caused to disintegrate. For example, some 175 MEV of energy are released in the splitting of one uranium atom. On this basis one can readily calculate that if one pound of uranium could be caused to disintegrate it would furnish as much energy as 800 tons of fuel oil. Scientists are still far from practical utilization of energy in this form, but the possibility appears less remote now than it did only a few years ago. Studies of disintegrations produced by extremely high energy particles may give just

[51] T. H. Osgood, *Jour. App. Phys.*, **13**, 15 (1942); see also, *Jour. App. Phys.*, **11**, 339 (1940).

the information needed to utilize this vast store of energy. These high energy particles are already being used in the preparation of many artificial radioactive substances, and some of these substances may prove even more effective in medical treatment than are the natural radioactive materials. Some of these artificial radioactive atoms are already proving valuable[52] as tracers in biological investigations. The high energy particles may themselves, or through the neutrons produced by them, have useful effects on malignant tissue.

It is always a positive ion that is given a high energy in the cyclotron; it is never the electron. As has already been shown, the resonance conditions necessary to have the charged particle arrive at the gap between dees always at just the right instant to cause it to be further accelerated by the alternating potential across this gap, are very simple when no account is taken of the change of mass of the particle with velocity. But the velocities of these high energy particles are sufficiently near that of light that this change of mass is far from negligible. A 5 MEV electron has a velocity approximately 0.996 that of light, while a 5 MEV proton has a velocity only 0.1 that of light. Calculation will show that the mass of an electron of this energy is increased over its rest value by a factor of approximately 11, whereas the mass of a proton of the same energy is increased by only ½%. It is therefore clear that approximate resonance conditions can be maintained at a far higher energy for the proton or other heavy ion than for the electron.

Kerst[52a] has recently developed a method suitable for giving electrons very high energies. A magnetic field between two peculiarly shaped pole faces serves to guide the electron repeatedly around an orbit in this field. As the electron moves in this orbit the magnetic flux through the orbit is changed rapidly, power to produce this changing flux being supplied by a 600 cycle alternator. The rapidly changing flux through the orbit induces in the orbit a high e.m.f. Thus the electron is accelerated. The apparatus is referred to as an "induction accelerator." The change of mass of the electron with velocity does not disturb the operation of this accelerator. As a consequence, very high energies can be given the electron. With the first apparatus built Kerst succeeded in producing electrons of 2.3 MEV energy. He has recently constructed a much larger apparatus. With this he has produced[52b] electrons having an energy of 20 MEV. This energy is higher than any yet given the proton in the cyclotron. Kerst has used these high energy electrons to produce X-rays. It is probable that their greatest application will be in this field.

[52] J. Chadwick, *Proc. Roy. Inst.*, **30**, 398 (1938); *Nature*, **142**, 630 (1938).

[52a] D. W. Kerst, *Phys. Rev.*, **58**, 841 (1940); **60**, 47 (1941); D. W. Kerst and R. Serber, *Phys. Rev.*, **60**, 53 (1941).

[52b] D. W. Kerst, *Phys. Rev.*, **61**, 93 (1942).

In the case of the cyclotron the difficulties introduced by even the relatively small change of mass of the heavy positive ion are serious. This change of mass, together with small inhomogeneities in the magnetic field, such as a slight falling off near the edge of the pole face, affects both the focusing[53–56] of the ion beam and the resonance conditions[53,54,57] necessary to produce extremely high energy particles. Both the focusing and the resonance conditions are extremely critical; they are affected seriously by changes of a small fraction of one percent in either mass or magnetic field. In order to establish resonance conditions it has been found necessary to place shims in the magnetic gap to cause the field to vary in the proper manner from the center of the pole face outward. Unfortunately the shimming required to produce resonance is not just that required for the best focusing.[54] As a result one is forced to strive for some medium in shimming the field, sacrificing some intensity of ion beam through lack of focusing to gain higher energy through resonance, or sacrificing higher energy in favor of the larger ion current obtained by careful focusing.

Because of the impossibility of shimming properly for both focusing and resonance at the same time, practical limitations are set on the highest energy obtainable with the cyclotron for a given alternating potential applied to the dees. These highest practical energies have been calculated[54] to be, for 50 kv. on the dees, approximately 15 MEV for protons, 21 MEV for deuterons, and 42 MEV for alpha particles. Another calculation,[57] assuming 100 kv. on the dees, leads to practical upper energy limits of approximately 22 MEV for protons, 31 MEV for deuterons, and 62 MEV for alpha particles. Only through an unreasonable further sacrifice in intensity can the upper energy limit be increased appreciably for a given potential on the dees. It is true that a higher alternating potential applied to the dees will lead to a higher particle energy, but the increase is not as rapid as one would like. Calculation shows that the particle energy increases only as the square root of this potential. Although the particle gains energy proportional to the dee potential each time it crosses the gap, the higher energy particle describes fewer turns of the irregular spiral before reaching the edge of the dee. These two effects combine to give a particle energy proportional to the square root of the dee potential.

### The Van de Graaff Machine

Another entirely practical and widely used apparatus for the production of high energy particles is that known as the Van de Graaff machine. Unlike

[53] H. A. Bethe and M. E. Rose, *Phys. Rev.*, **52,** 1254 (1937).

[54] M. E. Rose, *Phys. Rev.*, **53,** 392, 715 (1938).

[55] R. R. Wilson, *Phys. Rev.*, **53,** 408 (1938).

[56] L. H. Thomas, *Phys. Rev.*, **54,** 580 (1938).

[57] J. Khurgin, *Comptes Rendus* (Doklady) *de l'Acad. des Sciences*, U.R.S.S., **19,** 237 (1938).

the cyclotron, this apparatus does not utilize the repeated acceleration of a charged particle through a relatively small potential difference to give the particle its final high energy. In this method the full potential is actually developed.

The principle of operation of the Van de Graaff high voltage generator[58,59] is illustrated in Fig. 10. Belt $B$, made of silk, paper, rubber or other flexible insulating material, is run at high speed over the motor driven pulleys $P$. The belt runs between two conductors $A$ and $D$, one of which ($D$) has a smooth rounded surface and the other of which ($A$) consists of a

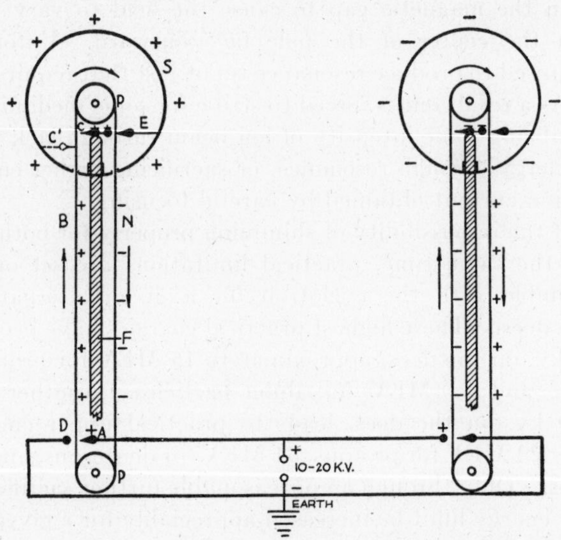


FIG. 10.—Illustrating the principle of the Van de Graaff machine.

number of needle points or of a small wire placed parallel to the belt and perpendicular to its motion. A d.c. potential difference of the order of 10 to 30 kv. is established between the conductors $A$-$D$. This potential is commonly obtained from a high voltage vacuum tube rectifier arrangement. $F$ represents an insulating column on the top of which is mounted a large hollow metal sphere $S$.

The operation of the apparatus is quite simple. The gap $A$-$D$ is adjusted to maintain a brush discharge from the point $A$. Positive charge is thus sprayed onto the belt as it moves by. The charge density which can be put onto the belt is limited only by the breakdown of the air near the belt's surface. This positive charge is carried up into the sphere $S$. In the simplest case the charge is taken off the belt by a sharp point $C'$ and transferred to the sphere. (In this simple type of instrument, points $C$ and $E$ of

[58] R. J. Van de Graaff, *Phys. Rev.*, **38**, 1919 (1931).

[59] R. J. Van de Graaff, K. T. Compton and L. C. Van Atta, *Phys. Rev.*, **43**, 149 (1933).

Fig. 10 would be omitted; likewise, there would be no negative charge $N$ on the belt leaving the sphere.) Since except for the charge on the belt all points inside the conducting sphere would be at the same potential, it follows that the positively charged belt will always be at a potential higher than that of point $C'$. Thus the charge passes readily from the belt to $C'$ regardless of how high a potential the sphere may assume. This continual transfer of positive charge onto the sphere maintains the sphere at a potential above that of the ground. By an exactly similar process, except that negative electricity is sprayed onto the belt and transferred to the sphere, another similar sphere is maintained at a potential below that of the ground. The full potential developed between spheres is, therefore, approximately twice that by which either sphere differs from the ground. The potential difference attainable is limited only by the corona breakdown in the air at the surface of the sphere. This depends of course on the radius of the sphere and the smoothness of the surface. It depends also upon the pressure of the surrounding air, and upon the moisture content of this air.

The current which can be drawn from the apparatus is determined by the rate at which the belt transfers charge to the sphere. This can be increased by using wide belts or multiple belts, and by running them at high speed. It can also be increased by arranging the apparatus so that the same belt which carries one sign of charge onto the sphere will carry a charge of opposite sign away. Omitting $C'$ and inserting $C$ and $E$ of Fig. 10 allows this to be done. The positive charge carried into the sphere is taken off by the point of collector $C$; this collector assumes a high positive potential. The other end of the collector, which end is relatively large and smooth, is placed near that part of the belt just ready to leave the sphere. This draws from point $E$, and thus from the sphere, a spray of negative charge. Thus, in this modification of the apparatus, the belt conveys positive charge to the sphere and carries negative charge away. The capacity of the apparatus to furnish current is greatly increased.

There exist a number of laboratory installations[49,58–67a] of this general type of high voltage generator. Details of the various installations vary

[60] R. G. Herb, D. B. Parkinson and D. W. Kerst, *Rev. Sci. Instr.*, **6**, 261 (1935); *Phys. Rev.*, **51**, 75 (1937).

[61] M. A. Tuve, L. R. Hafstad and O. Dahl, *Phys. Rev.*, **48**, 315 (1935).

[62] L. C. Van Atta, D. L. Northrup, C. M. Van Atta and R. J. Van de Graaff, *Phys. Rev.*, **49**, 761 (1936).

[63] W. H. Bennett, *Rev. Sci. Instr.*, **7**, 53 (1936).

[64] J. G. Trump, F. H. Merrill and F. J. Safford, *Rev. Sci. Instr.*, **9**, 398 (1938).

[65] D. B. Parkinson, R. G. Herb, E. J. Bernet and J. L. McKibben, *Phys. Rev.*, **53**, 642 (1938).

[66] W. H. Wells, R. O. Haxby, W. E. Stephens and W. E. Shoupp, *Phys. Rev.*, **58**, 162 (1940).

[67] R. G. Herb, C. M. Turner, C. M. Hudson and R. E. Warren, *Phys. Rev.*, **58**, 579 (1940).

[67a] T. Lauritsen, C. C. Lauritsen and W. A. Fowler, *Phys. Rev.*, **59**, 241 (1941).

considerably. In all cases the apparatus is very large, requiring laboratory space which is usually not available except by special construction. The insulating columns $F$ must be long and sturdy. The two metal spheres must be very large in order that the surface curvature shall be sufficiently small to prevent a corona discharge at the potential desired. One of the earliest installations[59] used spheres 2′ in diameter mounted on upright Pyrex insulators 7′ long. Using a 2.2″ silk belt run at a linear speed of 3,500 feet per minute, and using a 10 kv. supply for spraying the belt, this apparatus developed a potential difference of 1.5 million volts between spheres and furnished a current of 25 microamperes.

More modern installations are much larger. In one of the largest of these,[62] at Massachusetts Institute of Technology, the hollow spheres are 15′ in diameter and are made of aluminum alloy ¼″ thick. The insulating columns are cylinders of Textolite 22′ long, 6′ in diameter, and ⅝″ wall thickness. The belts are made of insulating paper, are 47″ wide, and run inside the Textolite cylinders. This generator has actually produced a potential difference of 5.1 Mv. between spheres, one sphere operating 2.4 Mv. above ground potential and the other 2.7 Mv. below ground. The voltage fluctuation is less than 0.1% over reasonable time intervals. Operating at this potential the apparatus will furnish a current of 1.1 milliamperes. Thus the generator will develop 5.6 kilowatts power at a potential of 5.1 million volts. Although it was originally planned to utilize the entire potential difference between the two spheres to accelerate positive ions, practical difficulties have led to the elimination of one of the spheres. It is desirable to have certain parts of the associated apparatus at ground potential, and the use of but one large electrode allows one to do so. Another large installation,[61] utilizing only one large electrode and differing considerably in many details of construction, is that of the Department of Terrestrial Magnetism of the Carnegie Institution. One of the most recent installations[66] is that at the Westinghouse Research Laboratory. This apparatus has developed 3.7 Mv., from its one metal electrode to ground, constant to 0.5% for times of several minutes and to 0.2% for one-half minute intervals. Another recent installation[67] at the University of Wisconsin, one incorporating a number of unusual features, is capable of developing a potential of 4.5 Mv.

Since the potential attained by the Van de Graaff machine is limited by the corona breakdown of the surrounding air, the maximum potential developed might be increased by operating the machine either in high vacuum or under a pressure much greater than atmospheric. Operation in vacuum presents a number of grave difficulties. On the other hand, operation under high pressure has been found entirely practical. By enclosing the entire apparatus[60,65–67a] in a steel tank in which an air pressure of from

75 to 100 pounds per square inch is maintained, it has been found possible to increase considerably the potential developed. It has also been found[65,68–70] that the addition of $CCl_4$, Freon or other similar vapor to the air increases the breakdown voltage. Herb and his associates[60,65,67] at Wisconsin have obtained remarkable results with a generator operating under pressure and in an atmosphere containing Freon. Their new generator[67] operating under an air pressure of 100 lbs./in.$^2$ develops 3.5 Mv. When Freon is added to the air this same generator develops 4.5 Mv. This is the highest potential yet attained for actual application across an accelerating tube. As yet the current at this high potential is limited to approximately 5 microamperes, but it will no doubt be made larger in the future. Generators operating under pressure and in an atmosphere of Freon have the distinct advantage of being much smaller and more compact than those operating at atmospheric pressure.

### Accelerating Tubes

Whereas in the cyclotron high energy particles are produced without the actual production of a high potential difference, in the Van de Graaff machine a high potential difference is developed directly and one has then to accelerate ions by means of this. The construction of an accelerating tube[60,61,65,66,71] across which this potential can be applied is a real problem in itself. The accelerating tube, including a source of ions at one end and the target to be bombarded at the other, must have sufficient length to prevent spark-over along the outside of the tube. The potential gradient along an ordinary insulating tube, regardless of how large or how long, is sufficiently nonuniform that the tube will almost certainly break down somewhere when a potential of a few million volts is applied across it. Furthermore, a single tube sufficiently long for the purpose would be both costly and difficult to handle. For these reasons, and it is mainly to secure a more nearly uniform potential gradient along the tube, modern accelerating tubes are built in sections. The insulator sections are usually of glass or porcelain, perhaps 10″ in diameter. The entire accelerating tube may be 15 or 20 feet long.

The general construction of the accelerating tube is illustrated in Fig. 11. Positive ions obtained from the gas in an arc or other electrical discharge at $S$ are focused into a narrow beam by one or more focusing cylinders $F$. They then proceed into the main accelerating tube. Between adjacent glass sections there is mounted a metal tube $T$ with rounded ends. From

[68] F. Joliot, M. Feldenkrais and A. Lazard, *Comptes Rendus*, **202**, 291 (1936).
[69] M. T. Rodine and R. G. Herb, *Phys. Rev.*, **51**, 508 (1937).
[70] C. M. Hudson, L. E. Hoisington and L. E. Royt, *Phys. Rev.*, **52**, 664 (1937).
[71] L. C. Van Atta, R. J. Van de Graaff and H. A. Barton, *Phys. Rev.*, **43**, 158 (1933).

the center of this tube a metal disk *D* passes out between the ends of the glass sections which are held firmly together. Gaskets or wax at these joints prevent leakage of air into the evacuated tube. To the outside rim of this projecting metal disk there is fastened a corona ring. Points on the corona rings, or adjustable gaps between the rings and a grounded conductor, are often used to maintain the desired corona discharge from each ring. With proper distribution of the corona leakage it is possible to maintain a more or less uniform potential gradient along the entire tube.

The details of construction vary greatly among the accelerating tubes that have been built. One early tube[71] consisted of a single cylindrical section of fiber, Textolite, 53 cm. long and 7″ in diameter. More or less uniform potential distribution was obtained by use of an artificial leak consisting of an India ink line drawn helically around the cylinder from one

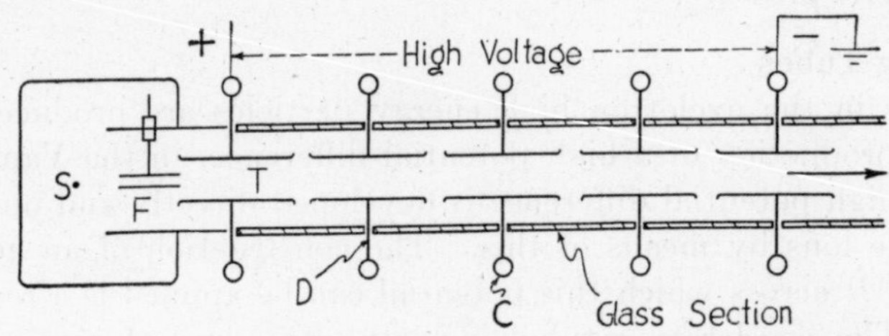


FIG. 11.—Illustrating the construction of an accelerating tube.

end to the other. This tube supported a potential difference of 300 kv. More recent tubes, designed to stand much higher potentials, have been far larger and more complex in structure. One such tube[61] consisted of 3 lead glass sections, two 64″ long and one 32″ long. This tube was 8″ in diameter and approximately 13′ long. A tube of this type withstood 1.2 Mv. Most tubes are built of more and shorter sections. Some[60,65,66] use porcelain instead of glass. Sometimes both the inner and outer surfaces of the porcelain are corrugated deeply to increase the length of the leakage path. One tube[60,65] consisting of 53 corrugated porcelain sections each 2½″ long and between 3″ and 4″ in diameter, was found to withstand a potential of 2.5 Mv. Another recently constructed tube[66] consists of 130 porcelain sections each 2⅛″ long and 15″ in diameter. Instead of corrugations these porcelain sections have projecting flanges both inside and out. This tube, having an over-all length of approximately 23′, has had applied to it a potential difference of 3.7 MEV.

It is necessary to evacuate these accelerating tubes to a pressure of the order of $10^{-5}$ mm. of mercury or less. Because of the large volume to be evacuated, and because of some leakage at the joints between sections, fast pumps are required. Large oil diffusion pumps are used; these are backed with a good mechanical oil pump. In order to facilitate high speed pumping the tube connecting the diffusion pump to the accelerating tube is quite large, usually 3″ or 4″ in diameter.

## 3. ARTIFICIAL DISINTEGRATION

Whereas in the days of Rutherford's early success in demonstrating the artificial disintegration of materials there were available as bombarding particles only the alpha particles given off by the natural radioactive stuffs, the development of the cyclotron and the Van de Graaff machine made available to investigators other energetic heavy ions. Energetic protons, deuterons, or alpha particles can be produced directly in the cyclotron, or the particles can be given high energies by accelerating them through the potential developed by the Van de Graaff machine. Such apparatus has also led to convenient sources of neutrons, for these can be produced by bombarding certain elements with those high energy particles which are produced directly. Thus there is now a wide choice of particles to use for the bombardment, and it is not surprising that experimenters have been able to produce almost unlimited disintegrations.[72–77] We shall attempt here only to call attention to the various types of disintegrations and to point out that nearly all elements can be disintegrated, many of them in numerous ways.

### Disintegration by Proton Bombardment

The first disintegration brought about by particles produced in the laboratory was one for which the proton was used as the bombarding particle. Cockcroft and Walton,[78] in 1932, bombarded Li with protons having energies from 100 to 700 KEV and observed that alpha particles were given off. These alpha particles were first detected through the scintillations they produced on a fluorescent screen, but the results were immediately verified by electrical methods of detection[78,79] and by photographing[78,80] the tracks of the particles in a cloud chamber. Photographs of these tracks,

72 Various Authors, *Rep. on Prog. in Phys.*, **1**, 269 (1934); **2**, 74 (1935); **3**, 66 (1936); **4**, 173, 198 (1937).

73 M. L. E. Oliphant, A. R. Kempton and E. Rutherford, *Proc. Roy. Soc.*, A, **149**, 406 (1935); **150**, 241 (1935).

74 G. Hevesy and F. A. Paneth (translated by R. W. Lawson), *A Manual of Radioactivity* (2nd ed.; London: Oxford University Press, 1938), pp. 108–125.

75 N. Feather, *An Introduction to Nuclear Physics* (London: Cambridge University Press, 1936).

76 F. Rasetti, *Elements of Nuclear Physics* (New York: Prentice-Hall, 1936).

77 H. A. Bethe and Others, *Rev. Mod. Phys.*, **8**, 82 (1936); **9**, 69, 245 (1937).

78 J. D. Cockcroft and E. T. S. Walton, *Proc. Roy. Soc.*, A, **137**, 229 (1932); *Nature*, **131**, 32 (1933).

79 M. L. E. Oliphant, B. B. Kinsey and E. Rutherford, *Proc. Roy. Soc.*, A, **141**, 722 (1933).

80 P. I. Dee and E. T. S. Walton, *Proc. Roy. Soc.*, A, **141**, 733 (1933).

one of which is reproduced[80] in Fig. 12, show that two alpha particles leave the point of disintegration and that these proceed with equal energies in almost opposite directions. The particles resulting from two distinct disintegrations are shown in the photograph, the two pairs of alpha particle tracks being $c_1$-$c_2$ and $d_1$-$d_2$. The range of each of these particles is approximately 8.3 cm., corresponding to an energy of approximately 8.6 MEV. Thus the products of disintegration have a combined energy of over 17 MEV even though the bombarding proton used to produce the disintegration possesses an energy of perhaps only 0.3 MEV. Thus again, just as in Rutherford's early work, the bombarding particle serves merely as a trigger

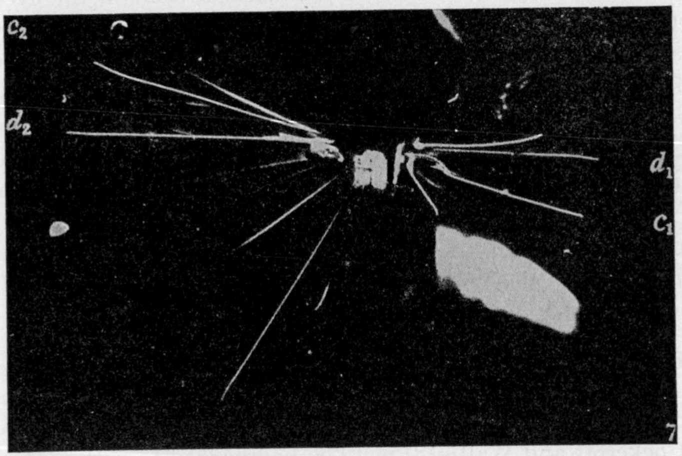


FIG. 12.—Showing the paired alpha particle tracks resulting from the disintegration of Li by proton bombardment.

to set off the nuclear explosion; the greater part of the energy of the products of disintegration comes from the disintegration itself.

Accurate measurements have been made of the energy released during the disintegration of $Li^7$ when bombarded with protons. One measurement[73,77] yielded a value 17.13 ± 0.06 MEV; another[81] gave 17.28 ± 0.03 MEV. The products of disintegration possess this much more kinetic energy than do the original particles. It has already been shown in Chapter 5 that this energy agrees closely with the value 17.25 MEV which one might expect if the loss of mass accompanying the disintegration is converted into energy. The laws of conservation of momentum and conservation of energy hold for each individual disintegration. Since two particles of equal mass are shot off in the case under discussion, these laws would necessitate that they be shot off in almost opposite directions, not quite opposite because of the forward momentum given them by the incident proton. Energy

[81] N. M. Smith, *Phys. Rev.*, **56**, 548 (1939).

calculations show that energy is always conserved in disintegration processes,[72] provided of course that mass is included as a form of energy.

In discussing nuclear disintegrations one finds it convenient to have some concise method of writing just what goes on. For the disintegration just discussed one writes

$${}_3Li^7 + {}_1H^1 \rightarrow {}_2He^4 + {}_2He^4$$

indicating that a Li atom of atomic number 3 and atomic weight 7 was bombarded with a proton of atomic number 1 and atomic weight 1, and that the products of the reaction were 2 alpha particles, each of atomic number 2 and atomic weight 4. The Li nucleus apparently absorbed the proton and was caused to split into two alpha particles. It was observed originally that protons with energy as little as 100 KEV were able to cause this disruption of the Li nucleus. Disintegrations have since been produced with proton energies as low as 20 KEV. In general the number of disintegrations produced per given number of bombarding protons increases rapidly as the energy of the proton is increased. In any case the yield is small. For protons of moderate energy bombarding Li it is of the order of one in $10^8$; even for 1 MEV protons there is only one Li nucleus disintegrated for every few thousand bombarding particles. It is often found that particles of a particular energy are more efficient in producing disintegrations than are particles of somewhat higher energy. Particularly is this true in the lower energy ranges. There appear to be certain so-called resonance values of energy for which the particle can enter the nucleus fairly readily even though its energy be small.

Early workers[79] observed that when Li is bombarded by protons there are given out other particles with ranges far less than 8.3 cm. One group has a range between 1 and 2 cm. while another has a range of approximately 0.5 cm. These shorter range particles apparently come from the disintegration of $Li^6$ by the proton, a disintegration represented by

$${}_3Li^6 + {}_1H^1 \rightarrow {}_2He^4 + {}_2He^3$$

It was recognized[78] from the first that many materials other than Li can be disintegrated by bombardment with protons having energies as low as 150 KEV. Since then these disintegrations have been verified and many others have been found. A few of the other disintegrations produced by proton bombardment are:

$${}_3Li^7 + {}_1H^1 \rightarrow {}_4Be^8 + h\nu$$
$${}_4Be^9 + {}_1H^1 \rightarrow {}_3Li^6 + {}_2He^4$$
$${}_4Be^9 + {}_1H^1 \rightarrow {}_4Be^8 + {}_1H^2$$
$${}_5B^{11} + {}_1H^1 \rightarrow {}_2He^4 + {}_2He^4 + {}_2He^4$$
$${}_{20}Ca^{44} + {}_1H^1 \rightarrow {}_{21}Sc^{44} + {}_0n^1$$

In each one of these reactions the energy released by the disintegration is just that which might be accounted for by the loss of mass suffered by the original particles in being transformed into the final particles. That this is the case is evident from Table IV which appears later.

**Disintegration by Deuteron Bombardment**

It was only a short while after it had been demonstrated that nuclear disintegration can be produced by proton bombardment that investigators[79,80,82] found that similar disintegrations could be produced by bombardment with deuterons. Since that time a large number of disintegrations by deuteron bombardment have been studied. The first reaction observed was again that of the Li nucleus, a disintegration represented by

$$_3Li^6 + {_1H^2} \rightarrow {_2He^4} + {_2He^4}$$

The ranges of the alpha particles ejected during this transformation have been studied both electrically[79] and photographically.[80] Each of the two particles has a mean range of 12.5 cm. The nuclear energy released in the disintegration process is unusually high, one observer[73,77] giving 22.07 ± 0.07 MEV and another[81] 22.20 ± 0.04. Again the observed energy released agrees closely with that expected on the supposition that the loss of mass suffered by the reacting particles is converted into kinetic energy. It is the many observations of this character that provide the unquestionable evidence that mass is simply another form of energy.

Just as in the case of proton bombardment, disintegrations produced by deuterons do not always yield alpha particles. Some disintegrations give off protons, some alpha particles and some neutrons. Gamma ray photons are often given off during the nuclear transformation. Many times the new nucleus formed in the process is stable, and it continues to exist as such. In many other cases, however, the newly formed nucleus is radioactive; it proceeds to disintegrate just as does any one of the natural radioactive materials. The disintegration follows the same laws of chance as are followed by the natural radioactive substances. One refers to these newly formed radioactive materials as being artificially radioactive. There is really nothing artificial about their radioactivity; they are artificial only in the sense that the material itself has been manufactured in the laboratory. In disintegrating, a majority of the artificial radioactive substances emit either an electron or a positron, though a number of them do disintegrate by some other process. We shall defer for the moment any further consideration of artificial radioactivity itself, contenting ourselves with consideration of the artificially produced disintegrations which give rise to the new material, sometimes stable and sometimes radioactive.

[82] G. N. Lewis, M. S. Livingston and E. O. Lawrence, *Phys. Rev.*, **44**, 55 (1933).

Returning again to the disintegration of Li by deuterons, attention might be called to the fact that disintegration has been observed to occur in three ways other than that already indicated. These are:

$$_3Li^6 + {}_1H^2 \rightarrow {}_3Li^7 + {}_1H^1$$
$$_3Li^7 + {}_1H^2 \rightarrow {}_2He^4 + {}_2He^4 + {}_0n^1$$
$$_3Li^7 + {}_1H^2 \rightarrow {}_3Li^8 + {}_1H^1$$
$$_3Li^8 \rightarrow {}_4Be^8 + \beta^- \qquad T = 0.88 \text{ sec.}$$

In the last case the newly formed Li of atomic weight 8 is radioactive; it proceeds to disintegrate by ejecting an electron, the half life period being 0.88 seconds.

An interesting case is that in which deuterons are used to bombard heavy hydrogen. The heavy hydrogen target usually consists of heavy water frozen on a surface cooled by liquid air, or of some other solid compound containing heavy hydrogen. The two disintegrations resulting[83] from the bombardment of heavy hydrogen with deuterons are:

$$_1H^2 + {}_1H^2 \rightarrow {}_2He^3 + {}_0n^1$$
$$_1H^2 + {}_1H^2 \rightarrow {}_1H^3 + {}_1H^1$$

The product $_2He^3$ formed in the first reaction is a rare but stable isotope of of helium. The second transformation is particularly interesting since all of the particles involved are isotopes of hydrogen. It has been shown recently[84] that the hydrogen isotope of atomic weight 3 is radioactive; it ejects electrons and has a half life period[85] of $(31 \pm 8)$ years.

A few of the many other disintegrations which have been produced by deuteron bombardment are:

$$_5B^{10} + {}_1H^2 \rightarrow {}_2He^4 + {}_2He^4 + {}_2He^4$$
$$_6C^{12} + {}_1H^2 \rightarrow {}_6C^{13} + {}_1H^1$$
$$_6C^{12} + {}_1H^2 \rightarrow {}_7N^{13} + {}_0n^1$$
$$_7N^{13} \rightarrow {}_6C^{13} + \beta^+ \qquad T = 9.93 \text{ min.}$$
$$_{11}Na^{23} + {}_1H^2 \rightarrow {}_{12}Mg^{24} + {}_0n^1$$
$$_{11}Na^{23} + {}_1H^2 \rightarrow {}_{11}Na^{24} + {}_1H^1$$
$$_{11}Na^{24} \rightarrow {}_{12}Mg^{24} + \beta^- \qquad T = 14.8 \text{ hr.}$$
$$_{13}Al^{27} + {}_1H^2 \rightarrow {}_{12}Mg^{25} + {}_2He^4$$
$$_{20}Ca^{40} + {}_1H^2 \rightarrow {}_{19}K^{38} + {}_2He^4$$
$$_{19}K^{38} \rightarrow {}_{18}A^{38} + \beta^+ \qquad T = 7.7 \text{ min.}$$
$$_{78}Pt^{196} + {}_1H^2 \rightarrow {}_{78}Pt^{197} + {}_1H^1$$
$$_{78}Pt^{197} \rightarrow {}_{79}Au^{197} + \beta^- \qquad T = 18 \text{ hr.}$$

[83] M. L. E. Oliphant, P. Harteck and E. Rutherford, *Proc. Roy. Soc.*, A, **144**, 692 (1934).
[84] L. W. Alvarez and R. Cornog, *Phys. Rev.*, **56**, 613 (1939); **58**, 197 (1940).
[85] R. D. O'Neal and M. Goldhaber, *Phys. Rev.*, **58**, 574 (1940).

The last transformation is interesting in two respects. First, although in general it is the elements of low atomic number which are most easily disintegrated by deuteron or other charged particle bombardment, it is nevertheless possible for these particles to cause disruption of some heavy nuclei. In general nuclei of high atomic number, and hence of high net positive nuclear charge, require that a charged particle have a very great energy before it can enter the nucleus. This is due to the large electrical repulsion. By using deuterons of 5 MEV it has been shown,[86] however, that heavy elements such as Pt can be disintegrated by charged particle bombardment. As already mentioned in connection with disintegration by protons, there appear to exist certain resonance energies, sometimes rather low, for which the bombarding particle is able to penetrate the nucleus. It is probably only because of this resonance phenomenon that elements of high atomic number can be disintegrated by charged particle bombardment.

The disintegration of Pt indicated above is interesting for a second reason. Here is a disruption of one of the noble metals. It is true that the disintegration proper results in another isotope of Pt, but this isotope is radioactive and proceeds to turn into Au. Here then is a transformation of one noble metal into another. The process would scarcely be profitable financially, for the platinum used is more costly than the gold obtained. Sherr and Bainbridge[87] have reported recently that both gold and platinum have been made from mercury by bombarding the mercury with neutrons. The small amounts of gold and platinum formed were detected through their radioactive properties. As far as is known no stable forms of these noble metals were produced, though the method of detection did not permit of finding these. In any case the total amount of gold and platinum formed was extremely small. The process of turning mercury into these metals would be far from profitable financially.

### Disintegration by Alpha Particle Bombardment

It was by means of alpha particles that Rutherford and his coworkers first produced disintegration of many of the normally stable elements. Within the past ten years investigators have not only verified many of Rutherford's original findings, but have also produced numerous other disintegrations by alpha particle bombardment. These additional transformations have been brought to light in part because of the most intense work in recent years and in part because there is now available, thanks to the cyclotron, a laboratory supply of alpha particles far more energetic

[86] J. M. Cork and E. O. Lawrence, *Phys. Rev.*, **49**, 205, 788 (1936).

[87] R. Sherr and K. T. Bainbridge, *Phys. Rev.*, **59**, 937 (1941); R. Sherr, K. T. Bainbridge and H. H. Anderson, *Phys. Rev.*, **60**, 473 (1941).

than those given off by any of the radioactive materials. Rutherford and his coworkers knew only that an energetic proton was given off during these disintegrations; and they had only a rough measure of the energy of this particle. In contrast with this it is now known that alpha particle bombardment can produce disintegrations resulting in either proton or neutron ejection; and quite accurate measurements have been made of the energies released by the disintegrations.

A few of the disintegrations now known to be produced by alpha particle bombardment are as follows:

$$
\begin{array}{lll}
{}_3\mathrm{Li}^7 + {}_2\mathrm{He}^4 \rightarrow {}_5\mathrm{B}^{10} + {}_0n^1 & & \\
{}_4\mathrm{Be}^9 + {}_2\mathrm{He}^4 \rightarrow {}_6\mathrm{C}^{12} + {}_0n^1 & & \\
{}_5\mathrm{B}^{10} + {}_2\mathrm{He}^4 \rightarrow {}_7\mathrm{N}^{13} + {}_0n^1 & & \\
\qquad {}_7\mathrm{N}^{13} \rightarrow {}_6\mathrm{C}^{13} + \beta^+ & & T = 9.95 \text{ min.} \\
{}_6\mathrm{C}^{12} + {}_2\mathrm{He}^4 \rightarrow {}_8\mathrm{O}^{15} + {}_0n^1 & & \\
\qquad {}_8\mathrm{O}^{15} \rightarrow {}_7\mathrm{N}^{15} + \beta^+ & & T = 126 \text{ sec.} \\
{}_7\mathrm{N}^{14} + {}_2\mathrm{He}^4 \rightarrow {}_8\mathrm{O}^{17} + {}_1\mathrm{H}^1 & & \\
{}_7\mathrm{N}^{14} + {}_2\mathrm{He}^4 \rightarrow {}_9\mathrm{F}^{17} + {}_0n^1 & & \\
\qquad {}_9\mathrm{F}^{17} \rightarrow {}_8\mathrm{O}^{17} + \beta^+ & & T = 70 \text{ sec.} \\
{}_{10}\mathrm{Ne}^{22} + {}_2\mathrm{He}^4 \rightarrow {}_{12}\mathrm{Mg}^{25} + {}_0n^1 & & \\
{}_{11}\mathrm{Na}^{23} + {}_2\mathrm{He}^4 \rightarrow {}_{12}\mathrm{Mg}^{26} + {}_1\mathrm{H}^1 & & \\
{}_{11}\mathrm{Na}^{23} + {}_2\mathrm{He}^4 \rightarrow {}_{13}\mathrm{Al}^{26} + {}_0n^1 & & \\
\qquad {}_{13}\mathrm{Al}^{26} \rightarrow {}_{12}\mathrm{Mg}^{26} + \beta^+ & & T = 7.0 \text{ sec.} \\
{}_{13}\mathrm{Al}^{27} + {}_2\mathrm{He}^4 \rightarrow {}_{14}\mathrm{Si}^{30} + {}_1\mathrm{H}^1 & & \\
{}_{13}\mathrm{Al}^{27} + {}_2\mathrm{He}^4 \rightarrow {}_{15}\mathrm{P}^{30} + {}_0n^1 & & \\
\qquad {}_{15}\mathrm{P}^{30} \rightarrow {}_{14}\mathrm{Si}^{30} + \beta^+ & & T = 2.55 \text{ min.} \\
{}_{24}\mathrm{Cr}^{50} + {}_2\mathrm{He}^4 \rightarrow {}_{26}\mathrm{Fe}^{53} + {}_0n^1 & & \\
\qquad {}_{26}\mathrm{Fe}^{53} \rightarrow {}_{25}\mathrm{Mn}^{53} + \beta^+ & & T = 8.9 \text{ min.} \\
{}_{46}\mathrm{Pd}^{108} + {}_2\mathrm{He}^4 \rightarrow {}_{47}\mathrm{Ag}^{111} + {}_1\mathrm{H}^1 & & \\
\qquad {}_{47}\mathrm{Ag}^{111} \rightarrow {}_{48}\mathrm{Cd}^{111} + \beta^- & & T = 7.5 \text{ da.}
\end{array}
$$

The fifth transformation shown in this group is of interest because it is no doubt the one originally observed by Rutherford. Protons were ejected from nitrogen bombarded with alpha particles. Although it seemed quite certain that these protons were actually ejected from the nitrogen nuclei, one could at first only speculate as to what became of the incident alpha particle and as to the nature of the newly formed nucleus resulting from the disruption of the nitrogen. Cloud chamber photographs by Blackett,[16,17] one of which is reproduced in Fig. 5, showed clearly that only two ionizing particles left the point of collision between the alpha particle and the N nucleus. One of these was clearly the ejected proton. The other was without question the recoiling disrupted nucleus. There was no third track representing the alpha particle leaving the scene of the collision. This particle most certainly was absorbed by the N nucleus in the disintegration process. If this be the case the original N nucleus of atomic number 7 and atomic weight 14 became, after gaining an alpha particle and losing a proton, an O nucleus of mass 17. That is, the disintegration must have been in accord with

$${}_7N^{14} + {}_2He^4 \rightarrow {}_8O^{17} + {}_1H^1$$

It was then shown by Blackett[16] that, assuming the laws of conservation of momentum and of energy, one can calculate the mass of the recoiling nucleus from the angles at which the particles leave the point of collision. This mass was calculated[16] to be $16.72 \pm 0.42$, a value entirely consistent with the formation of the $O^{17}$ nucleus. Further work[17,88] of the same character left little doubt of the correctness of this view.

Experiment shows that in the reaction written last above, energy is absorbed by the disintegration. That is, the sum of the kinetic energies of the proton and the recoiling oxygen nucleus is less than the kinetic energy of the incident alpha particle. Measurements of these energies show an absorption[77] of 1.16 MEV. The energy of the reaction is said to be $-1.16$ MEV, the negative sign indicating that energy is absorbed rather than freed. Absorption of energy occurs only in those reactions for which the sum of the masses of the final particles is greater than the sum of the masses of the original particles. In the reaction being discussed the sum of the original masses is 18.01139, while that of the final products is 18.01263. There is an increase in mass of 0.00124 atomic mass units. Since 1.000 atomic mass unit is equivalent to 931 MEV, this increase in mass represents an energy of 1.155 MEV. This is just the loss of kinetic energy observed. It is true that the mass of $O^{17}$ has not been measured with the mass spectrograph; the mass used in this calculation was obtained from nuclear disintegration studies. However, the mass of $O^{17}$ has been obtained accurately from a nuclear reaction other than the one being considered here. Its use in this calculation is therefore justified.

The capture of the bombarding particle seems to be the first step in all disintegrations produced by particle bombardment. The second step is the ejection of some other particle or particles. In the case of alpha particle bombardment the alpha particle is captured. Either a proton or a neutron is then ejected. Even though the same particle is used to bombard a particular material the nature of the ejected particle is not always the same, as is evident from the following transformations for Na:

$${}_{11}Na^{23} + {}_2He^4 \rightarrow {}_{12}Mg^{26} + {}_1H^1$$
$${}_{11}Na^{23} + {}_2He^4 \rightarrow {}_{13}Al^{26} + {}_0n^1$$

[88] P. M. S. Blackett and D. S. Lees, *Proc. Roy. Soc.*, A, **134**, 658 (1932).

Thus either Mg or Al may result from the bombardment of $Na^{23}$ with alpha particles. It is true that the $Al^{26}$ produced is radioactive and proceeds to eject positrons and become Mg. One might wonder why bombardment with alpha particles does not result sometimes in the ejection of a deuteron, or in the simultaneous ejection of a proton and a neutron. Calculation of the mass changes that would be involved shows that reactions of these types would in general absorb a great deal of energy, often of the order of 10 MEV. One could therefore not hope to produce such reactions without very energetic particles, and even then their production is improbable. Sherr[89] has recently obtained some evidence for a reaction of one or the other of these types when sulphur is bombarded with 22 MEV alpha particles.

In general it is quite difficult to disrupt heavy nuclei by alpha particle bombardment, due no doubt to the difficulty the doubly charged alpha particle has in entering a nucleus of high net positive charge. But just as for protons and for deuterons, except perhaps more noticeable still, there exist certain resonance energies for which alpha particles of only moderate energy can enter these nuclei. These resonance energy bands are fairly narrow, roughly[90] 0.25 MEV wide for Al. If the particle energy differs by more than half of this from the resonance value, it has an exceedingly small chance of entering the nucleus unless it has an energy in excess of some critical value characteristic of the material. These resonance energies are much more in evidence for some nuclei than for others. Their existence and their values are connected, at least theoretically, with the existence of empty energy levels inside the nucleus.

### Disintegration by Neutron Bombardment

With the discovery of the neutron in 1932 there was made available another particle which has since been found unusually effective in producing disintegrations. This particle is capable of penetrating rather readily the nuclei of even the heavy, highly charged atoms, no doubt because the particle itself bears no electrical charge. The forces which arise to prevent the particle from entering a nucleus are so small in the case of a neutron that even very low energy neutrons have been found extremely effective in producing disintegrations.

Of all the particles available for bombardment, many more disintegrations have been produced with neutrons than with any other. The reaction may give rise to any one of a number of particles, a proton, an alpha particle, more than one neutron, or a photon; in one case a deuteron is formed. A few typical reactions produced by neutron bombardment are the following:

[89] R. Sherr, *Phys. Rev.*, **57**, 937 (1940).

[90] J. Chadwick and J. E. R. Constable, *Proc. Roy. Soc.*, A, **135**, 48 (1932).

$$_1H^1 + {}_0n^1 \rightarrow {}_1H^2 + h\nu \quad (1)$$

$$_3Li^6 + {}_0n^1 \rightarrow {}_1H^3 + {}_2He^4 \quad (2)$$

$$_1H^3 \rightarrow {}_2He^3 + \beta^- \qquad T = 31 \text{ yr.}$$

$$_4Be^9 + {}_0n^1 \rightarrow {}_2He^6 + {}_2He^4 \quad (3)$$

$$_2He^6 \rightarrow {}_3Li^6 + \beta^- \qquad T = 0.8 \text{ sec.}$$

$$_5B^{10} + {}_0n^1 \rightarrow {}_3Li^7 + {}_2He^4 \quad (4)$$

$$_{11}Na^{23} + {}_0n^1 \rightarrow {}_9F^{20} + {}_2He^4 \quad (5)$$

$$_9F^{20} \rightarrow {}_{10}Ne^{20} + \beta^- \qquad T = 12 \text{ sec.}$$

$$_{12}Mg^{24} + {}_0n^1 \rightarrow {}_{11}Na^{24} + {}_1H^1 \quad (6)$$

$$_{11}Na^{24} \rightarrow {}_{12}Mg^{24} + \beta^- \qquad T = 14.8 \text{ hr.}$$

$$_{13}Al^{27} + {}_0n^1 \rightarrow {}_{12}Mg^{27} + {}_1H^1 \quad (7)$$

$$_{12}Mg^{27} \rightarrow {}_{13}Al^{27} + \beta^- \qquad T = 10.2 \text{ min.}$$

$$_{13}Al^{27} + {}_0n^1 \rightarrow {}_{11}Na^{24} + {}_2He^4 \quad (8)$$

$$_{11}Na^{24} \rightarrow {}_{12}Mg^{24} + \beta^- \qquad T = 14.8 \text{ hr.}$$

$$_{13}Al^{27} + {}_0n^1 \rightarrow {}_{13}Al^{28} + h\nu \quad (9)$$

$$_{13}Al^{28} \rightarrow {}_{14}Si^{28} + \beta^- \qquad T = 2.4 \text{ min.}$$

$$_{19}K^{39} + {}_0n^1 \rightarrow {}_{19}K^{38} + {}_0n^1 + {}_0n^1 \quad (10)$$

$$_{19}K^{38} \rightarrow {}_{18}A^{38} + \beta^+ \qquad T = 7.7 \text{ min.}$$

$$_{29}Cu^{63} + {}_0n^1 \rightarrow {}_{29}Cu^{62} + {}_0n^1 + {}_0n^1 \quad (11)$$

$$_{29}Cu^{62} \rightarrow {}_{28}Ni^{62} + \beta^+ \qquad T = 10.5 \text{ min.}$$

$$_{29}Cu^{65} + {}_0n^1 \rightarrow {}_{29}Cu^{66} + h\nu \quad (12)$$

$$_{29}Cu^{66} \rightarrow {}_{30}Zn^{66} + \beta^- \qquad T = 5 \text{ min.}$$

$$_{79}Au^{197} + {}_0n^1 \rightarrow {}_{79}Au^{198} + h\nu \quad (13)$$

$$_{79}Au^{198} \rightarrow {}_{80}Hg^{198} + \beta^- \qquad T = 2.7 \text{ da.}$$

These are but a few of the many disintegrations observed by neutron bombardment. Practically all elements can now be disintegrated in this way; a majority of them were disintegrated[91] only a few years after the discovery of the neutron. Some of the disintegrations produced by neutron bombardment require the use of very energetic neutrons, referred to as fast neutrons, while many others are produced even more effectively by slow neutrons. These slow neutrons are usually obtained by allowing the fast neutrons, produced by bombarding some material with energetic charged particles, to pass through some substance containing hydrogen. It has been found that neutrons having energies as low as those corresponding to thermal velocities are capable of producing numerous disintegrations.

Special interest may attach to several of the reactions listed above. The first one shown represents the conversion of ordinary hydrogen into heavy hydrogen by neutron bombardment. The second one results in the formation of $H^3$, a hydrogen isotope only recently recognized as definitely

[91] E. Amaldi, O. D'Agostino, E. Fermi, B. Pontecorvo, F. Rasetti and E. Segrè, *Proc. Roy. Soc.*, A, **149**, 522 (1935).

radioactive.[84,85] The sixth is interesting in that it is typical of a number of reactions in which the end product is identical with the original. The disintegration of $_{12}Mg^{24}$ by neutron bombardment leads to radioactive $_{11}Na^{24}$ which in turn decays by beta ray ejection, becoming again $_{12}Mg^{24}$. The tenth disintegration listed is typical of a number of reactions produced by neutron bombardment in which the one neutron is captured and two neutrons are ejected. Evidence has recently been reported[91a] that two neutrons and a proton, or three neutrons, are ejected in at least one instance. The last reaction shown is interesting in that it involves a change of gold from one isotope to another, the latter finally decaying into mercury.

Another interesting and very important aspect of disintegration by neutron bombardment is the recent discovery of nuclear fission. In all the disintegrations discussed so far the disrupted nucleus splits into two quite unequal parts. One of these is a proton, a neutron, a deutron or an alpha particle. It was shown in 1939, however, that neutron bombardment of uranium causes the uranium nucleus to split into two parts not far different in mass. This approximately equal splitting is called fission. While fission was first produced by neutron bombardment, it has since been produced by other particles. Because of the importance of the fission process, and because the process is produced also by particles other than neutrons, this type of disintegration will be discussed later in a special section devoted to it.

## Disintegration by Photon Bombardment

Many examples have been given of the disintegration of nuclei by bombardment with protons, deuterons, alpha particles, and neutrons. There is still another way in which the nuclei of a few elements can be torn apart, namely by bombardment with photons. One of these elements is heavy hydrogen. Chadwick and Goldhaber[92] discovered that when the penetrating gamma rays from ThC″, for which $h\nu = 2.62$ MEV, are allowed to fall upon the heavy isotope of H, the deuteron is split into a proton and a neutron. Thus

$$_{1}H^{2} + h\nu \rightarrow {}_{1}H^{1} + {}_{0}n^{1}$$

Irradiation with gamma rays from RaC, for which $h\nu = 2.198$ MEV, will also produce this reaction. The process is referred to as photodisintegration. It is interesting that just the reverse of this process has already been mentioned, namely

$$_{1}H^{1} + {}_{0}n^{1} \rightarrow {}_{1}H^{2} + h\nu$$

[91a] J. M. Cork and W. Middleton, *Phys. Rev.*, **58**, 474 (1940).

[92] J. Chadwick and M. Goldhaber, *Nature*, **134**, 237 (1934).

In one of these, heavy hydrogen splits into a proton and a neutron; in the other a proton and a neutron combine to form heavy hydrogen.

A calculation from the masses involved shows a loss of mass in the latter case and a gain in mass in the photodisintegration. This change of mass is 0.00233, representing an energy of 2.17 MEV. Thus 2.17 MEV of energy is released in the disintegration produced by neutron bombardment, whereas 2.17 MEV is absorbed in the photodisintegration process. One might therefore expect that the gamma rays used to produce this disintegration would have to be of a frequency sufficiently high that the photon possesses an energy of at least 2.17 MEV. This is found to be true. It has already been pointed out in Chapter 10 that the measured value of the energy absorbed[92,93] in the photodisintegration of ${}_1H^2$ is 2.17 MEV, and that use of this measured energy constitutes one of the most accurate ways of evaluating the mass of the neutron.

Another illustration of photodisintegration is that of ${}_4Be^9$. This reaction is

$${}_4Be^9 + h\nu \rightarrow {}_4Be^8 + {}_0n^1$$

Again, consideration of the masses involved shows that this reaction absorbs 1.69 MEV of energy. The incident gamma ray photon must therefore have at least this energy in order to produce the disintegration. A number of other similar cases of photodisintegration can be found in the literature.[94] In each case mass and energy are interchanged always in the same ratio as that found for disintegrations produced by particle bombardment.

### Different Ways of Producing the Same Material

It has been seen that materials can be disintegrated in a number of different ways. In general the same substance can be disintegrated to form any one of several new materials, the nature of the newly formed substance depending upon the particle used to produce the disintegration and upon the particle given off during the disintegration. As an example illustrating the several new substances that can be produced from a given original material, let us choose the case of ${}_{13}Al^{27}$, the only stable isotope of Al. This material has been made to undergo the following disintegrations:

$${}_{13}Al^{27} + {}_2He^4 \rightarrow {}_{15}P^{30} + {}_0n^1$$
$${}_{13}Al^{27} + {}_2He^4 \rightarrow {}_{14}Si^{30} + {}_1H^1$$
$${}_{13}Al^{27} + {}_1H^2 \rightarrow {}_{12}Mg^{25} + {}_2He^4$$
$${}_{13}Al^{27} + {}_1H^2 \rightarrow {}_{13}Al^{28} + {}_1H^1$$
$${}_{13}Al^{27} + {}_1H^1 \rightarrow {}_{14}Si^{27} + {}_0n^1$$

93 H. A. Bethe, *Phys. Rev.*, **53**, 313 (1938)
94 H. J. Walke, *Rep. on Prog. in Phys.*, **6**, 16 (1939).

$$_{13}Al^{27} + {_0n^1} \rightarrow {_{13}Al^{28}} + h\nu$$
$$_{13}Al^{27} + {_0n^1} \rightarrow {_{12}Mg^{27}} + {_1H^1}$$
$$_{13}Al^{27} + {_0n^1} \rightarrow {_{11}Na^{24}} + {_2He^4}$$

Seven of the eight newly formed materials are different. Thus it is possible to make $_{13}Al^{27}$ into at least seven different things. Five of these newly formed materials are radioactive while two of them, $_{12}Mg^{25}$ and $_{14}Si^{30}$, are stable. In view of the large number of different isotopes that can often be made from a given material, is there any wonder that there are known today something like 600 different nuclei?

In a similar manner it is possible to make a given substance by proper treatment of any one of a number of original materials. For example, the radioactive material $_{13}Al^{28}$ can be made in the following five ways:

$$_{12}Mg^{25} + {_2He^4} \rightarrow {_{13}Al^{28}} + {_1H^1}$$
$$_{13}Al^{27} + {_1H^2} \rightarrow {_{13}Al^{28}} + {_1H^1}$$
$$_{13}Al^{27} + {_0n^1} \rightarrow {_{13}Al^{28}} + h\nu$$
$$_{14}Si^{28} + {_0n^1} \rightarrow {_{13}Al^{28}} + {_1H^1}$$
$$_{15}P^{31} + {_0n^1} \rightarrow {_{13}Al^{28}} + {_2He^4}$$
$$_{13}Al^{28} \rightarrow {_{14}Si^{28}} + \beta^- \qquad T = 2.4 \text{ min.}$$

$_{13}Al^{28}$ results from each reaction, and it proceeds to decay to stable $_{14}Si^{28}$ by the ejection of negative beta particles, and with a half life period of 2.4 minutes, regardless of how it is made. The fact that a given radioactive material can often be made in a number of ways provides a greater possibility that a desired radioactive stuff can be produced in practical quantities and on an economical basis.

**The Mass Changes and Energies Associated with Disintegrations**

It has been emphasized repeatedly that when mass appears or disappears during a disintegration process there always disappears or appears a corresponding amount of energy in some other form. Several numerical examples have been given to illustrate this interchange between mass and energy, and to show how accurately one can calculate the conversion ratio. For a large number of reactions there are accurate data available on the energy released during the disintegration and on the masses of the atoms involved in the reaction. A number of these are shown in Table IV. A more extended table has been given by Bethe,[77] and still other examples are scattered through the literature since. Most of the observed energies of disintegration shown in Table IV have been taken from a table by Bethe,[77] though a few have been taken from more recent measurements.[81,93,95,96]

[95] T. W. Bonner, *Phys. Rev.*, **59**, 237 (1941).
[96] G. J. Perlow, *Phys. Rev.*, **58**, 218 (1940).

TABLE IV

Comparison of calculated and observed energies of disintegration

| Reaction | Decrease of mass | Energy released, MEV | |
|---|---|---|---|
| | | Calculated | Observed |
| $Li^6 + H^1 \rightarrow He^4 + He^3$ | .00412 | 3.84 | 3.95 |
| $Li^7 + H^1 \rightarrow He^4 + He^4$ | .01853 | 17.25 | 17.28 |
| $Be^9 + H^1 \rightarrow Li^6 + He^4$ | .00242 | 2.25 | 2.28 |
| $Be^9 + H^1 \rightarrow Be^8 + H^2$ | .00052 | .48 | .46 |
| $B^{11} + H^1 \rightarrow Be^8 + He^4$ | .00924 | 8.60 | 8.60 |
| $F^{19} + H^1 \rightarrow O^{16} + He^4$ | .00876 | 8.16 | 8.15 |
| $H^2 + H^2 \rightarrow H^3 + H^1$ | .00428 | 3.98 | 3.98 |
| $H^2 + H^2 \rightarrow He^3 + n^1$ | .00355 | 3.31 | 3.31 |
| $Li^6 + H^2 \rightarrow He^4 + He^4$ | .02381 | 22.17 | 22.20 |
| $Li^6 + H^2 \rightarrow Li^7 + H^1$ | .00528 | 4.92 | 5.02 |
| $Li^7 + H^2 \rightarrow Be^8 + n^1$ | .01606 | 14.95 | 14.55 |
| $Be^9 + H^2 \rightarrow Li^7 + He^4$ | .00770 | 7.17 | 7.19 |
| $Be^9 + H^2 \rightarrow Be^{10} + H^1$ | .00493 | 4.59 | 4.59 |
| $Be^9 + H^2 \rightarrow B^{10} + n^1$ | .00453 | 4.22 | 4.20 |
| $B^{10} + H^2 \rightarrow Be^8 + He^4$ | .01923 | 17.90 | 17.76 |
| $B^{10} + H^2 \rightarrow B^{11} + H^1$ | .00999 | 9.30 | 9.14 |
| $B^{10} + H^2 \rightarrow C^{11} + n^1$ | .00685 | 6.38 | 6.08 |
| $B^{11} + H^2 \rightarrow Be^9 + He^4$ | .00872 | 8.12 | 8.13 |
| $B^{11} + H^2 \rightarrow C^{12} + n^1$ | .01474 | 13.72 | 13.4 |
| $C^{12} + H^2 \rightarrow C^{13} + H^1$ | .00297 | 2.76 | 2.71 |
| $C^{13} + H^2 \rightarrow B^{11} + He^4$ | .00553 | 5.15 | 5.24 |
| $N^{14} + H^2 \rightarrow C^{12} + He^4$ | .01436 | 13.37 | 13.40 |
| $N^{14} + H^2 \rightarrow N^{15} + H^1$ | .00921 | 8.57 | 8.55 |
| $O^{16} + H^2 \rightarrow N^{14} + He^4$ | .00334 | 3.11 | 3.13 |
| $O^{16} + H^2 \rightarrow O^{17} + H^1$ | .00210 | 1.96 | 1.95 |
| $N^{14} + He^4 \rightarrow O^{17} + H^1$ | −.00124 | −1.15 | −1.16 |
| $F^{19} + He^4 \rightarrow Ne^{22} + H^1$ | .00164 | 1.53 | 1.58 |
| $Na^{23} + He^4 \rightarrow Mg^{26} + H^1$ | .00194 | 1.81 | 1.91 |
| $Mg^{24} + He^4 \rightarrow Al^{27} + H^1$ | −.00195 | −1.82 | −1.82 |
| $Al^{27} + He^4 \rightarrow Si^{30} + H^1$ | .00242 | 2.25 | 2.26 |
| $Si^{28} + He^4 \rightarrow P^{31} + H^1$ | −.00242 | −2.25 | −2.23 |
| $S^{32} + He^4 \rightarrow Cl^{35} + H^1$ | −.00271 | −2.52 | −2.10 |
| $H^2 + h\nu \rightarrow H^1 + n^1$ | −.00233 | −2.17 | −2.17 |
| $Be^9 + h\nu \rightarrow Be^8 + n^1$ | −.00181 | −1.69 | |

The agreement between calculated and observed energies in Table IV is remarkable. It is true that the masses used in calculating these energies are not all mass spectrograph values; some of them have been determined by the nuclear disintegration method. A few of the exact correspondences, such as that for the photodisintegration of heavy hydrogen, are therefore due to the fact that it was just this reaction from which one of the masses

TABLE V

Atomic weights used for the calculation of the mass and energy changes shown in Table IV. These have been taken from Table IV of Chapter 5. The values chosen are those suggested at the end of that table

| Atom | Atomic weight | Atom | Atomic weight |
|---|---|---|---|
| $n$ | 1.00893 | $N^{14}$ | 14.00750 |
| $H^1$ | 1.00813 | $N^{15}$ | 15.00489 |
| $H^2$ | 2.01473 | $O^{16}$ | 16.00000 |
| $H^3$ | 3.01705 | $O^{17}$ | 17.00450 |
| $He^3$ | 3.01698 | $F^{19}$ | 19.00452 |
| $He^4$ | 4.00389 | $Ne^{22}$ | 21.99864 |
| $Li^6$ | 6.01686 | $Na^{23}$ | 22.99680 |
| $Li^7$ | 7.01818 | $Mg^{24}$ | 23.99189 |
| $Be^8$ | 8.00792 | $Mg^{26}$ | 25.99062 |
| $Be^9$ | 9.01504 | $Al^{27}$ | 26.98960 |
| $Be^{10}$ | 10.01671 | $Si^{28}$ | 27.98639 |
| $B^{10}$ | 10.01631 | $Si^{30}$ | 29.98294 |
| $B^{11}$ | 11.01292 | $P^{31}$ | 30.98457 |
| $C^{11}$ | 11.01526 | $S^{32}$ | 32.98260 |
| $C^{12}$ | 12.00398 | $Cl^{35}$ | 34.98107 |
| $C^{13}$ | 13.00761 | | |

involved was determined. In almost all cases, however, these masses have been determined from more than the one reaction. This is true for the neutron whose mass is involved in the photodisintegration of heavy hydrogen. Approximately half of the masses used are mass spectrograph values, and for many of the others there exist mass spectrograph values inappreciably different from the nuclear masses used. In a few cases the atoms involved are radioactive, and for these no mass spectrograph measurements exist. The agreement between the calculated and observed disintegration energies leaves no doubt of the interchangeability of mass and energy. One would be scarcely more justified today in questioning the interchangeability of mass and energy than he would be in questioning the interchangeability of heat and energy.

## Fission

As early as 1934 it was realized by Fermi[97] that bombardment of uranium by neutrons might lead to the formation of elements of atomic number higher than 92. As is evident from the list of typical neutron disintegrations which has been given, these reactions often result in the formation of a radioactive isotope of the original material bombarded. This radioactive isotope often decays by ejecting a negative beta ray, thus becoming an element of atomic number one higher than the original element. If

[97] E. Fermi, *Nature*, **133**, 898 (1934).

then the bombardment of $_{92}U$ should result in the formation of an isotope of U which is radioactive, and if this isotope should decay by ejecting a beta ray, then there would be formed an element of atomic number 93. If by chance this element should also be radioactive and should disintegrate by the same process, an element of still higher atomic number would be formed. Each successive beta ray disintegration would increase the atomic number by one.

Now it was observed by Fermi and his associates[97,91] that the bombardment of uranium by neutrons does result in one or more radioactive products which emit negative beta particles. Four different half periods were observed for these products. It was natural to suppose that these may have come from a succession of beta particle disintegrations of elements having atomic numbers higher than 92. A great deal of effort was devoted to an attempt to isolate these products in order to ascertain the atomic numbers of the disintegrating elements. These many works have been well summarized in the recent literature.[98] It appeared for some time that elements 93, 94, 95, and 96 had been produced. Somewhat similar evidence concerning the products resulting from neutron bombardment of $_{90}Th$ was construed as indicating the presence of other previously unknown radioactive isotopes of the heavy elements.

Among those working on this problem were Hahn and Strassmann.[99] These workers finally secured unquestionable evidence that certain of the products resulting from neutron bombardment of uranium, which products had previously been thought to have atomic numbers greater than that of uranium, were in reality isotopes of $_{56}Ba$. Another was an isotope of $_{57}La$. The same situation was found to prevail among the products resulting from neutron bombardment of Th. Certain of the isotopes of Ba and La were ones which had already been recognized. For example, one product of the nuclear disruption was a Ba isotope having a half period of 86 minutes; this agrees almost exactly with the then recognized period of 85.6 minutes for $_{56}Ba^{139}$. In a similar way another product was a $_{57}La$ isotope having a half period somewhat less than 40 hours; this was identified with $_{57}La^{140}$ which was already known to have a half period of around 31 hours Another of the products appeared certain to be $_{56}Ba^{140}$.

These findings represented something entirely new. Although nearly all of the elements had previously been disintegrated by particle bombardment, in every previous case the new nucleus formed differed from the original only slightly in atomic number and atomic weight. When the bombarded nucleus disintegrated to form two or more particles, one of these was always a particle such as a proton, a neutron, or an alpha particle.

[98] L. A. Turner, *Rev. Mod. Phys.*, **12**, 1 (1940).

[99] O. Hahn and F. Strassmann, *Naturwiss.*, **27**, 11, 89 (1939).

Never before had there been observed a particle more massive than $_2He^4$ torn from the nucleus. In the case of neutron bombardment of uranium, however, there is definite evidence that the uranium nucleus is split into two approximately equal pieces one of which has an atomic weight of about 140. Since the atomic weight of $_{92}U$ is 234, 235 or 238, depending upon which isotope undergoes fission, and since the neutron is probably captured in the process, the remaining portions of the disrupted nucleus must have an atomic weight about 96 or 99 and an atomic number about 37. There is ample evidence for numerous fission fragments in this region. Among those[98,100] which have been identified are $_{35}Br^{83}$, $_{36}Kr^{83}$, $_{36}Kr^{88}$, $_{37}Rb^{88}$, $_{38}Sr^{89}$, $_{39}Y$, $_{40}Zr$, $_{41}Cb$, $_{42}Mo$ and element number 43. The products fall into two groups,[98,100] one of atomic number in the range from 35 to 43 and atomic weight in the range from 82 to about 100, the other of atomic number from 51 to 57 and atomic weight from 127 to about 150. Many of the products in each group are radioactive; others are stable. Among those in the heavier group are $_{51}Sb^{127}$, $_{52}Te^{129}$, $_{53}I^{131}$, $_{53}I^{133}$, $_{53}I^{135}$, $_{54}Xe^{139}$, $_{55}Cs^{139}$, $_{56}Ba^{139}$, $_{56}Ba^{140}$ and $_{57}La^{140}$. It is certain that the U nucleus is split into two or more fragments and that two of these have roughly equal masses.

The energy released in the disintegration of a nucleus results from the fact that the total mass of the final products is less than that of the original particles. Whereas energies from 1 to 20 MEV are commonly released in ordinary disintegrations, fission of the U nucleus releases an energy of a still higher order of magnitude. This would be expected, for the loss of mass accompanying the splitting of a heavy atom into two approximately equal parts is very large. Henderson[101] has measured calorimetrically the total energy released per fission of U. He obtained 177 MEV, with a probable error of about 1%. Kanner and Barschall[102] have measured the distribution of energy among the individual fragments of fission. They found one group of particles with energies distributed about a most probable value of 65 MEV and another group distributed about the value 98 MEV. The sum of these energies is 163 MEV. These investigators measured also the energy distribution under conditions such that the energy measured was the sum of the energies of the two fragments. This distribution curve was found to have one peak, at 159 MEV. While this value is somewhat below the later one of Henderson, the agreement is rather satisfactory in view of the fact that entirely different methods were used.

Mass considerations alone indicate that approximately 200 MEV should be released in the fission of U. An appreciable part[103] of this probably

[100] H. L. Anderson, E. Fermi and A. V. Grosse, *Phys. Rev.*, **59**, 52 (1941).

[101] M. C. Henderson, *Phys. Rev.*, **58**, 774 (1940).

[102] M. H. Kanner and H. H. Barschall, *Phys. Rev.*, **57**, 372 (1940).

[103] N. Bohr and J. A. Wheeler, *Phys. Rev.*, **56**, 426 (1939).

goes to excite the residual nuclei, however, and would not appear as kinetic energy of recoil. Some of this would certainly appear later as gamma radiation, and some of it might be dissipated by the ejection of electrons, positrons or neutrons. It is clear, therefore, that neither the ionization method used by Kanner and Barschall nor the calorimetric method used by Henderson would measure all of this energy. This probably accounts for the fact that both of these results are somewhat below the disintegration energy expected from mass considerations, and also for the fact that the two methods of measurement do not give exactly the same result.

If by any chance this fission process can be put on a practical basis there exists the possibility of a tremendous supply of energy. It turns out that secondary neutrons are ejected in the fission process. These secondary neutrons may themselves produce still more fissions, which in turn produce more secondary neutrons, and so on. Such a chain reaction would release terrific amounts of energy in a very short time. It has been calculated[104] that one cubic meter of $U_3O_8$ might develop $10^{12}$ kilowatt hours in less than 0.01 seconds. The problem today is not only to propagate such a chain reaction but also to control the speed of the reaction.

It is not only a single isotope of U that undergoes fission by neutron bombardment. Definite information concerning this has come from studies[105,106] of individual isotopes separated by a mass spectrograph. At least two U isotopes are split apart by neutron bombardment. Fast neutrons are required for the splitting of $U^{238}$; thermal neutrons produce the fission of $U^{235}$. It is the latter isotope which appears to hold the greater promise for the release of a practical supply of energy. This isotope comprises[107] $1/139$ of U. One of the real problems is to concentrate reasonable quantities of this isotope. Uranium is not the only heavy element which undergoes fission by neutron bombardment. Th and Pa have been shown to split apart in much the same way and with a comparable release of energy.

It has been found that fission can also be produced by bombardment with particles other than neutrons. The first charged particle used to produce fission was the deuteron. Gant[108] and Jacobsen and Lassen[109] have induced fission of both U and Th by deuteron bombardment. The efficiency of fission production was found to rise rapidly at deuteron energies of about 9 MEV. It was next shown by Fermi and Segrè[110] that the U nucleus

104 S. Flügge, *Naturwiss.*, **27**, 402 (1939).

105 A. O. Nier, E. T. Booth, J. R. Dunning and A. V. Grosse, *Phys. Rev.*, **57**, 546, 748 (1940).

106 K. H. Kingdon, H. C. Pollock, E. T. Booth and J. R. Dunning, *Phys. Rev.*, **57**, 749 (1940).

107 A. O. Nier, *Phys. Rev.*, **55**, 150 (1939).

108 D. H. T. Gant, *Nature*, **144**, 707 (1939).

109 I. C. Jacobsen and N. O. Lassen, *Phys. Rev.*, **58**, 867 (1940).

110 E. Fermi and E. Segrè, *Phys. Rev.*, **59**, 680 (1941).

can be split by alpha particle bombardment. After bombarding U with 32 MEV alpha particles, these investigators found present several of the iodine isotopes and in some cases tellurium. These are normal fission products. Care was taken to eliminate the possibility that this splitting was due to neutrons or to deuterons. The fission appears to have been produced by the alpha particles themselves. Even more recently Dessauer and Hafner[111] have found that proton bombardment of Th and of U causes fission. The protons used had an energy of 6.9 MEV. Care was taken to eliminate the possibility that the observed splitting was due to secondary neutrons. The proton is apparently captured by the bombarded nucleus, after which this nucleus undergoes fission.

In the meantime it had been discovered by Haxby, Shoupp, Stephens and Wells[112] that fission of both U and Th can be produced by gamma rays. The 6.3 MEV gamma radiation given off when $CaF_2$ is bombarded with protons was used for the purpose. The possibility that the observed effect may have been due to secondary neutrons was carefully considered. The fission observed was certainly induced by the gamma ray photons. Langer and Stephens[113] have identified two of the products of photo-fission as barium and strontium, two of the ordinary products of fission produced by neutrons. Yttrium building up from one of the radioactive fission fragments was also found among the products. Thus fission has been produced with neutrons, photons, protons, deuterons and alpha particles. Although it is not known that the products are identical in each case, there is no reason to believe that they are greatly different. Some of the products have been shown to be identical in a few instances.

It has already been pointed out that observations on what has since been shown to be the splitting of U were first interpreted incorrectly as showing the existence of elements of atomic number higher than that of U. Elements 93, 94 and probably 95 and 96 were at one time thought to exist, each being radioactive. Recognition of the fission process, however, removed the evidence for the existence of these elements. It is all the more interesting, therefore, that other evidence[114] obtained recently shows the existence of elements 93 and 94.

If U is bombarded with neutrons there appear two radioactive periods, one of 23 minutes and one of 2.3 days. Careful investigation of the products seems to show clearly the existence of element 93. It is probably formed as follows:

[111] G. Dessauer and E. M. Hafner, *Phys. Rev.*, **59**, 840 (1941).

[112] R. O. Haxby, W. E. Shoupp, W. E. Stephens and W. H. Wells, *Phys. Rev.*, **58**, 92 (1940); **59**, 57 (1941).

[113] A. Langer and W. E. Stephens, *Phys. Rev.*, **58**, 759 (1940).

[114] E. McMillan and P. H. Abelson, *Phys. Rev.*, **57**, 1185 (1940).

$$_{92}U^{238} + {}_0n^1 \rightarrow {}_{92}U^{239} + h\nu$$
$$_{92}U^{239} \rightarrow {}_{93}X^{239} + \beta^- \qquad T = 23 \text{ min.}$$

It has further been shown that element $_{93}X^{239}$ proceeds to decay with the emission of a negative beta particle, and with a half life period of 2.3 days. Thus

$$_{93}X^{239} \rightarrow {}_{94}X^{239} + \beta^- \qquad T = 2.3 \text{ da.}$$

Thus elements 93 and 94 again appear certain to exist, and it is not likely that this interpretation is in error. The question of what happens to element 94 after it is formed is still not settled. No radioactive properties have yet been detected. On the other hand, it is not likely that it would be stable. Further experiments will be necessary to settle this point.

## 4. ARTIFICIAL RADIOACTIVITY

### The Discovery and Extent of

It was only a decade ago, in 1933, that artificial radioactivity was discovered. At that time all of the radioactive elements known, with the exception of K and one or two others, were elements of high atomic number, above $_{82}$Pb. Since the original discovery of natural radioactivity by Becquerel in 1896, investigators had learned of some forty of these naturally occurring radioactive elements. Little did physicists suspect then that within the next seven years they would actually produce some 300 other radioactive elements which do not occur normally in nature.

Recall that the positron was discovered in 1932. In studying the positrons emitted by certain light elements when these are bombarded with alpha particles from polonium, Curie and Joliot[115] observed that certain of these continued to emit positrons after the alpha ray bombardment had ceased. The emission of positrons gradually decreased with time, finally approaching zero. This continued emission of positrons after removal of the bombarding alpha particles was originally observed for B, Mg and Al. The alpha ray bombardment of these materials appeared to form new substances, substances which were radioactive and which proceeded to decay just like a natural radioactive material. The only difference in behavior was that these new substances disintegrated by the ejection of positrons, whereas the natural radioactive substances disintegrate by ejecting either negative beta particles or alpha particles. Curie and Joliot found half life periods of 14 minutes, 2.5 minutes and 3.25 minutes, respectively, for the radioactive materials formed by alpha particle bombardment of B, Mg and Al.

[115] I. Curie and F. Joliot, *Comptes Rendus*, **198**, 254 (1934); *Nature*, **133**, 201 (1934).

Curie and Joliot suggested for the case of B that the alpha particle bombardment results in the disintegration

$$_5B^{10} + {_2He^4} \rightarrow {_7N^{13}} + {_0n^1}$$
$$_7N^{13} \rightarrow {_6C^{13}} + \beta^+$$

They suggested that $_7N^{13}$ emitted the positrons as it decayed to stable $_6C^{13}$. This has proved to be correct, though the half period is now known to be 9.93 minutes instead of the 14 minutes originally reported.

Since the original discovery of artificial radioactivity in 1933 some 300 artificially radioactive isotopes have been found. A great majority of these have been identified as to atomic number and atomic weight. One or more radioactive isotopes exist for practically all of the elements. The total number of isotopes existing, counting stable, naturally radioactive and artificially radioactive, is around 600. Several tables of both the stable[116–118] and the radioactive[117–119] isotopes are available in the literature. As early as 1938, just five years after the discovery of artificial radioactivity, one author [117] listed a total of 541 different nuclei, 287 stable and 254 radioactive. A more recent table,[118] a very complete and excellent one, lists 278 stable isotopes and over 300 artificially radioactive ones. It is interesting that the number of stable isotopes listed in this recent table is smaller than that given a few years ago[117]; a few that were originally thought to be stable have been found radioactive. In the meantime numerous other radioactive ones have been discovered.

### Types of Radioactive Decay

Although the first artificially produced radioactive materials disintegrated by ejection of positrons, it was soon found that even more disintegrated by ejecting electrons. These electrons are identical with the beta rays ejected by many of the natural radioactive elements. Regardless of whether positrons or electrons are ejected as the atoms decay, these particles are given off with velocities distributed over a wide range. These form a continuous velocity spectrum having a definite upper limit. The disintegration process seems to be identical with that of a natural radioactive material emitting beta rays. The upper limit of the continuous beta ray spectrum gives directly the total energy associated with the disintegration. Just why so many electrons are ejected with energies less than this maximum is understood no better than the similar phenomenon in natural radioactivity. It is presumed again that a neutrino is ejected simultaneously

[116] O. Hahn, S. Flügge, and J. Mattauch, *Phys. Zeits.*, **41**, 1 (1940).
[117] R. Grégoire, *Jour. de Physique et le Radium*, **9**, 419 (1938).
[118] J. J. Livingood and G. T. Seaborg, *Rev. Mod. Phys.*, **12**, 30 (1940).
[119] M. S. Livingston and H. A. Bethe, *Rev. Mod. Phys.*, **9**, 359 (1937).

with the beta ray, and that this still unobserved particle shares the total energy of disintegration with the disintegration electron. On this hypothesis the sum of the energies of the electron and the neutrino is exactly the same for each individual disintegration; the sum of these energies, which would be the same as the upper limit of the continuous beta ray spectrum, gives the energy of the reaction.

Disintegrations are known to occur also by processes other than the ejection of a nuclear positron or electron. A few of the artificially produced materials disintegrate by ejecting alpha particles. Far more of them disintegrate by a process known as $K$ electron capture. If a given nucleus normally ejects a positron as it disintegrates, there would exist a certain probability that this same nucleus might occasionally absorb an electron instead of emitting a positron. Since its own $K$ electrons are the most readily available, it seems reasonable that the nucleus might absorb one of these, the vacancy created in the $K$ shell being filled later by one of the outer electrons. A goodly number of the artificial radioactive nuclei do disintegrate in this way, decreasing their atomic number by one just as they would have by emission of a positron.

When an atom decays by $K$ electron capture one observes the emission of characteristic X-rays. Absorption of a $K$ electron by the nucleus leaves a vacancy in the $K$ shell, and as an outer planetary electron drops into this vacancy a characteristic line of the $K$ X-ray series is emitted. This emission of X-rays is the most characteristic external effect accompanying disintegration by this process. It was observation[120] of these characteristic X-rays in 1937 that constituted the first evidence of disintegration by $K$ electron capture. It was soon shown[120] definitely, by separation of the isotopes, that ${}_{31}Ga^{67}$ does actually disintegrate by this process. Accompanying this disintegration are the characteristic[120,121] $K_\alpha$ and $K_\beta$ X-ray lines of ${}_{30}Zn$. That is, the X-rays emitted are not those of the original atom but those of an atom one less in atomic number. The nucleus has actually changed, by absorption of the $K$ electron, before the X-rays are emitted. It will be recalled that some of the $\gamma$-rays accompanying the beta ray disintegration of a natural radioactive atom are really characteristic X-rays which follow the ejection of a planetary photoelectron by a nuclear gamma ray. And it will be remembered that these X-rays were not those of the original atom, but those characteristic of an atom of one higher atomic number. That is, the nucleus disintegrated preceding the ejection of the gamma ray. Thus those gamma rays which are really characteristic X-rays, and which are emitted by many both natural and artificial radioactive materials, are characteristic of the new element formed rather than of the original element.

[120] L. W. Alvarez, *Phys. Rev.*, **52**, 134 (1937); **54**, 486 (1938).
[121] P. Abelson, *Phys. Rev.*, **55**, 424, 876 (1939).

In the case of a $\beta$ disintegration the X-rays are those of an element of one higher atomic number, whereas in the case of a positron disintegration or a disintegration by $K$ electron capture they are characteristic of an element of one lower atomic number. For example,[121] $_{53}I^{131}$, which disintegrates by ejecting a $\beta$ particle, gives off the characteristic X-rays of $_{54}Xe$, while $_{29}Cu^{64}$, part of which disintegrates by ejecting a positron, gives the characteristic X-rays of $_{28}Ni$.

Characteristic X-rays are given off also by many atoms because of internal conversion of nuclear gamma rays, that is, through the ejection of a photoelectron from the planetary system of a given atom by absorption of a nuclear gamma ray emitted by this same atom. One must, therefore, be careful to distinguish between these X-rays and those which are considered as evidence of disintegration by $K$ electron capture. There is convincing evidence that certain nuclei disintegrate only by $K$ electron capture. The case of $_{23}V^{47}$ is quite conclusive. When this isotope is carefully separated it is found[122] to emit only characteristic X-rays. No disintegration $\beta$ rays or positrons have been detected, and no nuclear gamma rays are emitted. Furthermore, the characteristic X-rays are those of $_{22}Ti$. The nucleus $_{23}V^{47}$ must therefore change into $_{22}Ti$ by capture of a $K$ electron and by no other process.

It has been found that in a number of instances there exist nuclei with the same atomic number and the same mass number which nevertheless exhibit different radioactive properties. These are called nuclear isomers. That such isomers might exist among the natural radioactive substances was first suggested by Soddy,[123] and experimental evidence[124,125] for their existence was observed shortly thereafter. In recent years numerous isomers[94] have been found among the artificial radioactive nuclei. The first example of this was the case of $_{35}Br^{80}$. There are two half life periods associated with this, 4.4 hours for one isomer and 18 minutes for another. It seems that certain nuclei can exist for considerable time in an excited state, known as a metastable state. One would expect that sooner or later the nucleus would pass from the metastable state to the normal ground state, probably with the emission of a gamma ray representing the energy difference between the two states. Careful separation of the isomers of $_{35}Br^{80}$ has shown[126,127] conclusively that the 4.4 hour period is associated with the change from the upper to the lower isomeric state, while the 18 minute

[122] H. Walke, E. J. Williams and G. R. Evans, *Proc. Roy. Soc.*, A, **171**, 360 (1939).

[123] F. Soddy, *Nature*, **99**, 414, 433 (1917).

[124] O. Hahn, *Ber. Deutsch. Chem. Gesell.*, B, **54**, 1131 (1921).

[125] N. Feather and E. Bretscher, *Proc. Roy. Soc.*, A, **165**, 530 (1938).

[126] E. Segrè, R. S. Halford and G. T. Seaborg, *Phys. Rev.*, **55**, 321 (1939).

[127] D. C. DeVault and W. F. Libby, *Phys. Rev.*, **55**, 322 (1939).

period is associated with the decay of the lower isomeric form by $\beta$ ray emission. Similar information is available concerning a number of other isomeric pairs.[94]

In most instances it is very difficult or even impossible to observe the gamma rays associated with a change from one isomeric form to another. What one does observe is a group of fairly low energy electrons. These electrons have been ejected photoelectrically from the planetary system of the atom by absorption of the nuclear gamma ray accompanying the change from one isomeric state to the other. The gamma ray is absorbed in the same atom from the nucleus of which it was given out; it is internally converted. In many instances the internal conversion factor is very high, approaching unity in some cases. An internal conversion coefficient of unity means that each gamma ray photon emitted by the nucleus is absorbed in the planetary system of the same atom, ejecting thereby a photoelectron.

It is not only those atoms the nuclei of which undergo transition from one isomeric form to another that eject photoelectrons. There are nuclear gamma rays associated with many of the disintegrations in which electrons or positrons are emitted. Appreciable internal absorption of these results likewise in the ejection of photoelectrons, followed by the emission of characteristic X-rays. These electrons are obviously not those associated directly with the nuclear disintegration.

The approximate numbers of nuclei which disintegrate in different ways is of interest. According to a recent table by Livingood and Seaborg,[118] which includes a number of cases for which the evidence is not yet trustworthy, there are approximately 174 artificially produced nuclei which disintegrate by the ejection of electrons, 65 which disintegrate by emitting positrons, 3 by emitting alpha particles, and 35 by capturing a *K* electron. There are approximately 15 cases of a nuclear transition from an upper to a lower isomeric state. Gamma rays are known to accompany some 70 of the recognized radioactive changes. Internal conversion electrons are emitted from some 33 of these atoms. At least in one case, that of ${}_{29}Cu^{64}$, a given nucleus disintegrates in three different ways, by ejecting electrons, by ejecting positrons, and by *K* electron capture. It is of interest that this common source of electrons and positrons has been used quite recently[128] for a direct comparison of the ratio $e/m$ for positrons and electrons.

## The Possible Significance of These Materials

It is impossible to predict with any certainty the future value of the tremendous effort which has been put forth in recent years on the transmutation of the elements and on the study of the radioactive properties of

[128] A. H. Spees and C. T. Zahn, *Phys. Rev.*, **58**, 861 (1940).

artificially produced materials. Past experience has shown, however, that there is little need to fear that the store of knowledge which has come from these studies will not sooner or later be made to serve mankind. We have already emphasized the possible significance of the vast stores of energy which can be released by nuclear disintegration if one can but develop this process on a large scale and at the same time control it.

The application of knowledge gained through studies of the radioactive properties of artificially produced materials seems definitely assured. Many of these materials are already being used for various purposes. One of the most obvious uses is their substitution for natural radioactive materials in the treatment of diseased tissue. Certain advantages other than a possible saving in cost might result from this substitution. Among the artificial radioactive materials there are many which have relatively short half lives, say of the order of a few hours. Use of short lived materials eliminates the need of recovering these materials after treatment to prevent an excessive dose. The dose is controlled by using the proper amount of the material. Furthermore, the fact that the material need not be recovered allows it to be administered internally as well as externally. This may prove of utmost importance. It is well known that the physiological processes of the body carry certain materials mainly to definite parts of the body. By choosing a radioactive isotope of a material which the body localizes in some definite place, it may be possible to localize the desired treatment in that part of the body needing it. For example, it is known that a good part of the iodine taken internally goes to the thyroid gland. One can easily conceive of beneficial treatment of this gland with radioactive radiation. There exist radioactive isotopes of iodine, and if this iodine be taken internally the treatment will be localized in the thyroid. Experiments of this character are now being carried out in various laboratories. Other materials, and usually fairly common ones such as calcium and iron, go largely to certain parts of the body. The possibilities are at least intriguing.

As another example, it has been found that neutrons produce biological effects rather similar to those produced by X-rays and gamma rays. But whereas X-rays and gamma rays are absorbed much more rapidly in the bony tissue than in the fleshy tissue, neutrons are absorbed more rapidly in the fleshy tissue. Since radiation will produce effects only in those parts of the body where it is absorbed, it is possible that neutron radiation may prove advantageous for some treatments. The greater absorption of neutrons in the fleshy tissue no doubt results because of the greater concentration of hydrogen nuclei there. In fact the biological effect of neutrons comes probably not from the neutrons themselves but rather from the protons they project forward.

Perhaps the widest use to which artificially produced radioactive atoms have been put is as "tracers" in chemical, biochemical and biological studies. As a matter of fact it is not only the radioactive isotopes that are useful in these studies, but many of the stable ones as well. For example, H, C, N and O are found in over 90% of all chemical compounds known, and they are especially important in all biological problems. All of these elements have rather rare stable isotopes, $H^2$, $C^{13}$, $N^{15}$ and $O^{17}$, and each of these has been separated in amounts which are sufficient for many studies. Particular isotopes such as these serve as tags; they can be distinguished from other similar groups of atoms. Their use may clarify or make more certain the structures of many organic molecules. They can be used as tracers in many biological problems,[129] and this use has already yielded new information.

Radioactive atoms serve even more admirably[129,130] as tracers, for their radioactivity is a very sensitive and definite proof of their existence at any particular place. By feeding these elements to man and animals it is possible to study step by step their progress through and their absorption in the body. For example, the use of radioactive P has shown that 62% of the P absorbed goes into the bony structure within 5 days. By using calcium phosphate, in which the P has been made radioactive, the utilization of calcium by the rat has been studied. The greatest amount of calcium apparently goes to the front teeth. The storage and metabolism of iron in the body has been studied through use of radioactive Fe, and that of sugar through use of radioactive P. The absorption of minerals by plants has been studied[131] through use of radioactive Na and P. The use of these and other[132] radioactive isotopes will unquestionably contribute greatly to the future knowledge of living processes.

It is entirely possible also that the gamma rays from some of the artificial radioactive materials may be used instead of X-rays or natural gamma rays in the inspection of the structural members of machines. One of the radioactive isotopes of Y gives considerable promise[133] of being useful in this field. Using the gamma rays from this material, photographs have been taken through iron 2″ thick. These gamma rays are quite similar in hardness to those of radium, the material now used for such studies.

It is true that these artificial radioactive materials have not yet been produced on a really large scale. A number of them have been produced in amounts, however, which are sufficient for many purposes. For example,

[129] R. D. Potter, *Science Suppl.*, **89**, 8 (1939); **90**, 6 (1939).

[130] G. Hevesy, *Phys. Rev.*, **57**, 240 (1940).

[131] A. K. Brewer and A. Bramley, *Science*, **91**, 269 (1940).

[132] H. Walke, F. C. Thompson and J. Holt, *Phys. Rev.*, **57**, 177 (1940).

[133] C. Pecher, *Phys. Rev.*, **58**, 843 (1940); *Science Suppl.*, **92**, 8 (1940).

by one day's bombardment of sodium with deuterons one can now produce an amount of radioactive sodium, $_{11}Na^{24}$, having a gamma-ray activity equivalent to that of $10,000 worth of radium. Radioactive Sr is available in large quantities for therapeutic purposes. Ten hours of deuteron bombardment with the 60″ cyclotron at Berkeley will produce[133] about 12 milligrams radium equivalent of radioactive Y. Once the most useful of the radioactive isotopes is found it seems fairly certain that ways will be developed to produce the required amounts.

## Chapter 12

# COSMIC RAYS

### 1. THE EARLY HISTORY OF COSMIC RAYS

As has already been pointed out, experiments[1,2] carried out nearly 40 years ago showed that normal air is always slightly ionized. This residual ionization was made evident by demonstrating conclusively that considerable leakage normally occurs through the air surrounding the charged leaf system of an electroscope. It was found[3,4] immediately that this residual ionization could be decreased greatly by surrounding the electroscope chamber with lead or other absorbing material. It appeared clear, therefore, that at least a considerable part of this residual ionization was due to a rather penetrating radiation which came from outside the ionization chamber of the electroscope. At about this same time Rutherford and Soddy[5] showed that the radiations from spontaneously disintegrating radioactive materials were of three types, alpha, beta, and gamma rays. The gamma radiation had been found to be very penetrating, considerably more so than X-rays. Some gamma rays were capable of penetrating several centimeters of lead. It was therefore natural to suppose that the penetrating radiation responsible for the residual ionization was gamma radiation coming from small amounts of radioactive materials present in the rocks and soil. This supposition seemed all the more safe when it was later shown definitely that the earth's crust does contain such materials. While it was recognized that some penetrating radiation might come from the atmosphere, no evidence in favor of such a concept appeared for some years. Kurz,[6] reviewing all the evidence up to 1909, concluded that there was no evidence contradictory to the concept that the entire radiation came, either directly or indirectly, from materials in the earth's crust. The observed residual ionization might be produced directly by radioactive radiations

[1] C. T. R. Wilson, *Proc. Camb. Phil. Soc.*, **11**, 52 (1900); *Proc. Roy. Soc.*, A, **68**, 151 (1901); **69**, 277 (1901).

[2] H. Geitel, *Phys. Zeits.*, **2**, 116 (1900–01); J. Elster and H. Geitel, *Phys. Zeits.*, **2**, 560 (1900–01).

[3] J. C. McLennan and E. F. Burton, *Phys. Zeits.*, **4**, 553 (1902–03); *Phys. Rev.*, **16**, 184 (1903).

[4] E. Rutherford and H. L. Cooke, *Phys. Rev.*, **16**, 183 (1903).

[5] E. Rutherford and F. Soddy, *Phil. Mag.*, **4**, 370, 569 (1902); **5**, 576 (1903).

[6] K. Kurz, *Phys. Zeits.*, **10**, 834 (1909).

from the materials; or it might be produced by radiations from radioactive gases which diffuse from the earth into the lower atmosphere. Both of these processes are no doubt actually at work.

About 1910 there appeared, however, rather definite evidence that this was certainly not the whole story. Wulf,[7] through observations made on high towers, and Gockel,[8] through data obtained on several balloon flights, showed that the intensity of this ionizing radiation decreased but little if at all with increases in altitude above the earth's surface. At an elevation of 4500 meters, the highest attained by Gockel, the observed intensity was actually higher than that at the earth's surface. These were important observations, for if the radiation came directly from materials in the earth's crust, its intensity should decrease rapidly as one goes higher above the earth. It should[9] fall to one half its value at the earth's surface in going up a few hundred feet. A similar decrease of intensity with altitude would be expected even though the radiations might come from radioactive gases in the lower atmosphere, though the decrease might not become appreciable until somewhat higher altitudes are reached.

Recognition of the importance of such observations led to further and more extended balloon flights by Hess[10,11] and by Kolhörster.[12] The resulting observations established that the intensity does actually increase with altitude. There appeared to be no reason to question this conclusion. The experiments were carried out with sufficient quantitative accuracy, and they extended to sufficiently high altitudes, to prove the point beyond reasonable question. Altitudes of 5,200 and 9,000 meters were attained by Hess and Kolhörster respectively. Large increases in intensity were observed. At the higher altitudes the intensity appeared to be some 5 to 10 times as great as that observed at sea level. This astonishing increase, considered together with the fact that any ordinary radioactive radiation coming from the earth's surface should be almost completely absorbed in going up through the first one or two thousand meters of atmosphere, made it appear certain that the penetrating radiation has its origin either in or beyond the upper atmosphere. Hess[11] proposed as early as 1912 that the origin of this penetrating radiation was entirely beyond our atmosphere, and that it fell upon our atmosphere almost uniformly from all directions. Practically all of the detailed information gathered since that time has supported this view. The fact that this radiation produces observable

[7] T. Wulf, *Phys. Zeits.*, **10**, 152 (1909); **11**, 811 (1910).

[8] A. Gockel, *Phys. Zeits.*, **11**, 280 (1910); **12**, 595 (1911).

[9] A. S. Eve, *Phil. Mag.*, **21**, 26 (1911).

[10] V. F. Hess, *Wien. Ber.*, **120**, 1575 (1911); **122, 1053, 1481 (1913)**; *Phys. Zeits.*, **12**, 998 (1911).

[11] V. F. Hess, *Wien. Ber.*, **121**, 2001 (1912).

[12] W. Kolhörster, *Verh. Deutsch. Phys. Gesell.*, **15**, 1111 (1913); **16**, 719 (1914).

effects at sea level, and is therefore able to penetrate our entire atmosphere, shows that this radiation is far more penetrating than even the gamma rays from radioactive substances.

While most observers were convinced at an early date that this penetrating radiation from without truly existed, it was a number of years before investigators acquired accurate data regarding its rate of absorption in air and other matter. And it was still much later, actually only in quite recent years, that physicists have come to any general agreement as to the nature of the radiation. Several points regarding this nature are still not settled. Some details of absorption measurements will be discussed later. Of whatever the radiation may consist, it is exceedingly penetrating, far more so than the hardest gamma rays. Its penetration to several hundred meters depth of water has been observed.[13] Its effect has been measured after penetrating far into the earth's crust.[14–16] Wilson[14] measured the radiation after it had penetrated approximately a quarter of a mile of rock, equivalent to 1100 meters of water, and others[16] have observed it even deeper in the earth's crust. After passing through 1100 meters water equivalent of rock the intensity was of the order of 1/10,000 that incident upon the rock. Something of the order of 99 percent of the most penetrating radiation incident upon a meter thickness of water actually gets through this thickness. Thus at least a part of the radiation is exceedingly penetrating. As will be seen later, that part of the radiation which penetrates to great depths of water or rock is considerably more penetrating than the average cosmic ray observed at the earth's surface. And in turn that observed at the earth's surface is far more penetrating than the average which falls upon the upper atmosphere. In either case the less penetrating component has been absorbed to a much greater extent in passing through great thicknesses of matter, thus leaving the more penetrating component.

The nature of cosmic rays has been a much disputed question, and one not yet entirely settled. It was urged early by Millikan that the radiation consisted of electromagnetic waves, or photons, having wave lengths much shorter than the gamma ray. Evidence was presented[17] by him for the existence of radiation of several wave lengths of the order of $5 \times 10^{-12}$ cm. Somewhat later it appeared[18] that, on the photon hypothesis, there must be some waves as short as $0.8 \times 10^{-12}$ cm. This is only $\frac{1}{300}$ the wave length of the most penetrating gamma ray known. Evidence for both this

[13] J. Clay, *Physica*, **1**, 363 (1934).
[14] V. C. Wilson, *Phys. Rev.*, **53**. 204, 337 (1938).
[15] J. Barnóthy and M. Forró, *Phys. Rev.*, **55**, 870 (1939); **58**, 844 (1940).
[16] Y. Nishina, Y. Sekido, Y. Miyazaki and T. Masuda, *Phys. Rev.*, **59**, 401 (1941).
[17] R. A. Millikan and G. H. Cameron, *Phys. Rev.*, **28**, 851 (1926).
[18] R. A. Millikan and G. H. Cameron, *Phys. Rev.*, **31**, 921 (1928).

wave interpretation and the estimates of the wave length, were drawn largely from measurements of the rate of absorption in matter. This concept of their nature had considerable early evidence which seemed to support it, and, being rather appealing, became rather widely accepted by many working in the field of cosmic rays and by a great majority of those not so familiar with the field.

Subsequent data seem to have shown conclusively, however, that by far the greater part of cosmic radiation consists of charged particles such as electrons and positrons. A variety of evidence has been brought to bear upon this question. A long series of papers by Millikan and his coworkers, from about 1923 to the present, provides a wealth of information. And it is largely with this as a basis that one school maintained for so long the photon character of cosmic rays. In 1935 Millikan,[19] in an article entitled, "What to Believe about Cosmic Rays," summarized in a semipopular manner some of the more general findings. But there have been literally hundreds of other researches dealing with the subject. Some of these have been as extensive, or even more extensive than those of Millikan and his collaborators. Professor A. H. Compton of the University of Chicago has been extremely active in helping to mould the present concept of cosmic rays, and he has given an excellent summary[20] of researches which have caused physicists to conclude that the primary cosmic radiation consists largely of charged particles. More recent summaries[21–27] and many still more recent researches provide much additional information.

## 2. EVIDENCE BEARING ON THE NATURE OF COSMIC RAYS

It will be convenient to review the various aspects of cosmic ray studies under several heads. The literature on even any one phase of the subject is often overwhelming. Attention will be called to only the more basic or, in a few instances, the more interesting of these works.

### The Variation of Intensity with Altitude

The very discovery of the existence of a penetrating radiation coming from the upper atmosphere or from beyond this atmosphere, was made through observations of the intensity of radiation at various altitudes. While only rough measurements of relative orders of magnitude were neces-

[19] R. A. Millikan, *Science*, **81**, 211 (1935).
[20] A. H. Compton, *Rev. Sci. Instr.*, **7**, 71 (1936); *Phys. Rev.*, **50**, 1119 (1936).
[21] B. Rossi, *N. Cimento*, **15**, 43 (1938).
[22] R. Steinmaurer, *Gerlands Beitr. z. Geophys.*, Supplementband, **3**, 38 (1938)
[23] D. K. Froman and J. C. Stearns, *Rev. Mod. Phys.*, **10**, 133 (1938).
[24] T. H. Johnson, *Rev. Mod. Phys.*, **10**, 193 (1938).
[25] J. C. Stearns and D. K. Froman, *Amer. Phys. Teacher*, **7**, 79 (1939).
[26] K. K. Darrow, *Bell System Tech. Jour.*, **18**, 190 (1939).
[27] Various Authors, *Rev. Mod. Phys.*, **11**, 121 (1939).

sary to show the existence of the radiation, very careful measurements were desired to aid in arriving at a proper knowledge of its nature and origin. The pioneering balloon flights of Hess[10,11] and Kolhörster,[12] who attained respective altitudes of 5,200 and 9,000 meters, contributed some evidence regarding the manner of variation of intensity with altitude. No significant work followed these for some ten years, probably due to the intervention of the World War.

In 1922 Millikan and Bowen[28] undertook a series of measurements which was the forerunner of a number of important works dealing with the subject. Rather than to make observations in manned balloons, Millikan and Bowen chose to send up small balloons carrying sufficient recording apparatus to obtain the desired data. Higher altitudes could be attained in this way. The primary purpose of securing data at high altitudes at that time was to allow a decision as to whether the penetrating radiation had its origin in the uppermost atmosphere or beyond even the outer layers of this atmosphere. Four duplicate instruments were designed especially for the flights. Each of these included a recording electroscope, a recording thermometer and a recording barometer. The records were made on a moving photographic film driven by a clock spring. The largest over-all dimension of the assembled instrument was approximately six inches. The entire weight of the assembled apparatus was only 190 grams. These instruments were carried up by sounding balloons similar to those used for weather observations. Each instrument was carried by two balloons. It was hoped that after one balloon had broken at a high altitude, the other would carry the instrument back to earth without serious damage. The flights were made at Kelly Field, Texas. Three of the four instruments were recovered after the flight, and two of these had satisfactory records. These had attained altitudes of 11,200 and 15,500 meters, respectively. In qualitative agreement with previous work, these experiments showed a marked increase of intensity with altitude. But the increase was not as large as it appeared from the pioneering work of Hess and Kolhörster. The average intensity between the 5 and the 15 kilometer levels was some three times that at the earth's surface. These general findings were confirmed[29] shortly through measurements made on mountain tops and in airplanes.

In more recent years reliable observations on the change of intensity with altitude have been carried practically to the top of the atmosphere. These have been made possible through airplane flights, sounding balloon flights, and stratosphere manned-balloon flights. Many of the results and conclusions to be drawn from airplane studies made up to 29,000 feet and from three stratosphere balloon flights extending up to 60,000 feet, have

[28] R. A. Millikan and I. S. Bowen, *Phys. Rev.*, **22**, 198 (1923); **27**, 353 (1926).

[29] R. A. Millikan and R. M. Otis, *Phys. Rev.*, **27**, 645 (1926).

been summarized by Bowen, Millikan and Neher.[30] Two of the more recent illuminating studies are those carried out by Millikan and his coworkers at Fort Sam Houston, Texas,[31] and at Madras, India.[32] In each case observations were made with photographic recording instruments carried up by sounding balloons. These flights extended to within less than 2% of the top of the atmosphere. That is, 98% of the atmosphere, by weight, was below the instrument at the highest altitude reached. Fig. 1 reproduces

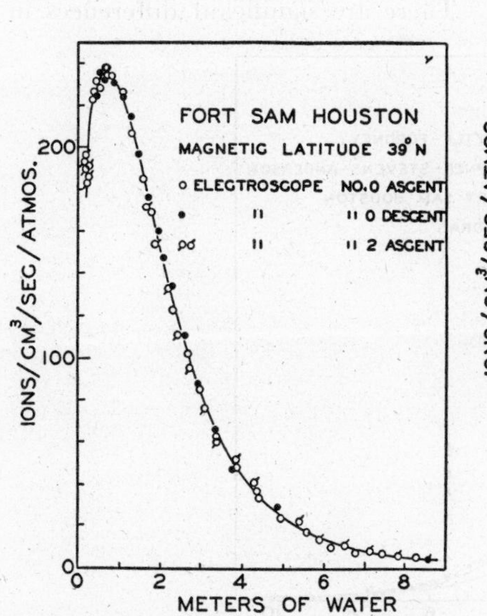


Fig. 1.—Showing the variation of cosmic ray intensity with altitude at Fort Sam Houston, Texas, magnetic latitude 39° N. Abscissae represent the distance below the top of the atmosphere in meters of water equivalent.

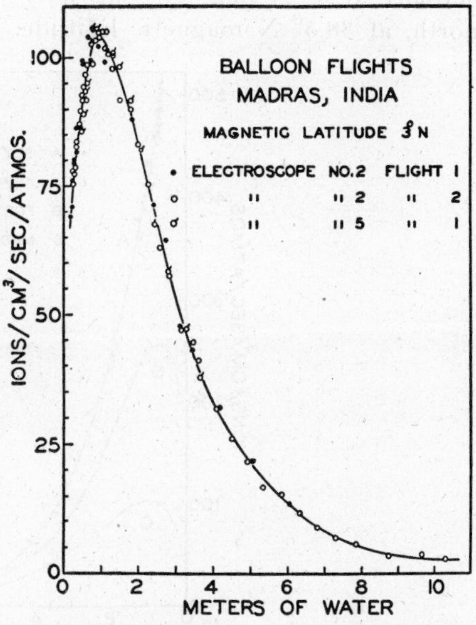

Fig. 2.—Showing the variation of cosmic ray intensity with altitude at Madras, India, magnetic latitude 3° N. Abscissae represent the distance below the top of the atmosphere in meters of water equivalent.

the results of the Fort Sam Houston study; Fig. 2 shows those obtained at Madras, India. In each case the ordinate represents the number of pairs of ions formed per cc. per sec. in an ionization chamber in which the pressure is one atmosphere. The abscissa represents, in a way, the altitude. Assuming that a layer of air has the same absorption as a layer of water having the same mass per unit area of surface, it is possible to express the absorption in a given layer of the atmosphere as that in an equivalent layer

[30] I. S. Bowen, R. A. Millikan and H. V. Neher, *Phys. Rev.*, **44**, 246 (1933); **46**, 641(1934).
[31] R. A. Millikan, H. V. Neher and S. K. Haynes, *Phys. Rev.*, **50**, 992 (1936).
[32] I. S. Bowen, R. A. Millikan and H. V. Neher, *Phys. Rev.*, **52**, 80 (1937).

of water. The mass of the entire atmosphere is approximately equal to that of a layer of water 10 meters thick. Accordingly the abscissae in Figs. 1 and 2 represent the "distance" below the top of the atmosphere expressed in meters of water equivalent. Ten meters of water equivalent would therefore correspond to sea level.

Results of studies at the two places are shown because of certain significant differences. Madras, India, is very close to the magnetic equator, actually at 3° N magnetic latitude. Fort Sam Houston is much farther north, at 38.5° N magnetic latitude. There are significant differences in

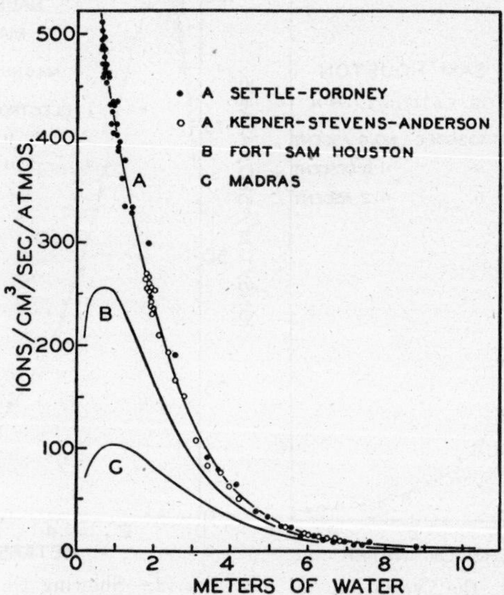


Fig. 3.—A comparison of the variations in cosmic ray intensity at Madras, India (magnetic latitude 3° N), Fort Sam Houston, Texas (magnetic latitude 39° N), and on two stratosphere balloon flights (magnetic latitude 53° N).

the curves obtained at the two places. We shall discuss later the variation of cosmic ray intensity with latitude and the reason for this variation. For the present it is sufficient to note that these two intensity-altitude curves are different. Although each has the same general form, and each reaches a maximum intensity well below the top of the atmosphere, the range of intensity variation is quite different. The intensity observed at high altitudes, say in the region of the maximum, is much greater at the higher latitude. Likewise, the altitude at which the intensity becomes a maximum is somewhat greater at the higher latitude.

These facts are all the more evident from Fig. 3, which shows the two curves already discussed, together[32] with a third which represents data taken at a still higher magnetic latitude, 53° N. This third curve results from data obtained on two stratosphere flights, the Settle-Fordney flight in 1933 and the Kepner-Stevens-Anderson flight in 1934. These were made at the same latitude. It is pleasing to see how well the data agree. This curve, corresponding to a still higher latitude, shows a still greater intensity of cosmic radiation at any given elevation. Even the higher of these stratosphere flights did not extend sufficiently near the top of the atmosphere to show the maximum at this latitude. This maximum occurs 90 percent of the way up near the equator, and about 93 percent of the way up at a latitude of 38.5°. The stratosphere flights at a latitude of 53° extended only 93 percent of the way up, not high enough to show any maximum which might exist. More recent data[33] taken at latitudes of 51° and 60° have extended much nearer the top of the atmosphere than did these stratosphere balloon flights. They have gone 98.8 percent of the way to the top. Curves obtained at both of these high latitudes show maxima occurring still closer to the top of the atmosphere. The actual ionizations corresponding to these maxima are somewhat less than would be expected from a continuation of the stratosphere flight curve shown in Fig. 3; but they are still much greater than those obtained at lower latitudes. Thus data extending to more than 98 percent of the way to the top of the atmosphere are available[33] at four different latitudes, 3°, 38.5°, 51° and 60° N. A maximum appears in each curve. The fact that the intensity increases to a maximum and then begins to fall off again appreciably below the top of the atmosphere, might at first seem to indicate that the cosmic radiation actually originates in the upper atmosphere. But such a conclusion is not at all necessary; there are other ways of accounting for the existence of this maximum. But if the primary radiation does come from entirely beyond the atmosphere, as everyone believes today, then the existence of such a maximum does show that the ionization in the atmosphere cannot be entirely due directly to the primary rays. The significant role probably played by secondary ionizing radiation will be discussed later.

Many other studies of the variation of intensity with altitude have of course been made. The results have been in general agreement with those of the works discussed above. Data have recently been obtained still nearer the top of the atmosphere. The development of small counter tubes for measuring cosmic ray intensity, and the development of small and light radio tubes and associated equipment, has made it possible to approach to within ½ percent of the top of the atmosphere. In several recent studies such counting apparatus has been carried up to very high altitudes by sounding balloons. The apparatus periodically transmits the existing pressure and counting rate back to earth by radio. Thus, success in gathering

[33] I. S. Bowen, R. A. Millikan and H. V. Neher, *Phys. Rev.*, **53**, 217, 855 (1938).

very high altitude data no longer hinges on recovering the observing apparatus. Instruments of this character have been described[34,35] for which the entire weight of the assembled instrument was only 5 pounds. Data have been obtained[34] in this manner up to an altitude of 21,300 meters (70,000 feet) in Lima, Peru, on the magnetic equator. Similar data taken[35] at Washington, D. C., 50° N magnetic latitude, extend up to 35,300 meters (116,000 feet) above sea level. The pressure at this altitude is approximately 4 mm. of mercury. Only ½ percent of the atmosphere remains still above the highest point at which observations were made.

These high altitude studies have furnished intensity-altitude data in essential agreement with those already discussed. The marked increase of high altitude intensity with magnetic latitude is confirmed. The data confirm also the existence of a maximum in the intensity-altitude curve, and the slight shift of the position of this maximum with magnetic latitude. They yield additional information regarding the decrease in intensity near the very top of the atmosphere. After the maximum is reached, the intensity continues to decrease rapidly up to the highest altitude attained. At an altitude of 35,300 meters the intensity[35] is approximately 1% of that at the maximum; it is approximately the same as that observed only 0.4 of an atmosphere above the earth. The fact that the intensity becomes very small as the top of the atmosphere is approached confirms the view that most of the cosmic ray phenomena observed are secondary effects produced in our own atmosphere. The primary rays are either of such a nature that they are not detected with usual apparatus, or they are few in number as compared to the secondaries produced in the upper atmosphere. It should be kept in mind, however, that this maximum of intensity, and the subsequent decrease at still higher altitudes, occurs very near the top of the atmosphere. The characteristic rapid rise of intensity with altitude continues 90 percent of the way to the top.

### The Absorption in Matter

Much can be learned from studies of the rate of absorption of cosmic radiation in matter. Absorption studies have been made not only in air, but also in water, in rocks of the earth's crust, and in lead and other similar materials. They have been made by a number of observers and by several different methods. It will be sufficient to call attention to a few of the typical studies, and to bring out the general findings resulting from such researches.

Air is not a very good absorber of really penetrating radiation, and it might at first appear hopeless to attempt studies of the rate of absorption

[34] S. A. Korff, L. F. Curtiss and A. V. Astin, *Phys. Rev.*, **53**, 14 (1938).

[35] L. F. Curtiss, A. V. Astin, L. L. Stockmann and B. W. Brown, *Phys. Rev.*, **53**, 23 (1938).

therein. Still, there is a lot of air above us, and the cosmic radiation must pass through all of this to reach the surface of the earth. Just as soon as one starts measuring the intensity of radiation at different altitudes, he begins acquiring data relative to the rate of absorption of the rays in air. From even the earliest work of Kolhörster it was possible to calculate a rough value for the absorption coefficient. This appeared to be of the order of 0.55 per meter of water equivalent, or of the order of 0.0007 per meter of air near the earth's surface. It has been remarked that the entire atmosphere is equivalent, as far as its absorption of the radiation goes, to approximately 10 meters of water. For one standard atmosphere of 76 cm. of mercury, the total mass of air above a square centimeter on the earth's surface is $76 \times 13.6 = 1034$ grams. Now a column of water one meter high and of one square centimeter cross section would have a mass of $100 \times 1 = 100$ grams. Hence, a standard atmosphere is equivalent to $1034/100 = 10.34$ meters of water. Since atmospheric pressure at sea level is normally somewhat less than the standard 76 cm., the normally prevailing atmosphere is closely equivalent to 10 meters of water. Authors therefore find it convenient to express the distance above sea level in meters of water equivalent, and to express absorption coefficients as the fraction of incident energy absorbed per meter of water equivalent penetrated. The original absorption coefficient calculated from the work of Kolhörster was soon recognized to be much too high to apply to the entire radiation. That is, at least a part of the radiation which reaches the earth's surface is far more penetrating than would be indicated by this rate of absorption. It is nevertheless interesting that even this early high value for the rate of absorption was less than 1/6 that of the corresponding absorption for the most penetrating gamma rays known. The absorption coefficient for these most penetrating gamma rays is of the order of 3 to 4 per meter of water.

In the early days of high altitude studies it was of course not certain that the penetrating radiation being observed was of cosmic origin; perhaps it came from our own atmosphere. Trustworthy conclusions regarding the rate of absorption in the atmosphere could not be drawn, therefore, until it was known definitely that this radiation came from outside the atmosphere. If it arose within the atmosphere the shape of the intensity-altitude curve would depend not only upon the rate of absorption, but also upon the distribution of the source of radiation throughout the atmosphere. One could imagine a source distribution which would lead to almost any kind of an intensity-altitude curve. Furthermore, the mere fact that the intensity-altitude curve depends markedly upon the magnetic latitude at which it is taken shows that the distribution of cosmic ray intensity throughout the atmosphere is not one determined by absorption alone. It was therefore natural that investigators turned rather early to the direct measurement of rates of absorption in water and other materials more dense than the atmosphere.

Kolhörster was perhaps the first to attempt direct measurement of the rate of absorption in water. This he did by sinking electroscopes to various depths in several different bodies of water near sea level, and by making observations in crevasses in glaciers at altitudes approximating 3000 meters. While the absorption coefficients obtained varied considerably, it was clear that the mean value was not more than one half that obtained from his early balloon measurements. He reported[36] a coefficient of 0.25 per meter of water. This lower value was at least more nearly consistent with the early sounding balloon results of Millikan and Bowen.[28]

The first really convincing experiments carried out under water were those of Millikan and Cameron[17] in 1926. Special water tight electroscopes were sunk to various depths in two snow fed lakes, Muir Lake and Arrowhead Lake. The first of these is at an elevation of 3595 meters; it is immediately adjacent to Mount Whitney, the highest peak in the United States. The second lake is in the San Bernardino mountains, at an elevation of 1555 meters. Observations were made at various depths extending to 20.4 meters beneath the surface of Muir Lake. Similar depths were reached in the second lake. The electroscopes were sufficiently sensitive that they detected measurable radiation at least 15.2 meters below the water surface. It is important that all electroscope readings in Arrowhead Lake corresponded to those taken at 1.8 meters greater depths in Muir Lake. Now the 2040 meters of atmosphere between the two lakes is equivalent to just 1.8 meters of water. It therefore appeared that the radiation observed in Arrowhead Lake was exactly that found in Muir Lake excepting for the fact that it had penetrated, and been somewhat absorbed in, the 2040 meters of atmosphere between. Hence it was concluded that no appreciable part of the radiation originated in that part of the atmosphere below Muir Lake. The atmosphere between lakes acted merely as an absorbing blanket, absorbing radiation coming from above. This fact, taken together with balloon observations then available, made it appear probable even at that time that the rays originate beyond the outer atmosphere.

Some of this cosmic radiation was found to be more penetrating than had previously been suspected. Since that part of the atmosphere above Muir Lake is equivalent to 7.0 meters of water, and since some radiation was detected 15.2 meters below the surface of the lake, it was clear that at least a measurable part of the radiation is capable of penetrating 22.2 meters of water. On the basis of equal masses per sq. cm. of absorber, this is equivalent to nearly 2 meters of lead. Approximately 2 percent of the

[36] W. Kolhörster, *Ber. Preuss. Akad. Wiss.*, **34**, 366 (1923).

most penetrating cosmic rays observed by Millikan and Cameron got through this thickness of water, whereas only something of the order of 1 part in $10^{31}$ of the hardest gamma rays known will penetrate this thickness. The more penetrating of the cosmic rays appeared from this work to be some 20 times more penetrating than the hardest gamma rays. Millikan and Cameron[17] concluded from this work that no one single absorption coefficient could be associated with all of the cosmic radiation striking the upper atmosphere, or even with all of that which reaches the surface of the earth. They felt that a considerable part of that radiation reaching the earth lay in two energy regions, one with an absorption coefficient of 0.30 per meter of water, and a more penetrating component with an absorption coefficient of 0.18 per meter of water. Their experiments under water showed definitely that there is a gradual hardening of the radiation as it passes through more and more matter. Just as for any other radiation made up of two or more components of different penetrating powers, the less penetrating components are filtered out first, leaving mainly the harder component after great thicknesses of matter have been traversed.

Numerous other underwater studies have been made. Millikan and Cameron[18,37] have extended their own measurements down to 72 meters beneath the surface of water, or 80 meters below the top of the atmosphere. The work has been made more accurate through certain refinements in electroscope design and through use of greater than atmospheric pressure in the ionization chamber of the electroscope. This last provides a greater amount of total ionization, and thus makes it more accurately measurable. The ionization continues to decrease down to the greatest depths attained. And the rate of absorption at these depths indicates an absorption coefficient of only 0.028 per meter of water for some of the radiation. Observations on mountain peaks showed, however, that the radiation at this higher level was much softer, having an absorption coefficient something like 0.35 per meter of water. Other observers have extended the measurements to still greater depths. Regener,[38] in a summary of extensive observations made by himself and his coworkers, both in the upper atmosphere and in lakes, gives data extending down to 240 meters depth of water. Fig. 4, reproduced from Regener's work, shows the manner in which the intensity falls off with increases in depth. The data yielding this curve are those obtained in a careful series of measurements carried out in two European lakes. From the observed rate of absorption in water, Regener found three absorption coefficients, 0.20, 0.073 and 0.020 per meter of water, corresponding to three different components of the radiation. A much softer component, with coefficient 0.85, is apparently present in the upper

[37] R. A. Millikan and G. H. Cameron, *Phys. Rev.*, **37**, 235 (1931).

[38] E. Regener, *Phys. Zeits.*, **34**, 306 (1933).

atmosphere. This conclusion is reached through consideration of the rate of absorption in the atmosphere.

Several other series of measurements extending to comparable depths of water have confirmed the existence of measurable radiation at these depths. Clay[13] made measurements down to 270 meters depth in the Red Sea. While the general trend of results was much the same as that of those already discussed, an entirely unexpected increase in intensity was observed as the depth increased from 200 to 250 meters. At depths less than 200 meters and at those greater than 250, the normal decrease of intensity with

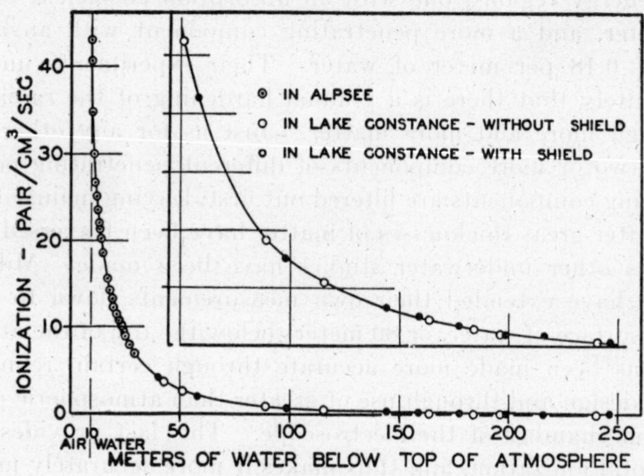


Fig. 4.—Showing the manner of decrease in cosmic ray intensity with increases in depth below the surface of water.

depth was observed. Although a similar increase has been observed[39] in a study carried out in a deep mine, the effect is probably not real. In the mine it was found to occur at a depth from 430 to 520 meters of water equivalent, whereas Clay found it from 200 to 250 meters. The observed increase in ionization was probably brought about by some extraneous effect,[13,40] rather than through an actual increase in cosmic ray intensity. Ehmert[41] has likewise made observations down to 240 meters in water, and he finds no indication of the peculiar increase. Clay and others[42] have recently extended these underwater studies to a depth of 440 meters.

Evidence of by far the greatest penetration through matter yet known has been reported recently by several investigators. Wilson[14] has made

[39] A. Corlin, *Annals of the Observatory of Lund*, **4**, (1934).

[40] W. F. G. Swann, *Phys. Rev.*, **46**, 432 (1934).

[41] A. Ehmert, *Zeits. f. Physik*, **106**, 751 (1937).

[42] J. Clay, A. Van Gemert and P. H. Clay, *Proc. Acad. Wetensch.*, Amsterdam, **41**, 694 (1938).

measurements in a deep mine, using a fourfold Geiger tube coincidence counter instead of an electroscope. The fourfold coincidence arrangement consisted of four Geiger tubes placed one above the other, and connected to the amplifying and counting system in such a way that the counter would operate only when an ionizing radiation went through the four tubes simultaneously. Such an arrangement is therefore directional; it counts radiation coming from one direction only. Because of this it is influenced to a lesser degree by stray radioactive radiation. With such apparatus Wilson made measurements down to a depth of approximately 384 meters in a mine. Measurable cosmic radiation penetrated this nearly one quarter mile of rock above the deepest observing station. This is equivalent to slightly over 1100 meters of water, an absorbing layer far thicker than that used by any previous observer. By tipping the apparatus so that it recorded only those rays coming obliquely through the earth, and hence through a greater thickness of rock, cosmic rays were detected at a depth equivalent to 1408 meters of water.

Ability to detect some cosmic radiation at these and even greater depths has been confirmed by others.[43,15,16] Gemert[43] detected radiation at a depth of 610 meters in a coal mine; the absorption is here equivalent to 1600 meters of water. Some of the cosmic rays are thus extremely penetrating. It is true that only one part in approximately 20,000 of the radiation incident upon the earth actually penetrates[14] to these great depths; but it is amazing that any measurable amount of it does. On the basis of equal masses per sq. cm. of absorber, the 1408 meters of water equivalent through which Wilson observed some radiation is equivalent to 124 meters of lead. Imagine any radiation getting through this! From observations made at 37 different effective depths, Wilson found the cosmic ray intensity to decrease continuously with increasing depth. There was no evidence whatever for any peculiar increase similar to that which had previously been found by two observers. From the rate of decrease of intensity, Wilson calculated[14] that the effective absorption coefficient decreases from 0.07 per meter of water at the earth's surface to 0.0025 at the greatest depth attained in the mine. This is by far the smallest rate of absorption, or the greatest penetrating power, yet reported. The data emphasize again the continuous hardening of the rays as more and more matter is penetrated.

Of course lead and other heavy materials are excellent absorbers of cosmic rays. But the radiation is so penetrating that its intensity cannot be cut down many fold by any practical thickness of even these materials. Considerable amounts of absorbing lead, or even gold, have nevertheless been used to advantage in numerous measurements. Several specific instances will be mentioned later. For the present only enough data will

[43] A. Van Gemert, *Physica*, **5**, 811 (1938).

be cited to show the general rate of absorption in such materials, and to bring out how measurements of this rate at different distances below the top of the atmosphere show the hardening of the cosmic radiation as it penetrates through more and more matter. Millikan and Cameron[37] found that a considerably greater percentage of the total radiation is capable of penetrating a 7.64 cm. thick lead screen at sea level than on top of Pike's Peak. Eleven observations taken between these two extremes of altitude show that the percentage of cosmic rays passing through the lead increases continuously from 61 percent on Pike's Peak to 76 percent near sea level. The hardening of the general radiation is apparent.

Nielsen and Morgan[44] have made similar observations of the rate of absorption in lead in a mine. The hardening effect produced by penetration through 60 meters water equivalent of earth is shown by the fact that the absorption coefficient in lead decreased from 0.0004 per gram per sq. cm. at the earth's surface to approximately one-half this value after penetration through this amount of earth. Nearly a half meter of lead was used in this study. These and other studies have made it quite clear that the general radiation consists of two main components, one relatively soft or easily absorbed, the other very hard or penetrating. Each component no doubt consists of a band of radiation of varying penetrating power. The marked difference in the penetrating powers of the two components is indicated by the fact that the absorption coefficient in lead is[45] something like 0.35 per centimeter for the soft component, whereas the penetrating component has[44] an absorption coefficient at least as small as 0.002 per centimeter. The number of penetrating cosmic rays which reach the earth's surface is not diminished[13] greatly by as much as 36 cm. of lead. On the other hand, this thickness of lead is more than sufficient to cut out practically all of the softer component.

Other workers have compared the rates of absorption in various materials. Studies[46] of the absorption of the soft component in lead, tin, copper, and aluminum indicate a considerable variation of the mass absorption coefficient from one material to another. The absorption of this soft component appears[23,45] to be roughly proportional to the square of the atomic number of the absorber. The hard component seems to obey an entirely different absorption law. Observations[47] of the rate of absorption of the hard component, made after filtering the radiation through 25 centimeters of lead, in the materials lead, iron, aluminum, copper, and paraffin having

[44] W. M. Nielsen and K. Z. Morgan, *Phys. Rev.*, **54**, 245 (1938).

[45] J. Crudup, *Phys. Rev.*, **54**, 483 (1938).

[46] P. Auger, L. Leprince-Ringuet and P. Ehrenfest, *Jour. de Physique et le Radium*, **7**, 58 (1936).

[47] A. Sittkus, *Zeits. f. Physik*, **108**, 421 (1937–38).

thicknesses between 100 and 1000 grams per square centimeter, show that approximately the same mass absorption coefficient holds for all. For cosmic rays of the hardness used, the absorption coefficient was approximately 0.00057 per gram per sq. cm. regardless of the material used as absorber.

### The Latitude Effect

The existence of some sort of a latitude effect is obvious from the fact that the cosmic ray intensity-altitude curve depends upon the latitude at which measurements are made. In 1927 Clay[48] found the cosmic ray intensity somewhat different in Holland and in Java. This difference was ascribed to the different effects the earth's magnetic field might produce at the two latitudes. Several expeditions by various workers failed to confirm Clay's findings, however, and it appeared[20,49] up to 1932 that no real latitude effect existed. Nevertheless, subsequent investigations have shown Clay's finding to be correct; they have shown conclusively the existence of a real latitude effect. That this effect is correlated with magnetic latitude rather than geographic latitude has been known since the discovery of the effect. It was recognized early that a careful study of this effect might yield highly important information regarding both the nature of, and the energy associated with, the radiation. As a result numerous studies have been made of the variation of intensity with latitude. A majority of these have been carried out near sea level, although some information is available concerning the effect at high altitudes.

The real nature of the latitude effect, and the quantitative manner of variation of intensity with latitude, can be brought out best by discussion of typical observations carried out at sea level. These are both far more extensive and more accurate than those made at high altitudes. Of the many series of observations available,[13,20,50–57] probably one of the most reliable is that by Compton and Turner.[54] It is true that an earlier investigation[50] comprising twelve different expeditions and including some eighty cooperating physicists, had provided measurements at more than a

[48] J. Clay, *Proc. Acad. Wetensch.*, Amsterdam, **30,** 1115 (1927); **31,** 1091 (1028); **33,** 711 (1930).

[49] G. Hoffmann, *Phys. Zeits.*, **33,** 633 (1932).

[50] A. H. Compton, *Phys. Rev.*, **41,** 111, 381 (1932); **43,** 387 (1933); *Trans. Amer. Geophys. Union*, p. 154 (1933).

[51] H. Hoerlin, *Nature*, **132,** 61 (1933); *Naturwiss.*, **21,** 822 (1933).

[52] R. A. Millikan and H. V. Neher, *Phys. Rev.*, **50,** 15 (1936).

[53] T. H. Johnson and D. N. Read, *Phys. Rev.*, **51,** 557 (1937).

[54] A. H. Compton and R. N. Turner, *Phys. Rev.*, **52,** 799 (1937).

[55] T. H. Johnson, *Phys. Rev.*, **54,** 151 (1938).

[56] P. S. Gill, *Phys. Rev.*, **55,** 1151 (1939).

[57] P. F. Gast and D. H. Loughridge, *Phys. Rev.*, **59,** 127 (1941).

hundred widely distributed points on the earth's surface. But the more recent work of Compton and Turner appears superior in several respects.

FIG. 5.—A general view of the Carnegie Model C cosmic ray meter.

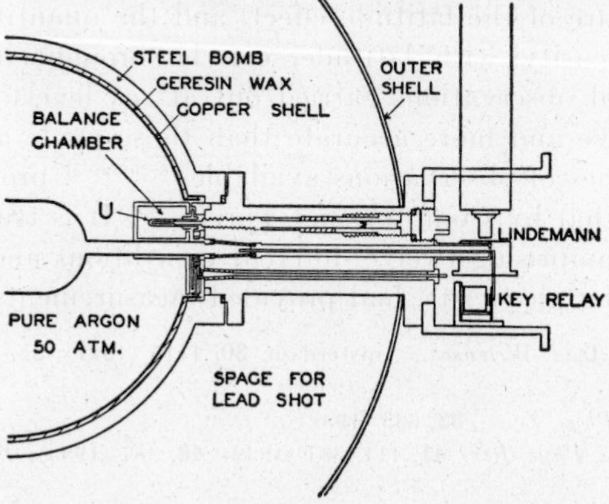


FIG. 6.—A more detailed view of the Carnegie Model C cosmic ray meter. The volume of the ionization chamber is 19.3 liters.

This series of measurements was made on 12 steamship voyages across the Pacific Ocean between Vancouver, Canada and Sydney, Australia. The observations thus extend from approximately 55° N to 42° S geomagnetic latitude, well into both hemispheres. The measurements were more or less continuous over the major part of a year, and therefore provide also excellent data regarding possible seasonal variation. The observations have been greatly extended in number by Gill,[56] who has summarized data gathered on 15 additional trips over the same route.

The records on all of these voyages were obtained with a "Carnegie model C" cosmic ray meter developed and described[58] several years earlier. The instrument is entirely automatic in recording. A general photograph of the instrument is reproduced[58] in Fig. 5; a cross section view showing more detail is reproduced in Fig. 6. The essential features of the instrument are: (1) A very large ionization chamber, 19.3 liters, consisted of a spherical steel bomb filled with argon gas at a pressure of approximately 50 atmospheres. The ionization produced by a given radiation is 1.60 times as great[58,59] in argon at atmospheric pressure as in air at the same pressure. While at normal pressures the ionization in a given gas is closely proportional to the pressure of the absorbing gas, this proportionality does not hold at high pressures. The ionization in argon at 40 atmospheres is 41.9 times[58] that in argon at atmospheric pressure. Thus the use of argon at high pressure provided an ionization 67.0 times that which would be produced in air at atmospheric pressure. (2) A balancing current was supplied by the ionization produced in a small auxiliary chamber by beta rays from metallic uranium. This balancing current was adjusted to approximate equality with the mean cosmic ray ionization current. Hence, the electrometer indicated directly small changes in cosmic ray intensity rather than the total intensity. This balancing action is illustrated by the photographic record reproduced in Fig. 7. Another advantage of this balancing method is that it automatically compensates for pressure or temperature changes of the gas in the ionization chamber. (3) The readings of the Lindemann electrometer, a barometer, and a thermometer were photographed continuously on a moving strip of bromide paper. One loading of paper was sufficient for a month's continuous run. (4) Once each hour the insulated

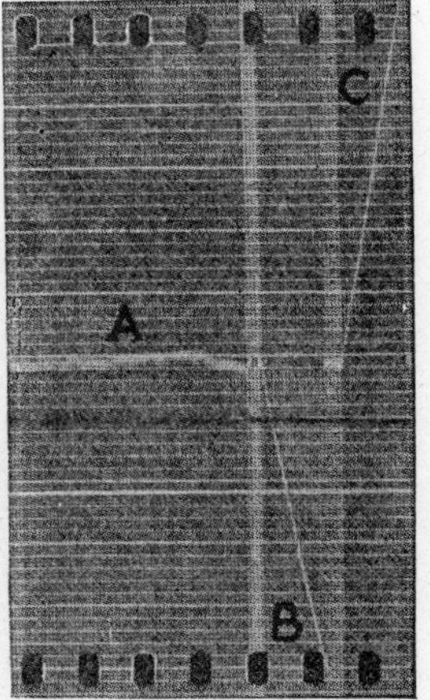

FIG. 7.—Illustrating the balancing action of the electroscope in the Carnegie Model C cosmic ray meter. *B* shows the drift of the needle due to cosmic rays alone. *C* shows the drift due to the auxiliary radioactive source alone. *A* shows that due to both sources. *A* corresponds to a drift over approximately 15 minutes.

[58] A. H. Compton, E. O. Wollan and R. D. Bennett, *Rev. Sci. Instr.*, **5**, 415 (1934).
[59] J. J. Hopfield, *Phys. Rev.*, **43**, 675 (1933).

section of the electrometer was grounded for 3 minutes; it was then left insulated for 57 minutes. During the latter interval it drifted a distance proportional to the difference between the average cosmic ray ionization current and auxiliary balancing current. At the end of every four hour period the sensitivity of the electrometer was automatically measured and recorded. (5) Shielding from a major part of stray radioactive radiations was provided by a layer of lead shot 17.3 cm. thick placed between the spherical ionization chamber and the larger outer sphere. This is equivalent to some 12 cm. of solid lead, depending somewhat upon the size of shot

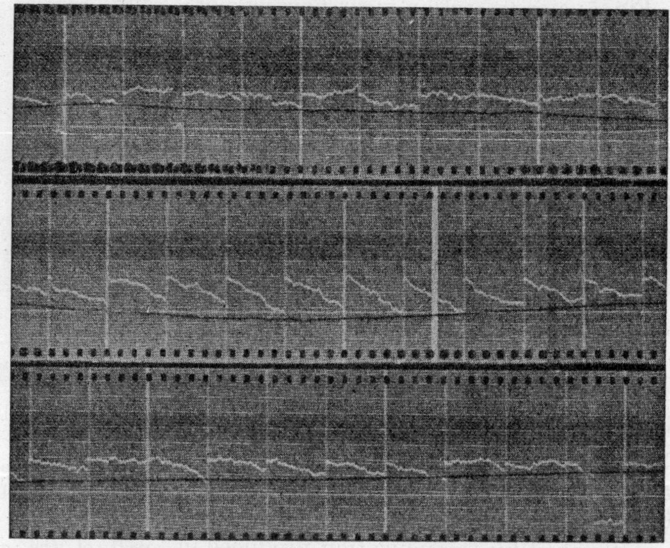

FIG. 8.—A typical record obtained with the Carnegie Model C cosmic ray meter. The vertical lines represent 15 minute intervals. In normal use, the camera is run more slowly and the vertical lines represent 1 hour intervals. The longitudinal wavy white line represents the position of the electrometer needle. The longitudinal continuous white trace is a record of temperature. The longitudinal continuous black trace is a record of pressure. There are three bursts shown here, two in the early part of the record and one near the end.

used. This thickness is sufficient to reduce the normal local radiation to not more than ½ percent of the cosmic ray ionization at sea level; and what is even more important, the variation in this small residual should not be more than 0.1 percent of the cosmic ray ionization.

A typical record obtained with one of these cosmic ray meters is shown in Fig. 8. Although cosmic ray bursts or showers will not be discussed until later, it is interesting that three such bursts are apparent in this record, two very near the beginning and one nearly at the end. These bursts produce a terrific momentary ionization, causing an abrupt jump of the electrometer needle. The effect of any such burst upon the observations can be eliminated by making allowance for the magnitude of the accompanying abrupt jump in electrometer reading. Instruments of this type have been used widely by Compton and his collaborators; they apparently yield entirely reliable information. Several other types of instruments, some of them quite similar in many respects to this one, have been used by other workers. References to descriptions of these are available in the literature.[50,52,58]

It was an instrument of the type just described that was used by Compton and Turner[54] on their 12 voyages across the Pacific Ocean. The same instrument was used by Gill[56] for the 15 additional voyages made later. Fig. 9 shows the observed variation of cosmic ray intensity with latitude. The ordinate represents the cosmic ray intensity in percent of the normal

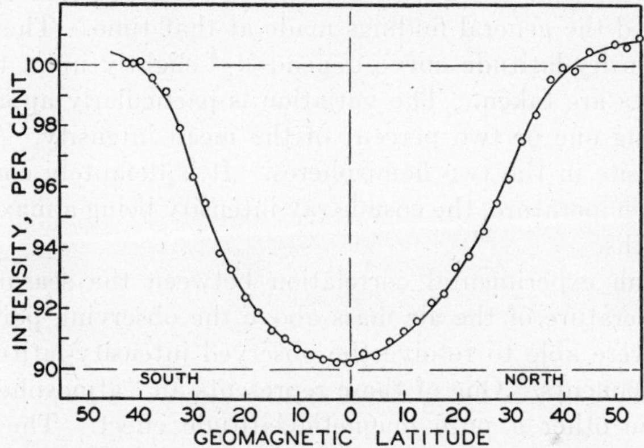


FIG. 9.—Showing the variation of cosmic ray intensity with magnetic latitude.

value observed at Chicago, corrected of course to standard atmospheric pressure and for residual ionization in the electroscope. Each point is the average of the average intensity observed by Compton and Turner and the average of that observed by Gill. The minimum intensity occurs at the magnetic equator. The intensity at this minimum is 10.3 percent less than that at Vancouver, at 55° N latitude. This same difference was observed by Compton and Turner and by Gill. The rate of variation of intensity with latitude becomes very small at the higher latitudes.

These general findings are in agreement with the results of other studies. For example, the 10.3 percent reduction at the equator observed in these works using a shield equivalent to 12 cm. of lead, is to be compared with the values 17 percent found with no shields,[60] 14 percent with a 6 cm. shield,[50] 13 percent with a 6.5 cm. shield,[20,54] 12.5 percent with a 12 cm. shield,[61] 11 percent with a 12 cm. shield,[52] and 10.1 percent with a 10 cm. shield. The

[60] J. Clay, *Proc. Roy. Soc.*, A, **151**, 202 (1935).

[61] R. A. Millikan and H. V. Neher, *Phys. Rev.*, **47**, 205 (1935).

shield filters out some of the softer radiation and thereby reduces the mean latitude variation. Although these percentages do not represent differences between the equator and exactly the same latitudes in all cases, they are comparable. Compton and Turner[54] found the "knee" of the latitude-intensity curve at from 35° to 40° latitude, whereas other observations place it at[50] from 40° to 45°, at[52] 41°, at[51] 55°, at[56] from 40° to 45°, at[62] 40°, somewhere below[63] 56°, and somewhere below[57] 53°.

There is definitely a small seasonal change in cosmic ray intensity. Although the literature[54] contains references to numerous previous observations dealing with a possible seasonal variation, Compton and Turner's Pacific Ocean data constituted the first major study of the effect. More recent studies by Gill,[56] by Forbush,[64] and by Millikan, Neher, and Smith[62] have confirmed the general findings made at that time. The shape of the observed intensity-latitude curve depends[54,56] slightly upon the season in which the data are taken. The variation is particularly apparent at high latitudes, being one or two percent of the mean intensity. The seasonal effect is opposite in the two hemispheres. It is definitely correlated with atmospheric temperature, the cosmic ray intensity being a maximum during the cold months.

Through an experimental correlation between the seasonal variation and the temperature of the air mass above the observing point, Compton and Turner were able to resolve the observed intensity-latitude variation into two components. One of these represents an "atmospheric" latitude effect and the other a pure magnetic latitude effect. The atmospheric latitude effect is somewhat larger at high latitudes than at the equator, representing one or two percent of the total, and shows seasonal variations. The true magnetic latitude effect is free from seasonal variations. Whereas Fig. 9 shows actually observed changes in intensity averaged over all seasons, Fig. 10 represents the variation[56] of intensity due to the true magnetic latitude effect. In plotting the curve for the true magnetic latitude effect no distinction has been made between data taken in the northern hemisphere and that taken in the southern hemisphere. The two sets of data are shown by different sets of points, however. The variations on the two sides of the magnetic equator are closely symmetrical. All observations fall on a smooth curve having a distinct minimum at the equator and a rather sharp knee at from 35° to 40°. Above this knee the intensity varies only slightly if at all.

The fact that seasonal variation in cosmic ray intensity is correlated with atmospheric temperature does not mean necessarily that temperature

[62] R. A. Millikan, H. V. Neher and D. O. Smith, *Phys. Rev.*, **56**, 487 (1939).

[63] T. H. Johnson, *Phys. Rev.*, **54**, 151 (1938).

[64] S. E. Forbush, *Phys. Rev.*, **54**, 975 (1938).

changes are directly responsible for the variation. It seemed[54] more probable from the first that some then unknown condition of the upper atmosphere, for which the temperature is an approximate index, is responsible for these changes in intensity. The electric potential gradient in the atmosphere and the height of the ionized Heaviside layer have been suggested as possible causes. What appears to be the real cause of it was suggested by Blackett[65] in 1938. The penetrating component of cosmic rays is known to consist of mesotrons, particles bearing the same charge as the electron, either positive or negative, but having a mass some 200 times as large. Evidence for the existence of these particles will be given in the

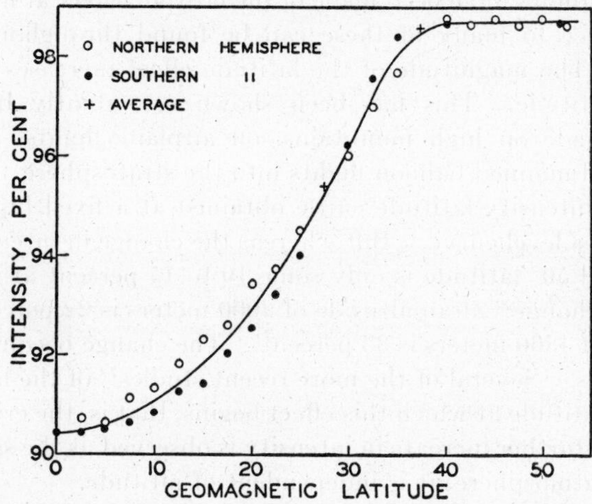


FIG. 10.—Showing the variation of cosmic ray intensity with magnetic latitude. The atmospheric latitude effect has been eliminated to obtain this curve. The curve is closely symmetrical about the equator.

next chapter. They are now known to be secondaries produced[66] high in the atmosphere. Previous to Blackett's interpretation it had been suggested that these mesotrons are radioactive, decaying with a half life period of a few microseconds. This radioactive property has now been established, as will be made evident in the next chapter.

Blackett[65] proposed to interpret the seasonal variation of cosmic ray intensity in terms of the radioactive decay of the mesotron. Blackett supposed that these mesotrons are secondary particles produced in the upper atmosphere, perhaps 15 to 20 kilometers above the earth's surface. If these particles are radioactive with a half life of a few microseconds, as is now known to be the case, some of them decay before reaching the earth's

[65] P. M. S. Blackett, *Phys. Rev.*, **54**, 973 (1938).

[66] M. Schein, W. P. Jesse and E. O. Wollan, *Phys. Rev.*, **57**, 847 (1940); **59**, 615 (1941).

surface. Now during the warm season the air mass is higher above the earth's surface on the average, and the production of mesotrons would be expected to take place at a greater altitude. Since the particles would then have to travel farther to reach the earth's surface, a greater fraction of them would disintegrate before arriving. The cosmic ray intensity would therefore be smaller during the warm season, as it is observed to be. Numerous works[65,67–70] have since indicated the essential correctness of Blackett's interpretation. It has even been found that a decrease in cosmic ray intensity accompanies the passing of a warm air front, no doubt due to an increase in the altitude of the air layer in which the mesotrons are produced.

Numerous studies have been made of the latitude effect at high altitudes. Specific reference to many of these can be found throughout the literature.[20,63,71–73] The magnitude of the latitude effect increases rapidly with increases in altitude. This has been shown consistently by nearly all observations made on high mountains, on airplane flights, and on both observation and manned balloon flights into the stratosphere. The general shape[71] of the intensity-latitude curve obtained at a fixed high altitude is similar to the sea level curve. But whereas the change in intensity between the equator and 50° latitude is only some 10 to 15 percent at sea level, the corresponding change[71] at an altitude of 2000 meters is 22 percent, and that at an altitude of 4360 meters is 33 percent. The change becomes very large at high altitudes. Several of the more recent studies[73] of the latitude effect show that the latitude at which this effect begins, that is, the critical latitude above which no further increase in intensity is observed, is the same throughout the whole atmosphere; it is independent of altitude.

The latitude effect has been of great significance in clarifying ideas regarding the nature of the cosmic radiation and in obtaining approximate values for the energy associated with the radiation. It has been remarked that one school maintained from the first, and with considerable supporting evidence, that the cosmic radiation consisted of unusually energetic photons. The radiation was thought to be of the same nature as gamma rays, except that the frequencies were very much higher. Measurements of the rate of absorption in matter indicated[18] the presence of wave lengths as short as $0.8 \times 10^{-12}$ cm. In fact it appeared that the general radiation might consist of several fairly well-defined bands of wave lengths. It was recognized

[67] D. H. Loughridge and P. F. Gast, *Phys. Rev.*, **57**, 938 (1940); **58**, 583 (1940).
[68] Y. Nishina, Y. Sekido, H. Simamura and H. Arakawa, *Phys. Rev.*, **57**, 663, 1050 (1940).
[69] N. F. Beardsley, *Phys. Rev.*, **59**, 233, 402 (1941).
[70] V. F. Hess, *Phys. Rev.*, **57**, 781 (1940).
[71] A. H. Compton, *Phys. Rev.*, **43**, 387 (1933).
[72] M. Cosyns, *Nature*, **137**, 616 (1936).
[73] B. Gross, *Phys. Rev.*, **55**, 112 (1939).

that the energies associated with these high frequency photons were enormous. The energy $h\nu$ of a quantum of radiation of wave length $0.8 \times 10^{-12}$ cm. is approximately 150 MEV. This is an energy which was unheard of before the study of cosmic rays.

The question of a possible origin of such energetic radiation was an intriguing one. Millikan[74] proposed to account for the radiation through the interchange of mass and energy in the annihilation of matter or in the creation of certain types of atoms from their component parts. Calculations showed that if the energy associated with the decrease of mass accompanying the creation of He from H were to be radiated as a photon, the frequency of the radiation would be essentially that of one of the more prominent cosmic ray bands. Other and more energetic radiation might well have come from the creation of O and Si out of H. Quantitative calculations seemed to carry some conviction that the origin of cosmic radiation was actually the creation of certain atoms out of H. There appeared to be little evidence of any radiation associated with the complete annihilation of an atom such as H. This theory stimulated a great interest in cosmic rays. It sometimes happens, however, that some of the most stimulating suggestions are finally shown to be in error. The evidence against the photon character of primary cosmic rays is overwhelming today. The existence of a latitude effect was one of the earlier pieces of evidence which spoke strongly against this supposed character. The mere existence of a magnetic rather than a geographical latitude effect shows immediately that the earth's magnetic field has some marked effect upon the intensity of cosmic radiation. And how could the earth's magnetic field affect in any way the number of photons coming to the earth's surface from interstellar space?

As a result of these difficulties it was suggested that the cosmic radiation coming from interstellar space consists of charged particles rather than of photons. The magnetic field of the earth would be expected to affect these. Following this suggestion, it was shown by Störmer[75] and by Lemaitre and Vallarta[76] that the earth's magnetic field would influence the motion of charged particles coming from outer space in such a way that it might explain quantitatively the observed variation of intensity with latitude. It is true that the supposed charged particles would have to possess tremendous energies in order to penetrate the earth's atmosphere and more. And it might be suspected that the relatively weak magnetic field about the earth would have a negligible influence upon the direction of such energetic particles. But when it is recalled that the earth's field extends hundreds or even thousands of miles above the earth's surface, it becomes apparent

[74] R. A. Millikan, *Phys. Rev.*, **32**, 533 (1928).

[75] C. Störmer, *Zeits. f. Astrophys.*, **1**, 237 (1930); *Oslo Obs. Publ.*, No. 10 (1934).

[76] G. Lemaitre and M. S. Vallarta, *Phys. Rev.*, **43**, 87 (1933).

that the total bending suffered by even a very high speed particle might be quite appreciable.

It has been calculated that the magnetic field 15,000 miles from the surface of the earth is approximately one percent of the value at the surface. In considering the magnetic field distribution over such an extended region it is permissible to regard the earth as a bar magnet having a magnetic moment[24] of $8.1 \times 10^{25}$ e.m.u. Now if a charged particle moves at any angle other than 0° with the direction of a magnetic field its motion is modified by the field. If the particle moves at constant speed in a direction perpendicular to a uniform field its path is a circle. The more energetic the particle the larger is the radius of the circular arc described. If the magnetic field is not uniform the path is a section of a spiral rather than the arc of a circle. If the particle moves at any angle other than 0° or 90° with the magnetic field, then it executes a helical path about the field lines.

Analytical treatment shows that if charged particles of various energies come equally from all directions of outer space, then the effect of the earth's magnetic field is to allow more particles to strike the earth at high latitudes than at low. Consider first a charged particle moving vertically toward the earth at one of the magnetic poles. This particle will be moving parallel to the magnetic field; it will not be deflected by this field. As a consequence, as far as any effect produced by the magnetic field is concerned, particles of all energies can reach the earth equally well at the poles. It is true that a particle must have considerable energy to penetrate the atmosphere, and this fact alone would exclude some of the lower energy particles from the group that reaches the earth. Consider next a particle moving vertically in the magnetic equatorial plane. This particle, or any other moving in this plane, has a direction of motion perpendicular to the magnetic field. Other factors being equal, it will be deflected a maximum amount. As an example, think of a particle moving vertically toward the earth but still 4,000 miles above the earth's surface. It is obvious that such a particle will never strike the earth if it describes an arc having an equivalent radius less than 4,000 miles. It would be possible to calculate the limiting paths which particles might describe and still reach the earth. Since the particle must describe a path having a not too small radius of curvature, it is apparent that there exists a critical energy below which it is impossible for a particle of given $e/m$ to reach the earth in the equatorial region. This critical energy is of the order of $10^{10}$ electron volts. All particles having an energy smaller than this critical value are bent sufficiently by the magnetic field that they turn away from the earth before striking it.

It is true that particles are incident from directions other than the vertical, and the paths of these are somewhat modified. Analysis shows that at a given latitude and for a particle of given energy, there exists a cone which defines the directions from which a particle may come and still strike the earth. The angular opening of this cone becomes larger with increases in the energy of the particle; it vanishes for that critical energy below which no particles can reach the earth. For particles of a given energy, the angular opening of the cone becomes larger as one proceeds to higher magnetic latitudes. It turns out that the minimum energy that a positive or negative electron can have and still reach the earth is somewhat larger at the magnetic equator than at higher latitudes. This critical energy in electron volts is given approximately by

$$V_0 = 1.92 \times 10^{10} \cos^4 \lambda$$

where $\lambda$ is the magnetic latitude. It is therefore clear that if cosmic rays consist of charged particles of different energies, then more of these will reach the earth at higher latitudes than at the equator. The actual manner in which the intensity would vary with latitude would depend upon the energy distribution among the cosmic ray particles. The existence of a rather well defined knee in the latitude curve at approximately 40° latitude, indicates that there must be present in the cosmic radiation an inappreciable number of particles having energies smaller than the critical value necessary to reach the earth at this latitude. In the absence of such low energy particles one would expect no further increase as one proceeds to higher latitudes.

The existence of a marked latitude effect, together with the straightforward interpretation of this in terms of the deflections suffered by charged particles, seems to demand that at least a part of the primary cosmic radiation consist of charged particles. As far as this interpretation goes these particles might be either positive or negative; they might be electrons, positrons, protons or alpha particles. The type of particle would have to be judged largely from other experiments. Although the latitude effect requires that an appreciable part of the radiation consist of charged particles, it by no means excludes the possibility of the presence of photons or neutrons. When combined with other evidence, however, it indicates pretty definitely that at least a very large fraction[20] of the primary cosmic rays are of the charged particle type. Quite recently there has appeared rather good evidence[66] that some of these particles are protons.

It has been remarked that the manner of variation of intensity with latitude would depend upon the energy distribution among the cosmic ray particles. Knowing the manner in which the intensity does vary with latitude, it is possible[77] to calculate an energy distribution which would lead to the observed manner of variation. This calculation makes use of the fact that the lowest energy, expressed in electron volts, which a charged

[77] H. Zanstra, *Naturwiss.*, **22**, 171 (1934).

particle can have and still proceed toward the earth at a magnetic latitude $\lambda$ is given approximately by

$$V_0 = 1.92 \times 10^{10} \cos^4 \lambda$$

Although a more rigorous expression for this energy has been given,[78] this relation is sufficiently good for the present purpose. If one combines this expression with experimental data on the ionization due to rays coming vertically to the earth at various latitudes, one can obtain the energy distribution of the incoming cosmic rays. Such considerations have led to various estimates of the energies possessed by these particles. Compton and Turner[54] conclude that there are two primary components at sea level. The more prominent of these is made up of particles having energies in excess

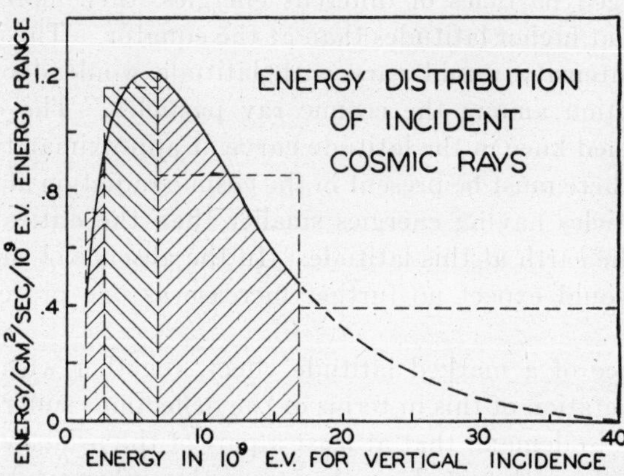


Fig. 11.—Showing the relative numbers of cosmic ray particles having various energies.

of $7.5 \times 10^9$ volts, and the weaker consists of particles of energy as low as $2.5 \times 10^9$ volts. Johnson[79] concludes that the average energy per cosmic ray particle coming in at the equator is $3 \times 10^{10}$ volts. The average of particles at higher latitudes is of course smaller, for particles with less energy are able to penetrate the earth's magnetic field at these higher latitudes.

One of the most recent and complete calculations of the energy distribution among the primary cosmic rays is one made by Bowen, Millikan and Neher[80] from observations they had obtained on numerous balloon flights at various latitudes. Fig. 11 shows the energy distribution obtained by them. Particles having energies approximately $6 \times 10^9$ volts are apparently most numerous, although there exist some particles with lower energies and many with considerably higher energies. While this distribution will

[78] G. Lemaitre and M. S. Vallarta, *Phys. Rev.*, **50**, 493 (1936).

[79] T. H. Johnson, *Phys. Rev.*, **53**, 499 (1938).

[80] I. S. Bowen, R. A. Millikan and H. V. Neher, *Phys. Rev.*, **53**, 855 (1938).

no doubt be modified in the future, it does not seem at all likely that the orders of magnitude can be changed. Quite recent calculations by Hilberry[81] have led to a similar distribution. These primary cosmic rays are truly high energy particles. The most energetic charged particle that can be produced directly in the laboratories today has an energy of the order of 50 MEV. The average cosmic ray particle possesses an energy some 200 times this, and many of them possess energies much higher. There is little hope ever to compete successfully with nature in the production of really high energy particles.

Johnson[79] has made some interesting calculations regarding the number of cosmic ray particles that strike the top of the earth's atmosphere per second. Using experimental data for the total energy spent in producing ionization in the atmosphere, and a calculated value for the average energy of the cosmic ray particle capable of getting through the earth's magnetic barrier, he found that approximately $8.0 \times 10^{17}$ primary cosmic ray particles are incident per second upon the earth's atmosphere. The total power carried by these primary cosmic rays is approximately 1,000,000 kilowatts. If all of the primary cosmic ray particles are positively charged, this stream of charged particles coming to the earth represents an electrical current of 0.13 amperes. If there were no compensating effects this would increase the electrical potential of the earth at the rate of 180 volts per second. It will be pointed out later that, although most of the primary particles responsible for the penetrating component at sea level appear to be positively charged protons, those primary particles responsible for the intense soft component observed high in the atmosphere are apparently electrons, about

TABLE I

Probable characteristics of cosmic rays falling upon the top of the atmosphere at various magnetic latitudes. All energies are given in electron volts

| | Geomagnetic latitude | | |
|---|---|---|---|
| | 3° | 39° | 52° |
| Energy falling per sec. on each sq. cm. of the atmosphere | $1 \times 10^9$ | $1.7 \times 10^9$ | $3.2 \times 10^9$ |
| Total number of ions formed per sec. below each sq. cm. of the upper surface of the atmosphere | $3 \times 10^7$ | $5.4 \times 10^7$ | $10 \times 10^7$ |
| Low energy limit imposed by the earth's magnetic field | $15 \times 10^9$ | $8 \times 10^9$ | $2 \times 10^9$ |
| Average energy per particle striking the atmosphere | $3 \times 10^{10}$ | $1.6 \times 10^{10}$ | $0.88 \times 10^{10}$ |
| Probable number of particles striking each sq. cm. of surface of the atmosphere per min | 1.9 | 6.5 | 21.8 |

[81] N. Hilberry, *Phys. Rev.*, **59**, 763 (1941).

half positive and half negative. Certain other interesting results are shown in Table I. It is interesting that so few particles strike any small area of the atmosphere; the present estimate is only 1.9 per sq. cm. per minute near the magnetic equator. The number of particles, including both primary and secondary, that arrive per minute per sq. cm. of the earth's surface is even smaller. Experiments[82] indicate that approximately 1.5 particles per sq. cm. per minute arrive at sea level. Many of the primaries and many of the large number of secondaries formed high in the atmosphere are unable to penetrate the entire atmosphere.

This number should not be confused with the number of ions formed by the cosmic rays per cc. per second at sea level. Numerous measurements of this latter quantity have been made. It is much easier to make accurate relative measurements of the ionization produced by cosmic rays than it is to make absolute determinations of the ionization. Variations among ionization chambers, shields, calibrations, and methods of reducing data introduce far greater probable errors in the absolute measurements. And often the relative measurements give the essential information desired. For example, variations of intensity with latitude are shown just as well by the relative ionizations produced as they would be by absolute ionizations. Hence, many of the ionization data are expressed relative to some more or less arbitrary zero. Even these relative measurements require correction for ionization due to radioactive contamination of the walls of the ionization chamber. This ionization is measured by taking the instrument to a great depth of water, or down in a mine; the cosmic ray contribution at sufficient depths becomes inappreciable.

There have been a number of determinations of the absolute ionization produced by cosmic rays at sea level. These do not show the consistency one might expect. The value obtained of course depends upon whether some of the cosmic radiation has been cut off by shields used to eliminate the effect of stray radioactive radiations. For example, an 11 cm. lead shield has been found by one observer[83] to decrease the ionization due to cosmic rays at sea level from 2.48 to 1.75 ion pair per cc. per second in air at one atmosphere. The reduction allowed by another observer,[84] however, for a 12.5 cm. lead shield is only from 1.28 to 1.10. A third value obtained[58] after filtering through 12 cm. of lead is 1.22. There is thus considerable variation among the values 1.75, 1.10 and 1.22, all obtained after filtering the cosmic rays through essentially the same thickness of lead.

To obtain the absolute ionization due to the entire cosmic radiation, it is of course necessary to make a correction for whatever shield is used.

[82] J. C. Street and R. H. Woodward, *Phys. Rev.*, **46**, 1029 (1934).

[83] R. A. Millikan, *Phys. Rev.*, **39**, 397 (1931).

[84] J. Clay and H. F. Jongen, *Physica*, **4**, 245 (1937).

Since observations carried on over water relatively free from radioactive contamination require thinner shields and therefore smaller corrections than observations over land, several measurements have been made over water. Typical values obtained over both land and water for the total sea level ionization at a pressure of one atmosphere of air are 1.37,[17] 1.6,[18] 2.48,[83] 1.28,[84] and 1.63[85] ion pairs per cc. per second. While it is true that these values were not all obtained at the same latitude, the variation is far greater than the 10% which might be introduced by the latitude effect. The last value, (1.63 ± 0.05), is one of the most recent and probably one of the most reliable. It represents the ionization in air at atmospheric pressure and 15° C due to all cosmic rays coming through an atmosphere corresponding to 76 cm. of Hg; it represents the ionization at magnetic latitudes greater than 50°, latitudes sufficiently large that there is no further variation of intensity with latitude. The ionization in gases other than air is of course different. For example, an ionization of (2.35 ± 0.06) ion pairs per cc. per second is found[85] in argon at one atmosphere pressure when the pressure of the atmosphere is 76 cm. of Hg. For a barometer reading less than 76 cm. of Hg the ionization is somewhat greater due to the smaller absorption of the radiation in the atmosphere. The change is[85] approximately 5 percent per centimeter of Hg change in pressure of the atmospheric air.

**Seasonal, Diurnal and Other Changes in Intensity**

That there exist seasonal changes in cosmic ray intensity amounting to several percent of the total has already been mentioned in the discussion of the latitude effect. And it has been pointed out that at least a large part of this change is closely correlated with atmospheric temperature. There have been many investigations attempting to prove or disprove the existence of seasonal, daily, and erratic changes of one type and another. While many studies have been described in the literature, one of the most recent and extensive is that by Forbush.[64] The problem of unraveling possible seasonal, solar diurnal, sidereal diurnal and erratic variations is complicated at best. Investigators have been further handicapped by the fact that all of these are small and some, if they exist at all, are barely large enough to be detected.

The question of the existence of a diurnal variation of intensity with sidereal time has been considered of great importance. It was pointed out[86] in 1935 that if the cosmic radiation originates outside of our own galaxy then the motion of our galaxy as a whole, combined with the earth's rotation, should lead to a small daily variation with sidereal time. Astronomical evidence indicates that our entire galaxy is rotating with a small angular

[85] J. Clay and P. H. Clay, *Physica*, **5**, 898 (1938).

[86] A. H. Compton and I. A. Getting, *Phys. Rev.*, **47**, 817 (1935).

velocity. Since our own planetary system is at a considerable distance from the center of this galaxy, it results that the sun and its planets are moving through space at a speed of approximately 300 kilometers per second. A recent investigation[87] indicates that this velocity may be nearer 200 than 300 kilometers per second. At the present time this motion is toward Cepheus, 47° N declination, 20 hours and 55 minutes right ascension. Since the angular velocity of the galaxy is small, the direction of this motion will be approximately that just stated for years to come.

If the cosmic radiation comes from beyond our own galaxy, then the intensity observed in the northern hemisphere should be greater than that observed in the southern hemisphere. A difference in intensity would be expected whether the cosmic radiation consist of charged particles or of photons. If the rays are charged particles, then our motion through space would cause more particles per second to strike the northern hemisphere. This hemisphere is the forward face of the earth as it moves through space. If the rays are photons, there would be a Doppler effect with a resultant increase in frequency, and hence in energy and intensity, in the northern hemisphere. On either concept of the nature of cosmic rays, the intensity observed at high north magnetic latitudes should exceed that observed at high south latitudes by 0.5 percent. Early experiments appeared[20] to bear out this expectation. Since the motion of our galaxy is not exactly to the north, then rotation of the earth would be expected to lead to a small daily variation with sidereal time. The magnitude of this variation should depend upon latitude. It was calculated that the magnitude of the daily variation should be of the order of 0.1 percent if the cosmic rays consist of charged particles; it should be from 2½ to 10 times larger[20] if the primary cosmic rays are photons. In either case, the maximum intensity should occur at 20 hours and 40 minutes sidereal time. More rigorous theoretical treatment[88] has since modified these expected values slightly, but it has not changed the general conclusions.

Even when this galactic rotation effect was first suggested, some experimental data[86] bearing on the question was available. These data appeared to speak strongly in favor of the existence of such an effect. The phase of the variation agreed almost exactly with that predicted; and the amplitude of the apparent effect was essentially that expected on the supposition that the primary cosmic radiation consisted of charged particles. Later evidence[20] seemed to speak even more convincingly in favor of the existence of the effect. Most workers felt that both the north-south effect and the sidereal diurnal variation were real.

[87] G. L. Camm, *Roy. Astron. Soc.*, M.N., **99**, 71 (1938).

[88] M. S. Vallarta, C. Graef and S. Kusaka, *Phys. Rev.*, **55**, 1 (1939).

Although a few years ago the evidence seemed to be quite strong in favor of the existence of a variation of cosmic ray intensity with sidereal time, the existence of the effect is by no means as certain today. There is rather good evidence now that if such an effect does exist it is quite small, no larger than the experimental errors present in the most reliable observations. This change of view has been brought about through recent success in unraveling the seasonal, solar diurnal, and other variations. Compton and Turner's Pacific Ocean data[54] seemed at first[20] to show a definite sidereal time effect, and a slightly greater intensity in the northern hemisphere. The apparent existence of these effects appeared consistent with the results of other studies.[89,90] A more complete treatment[54] of these data indicated, however, that there was no significant difference between the intensities observed at equal north and south latitudes. Any difference which might exist was much smaller than that theoretically expected. There still appeared to be a real sidereal time variation, but it was considerably smaller than the predicted value.

Thompson[91] has shown that even this smaller sidereal time effect is probably fictitious. When the data are properly analyzed, making due allowance for the solar diurnal and for the seasonal changes, there remains no significant variation associated with sidereal time. Workers are fairly generally agreed today that no significant sidereal effect exists. Still more precise data will be required before one can feel quite safe in saying definitely that no galactic rotation effect exists. If it does exist, however, it must certainly be smaller than suspected. This may be due in part to a too high original estimate of the velocity of our galaxy through space. If one accepts the theory behind such a possible effect, then one is almost forced to conclude[27] that the cosmic rays originate within our own galaxy. Workers in this field have thus completely about faced within the past few years. Several years ago it appeared quite certain that the cosmic rays originate outside of our own galaxy. Now there is equally good reason for concluding that they originate within this galaxy. If they do originate from without, then one must assume that before reaching us they have acquired in some way the motion of our galaxy.

As the reader will have inferred from previous remarks, there do exist other recognized intensity variations. There can be no doubt of the existence of a seasonal variation. This was shown conclusively by Compton and Turner's Pacific Ocean data,[54] as well as by numerous other extensive works. The amplitude of this seasonal variation is zero at the magnetic equator; it increases as one proceeds to higher latitudes. Forbush[64] has

[89] W. Illing, *Terr. Mag.*, **41,** 185 (1936).

[90] B. F. J. Schonland, B. Delatisky, and J. Gaskell, *Nature*, **138,** 325 (1936).

[91] J. L. Thompson, *Phys. Rev.*, **55,** 11 (1938).

recently reported the results of continuous cosmic ray intensity observations made over periods exceeding 17 months at four different observing stations. The locations of these stations ranged from 48° S to 50° N magnetic latitude. The seasonal variation, which has a period of 12 months, has an amplitude ranging from zero at the equator to 1 or 2 percent of the total intensity at a latitude of 50°. The maximum of this seasonal variation occurs during the month of January in the northern hemisphere. The variation is in opposite phase in the southern hemisphere, the maximum occurring there in July. The maximum seems to occur always during the colder part of the year.

The cause of the seasonal variation has already been discussed in connection with the variation of intensity with latitude. The generally accepted interpretation[65] is that in terms of the decay of the mesotrons formed high in the atmosphere, and a seasonal shift in the height of the layer of atmosphere in which the mesotrons are produced. The possibility[92] that it might be due to a magnetic field about the sun is ruled out by the fact that the phase of the observed effect is just opposite[64] that which such a magnetic field would cause.

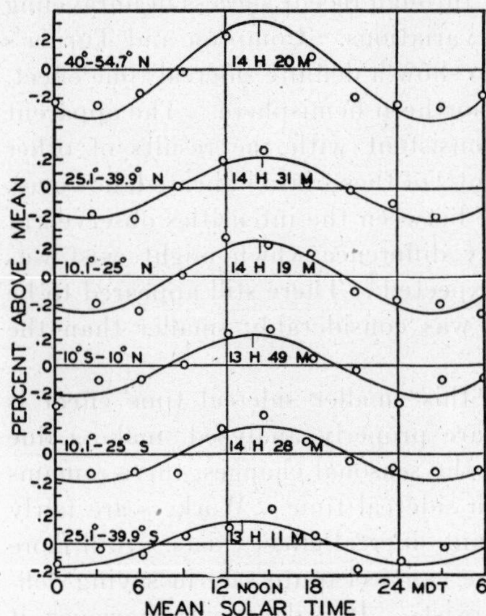


FIG. 12.—Showing the variation of cosmic ray intensity with solar time of day. The curve is essentially independent of the latitude in which the data are taken.

There appears definitely to exist also a variation of cosmic ray intensity with solar time of day. Such an effect appeared in Compton and Turner's[54] Pacific Ocean data. The cosmic ray intensity was consistently above average about noon. These data have been analyzed critically by Thompson[91,93] who finds a definite variation with solar time of day. The cosmic ray intensity is consistently large slightly after noon, at approximately two o'clock; it is a minimum shortly after midnight. The magnitude of the variation is small, the amplitude given by Thompson being 0.23% of the total intensity. These findings agree approximately with those of another study[94] which indicated a variation with an amplitude of 0.20% and a maximum at noon. This latter study utilized continuous observations made

[92] M. S. Vallarta, *Nature*, **139**, 839 (1937).

[93] J. L. Thompson, *Phys. Rev.*, **54**, 93 (1938).

[94] V. F. Hess and H. T. Graziadei, *Terr. Mag.*, **41**, 9 (1936).

over a three year period. The solar diurnal variation of cosmic ray intensity appears to be independent of latitude. Fig. 12 shows results[93] obtained at different latitudes between 40° S and 55° N. No appreciable variation in either the magnitude or the position of the maximum of the effect is evident. A comparison of results obtained from studies[93] carried out at sea level with those obtained in a similar study[94] at an altitude of 2300 meters indicates that this solar variation is essentially independent of altitude.

The cause of the solar diurnal variation is not known. The time at which the maximum intensity occurs might indicate the possibility of some cosmic rays coming directly from the sun. All evidence indicates, however, that if any such contribution exists it must be very small. One might also hope to interpret the diurnal variation in terms of a shift in air mass accompanying a change in temperature, much as is done for the seasonal variation. Unfortunately the phase of the effect which would be expected on this basis is opposite that of the observed effect. There have been several suggestions that small variations of this character may be attributable to a magnetic field about the sun. One recent treatment[95] of the possible effects of a solar magnetic field has indicated that such a field might influence considerably the actual cosmic ray intensity observed upon the earth. It appears further that it might introduce small annual and diurnal variations. These variations might be of a proper order of magnitude to account for the daily variation observed.

There exist other more or less erratic changes in cosmic ray intensity. Significant changes[24,96] have often been observed during major magnetic storms. These seem to occur simultaneously at all points on the earth. They often amount to several percent. It is generally supposed that the change in intensity accompanying these storms is due directly to the change in the effect of the abnormal magnetic field upon the charged particles constituting the cosmic radiation. There is some difficulty with such an interpretation, however. The changes in cosmic ray intensity are often far larger than one would expect from the observed accompanying changes in magnetic field. It has been calculated[96] that the change in the magnetic moment of the earth during the storm would, to account for the observed changes in cosmic ray intensity, have to be some 150 times as great as any change reconcilable with the observed variation in magnetic field. In addition to these major changes accompanying recognized magnetic storms, there are small erratic changes of variable magnitude. Recent and rather extensive investigation of these has shown that they occur at all points of the world simultaneously. The magnitude of such changes increases rapidly with increases in altitude. It appears to increase rapidly also, particularly at high altitudes, as one goes to higher latitudes. These

[95] P. S. Epstein, *Phys. Rev.*, **53**, 862 (1938).

[96] T. H. Johnson, *Terr. Mag.*, **43**, 1 (1938); *Rev. Mod. Phys.*, **10**, 222 (1938).

changes are apparently symmetrical about the magnetic equator. The origin of such small changes is not known. The fact that the ratio of magnitudes of these small erratic changes at different stations is essentially equal to the ratio of the changes produced at these same stations by major magnetic storms, leads one to suspect that the same mechanism may be responsible for both. Perhaps there are miniature magnetic storms in progress continually.

### The East-West Directional Effect

If cosmic rays consist of charged particles, and if particles of one sign of charge should be more numerous than those of opposite sign, then one should find an east-west asymmetry in the cosmic ray intensity. Consider a positively charged particle coming from interstellar space. For simplicity choose a particle coming from directly overhead. As this particle proceeds through the earth's magnetic field it will follow a curved path. Knowing the direction of the horizontal component of the earth's magnetic field, and knowing the direction of motion of the positively charged particle, it is easily argued that this particle will appear to have come from a somewhat westerly direction. In a similar manner, it can be argued that negatively charged particles would appear more abundant from an easterly direction. Of course not all positive particles would appear to come from the west; nor would all negatives appear to come from the east. A positive particle coming from the eastern horizon would appear to come from the east; but the curvature of its path would cause it to come in at a smaller zenith angle than it would were it not for this bending. In a similar way a negative particle coming from near the western horizon would appear to come from the west. The deflections in the earth's magnetic field, however, result in a preponderance of positives from the west and of negatives from the east. If the cosmic radiation consists of equal numbers of similar positive and negative particles there would be no east-west asymmetry in intensity. The two effects would just balance. It becomes clear, therefore, that important information regarding the nature of cosmic rays might be gathered from observations relative to the possible existence and possible magnitude of an east-west asymmetry.

The literature[20,96–103] contains many references to studies of this character. It has been recognized for some years that such an east-west effect

[97] T. H. Johnson, *Phys. Rev.*, **45**, 569 (1934); **48**, 287 (1935).
[98] B. Rossi, *Phys. Rev.*, **45**, 212 (1934).
[99] K. K. Darrow, *Bell System Tech. Jour.*, **18**, 190 (1939).
[100] T. H. Johnson and J. G. Barry, *Phys. Rev.*, **55**, 503 (1939); **56**, 219 (1939); **57**, 245 (1940).
[101] F. G. P. Seidl, *Phys. Rev.*, **59**, 7 (1941).
[102] T. H. Johnson, *Phys. Rev.*, **59**, 11 (1941).
[103] D. J. Hughes, *Phys. Rev.*, **57**, 592 (1940).

does exist. Quantitative measurements of the magnitude of the effect are ordinarily made through use of several coincidence counter tubes. These are placed in line so that only that radiation coming from a definite direction can pass through all counter tubes. Associated apparatus is arranged so that no count is recorded unless the radiation passes through all tubes. By tipping the apparatus one can measure the intensity of radiation coming in at various angles with the vertical. It has been found consistently that the intensity from the west exceeds that from the east. This is true for all zenith angles. That is, the intensity from a direction 30° west of vertical in an east-west plane exceeds that from a direction 30° east of vertical. Similarly, that from 45° west of vertical exceeds that from 45° east. This general finding indicates definitely that there is at least an excess of positively charged particles in the cosmic radiation.

The magnitude of the east-west asymmetry depends upon the latitude, altitude and zenith angle at which observations are made. The effect is a maximum at the equator, falling off rapidly at the higher latitudes. A small asymmetry exists[101,102] even at latitudes higher than that corresponding to the knee of the intensity-latitude curve. Near sea level the asymmetry increases somewhat with altitude,[97] though at high altitudes it almost vanishes.[100] The greatest asymmetry is found at zenith angles of from 45° to 60°. The theory of the bending of charged particles in the earth's magnetic field leads one to expect a maximum asymmetry at the equator, and an asymmetry which increases with zenith angle. A maximum is observed at the equator. Were it not for the absorption in the atmosphere one would expect the asymmetry to increase continually with zenith angle. But radiation coming from near the horizon must penetrate a great deal more atmosphere than that coming from above. For large zenith angles, therefore, the low energy rays are absorbed to a greater extent than are the high energy particles. This results in an actual decrease of asymmetry beyond zenith angles of about 60°.

It is customary to define the percent asymmetry as

$$\text{Percent asymmetry} = 2 \times \frac{W - E}{W + E} \times 100$$

where $W$ and $E$ represent the intensities from a westerly and an easterly direction, respectively. At sea level locations near the magnetic equator, the asymmetry between west and east zenith angles of 45° is[97] some 14 percent. One observer,[98] having filtered out the softer component with an 8 cm. lead shield, found near the equator and at 45° zenith angle, an asymmetry of 27 percent. The asymmetry of the unfiltered radiation decreases to 2 or 3 percent at latitudes of 40°. Only a slight asymmetry, but apparently definite,[101,102] has been observed at latitudes greater than 50°.

The magnitude of the east-west asymmetry allows one to estimate the relative abundance of positive and negative charged particles making up the primary radiation. The magnitude of the effect at sea level shows[96,97] that practically all of the primary radiation responsible for the cosmic ray effects at sea level must be positively charged. Only a small fraction could be negative. Since it is now known that the penetrating radiation observed at sea level consists largely of mesotrons, it must be that these mesotrons are formed in the upper atmosphere almost entirely by positive primaries. Several investigators[27,100,104–106] have suggested that these primaries are protons, and a recent investigation[66] of the production of mesotrons in the upper atmosphere has made it fairly certain that they are.

The conclusion that the primary cosmic rays responsible for the penetrating component at sea level are all positives raised another serious difficulty.[106–109] It has already been pointed out that this stream of positive particles coming to the earth would increase the potential of the earth by some 180 volts per second. This tendency might of course be offset by the gradual diffusion and attraction of negatives which might not possess sufficient energy to reach the earth. Surely the radiation coming to the earth must be statistically neutral in space. If it were all positive tremendous potential differences would be developed between points relatively close together in interstellar space. The potential between two points one light year apart would[106] be of the order of $7 \times 10^{18}$ volts. It therefore seems necessary to postulate a sufficient number of negative particles to maintain electrical equilibrium. It may be that these have energies too small to penetrate the earth's magnetic field. Or what seems more likely, as Johnson[100,104,106] argued, the positively charged particles may be of greater mass than the negative electrons. Johnson argued that these positives might well be protons, a suggestion that appears to have been confirmed by the recent experiments of Schein, Jesse and Wollan.[66] The possibility that this heavy primary component might consist of mesotrons is ruled out by the fact that the mesotron is radioactive.

It has been remarked that the east-west asymmetry is very small at high altitudes.[100] This is a quite recent finding and one which bears directly on the nature of the soft component of the primary radiation. The near absence of this effect at high altitudes means that there is near equality between the positive and the negative components of the primary

[104] T. H. Johnson, J. G. Barry and R. P. Shutt, *Phys. Rev.*, **57**, 1047 (1940).
[105] W. F. G. Swann, *Phys. Rev.*, **59**, 770, 836 (1941).
[106] T. H. Johnson, *Phys. Rev.*, **54**, 385 (1938).
[107] W. F. G. Swann, *Phys. Rev.*, **44**, 124 (1933).
[108] H. Alfvén, *Phys. Rev.*, **55**, 425 (1939).
[109] F. Evans, *Phys. Rev.*, **59**, 1 (1941).

radiation responsible for phenomena in the upper atmosphere. Thus the total primary radiation is now thought to be made up of two components, one consisting of high energy protons which produce in the upper atmosphere the penetrating mesotron radiation, the other consisting of approximately equal numbers of electrons and positrons which constitute the more easily absorbable radiation.

## Coincidence and Cloud Chamber Studies

Much valuable information has been gathered from various types of coincidence studies. Many of these have had to do with the absorption of cosmic rays in materials such as lead. Others have been concerned with directional effects. The interpretations of such studies have until recently been somewhat clouded by the possible presence of secondary effects. It is well known that the primary cosmic rays produce in the atmosphere or other matter a great deal of secondary radiation. These so-called secondaries may be either electrically charged particles or photons. As will be seen later, many of these secondaries start out almost simultaneously from a given locality. The question arises, therefore, as to whether multiple coincidence tubes in line are set off simultaneously by a single particle moving in such a direction as to pass through all tubes, or whether these tubes may be set off simultaneously by different secondary radiation passing through each tube. Certain interpretations of coincidence studies depend considerably upon which action is responsible for the impulse counted.

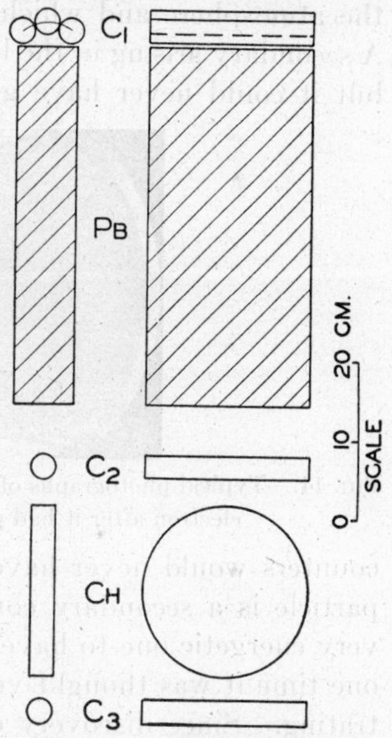


FIG. 13.—Showing the arrangement of apparatus used by Street, Woodward and Stevenson in photographing the tracks of cosmic ray particles.

Fortunately there are several experimental arrangements[110,111] which show quite definitely whether the particles producing coincidence counts under given conditions are mainly primary or secondary radiation. Fig. 13 shows an arrangement of three counter tubes $C_1$, $C_2$, and $C_3$. A lead block some 45 cm. thick can be placed between $C_1$ and $C_2$. A Wilson cloud chamber is placed between counters $C_2$ and $C_3$. Street, Woodward and Stevenson[111] found that a majority of photographs taken when the cloud chamber is tripped by a

[110] P. Auger and P. Ehrenfest, *Comptes Rendus*, **199**, 1609 (1934).
[111] J. C. Street, R. H. Woodward and E. C. Stevenson, *Phys. Rev.*, **47**, 891 (1935).

particle going through counters $C_1$, $C_2$ and $C_3$, show single straight paths of very high energy particles. As many as 90% of the photographs show this.

Typical photographs are reproduced in Fig. 14. It seems quite certain that the particle leaving this track is the same one that affected the coincidence counters. It has been shown[112] that about half of these particles will penetrate a lead block one meter thick, a thickness approximately equivalent to the atmosphere. This is about the same rate of absorption as that measured by the ionization the cosmic rays produce. The indication is strong, therefore, that these particles themselves are primary cosmic rays. If they are not primaries then they must be secondaries produced high in the atmosphere and which produce most of the ionization near sea level. A secondary arising in the lower part of the lead might provide such a track, but it could never have gone through counter $C_1$; hence the coincidence

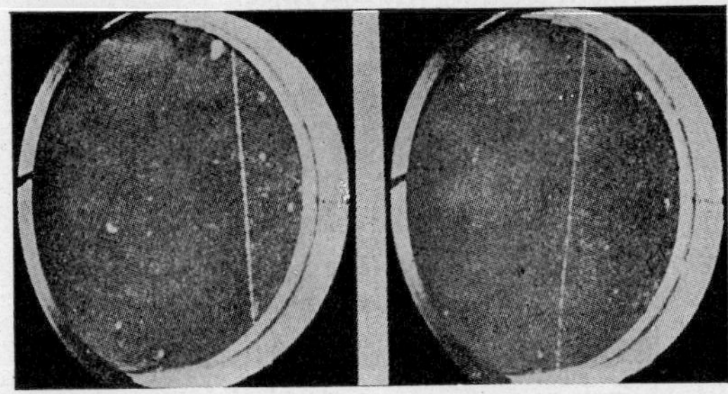

Fig. 14.—Typical photographs of single particle tracks. Each of these tracks was left by an electron after it had passed through the lead block shown in Fig. 13.

counters would never have tripped the cloud expansion chamber. If the particle is a secondary coming from above the lead it must have been a very energetic one to have gotten through the great thickness of lead. At one time it was thought very unlikely that secondaries could be this penetrating. Since discovery of the mesotron, however, and proof that these are exceedingly penetrating secondaries formed high in the atmosphere, it appears probable that many of the tracks observed were actually due to secondaries.

That the particles producing coincidence counts are not secondaries arising near the apparatus, particularly in the lead, is shown by another type of experiment.[112–114] Fig. 15 reproduces the experimental arrangement used by Hsiung.[114] The three Geiger-Muller tubes shown in a vertical line were so arranged that any particle coming through tubes 1 and 2 would record a coincidence on one mechanical counter. A second counter was so

[112] B. Rossi, *Naturwiss.*, **20**, 65 (1932); *Zeits f. Physik*, **82**, 151 (1933).
[113] B. Rossi, *Proc. Lond. Conf. on Nuclear Physics*, **1**, 233 (1934).
[114] D. S. Hsiung, *Phys. Rev.*, **46**, 653 (1934).

arranged that it registered only when a particle passed simultaneously through tubes 1, 2, and 3. Thus, double coincidences in the two upper tubes and triple coincidences in the three tubes were recorded simultaneously. Counter tube number 3 was always inclosed in a lead cylinder whose wall was 2½ cm. thick. This shield is sufficient to absorb practically all secondary radiation produced nearby, particularly in a block of lead used in different positions with respect to the several counter tubes. A block of lead 20 cm. thick could be used in three positions, completely removed from the apparatus (*A*), between counters 1 and 2 (*B*), or above the upper-most counter (*C*). Under condition *A* the apparatus records double coincidences produced by single primary or secondary rays from above and by stray secondary rays, together with triple coincidences produced alone by energetic rays from above. Under condition *B* one would expect a decrease in both the double and triple coincidences. Although insertion of the lead block causes the production of a greater number of secondaries, these are not recorded; the highly absorbing lead is between the two tubes sensitive to secondary rays. The presence of the lead block does reduce both double and triple coincidences due to rays from above; lead 20 cm. thick absorbs an appreciable fraction of these.

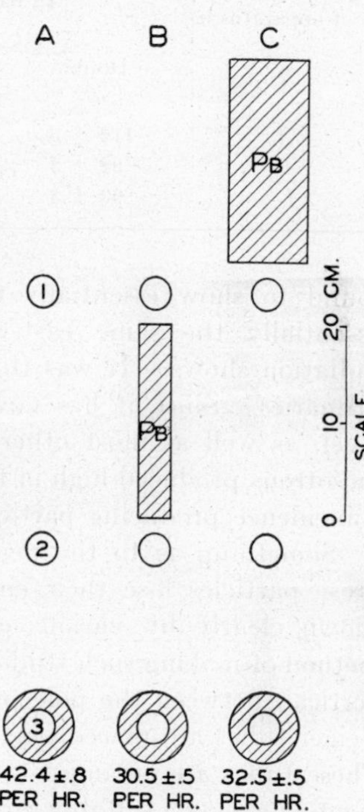


FIG. 15.—The arrangement of apparatus used in the Hsiung coincidence experiment to show that the penetrating coincidence particles are not secondaries produced in the apparatus.

Table II shows this decrease for data taken in a basement and for data taken on the roof of a building. Under condition *C* secondaries produced near the bottom of the lead block will produce double coincidences in tubes 1 and 2; the block will here absorb the same rays from above as it did in position *B*. The table shows that the triple coincidences under condition *C* are essentially equal to those under *B*; but the double coincidences, many of them due to local secondaries, are more numerous with the block in position *C*. It seems clear that, although there are many secondaries produced near the apparatus, all of the triple coincidences produced are due to very energetic radiation coming from far above the apparatus. These coincidence producing particles have been

TABLE II

Showing the number of coincidences per hour observed with the apparatus of Fig. 15. Preliminary observations were made in the basement of the laboratory. Final data were taken on the roof

| Arrangement of apparatus | Number of coincidences per hour | | | |
|---|---|---|---|---|
| | In basement | | On roof | |
| | Double | Triple | Double | Triple |
| *A* | 112 ± 3 | 27 ± 1 | 202.4 ± 1.8 | 42.4 ± 0.8 |
| *B* | 92 ± 3 | 23 ± 1 | 124.5 ± 1.5 | 30.5 ± 0.5 |
| *C* | 99 ± 3 | 23 ± 1 | 142.2 ± 1.1 | 32.6 ± 0.5 |

found to show essentially the same sea level latitude effect[115,116] and essentially the same east-west asymmetry[98,117,118] as the total cosmic radiation shows. It was therefore felt for some years that they must be primaries. Since it has now been found that the east-west effect at sea level, as well as most other sea level effects, is due largely to secondary mesotrons produced high in the atmosphere, it appears that the penetrating coincidence producing particles are really mesotron secondaries.

Something as to the penetrating power and as to the rate at which these particles lose their energy in passing through material[99] has been shown clearly by various cloud chamber experiments.[119–125] The usual method of making such studies is to arrange a cloud chamber, with its plane vertical, between the pole pieces of a strong electromagnet. Coincidence Geiger tubes are placed one above and one below the expansion chamber. These tubes are arranged to trip the cloud chamber and camera arrangement whenever a suitably directed particle passes through the system. The automatic tripping arrangement greatly increases the probability of obtaining satisfactory photographs for a large fraction of the exposures made. Stereoscopic views are usually taken. One of these is often a mirror view,

115 P. Auger and L. Leprince-Ringuet, *Nature*, **133**, 138 (1934).

116 J. Clay, *Physica*, **2**, 299 (1935).

117 T. H. Johnson, *Phys. Rev.*, **43**, 834 (1933); **44**, 856 (1933).

118 L. Alvarez and A. H. Compton, *Phys. Rev.*, **43**, 835 (1933).

119 C. D. Anderson and S. H. Neddermeyer, *Phys. Rev.*, **50**, 263 (1936).

120 J. Crussard and L. Leprince-Ringuet, *Comptes Rendus*, **204**, 112, 240 (1937).

121 S. H. Neddermeyer and C. D. Anderson, *Phys. Rev.*, **51**, 884 (1937).

122 P. M. S. Blackett and J. G. Wilson, *Proc. Roy. Soc.*, A, **160**, 304 (1937).

123 P. Ehrenfest, *Comptes Rendus*, **207**, 573 (1938).

124 J. G. Wilson, *Proc. Roy. Soc.*, A, **166**, 482 (1938).

125 P. M. S. Blackett, *Proc. Roy. Soc.*, A, **165**, 11 (1938).

taken by placing a mirror at such an angle as to view the track from an entirely different direction.

Photographs of this character allow determination of the actual geometry of the path described by the particle in passing through the magnetic field. From the amount of bending observed it is possible to evaluate the energy of the particle. This statement needs some qualification, for in order to evaluate the energy it is necessary to know, in addition to the bending suffered, both the charge and the mass of the particle. On the other hand, the momentum of the particle can be evaluated from the amount of bending if only the charge carried is known; the mass of the particle does not enter this calculation. The truth of these statements is evident from the following elementary considerations. A particle of mass $m$ and charge $e$, moving with a velocity $v$ perpendicular to a magnetic field $H$, will describe a circle of some radius $\rho$. If all quantities are expressed in the same system of units the relation

$$Hev = \frac{mv^2}{\rho}$$

holds for the quantities involved. The mass $m$ is of course the actual mass of a particle having a velocity $v$; it might be replaced by the quantity $m_0/\sqrt{1 - \beta^2}$ where $m_0$ is the rest mass. If this equation is solved for the momentum of the particle one obtains

$$\text{Momentum} = mv = eH\rho$$

Thus, the quantity $H\rho$ is a measure of the momentum, provided the charge of the particle is known.

Calculation of the velocity of the particle, or of the energy of the particle, in general involves the mass as well as the charge. If in the above expression for the momentum of a particle one substitutes $m_0/\sqrt{1 - \beta^2}$ for $m$ and $\beta c$ for $v$, one obtains

$$\frac{m_0\beta c}{\sqrt{1 - \beta^2}} = eH\rho$$

By squaring each side of this equation, solving explicitly for $\beta^2$, and then extracting the square root,

$$\beta = \frac{H\rho}{\sqrt{(m_0c/e)^2 + (H\rho)^2}}$$

This involves both the rest mass and the charge of the particle. It is apparent that for very high speed particles, for which $\beta$ approaches 1, the quantity $(H\rho)^2$ must become very large as compared to $(m_0c/e)^2$. This fact is important in that it allows one to calculate the energy of a very high speed particle without knowing the mass of the particle. If K.E. represents the kinetic energy of a particle, R.E. the "rest energy" due to its mass, and T.E. the total energy of this particle, then

$$\text{T.E.} = \text{K.E.} + \text{R.E.} = m_0c^2\left(\frac{1}{\sqrt{1-\beta^2}} - 1\right) + m_0c^2 = \frac{m_0c^2}{\sqrt{1-\beta^2}} = mc^2$$

But $mc^2 = mv\frac{c^2}{v}$, and the momentum $mv$ is given, from above, by $mv = eH\rho$. Hence,

$$\text{T.E.} = eH\rho\frac{c^2}{v} = \frac{eH\rho c}{\beta}$$

Putting the value of $\beta$ obtained above in this, one obtains

$$\text{T.E.} = ec\sqrt{\left(\frac{m_0c}{e}\right)^2 + (H\rho)^2}$$

Thus the expression for the total energy of the particle involves not only the quantity $H\rho$ but also the mass and charge of the particle.

The kinetic energy of the particle is really less than this total energy by an amount $m_0c^2$, but for an electron this amounts to only 0.511 MEV, an entirely negligible amount as compared to the kinetic energy of a cosmic ray electron. As a matter of fact, for really high energy electrons, the quantity $(m_0c/e)^2$ becomes negligible as compared to $(H\rho)^2$ and the above expression for the total energy reduces to

$$\text{T.E.} = ecH\rho$$

Thus, if one is certain that the quantity $(m_0c/e)^2$ is negligible as compared to $(H\rho)^2$, one can evaluate the energy of the particle without knowing its mass. If it is certain that one is dealing with an electron, and not a more massive particle, then this approximation is justified for most cosmic rays. By putting into the last expression for the total energy the values of known constants, and by introducing an appropriate factor to convert this energy into electron volts, it is found that the energy of a cosmic ray electron is given by

$$\text{T.E.} = 300H\rho$$

where the energy is in electron volts and where $H\rho$ must be expressed in oersted-cm.

It is not a simple matter to evaluate the mass of a particle from the track it leaves in a cloud chamber placed in a magnetic field. The degree of ionization along the path depends almost altogether upon the charge and the velocity of the particle; the mass of the particle seems to have little effect. By trial, however, it is possible to find a mass which seems to fit best all of the evident characteristics of the particle. Details of this procedure will be made more clear when we discuss, in the next chapter, the recently discovered mesotron.

Let us return now to experimental studies of the energy losses suffered by high energy particles in passing through appreciable thicknesses of materials such as lead. Fig. 16 shows the path of a heavily ionizing particle obtained[119] in a cloud chamber placed in a strong magnetic field. This path appears to be one of a proton having an energy of 150 MEV; its velocity is

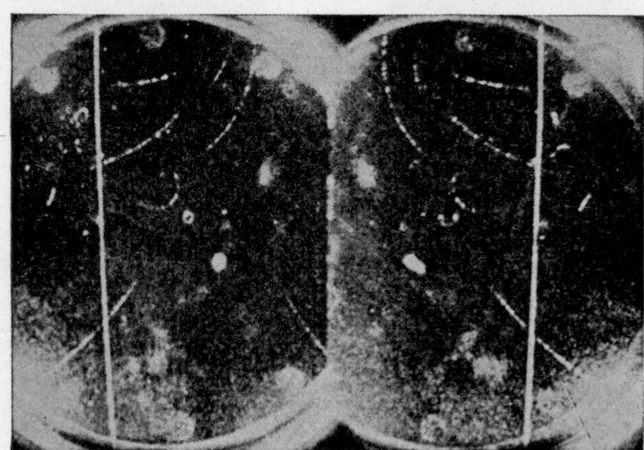

Fig. 16.—The track of a strongly ionizing particle moving in a magnetic field of 7900 oersteds. The particle is judged to be a proton having an energy of 150 MEV and a velocity 0.5 that of light.

approximately one-half that of light. In many such studies there is placed within the cloud chamber, and in such a position that the particle will have to pass through it, a sheet of Pb, Cu or other material. In this way it is possible to evaluate the energy of the particle before and after passing through the known thickness of material; hence the rate of energy loss in this material can be found. Fig. 17 shows the tracks[124] of two different penetrating particles which were made to pass through a 2 cm. sheet of Cu. In (*a*) there is no apparent change of curvature of the path as the particle passed through the Cu; the energy loss was therefore not measurable. The fact that the fractional change of energy was too low to measure does not mean necessarily that this was an unusually energetic particle. In fact as such particles go, this represents a relatively low energy one; its energy was approximately 470 MEV. It just happens that particles of about this energy do not lose energy rapidly in passing through the Cu. In Fig. (*b*) the curvature of the track is measurably greater after the particle passed through the Cu. Calculations show that the particle had an energy of 640 MEV before passing through the plate and only 360 MEV after penetrating the plate. Thus it lost 280 MEV of energy in passing through the 2 cm. of Cu. Similar studies have been made using, in place of the Cu, plates of Pb,[119,120,122] Al,[122] Au,[123] Pt,[121] and other materials. It is interesting that blocks of platinum 1 cm. thick and of gold 9 cm. thick have been used. In the work[123] employing the 9 cm. Au block, the penetrating particles were

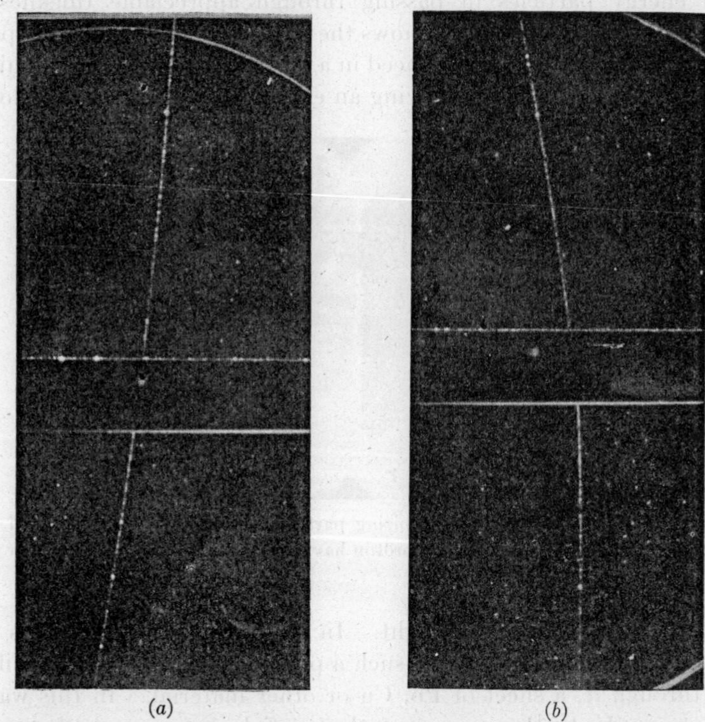

(a) (b)

FIG. 17.—Showing the tracks of two penetrating cosmic ray particles before and after passing through a copper plate 2 cm. thick. The small change of curvature caused by penetration of the plate shows that the particles lose a surprisingly small amount of energy.

made to pass through an additional 16 cm. of Pb before entering the cloud chamber. Thus only the more penetrating particles were studied.

Studies of this and other types have shown the existence of two components of the cosmic radiation. One of these is fairly easily absorbed. This component apparently consists of free electrons and positrons. It is this component that is mainly responsible for the so-called showers which we shall soon discuss. The experiments show also the presence of another component which loses a relatively small amount of energy in passing through any reasonable thickness of Pb or other material. The particles making up this component appear to be absorbed in an entirely different way. It seemed from the first that the particles could not be electrons, either positive or negative. It was presumed that they were particles having the same charge as an electron, either positive or negative, but a mass considerably greater. At first it appeared barely possible that they might be protons. More recent experiments have shown conclusively, however, that this penetrating component consists of mesotrons. Cloud expansion studies similar to those mentioned have allowed investigators to measure directly the energies of particles up to slightly over 10,000 MEV. For higher energy particles the curvature of the path in any magnetic field that is practicable is so slight that it cannot be detected. Magnetic fields as high as 20,000 oersteds have been used in attempts to bend the paths of these energetic particles.

The presence of both an easily absorbable and a penetrating component, together with the fact that particles of different energies may lose a major portion of this energy in different ways, complicates the interpretation of studies of the rate of energy loss. It is convenient to speak of the relative energy loss of a particle rather than of its absolute energy loss. If $R$ represents the rate of relative energy loss, then

$$R = \frac{1}{E}\frac{dE}{dx}$$

where $E$ is the energy of the particle and where $dE/dx$ represents the rate of energy loss as this particle penetrates the absorber. Experiments show that the relative energy loss depends markedly upon the energy of the particle being studied. It appears[122] that the relative energy loss $R$ for particles having an energy less than 200 MEV is of the order of 1 to 1.5, if energies are measured in MEV and distances in cm. As the energy of the particle increases above this the relative energy loss decreases rapidly. Particles having energies of the order of 500 MEV seem[124,125] to suffer a minimum loss in this region of energies, a relative loss of the order of $\frac{1}{10}$ that experienced by the less energetic particles. These same studies indicate that at least in lead and copper the relative energy loss then rises slightly, reaching a maximum for particles having energies of the order of 1500 MEV. The absorption corresponding to this maximum is still quite small; it is larger than that for particles of 500 MEV energy, but much less than that for particles having less than 200 MEV. For still higher energy particles the relative energy loss steadily decreases, becoming still smaller than that corresponding to the minimum existing in the energy range around 500 MEV. It can not be said with certainty whether these small fluctuations in energy loss, which may be characteristic of the absorbing material, are all real or whether they may be due in part to errors of measurement. In any case the rate of energy loss shows a general decrease for particles of increasing energy.

Fig. 18 reproduces some early measurements by Neddermeyer and Anderson[121] on the loss of energy of particles passing through 1 cm. of Pt. Similar curves representing other measurements are available in the literature.[122,125] In the figure shown here the actual energy loss per centimeter, rather than the relative energy loss per centimeter, is plotted against the energy of the particle. Particles for which measurements were made were

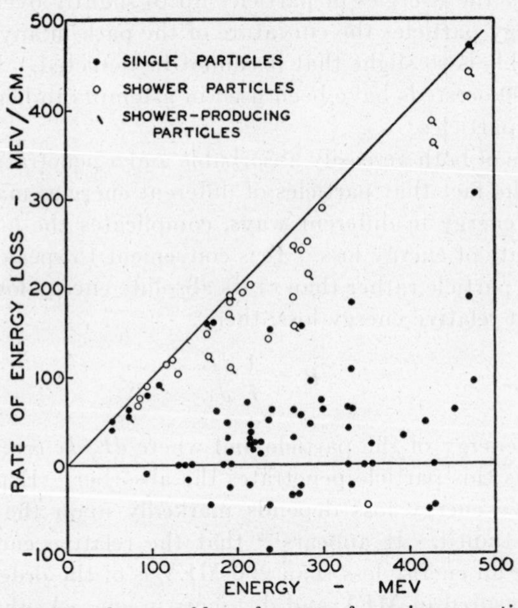


Fig. 18.—Showing the rate of loss of energy of cosmic ray particles in Pt.

of three types, shower particles, shower producing particles, and particles which do not produce showers. The shower particles and the shower producing particles lose energy at a relatively high rate, and at a rate which is apparently equal for the two. This is consistent with the view that both the shower particles and the shower producing particles are ordinary electrons and positrons. Those penetrating particles which lose energy at a much lower rate, and which do not produce showers, have been shown to be mesotrons. They are more penetrating not fundamentally because they are more energetic, but rather because they are a different type of particle. Relatively few low energy mesotrons are found, for the mesotron is radioactive and decays with a half life of a few microseconds into an easily absorbable electron or positron.

Physicists are just beginning to understand the mechanism by which the cosmic ray particles dissipate their energy. It is recognized that energetic charged particles give up their energy in several ways as they pass through material. Very low energy particles give up most of their energy by excitation and ionization of atoms near which they pass. As the particle energy becomes greater, however, large amounts of energy may be lost by several other processes. Among these processes are the following: losses by intimate collisions with the more firmly bound electrons within the atom, resulting in subsequent characteristic X-radiations; losses by actual disintegration of atomic nuclei; losses by impulse radiation excited during close encounters with nuclei. On the other hand, photons having energies no higher than those corresponding to the X-ray or gamma ray frequencies lose their energy by the ejection of photoelectrons from atoms. This of course results in the subsequent radiation of lower energy photons. It has already been pointed out, however, that there is another important process by which a high energy photon can lose its energy. This is by production of electron-positron pairs. The entire energy of a photon, provided it is sufficiently large, may disappear abruptly. There appears in its place an electron-positron pair having a kinetic energy equal to the difference between the photon energy and the energy represented by the masses of the newly formed electron and positron. Very high energy photons no doubt lose much of their energy through this pair production process. Thus the manners of absorption of both high energy photons and high energy charged particles such as found in the cosmic radiation may be quite different from those with which physicists have been familiar in the past.

Bethe and Heitler[126] have presented a theory of the nuclear absorption of high energy particles. In order to understand the basis of this theory it will be well to recall a few facts regarding the production of X-rays. When high speed electrons strike the target of an X-ray tube there are produced in general two types of radiation. One consists of photons whose frequencies are characteristic of the target. The other is the continuous radiation or impulse radiation. It has been found that a greater and greater fraction of the total X-ray energy goes into impulse radiation as the bombarding electron energy is made greater. For X-rays produced by the application of several million volts across the tube, the relative energy represented by the characteristic radiation has become quite negligible. Bethe and Heitler supposed that when an energetic charged particle comes close to an atomic nucleus it suffers large decelerations. As a result energy is transformed into impulse radiation. The interaction between the charged particle and the nucleus which results in this impulse radiation is called a radiative collision. This distinguishes it from the so-called ionizing

[126] H. Bethe and W. Heitler, *Proc. Roy. Soc.*, A, **146**, 83 (1934).

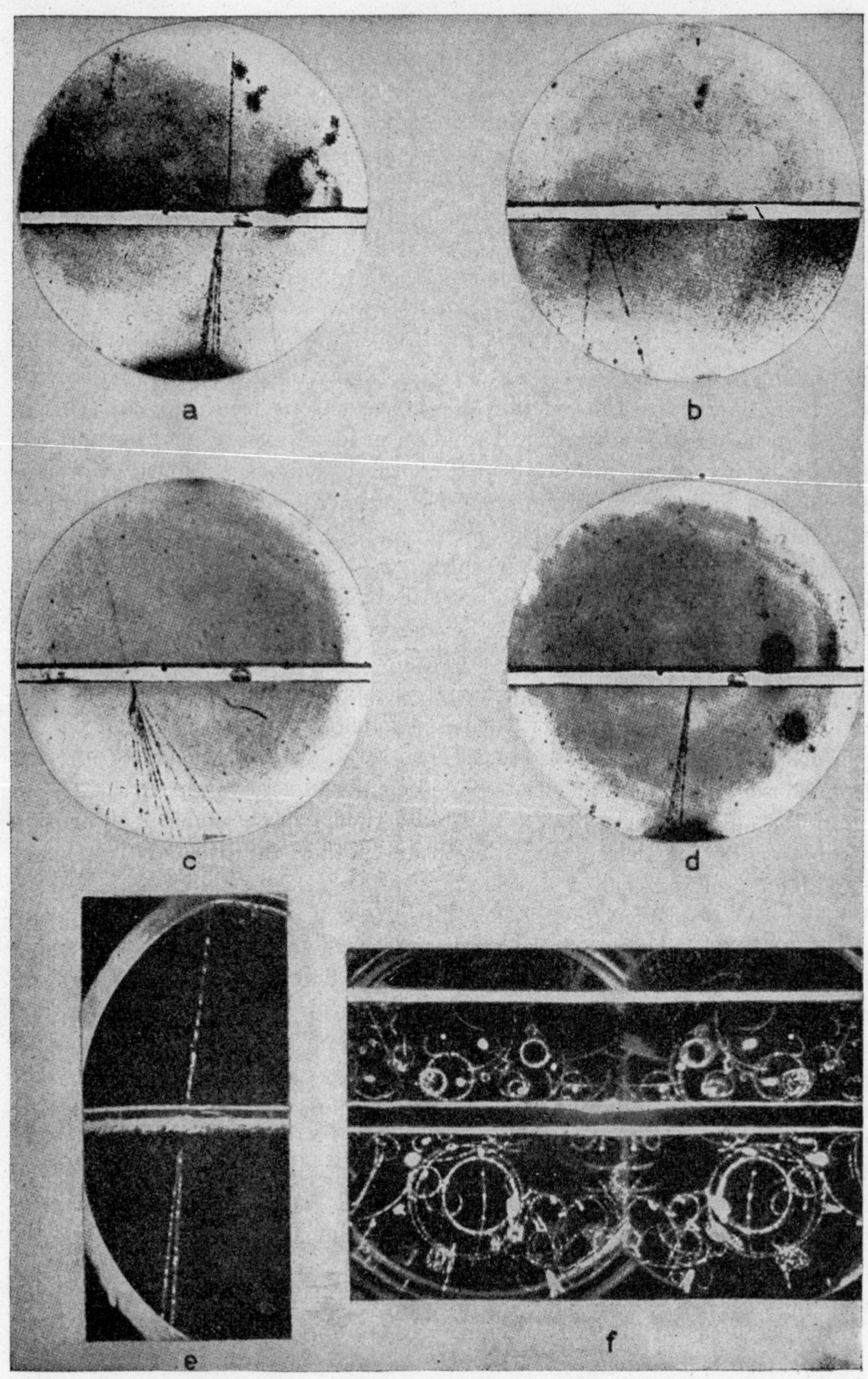


FIG. 19.—For descriptive legend see opposite page.

collisions, suffered by lower energy particles, which result in subsequent characteristic photon radiation. The photons making up this impulse radiation are then supposed to lose their energy through the production of electron-positron pairs. These in turn produce new photons. The process is repeated until the energy originally possessed by the single particle has been dissipated finally in the formation of lower and lower energy particles or photons. It has been possible to develop this theory quantitatively,[127] and to test it in a rough way by experimental data. While definite proof of its correctness will require more accurate experimental data, it appears fairly certain that the underlying concepts are essentially correct.

### Showers and Bursts

The occurrence of extremely high momentary ionizations in an ionization chamber has been recognized for some years. These excessive ionizations were first evidenced[23] clearly by abrupt jumps in the photographic trace of a recording cosmic ray electroscope. Such abrupt jumps have been observed many times since Hoffmann first found them in 1927. There are three recorded in the photographic trace reproduced in Fig. 8. The cosmic ray phenomenon responsible for such excessive momentary ionizations is referred to as a burst. Unfortunately, little can be learned regarding the nature of and the cause of these bursts through electroscope ionization studies. In more recent years, however, two other methods of study have revealed a phenomenon which is in all probability identical with the burst. The two methods of study are that employing coincidence counters and that utilizing the cloud chamber.

If a three or more tube coincidence counter is arranged with the several tubes out of line, it would appear that the number of counts registered would be extremely small. A count is registered only when an ionizing particle affects each tube simultaneously. No single particle could do this, and the chance of two independent particles doing it simultaneously is very small. The fact is, however, that an appreciable number of counts are registered; and these counts are still more numerous if a lead shield approximately a centimeter thick is placed above the apparatus. A natural inference would be that the various tubes were affected by two or more secondary particles produced simultaneously by a single cosmic ray as it penetrates the lead or other material nearby. Cloud chamber studies have shown that such secondary effects are produced, and the number of secondary

[127] W. Heitler, *The Quantum Theory of Radiation* (Oxford: The Clarendon Press, 1936).

FIG. 19.—Showing various types of showers. Those represented by *a*, *c* and *e* are produced by ionizing particles; *b*, *d* and *f* are produced by non-ionizing radiation, no doubt photons. The many low energy electrons of *f* show no common origin; they were probably produced by numerous soft photons from a shower near the cloud chamber.

particles arising at one time often runs surprisingly high. This phenomenon observed in the cloud chamber, and undoubtedly responsible for triggering off the three out-of-line counter tubes, is called a cosmic ray shower. Although the evidence is not particularly direct, there can be little doubt but that these showers are identical with the bursts mentioned above. The size of the burst, as measured by the excess number of ions produced, is no larger than that which would be produced by some of the larger showers observed. And the frequency with which showers occur seems to be sufficient to account for the number of bursts observed.

Present knowledge of these cosmic ray showers and bursts has been well summarized by Froman and Stearns.[23,25] The number of works, both

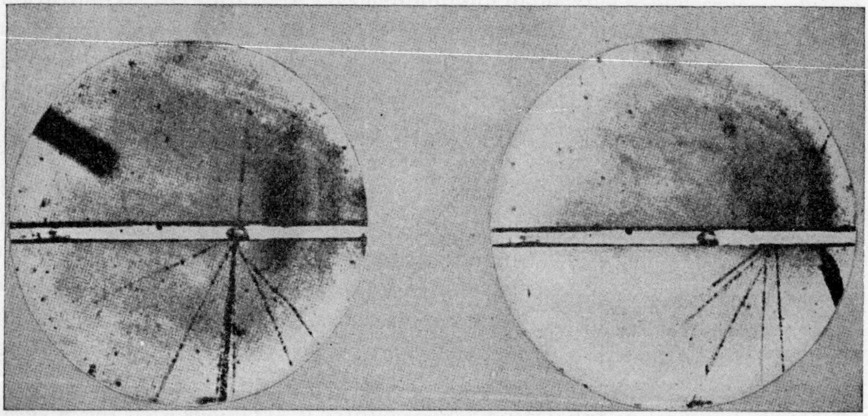

Fig. 20.—Two typical showers, each showing more than one origin. Each of these was produced by an ionizing particle which passed through one of the two foci.

experimental and theoretical, dealing with even this rather restricted field of cosmic radiation is quite impressive. We shall call attention to only a few of the more general and perhaps more important findings. Let us first see what evidence has been obtained from cloud chamber photographs. Fig. 19 reproduces photographs[23] of several showers. In (*a*), (*c*) and (*e*) the track of the particle responsible for the shower is evident. An ionizing particle produced each of these showers as it passed through the lead sheet; the track of the approaching particle can be seen. The fact that many of the particles resulting from the shower leave tracks shows that many of the shower particles are charged. There are no doubt other shower particles also, photons, which leave no track in the cloud chamber. The number of charged particles resulting from the shower shown in (*c*) is quite large. One has no way of judging from the photograph how many photons may have been present in the shower. Other types of measurements indicate that the number of photons present in a large shower is comparable to the number of ionizing particles. In fact some evidence[128] indicates that there may be a preponderance of photons. The showers of (*b*), (*d*) and (*f*) must have been produced by photons as they penetrated the lead; there is no track of the shower producing particle approaching the lead.

While many showers show a somewhat definite place of origin, others do not. That shown in (*f*) seems to have started simultaneously at many points. These shower particles were no doubt produced by numerous rather soft photons arising from another shower in the vicinity of the cloud chamber. Photographs of the type shown in Fig. 19 make it clear that showers

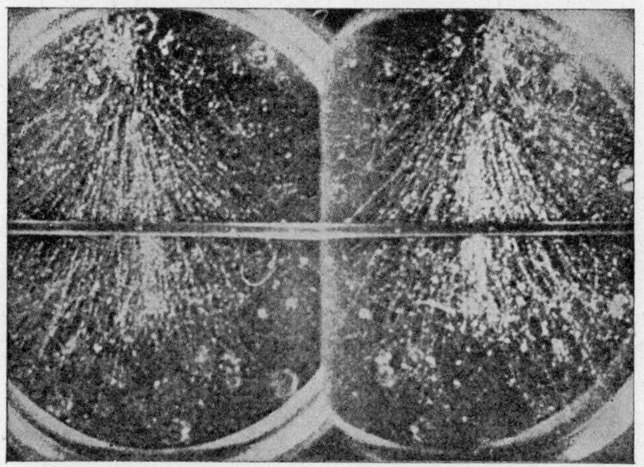

FIG. 21.—A very large shower consisting of some 300 electrons and positrons. Curvature of the tracks is caused by a magnetic field of 7900 oersteds. The total energy, summed for all shower particles, is of the order of 15,000 MEV.

may be induced by either a photon or an ionizing particle. There is available no accurate information as to the fractional number of showers produced by these two types of radiation. Present evidence indicates that roughly one-half of the showers are produced by either type of radiation. Fig. 20 shows two other showers,[23] each produced by a charged particle, and each showing two distinct foci. One of these foci probably locates the original shower, while the other represents the location of a second shower produced by one of the first shower particles. Fig. 21 reproduces stereoscopic views[129] of a very large shower. The magnetic field in which the chamber was placed has bent some of these particles to the right and others to the left. Hence, both positive and negative particles are present in the shower. The total number of charged particles constituting this shower has been estimated as 300. The total energy, summed for all particles, is of the order of 15,000 MEV.

[128] H. Geiger and O. Zeiller, *Zeits. f. Physik*, **108**, 212 (1938).

[129] C. D. Anderson and S. H. Neddermeyer, *Phys. Rev.*, **50**, 265 (1936).

In most of those photographs already referred to the numerous particles constituting the shower appear to leave the point of origin within a cone having an angle of 40° or less. Measurements of the distribution of particles at various angles are still none too certain. It appears, however, that the maximum number of shower particles diverge at an angle of approximately 20° or less. This mean angle of divergence seems to increase slightly with the thickness of the material used for producing the showers. It is interest-

FIG. 22.—A photograph of the relatively rare non-collimated type of shower.

ing that when a cosmic ray forms a single electron-positron pair these two particles seldom diverge at an angle exceeding 30°. Writers speak of these showers as being well collimated. A large fraction of the momentum of any given shower particle lies along the direction of travel of the shower producing particle. Measurements show that the transverse momenta possessed by such shower particles correspond to energies of only a few MEV. The great preponderance of momentum in the forward direction is to be expected if these shower particles obtained most of their energy directly from the primary shower producing ray. A large fraction of all showers observed is of this collimated type. When these showers are large they often exhibit no well defined focus.

Fig. 22 reproduces an entirely different and relatively rare type of shower. As for the more common type, this shower consists of photons, electrons and positrons. But in this case the shower particles do not appear to be at all collimated; they leave the place of origin in all directions, some of them proceeding backward. The total number of particles involved in this rarer type of shower is seldom large. Some of these particles, however, possess transverse momenta corresponding to energies of the order of 100 or more MEV. It is evident, therefore, that there are two distinct types of showers. Their distinctly different appearances indicate an entirely different mechanism of production. The fact that all particles in the collimated type of shower have a preponderance of momentum in the forward direction indicates that these particles acquired most of their energy directly from the shower inducing radiation. The existence of large transverse momenta and even of momenta in the backward direction among the particles constituting the rarer non-collimated type of shower, indicates that these particles may have acquired the greater part of their energies from the disintegration of an atom.

The question of what mechanism may be responsible for the usual type of shower has received considerable attention in recent years. The theoretical treatment of the production of electron-positron pairs by photons was started[130,131] in 1933. Shortly afterwards Bethe and Heitler[126] published their theory of the impulse radiation from an electron under the influence of a strong nuclear field, that is, of the radiation given out during the so-called radiative collision suffered by the electron. Heitler[127] has given a comprehensive account of various aspects of the theory of electromagnetic radiation and of electron-positron pair creation in nuclear fields. The so-called cascade theory of burst or shower formation was suggested[132,133] almost immediately. On this theory shower formation consists of a series of radiative collisions resulting in photon production, and of pair creations resulting in the charged particle component of the shower. It was soon shown that this theory could be put upon a quantitative basis and theoretical expressions were derived,[134,135] for the number of shower particles, positive and negative electrons, and photons, which should result per unit time when radiation of a given energy falls upon a given shower producing material of some definite thickness.

[130] G. Beck, *Zeits. f. Physik*, **83**, 498 (1933).
[131] J. R. Oppenheimer and M. S. Plesset, *Phys. Rev.*, **44**, 53 (1933).
[132] C. G. Montgomery, *Phys. Rev.*, **45**, 62 (1934).
[133] P. Auger, *Nature*, **135**, 820 (1935).
[134] H. J. Bhabha and W. Heitler, *Proc. Roy. Soc.*, A, **159**, 432 (1937).
[135] J. F. Carlson and J. R. Oppenheimer, *Phys. Rev.*, **51**, 220 (1937).

The cascade theory of showers leads to several conclusions which can be tested experimentally. Although the experimental tests are often not precise they are nevertheless rather consistently in accord with the general theory. For example, the theory leads one to expect that the size of the shower should increase in passing from a material of low to one of high atomic number. However, the size of the shower should depend only upon the second material after it has passed through a sufficient thickness of this second absorber. Experiment[136] is in qualitative agreement with this expectation. Another prediction of the theory is that the thickness of

FIG. 23.—Showing the growth of a shower as it proceeds through successive sheets of lead. This shower was produced by an ionizing particle.

absorber yielding a maximum number of showers of a given size should increase slightly with the size of the shower. Experimental evidence in accord with this prediction will be shown later.

Perhaps the most direct evidence in favor of the cascade theory of shower production comes from cloud expansion photographs of showers produced in successive lead plates within the chamber. Fig. 23 sheds light upon the manner of growth of a shower. The single shower producing particle coming from above causes a shower consisting of a few particles as it penetrates the upper plate. One of these shower particles produces at the second plate a much larger shower. At the third plate there is a still further increase in the size of the shower. The growth of a shower of this

[136] K. Z. Morgan and W. M. Nielsen, *Phys. Rev.*, **52**, 564 (1937).

type continues until the energies of the shower particles become so small that the probability of further photon production and electron-positron pair creation decreases sufficiently that no further increase in the size of the shower occurs. As the particles lose still more energy the shower begins to decay; each successive shower becomes on the average smaller and smaller. While the growth of the shower is illustrated beautifully in Fig. 23, a sufficient number of successive showers to show the gradual decay is not shown. Fig. 24 shows a somewhat similar series of showers, some of which are produced by ionizing particles and others of which are produced by photons.

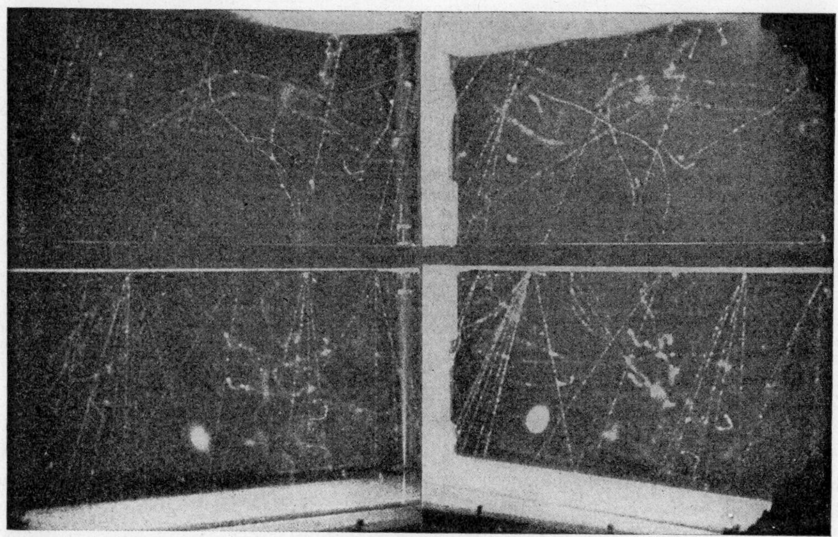

FIG. 24.—Showing numerous showers, some produced by ionizing particles and some by photons. Some of the showers consist of single pairs while others consist of many particles.

It has been remarked that the number of shower particles produced within a given region is increased markedly if one places above the region a sheet of absorbing material. The number of showers produced continues to increase as one increases the thickness of this absorber until a certain optimum value is reached. For thicknesses beyond this the number of showers decreases. A number of observers have determined the manner in which the number of showers depends upon the thickness of the absorbing shield. Fig. 25 summarizes[23] the results of numerous workers. A curve of this character is referred to as a Rossi curve. The lower curve represents the number of showers of three or more particles produced in lead of various thicknesses. The middle curve gives the same type of information for showers consisting of two or more particles. The upper curve represents results obtained for all showers, counting even those which have but a single secondary particle. A distinct maximum appears in each curve; there is an optimum thickness of lead shield for the most efficient production of showers. The optimum thickness is about 2 centimeters for showers of three or more particles, 1½ centimeters for showers of two or more particles and about 1 centimeter for the production of some type of shower.

It was remarked that the cascade theory of shower production leads one to expect that a somewhat thicker shield is required for the production of a

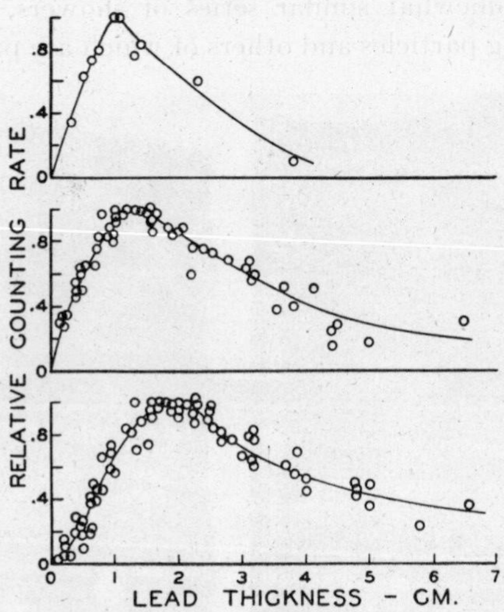


Fig. 25.—Showing the way in which the number of showers produced depends upon the thickness of lead used for production. The lower curve counts no shower having less than three ionizing particles. The middle curve counts no shower of less than two particles. Showers of even one particle are counted in the uppermost curve.

maximum number of large showers than is required for the production of a maximum number of some smaller sized shower. The observations reproduced in Fig. 25 are in agreement with this expectation. It will be noticed that these curves are extended to only 6½ centimeters thickness of lead. This corresponds to 75 grams of absorbing material per square centimeter of surface. Actually such curves have been extended to much greater thicknesses.[23,136–142] Thicknesses of nearly 600 grams per square centimeter

[137] J. E. Morgan and W. M. Nielsen, *Phys. Rev.*, **50**, 882 (1936).

[138] R. H. Woodward, *Phys. Rev.*, **49**, 711 (1936).

[139] K. Schmeiser and W. Bothe, *Naturwiss.*, **25**, 173, 669 (1937); *Ann. d. Physik*, **32**, 161 (1938).

[140] A. Ehmert, *Zeits. f. Physik*, **113**, 234 (1939).

[141] W. M. Nielsen, J. E. Morgan and K. Z. Morgan, *Phys. Rev.*, **55**, 995 (1939).

[142] N. N. Das Gupta, *Proc. Nat Inst. Sci. India*, **6**, 65 (1940).

of lead and iron have been used.[136] Aluminum shields of 200 grams per square centimeter have been used.[137] Several studies involving great thicknesses of absorber show the presence of a second peak in the Rossi curve. This peak is very small as compared to the first. For lead it occurs at a thickness of 18 or 20 cm. This thickness corresponds to an absorber of about 200 gr./cm.$^2$ The recent observations of Nielsen, Morgan and Morgan[141] throw into serious question the actual existence of this second peak. They found no second peak when a four tube coincidence counting system was used. On the other hand, they did find the peak when three tube coincidences were counted. The shape of the Rossi curve at great thicknesses depends appreciably upon what allowance is made for background counts. Since the four tube coincidence system reduces the background count to a much lower level than the three tube system, and since Rossi curves showing the second peak have been obtained generally with a three tube system, these authors feel that the second peak may be introduced by failure to take proper account of the background count. Some[143] believe, however, that the four tube system used by Nielsen, Morgan and Morgan was such that it actually produced a masking effect on the second peak. Just recently other good evidence[143a] for the existence of this second peak has been obtained through a cloud chamber study of the showers produced by thicknesses of lead near this second maximum. These observations, which are free from the questionable correction for background count, show a small but definite second maximum at about 17 cm. thickness of lead.

It has been pointed out that the general cosmic radiation consists of two main components, a soft component which is practically all absorbed at sea level in 10 centimeters of lead, and a hard component which is capable of penetrating much greater thicknesses of matter. The soft component consists of electrons, positrons and photons, the last of which are probably all of secondary character. The hard component consists of mesotrons, both positive and negative. It has been found that the intensity of shower production is approximately proportional to the intensity of the soft component of cosmic rays. Furthermore, many observations[23] have shown that the absorption coefficient of the shower producing rays agrees fairly well with the absorption coefficient of the soft component of the cosmic radiation. These and other facts make it appear certain that a great majority of the showers are produced by the soft component. On the other hand, the fact that showers are produced by cosmic radiation which has penetrated great thicknesses of the earth's crust shows that the hard component of the radiation is capable of producing showers. If the second peak of the Rossi

[143] A. K. Dutta, *Indian Jour. Phys.*, **14**, 79 (1940).

[143a] L. Broussard and A. C. Graves, *Phys. Rev.*, **60**, 413 (1941).

curve proves to be real it may well be due to showers produced by the penetrating component.

The frequency with which showers are produced varies rapidly with altitude. It has been found that the frequency of shower production in a given material increases with altitude much faster than does the total cosmic ray intensity. This is in agreement with the fact that the softer component of cosmic rays increases with altitude much faster than does the hard component, and with the view that the soft component is responsible for most of the showers.

The intensity of showers varies with magnetic latitude.[23,144–146] The manner of variation is similar to that found for the total radiation, but the magnitude of the variation between the equator and high latitudes is somewhat less for showers. Neher and Pickering[144] found a minimum number of showers produced at the equator, and a 6 or 7 percent greater number produced at a latitude of 30°. There is some evidence[23,144] that the shower intensity-latitude curve has a knee at about 30° latitude, and that there is no further increase in shower production above this knee. Several earlier observers had found a small latitude effect agreeing essentially with that reported by Neher and Pickering. It seems to be well established that the shower latitude curve varies less from the equator to a high latitude than does the entire cosmic radiation. On the other hand, the percentage variation between the equator and 30° latitude appears to be about the same for the two. One recent observer[145] has reported only a very small shower latitude effect over a range of latitude for which the cosmic ray intensity varied by 10 percent. This, however, has not been the usual finding.

Observations[146] indicate that there may be a much larger latitude effect for very large bursts than for all types of showers considered as a group. The increase of frequency of large bursts with latitude continues up to about the knee of the intensity-latitude curve; and the increase between the equator and this latitude is approximately 30 percent. These large bursts were observed under 12 cm. of lead shielding, and were probably produced by mesotrons rather than by the normal shower producing radiation. This probably accounts for the different variation with latitude.

There may exist a slight east-west effect for showers at sea level, but its magnitude is much smaller than that for the total cosmic radiation. This probable small effect vanishes at higher altitudes. The non-existence of an appreciable effect is consistent with the view that most of the showers are produced by the soft component and with the fact that it is the pene-

[144] H. V. Neher and W. H. Pickering, *Phys. Rev.*, **53**, 111 (1938).

[145] G. Occhialini, *Comptes Rendus*, **208**, 101 (1939); *Ricerca Scientifica*, **11**, 231 (1940).

[146] W. P. Jesse and P. S. Gill, *Phys. Rev.*, **55**, 414 (1939).

trating component that shows a high east-west asymmetry at sea level. There is no evidence for any daily or seasonal variation of shower intensity.

It has been remarked that the cosmic ray burst is probably identical with the shower. The bursts make themselves apparent through abrupt jumps of a recording electroscope. Such momentary increases in ionization were no doubt responsible for Hoffmann's[147] observation that the total ionization in an ionization chamber increased when this chamber was surrounded by thin absorbers. It is known now that these absorbers would cause the production of showers in the chamber. The equivalence of bursts and showers is indicated by the fact that both vary in much the same manner with altitude, latitude and thickness of material in which the effect is produced. It has been found[23,148,149] that the frequency of bursts increases with altitude more rapidly for large bursts than for small, and that the size of the large burst increases rapidly with altitude.

It is true that many of the large bursts correspond to an increase in ionization greater than that which could be associated with many of the showers observed. Increases in ionization due to showers involving not more than ten ionizing particles are probably too small to be distinguished from statistical fluctuations in present day ionization apparatus. When a large ionization chamber is utilized, showers of less than 100 particles are probably insignificant. On the other hand some of the larger showers involve a sufficiently large number of particles to account for the bursts observed. Both the bursts[150] and the showers are distributed at random in time. And the frequency with which showers occur seems to be sufficient to account for the burst phenomenon. It seems almost certain, therefore, that bursts occurring in ionization chambers are really large showers produced in the walls and shield about the chamber.

[147] G. Hoffmann, *Schr. Konigsb. Gel. Gesell.*, **4**, 1 (1927).
[148] R. D. Bennett, G. S. Brown and H. A. Rahmel, *Phys. Rev.*, **47**, 437 (1935).
[149] C. G. Montgomery and D. D. Montgomery, *Phys. Rev.*, **47**, 429 (1935); **48**, 969 (1935).
[150] C. G. Montgomery and D. D. Montgomery, *Phys. Rev.*, **44**, 779 (1933).

Chapter 13

# THE MESOTRON

## I. DISCOVERY OF THE MESOTRON

### Early History

It has already been pointed out that previous to 1932 the physicist was aware of only two fundamental particles, the negative electron and the proton. It might be said that he was familiar with three if one wished to include as a fundamental particle the photon of radiant energy. The number of recognized elementary particles was doubled with the discovery of the positron and the neutron in 1932. Information leading to the discovery of these was made possible by the development of modern techniques of studying the characteristics of particles, one of the most notable of these techniques being that of the cloud chamber. Even with these improved techniques available, it is remarkable that still another particle was discovered in 1936. This particle, the mesotron, was the third new particle to be discovered in the short span of four years.

Shortly after Carl D. Anderson had been awarded the Nobel Prize for the discovery of the positron, this same investigator[1] announced that he had found still another unknown particle. He found that cosmic rays include electrical particles which make tracks in a cloud chamber much like those left by electrons, but which appeared to have other characteristics differing from those of the electron. These new particles were unusually penetrating; they did not knock electrons out of matter as readily as the usual electron; they often proceeded through lead plates without producing any perceptible secondary effects. At that time Anderson was not certain as to the exact nature of the new particle. The indications were that it bore the same charge as the electron, but possessed a mass considerably greater than that of the electron.

Fig. 1 reproduces[2] one of the first cloud chamber photographs indicating the possible existence of this new type of particle. The particle responsible for this track was tentatively interpreted as a proton but it was recognized that the range, the degree of ionization, and the radius of curvature in the magnetic field were scarcely consistent with this interpretation. In fact

[1] *Science Suppl.*, **84**, 9 (1936).

[2] C. D. Anderson and S. H. Neddermeyer, *Phys. Rev.*, **50**, 270 (1936).

Anderson and Neddermeyer[2] stated in their original article that, "If the observed curvature were produced entirely by magnetic deflection it would be necessary to conclude that this track represents a massive particle with an $e/m$ much greater than that of a proton or any other known nucleus." The authors were not certain how much of the apparent curvature may have been caused by scattering of the supposed low energy proton. They therefore deferred final judgment as to the nature of the particle until further information could be obtained.

Other evidence was forthcoming immediately. This soon became sufficiently extensive that one could say with certainty that such a particle does exist. This new particle has gone under several names. At first it was referred to as the heavy electron. Shortly the name barytron was introduced, and it was taken up immediately by many writers. Soon afterward the name mesotron, meaning intermediate particle, was introduced, and this is rather generally accepted today. Some writers now shorten this name to meson.

The evidence for the existence of the mesotron has come principally from two types of studies. Both of these have grown out of cosmic ray investigations. The one line of evidence came from cosmic ray studies having to do with the rate of absorption of the radiation. Although this evidence was somewhat indirect, it was nevertheless rather convincing. The second line of evidence came from studies of the paths left by particles while passing through a cloud chamber. These studies have now become sufficiently numerous that there can be no question as to the existence of a heavy electron having a mass some 200 times the mass of the normal electron. Several summaries[3,4] of the evidence for such a particle are available in the literature.

### Evidence from Cosmic Ray Studies

As has already been pointed out in the preceding chapter, cosmic radiation has been shown to consist of two main components, a so-called soft component chiefly responsible for showers, and a so-called hard component which is almost unbelievably penetrating. Whereas the soft component at sea level, which is presumed to consist of electrons, positrons and photons, is almost completely absorbed in 10 cm. of Pb, the hard component is but little affected by this amount of Pb. It was also pointed out that the soft component increases much more rapidly with altitude than does the hard component. Furthermore, the manner of absorption of the two components is different. For the soft component the absorption per atom is roughly

[3] D. K. Froman and J. C. Stearns, *Rev. Mod. Phys.*, **10**, 176 (1938); *Amer. Phys. Teacher*, **7**, 95 (1939).

[4] K. K. Darrow, *Bell System Tech. Jour.*, **18**, 190 (1939).

proportional to the square of the atomic number. The hard component obeys roughly a mass absorption law. It might appear possible at first to interpret this penetrating component as a group of unusually energetic electrons, both positive and negative. One can calculate theoretically the approximate energy that such a particle would have to possess in order to penetrate the thicknesses of matter that it does. Such a calculation shows that the energy required is out of all reason; it is very much larger than any of the energies associated with cosmic ray particles. One is therefore almost forced[5] to one of two conclusions: (1) the theoretical expression for the rate of energy loss of fast electrons must break down for energies above some critical value; or, (2) the penetrating component of cosmic rays does not consist of ordinary electrons, either + or −, but must consist of some particle having a much greater mass, probably intermediate between that of the normal electron and that of the proton.

For several years it was generally supposed that the first conclusion was the more likely. As experimenters began to measure the rate of energy loss for normal electrons of higher and higher energies, however, there appeared no direct evidence whatever for the breakdown of the modern theory of energy loss; and there appeared no real grounds for supposing that this theory breaks down for energies higher than those used by experimenters. From consideration of the atmospheric absorption curve, Heitler[6] has shown that if a breakdown of the theoretical expression for the rate of energy loss of normal electrons does take place, then it must be at energies higher than 5,000 MEV. From still later observations of the shape of the absorption curve in the upper atmosphere, others[7] have concluded that there is no breakdown at energies below 10,000 MEV. Furthermore, calculation based upon the modern theory of energy loss by normal electrons shows[8] that there is a negligible chance of a normal electron with energy less than 10,000 MEV reaching sea level. Although normal electrons of energy greater than 10,000 MEV should not show a sea level latitude effect at magnetic latitudes greater than approximately 35°, variations of intensity with latitude actually extend to appreciably higher latitudes. It is apparent, therefore, that the assumption of a breakdown in the theory of the rate of energy loss for normal electrons does not rid one of all of the difficulties. On the other hand, if one assumes the existence of a particle having the same charge as the electron, either + or −, but a mass some 200 times as great, then practically all of these observations can be correlated in an orderly manner. In fact Bhabha,[5] in an excellent article on the penetrating component of cosmic

[5] H. J. Bhabha, *Proc. Roy. Soc.*, A, **164**, 257 (1937).

[6] W. Heitler, *Proc. Roy. Soc.*, A, **161**, 261 (1937).

[7] I. S. Bowen, R. A. Millikan and H. V. Neher, *Phys. Rev.*, **52**, 80 (1937).

[8] H. J. Bhabha and W. Heitler, *Proc. Roy. Soc.*, A, **159**, 432 (1937).

radiation, regards cosmic ray evidence of this character as excellent evidence for the existence of a new particle.

It is apparent that a heavy electron having a mass some 200 times that of the normal electron, would, for a given high energy, be much more penetrating than the normal electron. High energy electrons dissipate a considerable part of their energy during so-called radiative collisions with nuclei. During these abrupt decelerations of the particle, impulse radiation is given off as photons. These photons in turn produce electron-positron pairs. These new electrical particles in turn suffer radiative collisions and the process is repeated. In this way the energy of the original electron is dissipated at rate which can be calculated. Now the particles making up the penetrating component of cosmic rays apparently do not lose energy this rapidly. If one is to suppose that the theoretical considerations are still correct, then the difficulty could be eliminated by assuming that these penetrating particles possess masses greater than that of the ordinary electron. In this way their decelerations, and hence their radiative collision energy losses, would be smaller than those for the normal electron. While evidence of this character is neither very direct nor entirely convincing, it did point strongly toward the existence of a new particle.

### Evidence from Cloud Chamber Photographs

The number of protons found in cosmic rays by cloud expansion photographs is very small, and this in spite of the fact that numerous workers have searched for them. As an example, Blackett,[9] from a total of 1500 photographs of nearly vertical cosmic ray tracks, 150 of which were left by particles having less than 600 MEV energy, found not a single track he could definitely attribute to a proton. In another series of experiments the observers[10] reported 14 protons among 8,500 tracks. In still another series the experimenters[11] reported only two or three protons among 2,000 tracks. Thus the number of protons which can be identified by the greater ionization along the tracks left in a cloud chamber is very small near sea level, perhaps 0.2 percent of the total number of particles leaving tracks. The actual number of protons present in the cosmic radiation may of course run much larger than this, for those of high energy cannot be distinguished from electrons merely by the degree of ionization along the track. It has been estimated that no more than 10 to 15 percent of the penetrating component at sea level can be protons. On the other hand, it now appears[12] rather

[9] P. M. S. Blackett, *Proc. Roy. Soc.*, A, **159,** 1 (1937).

[10] R. B. Brode, H. G. MacPherson and M. A. Starr, *Phys. Rev.*, **50,** 581 (1936).

[11] C. D. Anderson and S. H. Neddermeyer, *Internat. Conf. on Nuclear Physics*, London, p. 171 (1934).

[12] M. Schein, W. P. Jesse and E. O. Wollan, *Phys. Rev.*, **59,** 615 (1941).

definite that that part of the primary cosmic radiation responsible for the penetrating component consists largely of protons incident on the upper atmosphere. On this view a greater number of protons might be found at high altitudes. Herzog[13] has found a relatively large number of proton tracks in cloud chamber photographs taken at altitudes from 15,000 to 29,000 feet.

In the course of such studies there have often been observed tracks showing greater ionization than that due to an electron, yet tracks which certainly cannot be due to protons. Knowing the value of $H\rho$ for a proton in a given magnetic field, one can calculate the energy of the proton and thence the range of this particle. For example, the range of a proton having an $H\rho = 2 \times 10^6$ oersted-cm., or an energy of 176 MEV, is[9] 18 gms/sq cm. The range appropriate to a proton of any measured $H\rho$, and hence of a given energy, can be calculated.[14] If the actual range of the observed particle agrees with this, then the assumption that a proton was responsible for the track is probably correct. If on the other hand the observed range of the particle describing the observed circular path is distinctly different from the calculated range, then the assumption that the particle was a proton is probably in error.

Now numerous photographs have been obtained of tracks left by particles which ionize more than do normal electrons, but which have ranges far greater than would be possible were the particles protons having the observed values of $H\rho$. Since these particles ionize more intensely than do normal electrons, and since they have penetrating powers far greater than do normal electrons, it is almost impossible to avoid the conclusion that the particle is a newly discovered one. Since the specific ionization produced is but slightly greater than that by a normal electron, it appears that this new particle must bear the same charge as does the normal electron. In order to account for its great penetrating power, and for its specific ionization, it is necessary to attribute to this particle a mass intermediate between that of the electron and that of the proton. Various estimates of this mass will be mentioned shortly. Let us first review in a bit more detail the actual evidence for the existence of this particle.

The first evidence pointing to the existence of the mesotron was reported by Anderson and Neddermeyer[2] in 1936. Fig. 1 reproduces one of two similar photographs they obtained during a cloud chamber study of cosmic rays on Pike's Peak. This particle has a range of approximately 4 cm. and an apparent $H\rho$ approximately $5.5 \times 10^4$ oersted-cm. The energy of a proton having the observed range would be 1.5 MEV. But a proton of this energy would have a value of $H\rho = 1.7 \times 10^5$, or a radius of 20 cm. in the

[13] G. Herzog, *Phys. Rev.*, **59**, 117 (1941).

[14] M. S. Livingston and H. A. Bethe, *Rev. Mod. Phys.*, **9**, 269 (1937).

magnetic field used. This radius is 3 times that obtained from the photograph. At that time the authors felt that the apparent curvature might be affected appreciably by factors other than the magnetic field. They concluded that if the observed curvature were produced entirely by magnetic deflection the track must have been left by a massive particle with an $e/m$

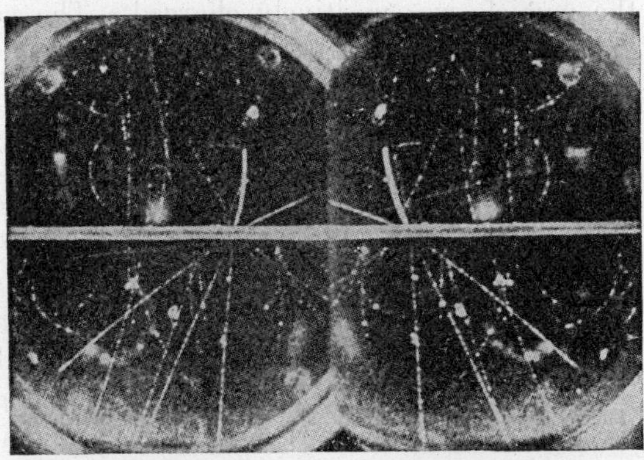

FIG. 1.—The first photograph in which was recognized a track of a particle which seemed to have a mass intermediate between that of an electron and that of a proton. Of the six ionizing particles ejected from the same point of the lead plate by a non-ionizing ray, one produces far more dense ionization than do the others. This one is the particle in question.

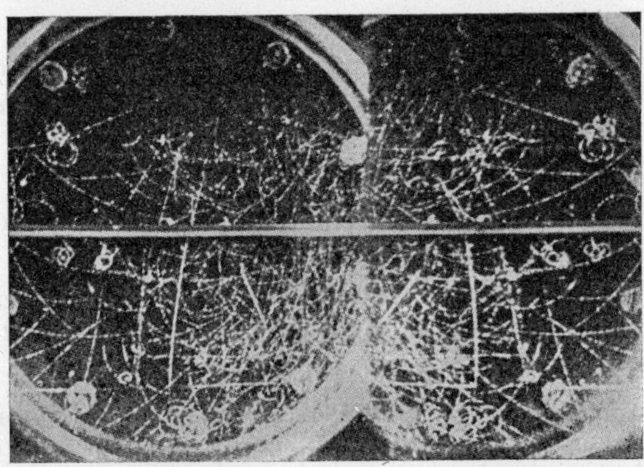

FIG. 2.—Another early photograph of a track left by a positive heavy electron. The track near the center of the photograph and below the lead plate is inconsistent with the assumption that it was left by a normal electron; it is likewise inconsistent with the supposition that the particle responsible for it was a proton.

much greater than that of a proton. This would necessitate a particle having a mass smaller than that of the proton but still far larger than that of the normal electron.

Fig. 2 reproduces another early photograph obtained at the same time by Anderson and Neddermeyer. At almost the center of the cloud chamber there appears a nearly vertical track which indicates that a particle has passed through the 0.35 cm. Pb plate. Above the plate the specific ionization is essentially that of a normal electron. Below the plate, however, the track indicates a much greater specific ionization. The direction of curvature in the magnetic field showed that the particle was positively charged. The value of $H\rho$ is approximately $1.4 \times 10^5$ oersted-cm. If this particle is a proton then in order to be bent in such a manner as to give this value of $H\rho$ it would have to possess an energy of 1 MEV. The range of a proton of this energy would be 2 cm. The observed range of this particle in the cloud chamber was at least 5 cm.; it was probably greater than this for the particle apparently went out of good focus in the photograph. Thus again there was indicated a particle having a mass intermediate between that of the proton and that of the normal electron. It is interesting that both of the particles originally reported by Anderson and Neddermeyer bore a positive charge; they were really heavy positrons. Other workers have since detected similar particles bearing a negative charge. Thus heavy electrons, or barytrons, or mesotrons, or mesons, as one chooses to call them, may be either + or −.

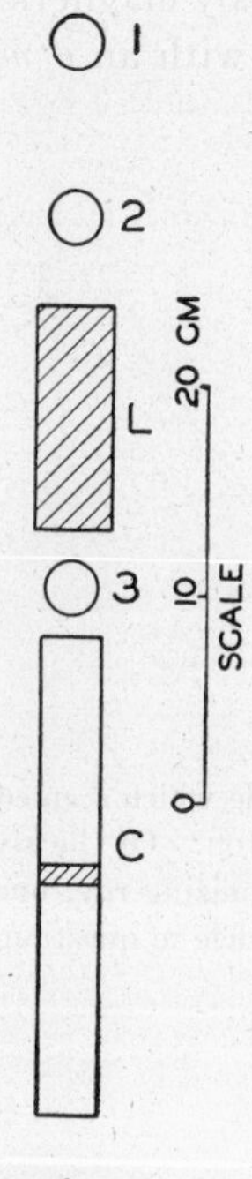


Fig. 3.—Experimental arrangement used by Street and Stevenson, whereby the probability of photographing a particle nearing the end of its range was increased.

Street and Stevenson,[15] seeking a somewhat critical test for the existence of a particle of intermediate mass, arranged a cloud chamber so as to observe the tracks of only those penetrating particles which were nearing the ends of their ranges. The arrangement of apparatus whereby the photographs taken were so limited is shown in Fig. 3. Any particle passing vertically through the cloud chamber *C* had to pass first through the 11 cm. Pb block *L*. Thus only penetrating particles were observed. Geiger tubes 1, 2, 3 and 4 were so arranged that the cloud chamber was expanded only when a particle passed through tubes 1, 2 and 3 but not through tube 4. Thus only those particles which terminated their paths before reaching 4 were photographed. By confining their studies to particles nearing the ends of their ranges the differences in specific ionization and in curvature which would result from various types of particles were made more definitely observable. In order to permit a better estimate of the degree of ionization along the track, the expansion was automatically

[15] J. C. Street and E. C. Stevenson, *Phys. Rev.*, **52**, 1003 (1937).

delayed about a second after the particle passed through the chamber. In this time interval the ions diffused sufficiently that the droplets condensed thereon during the expansion were sufficiently separated along the resulting broad track that a fair estimate could be made of the number of ions/cm. length of path.

Fig. 4 reproduces one of the photographs obtained by Street and Stevenson.[15] If, as seems likely, this particle entered the chamber from above, then the particle bore a negative charge. The particle produced an ionization approximately 6 times that of a normal electron, had an $H\rho = 9.5 \times 10^4$ oersted-cm., and had a visible range of 7 cm. The track cannot possibly be that of a proton, for a proton of this $H\rho$ would have an energy of only 0.44 MEV, and a range of only 1 cm. The range of this particle was at least 7 cm. It was probably somewhat greater than this; the particle passed out of the lighted region within the chamber before coming to the end of its range. The evidence is quite convincing that the particle responsible for this track was not a proton; nor was it a normal electron. It was a new particle, one having a mass intermediate between that of the proton and that of the normal electron.

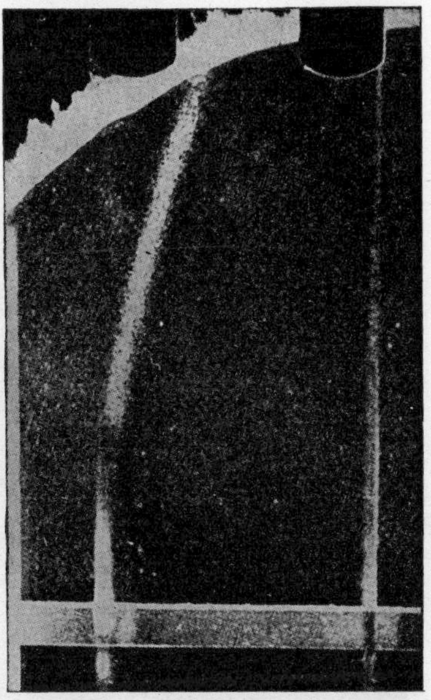

FIG. 4.—The track of a negative mesotron. The expansion was delayed approximately one second after passage of the particle in order that the resulting ions might diffuse appreciably before droplets condensed upon them.

One additional photograph of this character will be mentioned, one which probably provides the most convincing single piece of evidence available. Fig. 5 reproduces[16] a recent photograph of a particle coming up to, passing through, and emerging from a Geiger tube which had been placed inside of a cloud expansion chamber. The use of this tube, together with one placed above the apparatus, to trigger off the expansion increased the probability of observing particles nearing the ends of their ranges. This photograph is remarkable in that it shows a particle having 10 MEV energy passing into the Geiger tube, and presumably this same particle with its energy reduced to 0.21 MEV emerging from the Geiger tube. This particle, which was positively charged, could not have been a normal

[16] S. H. Neddermeyer and C. D. Anderson, *Phys. Rev.*, **54**, 88 (1938).

positron. The specific ionization of the particle before it traversed the counter tube was definitely greater than that of an electron having the curvature shown. If the particle was a proton then the curvature above the counter tube indicates that it had an energy of 1.4 MEV. Such a proton would form at least 30 times as many ions per cm. of path as are indicated in the photograph.

Consider next the path described by this same particle after it penetrated the Geiger tube. If the particle was a normal electron the curvature

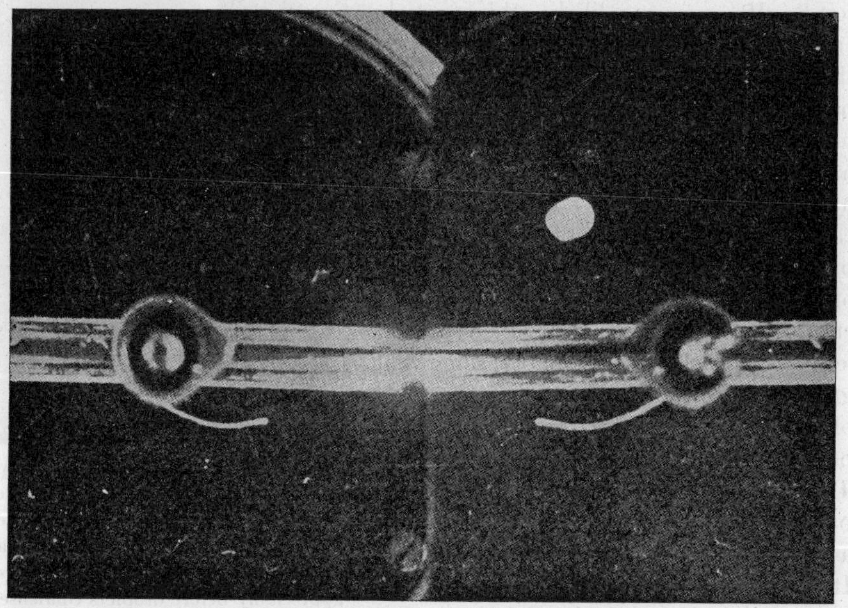

FIG. 5.—Reproduction of a photograph which is at present regarded as the most convincing single piece of evidence for the existence of the mesotron. This positively charged particle has passed through a Geiger tube placed within the expansion chamber, and has come to rest within the chamber.

of the track indicates that its energy was approximately 7 MEV. An electron of this energy would produce a low specific ionization, resulting in a thin track. Furthermore, such an electron would have a range of at least 3000 cm. in air under standard conditions. The actual range observed was only 1½ cm. If the particle below the counter is regarded as a proton then the curvature of its track indicates an energy of only 25000 electron volts. Such a proton would have a range in air of less than 0.02 cm., whereas the actually observed range was 1½ cm. Again there is no escape from the conclusion that this entire track was left by a new particle, a particle having a mass intermediate between that of the proton and that of the normal electron.

And so it has gone. As other observers have reported similar evidence the actual existence of the mesotron has become more and more certain. Some of these additional works[17–20] have shown the existence of positively charged heavy electrons; others[17,21] have shown the existence of negatively charged heavy particles. The mesotron may thus be either positive or negative. There is every reason to believe it bears a single electronic charge. Its mass is definitely intermediate between that of the proton and that of the normal electron. There is no question as to the actual existence of the particle.

## 2. THE MASS OF THE MESOTRON

It would be quite satisfying if the ratio $e/m$, and thence the mass, of the mesotron could be measured much after the fashion of that for the normal electron. This has so far been quite impossible for two reasons. First, there is available no convenient localized source of mesotrons. Second, the cosmic ray mesotrons which are available are so energetic that they are very difficult to bend appreciably by even the strongest magnetic fields. Fortunately there are other ways of obtaining the mass of the particle. These are none too direct and are far from precise. Nevertheless, they have allowed a good estimate of the magnitude of this mass. Although attention has not been called to the fact, most of the observers who have reported evidence for the existence of the mesotron have likewise reported a value for its mass.

The mass of the mesotron can be evaluated in any one of several indirect ways. Various quantities which can be obtained from cloud chamber photographs are the curvature of the track, the range of the particle, the ionization per centimeter of path, and the rates of change of these quantities as the particle proceeds along its path. These several quantities depend in fairly well known ways upon the charge, the mass, and the velocity of the particle. If certain of those which involve the mass of the particle are known it should be possible to evaluate this mass. Although the specific ionization depends very little upon the mass of a particle, it is nevertheless an important item in determining this mass. This ionization does depend upon the velocity of a particle. Hence two particles having the same $H\rho$ but different masses will ionize to perceptibly different degrees. Corson and Brode[20] have prepared a nomograph connecting these several quantities with the mass of the particle. This is reproduced in Fig. 6.

[17] Y. Nishina, M. Takeuchi and T. Ichimiya, *Phys. Rev.*, **52**, 1198 (1937).
[18] P. Ehrenfest, *Comptes Rendus*, **206**, 428 (1938).
[19] A. J. Ruhlig and H. R. Crane, *Phys. Rev.*, **53**, 266 (1938).
[20] D. R. Corson and R. B. Brode, *Phys. Rev.*, **53**, 773 (1938).
[21] Y. Nishina, M. Takeuchi and T. Ichimiya, *Phys. Rev.*, **55**, 585 (1939).

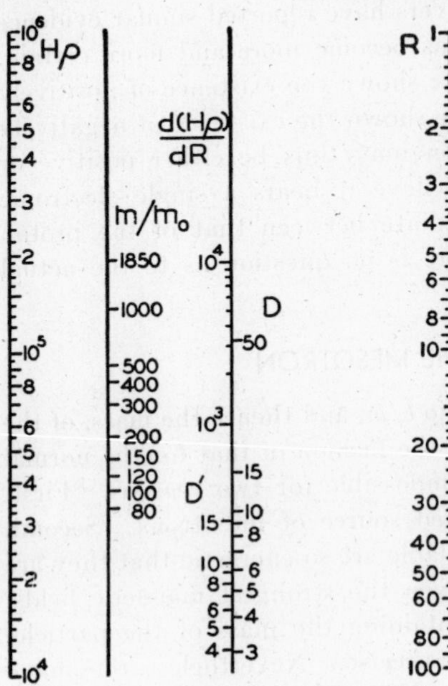


FIG. 6.—A nomograph, prepared by Corson and Brode, connecting the mass of the mesotron with various observable characteristics of the track left by the particle. $H\rho$ represents the product of magnetic field strength and radius of curvature of the track, the product being in oersted-cm. The quantity $m/m_0$ represents the ratio of the rest mass of the particle responsible for the track to the rest mass of the normal electron. $R$ is the range of the particle in cm. of air at 15° C and 750 mm. of Hg pressure. $D$ is the ratio of the specific ionization produced by the particle to the minimum specific ionization actually produced by a normal electron possessing the energy for which it produces this minimum ionization. $D'$ represents the ratio of the specific ionization produced by the particle in question to the specific ionization a normal electron would be expected to produce if its ionization were inversely proportional to $v^2$. Any straight line drawn across the nomograph gives a consistent set of values for all of the variables plotted.

This nomograph is constructed in such a way that the mass of the particle is given, as a multiple of the rest mass of the normal electron, by the intersection on the $m/m_0$ line of a straight line drawn between those points representing any two characteristics appropriate to the particle. For example, if $H\rho$ and the range $R$ are known, a straight line is drawn between the two points representing the values of these two quantities. The ratio $m/m_0$ can then be read directly from the nomograph. By way of example, consider the original particle photographed by Anderson and Neddermeyer.[2] As already stated, this particle had an $H\rho$ of $5.5 \times 10^4$ oersted-cm. and a range $R$ of approximately 4 cm. A straight line drawn between these values of $H\rho$ and $R$ intersects[20] the $m/m_0$ line at 350. Hence the particle responsible for this original track had a rest mass approximately 350 times the rest mass of the normal electron. It is not necessary to know both $H\rho$ and $R$ to obtain this mass. If some one of the quantities indicated along the third line of the nomograph is known, this coupled with either $H\rho$ or $R$ leads to a value of the mass. It is interesting, however, that either $H\rho$ or $R$ must be known. Even were all three quantities shown along the third line known, they would in no way determine $m/m_0$.

As Corson and Brode[20] point out, it is apparent from the nomograph that if all measurable quantities are known to the same degree of accuracy, then use of the $H\rho$ and $R$ values affords the most accurate method of evaluating the mass. The use of $H\rho$ and the specific ionization $D$ also affords a good determination of $m/m_0$, for a relatively large percentage change in $D$ produces a relatively small change in $m/m_0$. Combining the specific

FIG. 7.—A typical photograph taken for the express purpose of making an accurate ion count. The expansion has been delayed approximately one second after passage of the particle in order to allow the ions to separate by diffusion.

ionization $D$ with the range $R$ yields a value of $m/m_0$, but it is a relatively poor way of evaluating the mass; $D$ must be fairly accurately known to yield a good value for the mass. It is true that this last method does not involve the curvature of the track, a quantity which, when small, is often influenced by turbulence within the chamber. Evaluation of the specific ionization $D$ involves a reliable count of the droplets formed on ions during expansion of the cloud chamber. A reasonably accurate count can be obtained only by allowing a time of the order of 1 second to elapse between the passage of the particle and the subsequent expansion of the chamber. During this time the ions diffuse, forming a broad track. One such delayed photograph has been shown in Fig. 4. Another,[20] taken for the specific purpose of making an accurate ion count, is shown in Fig. 7. A count of the ions shows that this particle produced a density of ionization 5.5 times that of an ordinary electron. Curvature of the track shows that $H\rho = 1.5 \times 10^5$. These values, as is evident by reference to the nomograph, yield a rest mass of 250 times that of the normal electron. This track is therefore one produced by a mesotron.

Using methods of this character, many investigators have obtained values for the mass of the mesotron. As one would expect from consideration of the methods, the results have associated with them rather large probable errors. In fact these probable errors are so large in most determinations that one can be certain of little more than the order of magnitude of the mass. These methods have given definitely, however, the order of magnitude. It is interesting that a number[22] of cloud chamber photographs of an elastic collision between a mesotron and an electron have been obtained. While the curvatures of the tracks are not appropriate in most cases for accurate measurement, in one instance[22] these could be determined rather accurately. These measurements allow one to evaluate the mass of the mesotron directly from collision data. The value so obtained agrees with values obtained by other methods. Table I summarizes a number of the values that have been obtained for the mass of the mesotron.

It is useless to take an average of such widely divergent values. One can be certain only that the mass of the mesotron is approximately 200 times that of the normal electron. It has often been suggested that this particle may have no one characteristic mass; it may take on, with an equivalent energy change, any mass over a rather wide range. Certainly there exist no experimental data showing that the particle does exhibit different masses under different circumstances. On the other hand, measurements are still so crude that one can scarcely be certain that it does not.

It is indeed interesting that the existence of a particle having properties at least closely similar to those of the heavy electron was predicted from theoretical considerations before any experimental evidence was available. Considerations of the forces between particles going into the nuclear struc-

[22] L. Leprince-Ringuet, S. Gorodetzky, E. Nageotte and R. Richard-Foy, *Phys. Rev.*, **59**, 460 (1941).

TABLE I

A summary of experimental values of $m/m_0$, the ratio of the rest mass of the mesotron to the rest mass of the normal electron

| Author | Date | Reference | $m/m_0$ |
|---|---|---|---|
| Anderson and Neddermeyer | 1936 | 2 | Intermediate |
| Street and Stevenson | 1937 | 15 | 130 |
| Nishina, Takeuchi and Ichimiya | 1937 | 17 | 180–260 |
| Auger | 1938 | 25 | 100 |
| Corson and Brode | 1938 | 23 | 350 |
| Ruhlig and Crane | 1938 | 19 | 120 ± 30 |
| Corson and Brode | 1938 | 23, 20 | 250 |
| | | 24, 20 | <200 |
| | | 15, 20 | 160 |
| | | 2, 20 | 350 |
| | | 2, 20 | <1000 |
| | | 19, 20 | <110 |
| | | 17, 20 | 200 |
| Ehrenfest | 1938 | 18 | 200 |
| Neddermeyer and Anderson | 1938 | 16 | 240 |
| Williams and Pickup | 1938 | 26 | 220 ± 50 |
| | | | 190 ± 60 |
| | | | 160 ± 30 |
| | | | <430 |
| Nishina, Takeuchi and Ichimiya | 1939 | 17, 21 | 180 ± 20 |
| | | 21 | 170 ± 9 |
| Neher and Stever | 1940 | 27 | 160 |
| Leprince-Ringuet, Gorodetzky, Nageotte and Richard-Foy | 1941 | 22 | 240 ± 20 |

ture of atoms led Yukawa[28,29] to conceive of a then unknown particle which has since been referred to as the "Yukawa particle." The existence of such a particle seemed more or less essential to this worker's view of nuclear structure. Yukawa assigned to this then hypothetical particle a mass intermediate between that of the normal electron and the proton. He assigned, again from purely theoretical considerations, one further property. The particle was predicted to be unstable; it disintegrated, supposedly in accord with the usual laws of radioactivity, into a normal electron and a neutral particle. The half life period was predicted to be very short, some-

[23] D. R. Corson and R. B. Brode, *Phys. Rev.*, **53**, 215 (1938).
[24] R. B. Brode and M. A. Starr, *Phys. Rev.*, **53**, 3 (1938).
[25] P. Auger, *Comptes Rendus*, **206**, 346 (1938).
[26] E. J. Williams and E. Pickup, *Nature*, **141**, 684 (1938).
[27] H. V. Neher and H. G. Stever, *Phys. Rev.*, **58**, 766 (1940).
[28] H. Yukawa, *Proc. Phys. Math. Soc. Japan*, **17**, 48 (1935).
[29] H. J. Bhabha, *Nature*, **141**, 117 (1938).

thing of the order of one millionth of a second. Since convincing experimental evidence for the existence of the mesotron has been found the question arises as to whether this mesotron is the new particle predicted theoretically by Yukawa. The mesotron appeared from the first to have all the essential characteristics of this particle except possibly for the radioactive property, and during the last few years it has been shown rather definitely to be radioactive.

## 3. RADIOACTIVE DECAY OF THE MESOTRON

Evidence that mesotrons are unstable comes mainly, though not entirely, from observations that the absorption these particles suffer depends not only upon how much matter they traverse but also upon how long it takes the particles to pass through this matter. Lead is a very much better absorber of mesotrons than air, for a given thickness, but it is not as much better as one would expect from the known densities of the two materials. Carbon[30,31] is also a much better absorber than air, but it likewise is not as much better as one might expect. In fact, a thick layer of rarified air appears to absorb mesotrons better than a thin layer of air at higher pressure, even though the two layers contain the same mass per unit area of surface.

It has been recognized for several years that the mesotrons constituting the penetrating component of cosmic rays are absorbed in coming through the atmosphere more rapidly than can be accounted for by the mass of air they pass through. The most logical interpretation of this fact seems to be that some of the mesotrons disintegrate during the time required to pass through the atmosphere. Early discussions of this concept, together with references to the early experimental work, can be found in the literature.[4,32–34] That the mesotron is actually radioactive has been shown rather definitely by a number of more recent experiments.[30,31,35–39] Some of these experiments[30,31,35,36] have been designed to test more accurately the relative absorption of mesotrons in the atmosphere and in supposedly equivalent layers of more condensed material. Others[37–39] have been designed to

[30] B. Rossi, N. Hilberry and J. B. Hoag, *Phys. Rev.*, **56**, 837 (1939).

[31] W. M. Nielsen, C. M. Ryerson, L. W. Nordheim and K. Z. Morgan, *Phys. Rev.*, **59**, 547 (1941).

[32] H. Euler and W. Heisenberg, *Ergeb. d. exakt. Naturwiss.*, **17**, 1 (1938).

[33] T. H. Johnson and M. A. Pomerantz, *Phys. Rev.*, **55**, 104 (1939).

[34] B. Rossi, *Rev. Mod. Phys.*, **11**, 296 (1939).

[35] B. Rossi and D. B. Hall, *Phys. Rev.*, **59**, 223 (1941).

[36] H. V. Neher and H. G. Stever, *Phys. Rev.*, **58**, 766 (1940).

[37] F. Rasetti, *Phys. Rev.*, **59**, 706 (1941); **60**, 198 (1941).

[38] E. J. Williams and G. E. Roberts, *Nature*, **145**, 102 (1940).

[39] E. J. Williams and G. R. Evans, *Nature*, **145**, 818 (1940).

detect the actual disintegration of the mesotron by observing the disintegration particle.

In the first group are the experiments of Rossi, Hilberry and Hoag,[30] of Neher and Stever,[36] of Rossi and Hall,[35] and of Nielsen, Ryerson, Nordheim and Morgan.[31] Rossi, Hilberry and Hoag,[30] using Geiger counter tubes shielded from cosmic ray showers with 10 cm. of lead and from the soft component in general with 12.7 cm. of lead, measured the absorption of mesotrons in air by making observations of the intensity at different altitudes varying from that of Chicago to that of Mt. Evans. The absorption in carbon was measured by placing graphite layers of various thicknesses above the counters. It was found that the mass absorption in air is greater than that in carbon. For example, the air layer of 82 gr/cm.$^2$ between Echo Lake (elevation 10,600 feet) and Mt. Evans (elevation 14,000 feet) reduced the mesotron intensity more than twice as much as did a graphite layer of 84 gr/cm.$^2$ Nielsen, Ryerson, Nordheim and Morgan[31] obtained similar data by a somewhat different method. Neher and Stever[36] have compared the absorption in air and water by making measurements with a recording electroscope at various depths in two lakes at widely different altitudes. The air layer between lakes was found to be a better absorber than a layer of water having the same mass per unit area of surface. Rossi and Hall,[35] again using Geiger tubes, have compared the absorption in the air layer between Denver and Lake Echo (difference in elevation 5,330 feet) with that in a supposedly equivalent thickness of iron. A greater relative absorption was found to occur in the air.

All of these experiments show definitely that some of the mesotrons disappear by some process other than true absorption, and that the number disappearing in this way becomes appreciable only when the particles have to travel a great distance in passing through the absorber. One can scarcely escape the conclusion that these mesotrons disintegrate. In fact one can calculate the mean life of the mesotron from observations of this character. It is of the order of $2 \times 10^{-6}$ seconds. Various values of the mean life obtained by different experimenters are given in Table II. It is possible to calculate also the average distance the mesotron goes before disintegrating. A few of the values reported for this mean free path are $8.5 \times 10^5$ cm.,[30] $(8.0 \pm 0.8) \times 10^5$ cm.,[31] $(4.5 \pm 0.6) \times 10^5$ cm.,[35] and $(13.3 \pm 0.9) \times 10^5$ cm.[35] There is some indication[35] that the mean free path may be longer, and the mean life correspondingly longer, for high energy mesotrons than it is for low energy mesotrons.

It is clear from the table that the mean life period of the mesotron is of the order of 2 microseconds. It is possible that this mean life is not constant but depends upon the energy of the particle.[35] In any case the mean life is not far from that predicted for the Yukawa particle. The fact that the

TABLE II
Typical values for the mean life period of the mesotron

| Author | Date | Reference | Mean life in microseconds |
|---|---|---|---|
| Peierls | 1939 | 40 | 2–4 |
| Rossi, Hilberry and Hoag | 1939 | 30 | 2 |
| Cocconi | 1940 | 41 | 2 |
| Neher and Stever | 1940 | 36 | 2.8 |
| Rossi and Hall | 1941 | 35 | 2.4 ± 0.3 |
| Fedorenko | 1941 | 42 | 2.5 |
| Nielsen, Ryerson, Nordheim and Morgan | 1941 | 31 | 1.25 ± 0.3 |
| Rasetti | 1941 | 43 | 3.1 ± 1.5 |
| Rasetti | 1941 | 37 | 2 |
| Rasetti | 1941 | 37 | 1.5 ± 0.3 |

mesotron is radioactive eliminates the possibility that these particles, which are known to constitute the penetrating component of cosmic rays, are the primary cosmic rays themselves. The mean life is too short for the particle to have reached the earth's atmosphere before decaying. The mesotrons themselves must be of secondary origin. It appears[44] now that the primary cosmic radiation responsible for the penetrating component observed at sea level consists largely of protons. The mesotrons are apparently formed[45] by the bombardment of these protons on the earth's atmosphere. Most of the production occurs high in the atmosphere,[46] and the number of mesotrons found[44] in the atmosphere decreases with decreasing altitude due to the subsequent disintegrations. The decaying mesotrons probably give rise to electrons which in turn account either directly or indirectly for at least a part of the soft component of cosmic radiation.

A few experiments have been designed to detect the disintegration particle given out by the mesotron. The first[47] of these was unsuccessful. More recently the presence of the disintegration particle has been indicated by experiments of two types. Williams and Roberts[38] have obtained a cloud chamber photograph of tracks which appear to represent a positive electron arising from the disintegration of a positive mesotron. The low

[40] R. Peierls, *Rep. on Prog. in Phys.*, **6**, 78 (1939).
[41] G. Cocconi, *Phys. Rev.*, **57**, 61 (1940).
[42] N. Fedorenko, *Phys. Rev.*, **59**, 461 (1941).
[43] F. Rasetti, *Phys. Rev.*, **59**, 613 (1941).
[44] M. Schein, W. P. Jesse and E. O. Wollan, *Phys. Rev.*, **59**, 615 (1941).
[45] J. F. Carlson and M. Schein, *Phys. Rev.*, **59**, 840 (1941).
[46] M. Schein, W. P. Jesse and E. O. Wollan, *Phys. Rev.*, **57**, 847 (1940).
[47] C. G. Montgomery, W. E. Ramsey, D. B. Cowie and D. D. Montgomery, *Phys. Rev.*, **56**, 635 (1939).

energy mesotron apparently gives to the disintegration electron approximately half of its rest mass energy. In order to allow the conservation of energy and momentum, it is postulated that a neutrino also results from the disintegration. A second somewhat less convincing photograph of tracks by an original mesotron and its disintegration electron has been obtained by Williams and Evans.[39]

Rasetti[37] has detected what appear to be disintegration electrons by an entirely different method. A beam of mesotrons selected by a fourfold coincidence system of counter tubes was allowed to pass through iron **10** cm. thick. The number of mesotrons absorbed in the iron was determined by an auxiliary counter arrangement. It was found that a certain fraction of the mesotrons stopped in the iron is associated with the emission of ionizing particles from the iron. The emission of these particles was found to lag by a few microseconds the passage of the mesotrons. It is presumed that these ionizing particles are electrons arising from the disintegration of those mesotrons which were stopped by the iron. The mean life of the mesotron obtained[37,43] from measurements of this character agrees with that obtained by other methods. All of these different experiments leave no doubt that the mesotron is radioactive, and it appears that the disintegration electrons have been detected by two methods. The fact that the mesotrons disintegrate accounts for the rarity[15,48] of tracks left by mesotrons nearing the end of their range.

In Rasetti's[37] experiment the number of disintegration electrons observed was slightly less than half the number of mesotrons absorbed in the block of absorbing material. While the measurements are subject to fairly large errors, the indication is that only half the mesotrons disintegrate with the ejection of an electron. Now experiments show that roughly equal numbers of positive and negative mesotrons are present at sea level. Furthermore, certain theoretical considerations lead one to expect that it is only the positive mesotrons that disintegrate with the ejection of an electron when the mesotrons are stopped in an absorber. The negative mesotrons have a high probability of being absorbed in the nuclei of the absorber. Thus Rasetti's observation that there is about one disintegration electron for each two mesotrons absorbed, is consistent with the concept that it is only the disintegrations of the positives that are observed under such conditions.

[48] G. Herzog, *Phys. Rev.*, **55**, 1266 (1939).

## Chapter 14

# PARTICLES?—OR WAVES?

There has been presented in preceding chapters a great deal of evidence that light, X-rays, and gamma rays behave as photons. On the other hand, the phenomena of propagation, reflection, refraction, diffraction, interference, and polarization are logically and naturally interpreted by supposing that these are waves. In fact the phenomena of diffraction, interference and polarization had convinced physicists at one time that light, X-rays and gamma rays are definitely of wave character. Then came Planck's interpretation of the energy distribution of the radiation from a black body, Einstein's interpretation of the photoelectric effect, Bohr's interpretation of the emission and absorption of line spectra, Compton's interpretation of the scattering of X-rays, etc. The successes of these interpretations convinced everyone of the photon character of radiant energy. It appears that radiant energy sometimes exhibits the properties attributable to waves while under other circumstances it exhibits those properties which are associated definitely with the photon, or "particle," of energy. This dual character[1,2] of radiant energy stimulated a great deal of speculation as to the actual nature of light. While some progress had been made toward a more general concept of the actual nature of light, as a logical consequence of which this dual character might result, physicists were still far from a satisfactory solution when de Broglie offered in 1925 a suggestion of far-reaching consequence.

### 1. DE BROGLIE'S THEORETICAL CONSIDERATIONS

Among those attempting to reconcile existing concepts with the dual character of radiation was L. de Broglie. De Broglie[3] argued that if radiant energy behaves in some experiments as waves and in other experiments as particles, or photons, then might not one expect those entities which ordinarily behave as particles to exhibit the properties of waves under appropriate circumstances. That is, although electrons, protons, neutrons, atoms and molecules appear definitely to behave as particles in all experi-

[1] K. K. Darrow, *Bell System Tech. Jour.*, **4**, 280 (1925).

[2] A. H. Compton, *Jour. Frank. Inst.*, **205**, 155 (1928).

[3] L. de Broglie, *Ann. d. Physique*, **3**, 22 (1925).

ments previously tried, might not one devise other experiments in which these entities of matter show all the characteristics of waves.

Recall that the energy of a photon of radiation is given by $E = h\nu$. On the mass-energy equivalence concept one must assign to this photon a mass $m$ such that $E = mc^2$. By equating these two expressions for the energy one finds that $mc = h\nu/c = h/\lambda$. The quantity at the left is the momentum of the photon having a mass $m$ and traveling with a velocity $c$. Hence, in terms of wave characteristics, the momentum is given by $h\nu/c$ or $h/\lambda$. That is, one can express the momentum of radiant energy either in terms of the wave characteristic $\lambda$ or in terms of the mass and velocity characteristic of the equivalent particle. De Broglie[3] carried this idea over to those entities which had previously been regarded definitely as particles. If a particle such as an electron has a mass $m$ and travels with a velocity $v$, its momentum is given by $mv$. Arguing that this particle should sometimes behave as a wave, de Broglie equated this momentum to that of the equivalent wave. Thus

$$mv = \frac{h}{\lambda}$$

From this the wave length of the wave equivalent to a particle is found to be

$$\lambda = \frac{h}{mv}$$

That is, a particle of mass $m$ having a velocity $v$ should under proper experimental conditions exhibit the characteristics of a wave whose wave length is $h/mv$. This equation has become one of the most important of modern physics; it is known as the de Broglie equation. While Schrödinger, Dirac and others have greatly extended the original wave ideas into an elaborate theoretical treatment now known as wave mechanics, these various theoretical treatments all embody the original de Broglie equation.

At the time de Broglie advanced this hypothesis there was no experimental evidence whatever to indicate that electrons, protons, atoms, etc., ever exhibit properties other than those logically attributable to a particle. De Broglie's hypothesis would require that every particle of matter behave as a wave when studied under proper experimental conditions. It necessitates that all entities which had previously been regarded as simple particles should show the dual particle-wave characteristics just as does radiant energy. The wave length attributable to any particular particle can be calculated from the de Broglie equation. The wave lengths associated with a few typical particles are shown in Table I.

On the wave concept of the electron, or of matter in general, one does not conceive of any entity as a particle in the classical sense of the word.

TABLE I
The theoretical de Broglie wave lengths associated with various particles and bodies of gross matter

| Particle | Mass in grams | Velocity in cm/sec. | de Broglie wave-length in A° |
|---|---|---|---|
| 1-volt electron | $9.1 \times 10^{-28}$ | $5.9 \times 10^{7}$ | 12. |
| 100-volt electron | $9.1 \times 10^{-28}$ | $5.9 \times 10^{8}$ | 1.2 |
| 10,000-volt electron | $9.1 \times 10^{-28}$ | $5.9 \times 10^{9}$ | 0.12 |
| $H_2$ molecule at 200° C | $3.3 \times 10^{-24}$ | $2.4 \times 10^{5}$ | 0.82 |
| 100-volt proton | $1.67 \times 10^{-24}$ | $1.38 \times 10^{7}$ | 0.029 |
| 100-volt $\alpha$ particle | $6.6 \times 10^{-24}$ | $6.9 \times 10^{6}$ | 0.015 |
| $\alpha$ particle from radium | $6.6 \times 10^{-24}$ | $1.51 \times 10^{9}$ | $6.6 \times 10^{-5}$ |
| 22 rifle bullet | 1.9 | 32,000 | $1.1 \times 10^{-23}$ |
| Golf ball | 45 | 3,000 | $4.9 \times 10^{-24}$ |
| Baseball | 140 | 2,500 | $1.9 \times 10^{-24}$ |

The electron is not pictured as a particle of definite dimensions. Rather, it is pictured as a reinforcement in the standing wave pattern formed by two hypothetical wave trains moving in opposite directions. Instead of being localized, the electron charge is supposed to be distributed over a considerable space. The distribution of charge can be obtained mathematically from the standing wave pattern. Carrying this picture over into the atom, these hypothetical wave trains are supposed to move about the nucleus of the atom. The Bohr orbits are supposed to be those paths for which the wave has to travel some whole number of wave lengths in encircling the nucleus. For these paths there is formed a standing wave pattern, a number of nodes and antinodes. The electrons in this shell are represented by the reinforcements in this standing wave pattern. The number of electrons in a particular shell is given by the number of reinforcements. It was pointed out early that in order to account for the Bohr nonradiating orbits on this view, it was necessary that the wave length of these assumed electron waves be given by $\lambda = h/mv$, where $m$ is the mass and $v$ the velocity of the electron.

It turns out theoretically that these electron waves travel with a velocity greater than that of light. The product of the electron wave velocity $w$ and the electron particle velocity $v$ can be shown to be equal to the square of the velocity of light. That is, $wv = c^2$. For those entities commonly regarded as material particles $v$ is always less than $c$. It follows that the wave velocity associated with these is always greater than $c$. In the case of electromagnetic waves propagated with a wave velocity $w = c$, the equivalent particle velocity $v$ also turns out to be equal to $c$. The equivalent particle, the photon, thus travels with the velocity of light.

Many other interesting parallelisms can be drawn between the wave and the particle. Much more extended discussions of this character can be found elsewhere.[4,5] It is our primary purpose to present the more important experimental evidence bearing on present concepts, and to hold closely to this insofar as possible. There is definite evidence that electrons do exhibit those properties which one associates only with a wave, namely, diffraction and interference. Let us therefore consider this evidence.

## 2. EXPERIMENTAL OBSERVATIONS OF THE DIFFRACTION OF ELECTRONS

### Reflection from Crystals

Shortly after de Broglie's theoretical treatment of the wave properties of particles such as electrons, it was recognized that the wave length associated with relatively low energy electrons is essentially that of an X-ray. Consider, for example, a 100-volt electron. Ignoring the negligible change of mass of this low energy particle with velocity, the velocity of the electron can be calculated from

$$\frac{1}{2}mv^2 = Ve \quad \text{or} \quad v = \sqrt{\frac{2Ve}{m}}.$$

The de Broglie wave length associated with this particle is, therefore,

$$\lambda = \frac{h}{mv} = \frac{h}{m\sqrt{2Ve/m}} = \frac{h}{\sqrt{2meV}}$$

For $V = 100$ volts this yields a wave length of 1.2 A°, a wave length equal to that of a typical X-ray. Since the spacing of atomic planes in a crystal is of the proper size to produce clear-cut diffraction and interference effects with X-ray waves, then why should a crystal not diffract these electron waves in a similar manner?

A successful attempt to diffract electrons by a crystal was first carried out by Davisson and Germer[6,7] of the Bell Telephone Laboratories. The essentials of their complicated experimental arrangement are shown in Fig. 1. Electrons from a hot filament $F$ were accelerated through a potential difference of the order of 100 volts. A narrow beam of these, defined by openings in the plate $P$, was allowed to strike the face of a Ni crystal $C$ perpendicularly. An electrode $E$ connected to a sensitive galvanometer

[4] H. Semat, *Introduction to Atomic Physics* (New York: Farrar & Rinehart, 1939), pp. 134–159.

[5] G. P. Thomson and W. Cochrane, *Theory and Practice of Electron Diffraction* (London: Macmillan, 1939).

[6] C. Davisson and L. H. Germer, *Phys. Rev.*, **30**, 705 (1927); *Proc. Nat. Acad. Sci.*, **14**, 317, 619 (1928).

[7] L. H. Germer, *Zeits. f. Physik*, **54**, 408 (1929).

was then set to intercept those electrons scattered at first one and then another angle $\phi$. The experimental results, plotted in polar coordinates, are reproduced[6,4] in Fig. 2. The intensity in any particular direction is represented by the length of a line drawn in this direction from the origin to the curve. First, it is important to note that electrons are scattered in all directions, not just straight backward as one might expect of particles being reflected at the surface. Second, the distribution of the scattered electrons is definitely a function of the energy of the incident beam. As the accelerating potential is increased from 40 to 68 volts a characteristic peak, which was entirely absent at 40 volts, gradually appears and then disappears. This peak reaches a maximum, occurring at an angle of 50°, for electrons of 54 volts energy.

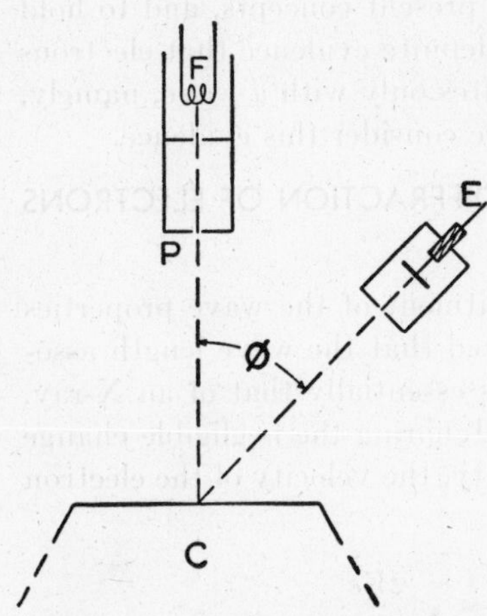


FIG. 1.—Showing the essential arrangement used by Davisson and Germer in studying electron diffraction by reflection from a nickel crystal.

Davisson and Germer interpreted this peak as due to a Bragg reflection, that is, reinforcement of electron waves reflected from a certain set of regularly spaced atomic planes within the crystal. A set of planes which might be responsible for the peak is shown in Fig. 3. In order to produce the normal Bragg reflection this set of planes must be perpendicular to a line bisecting

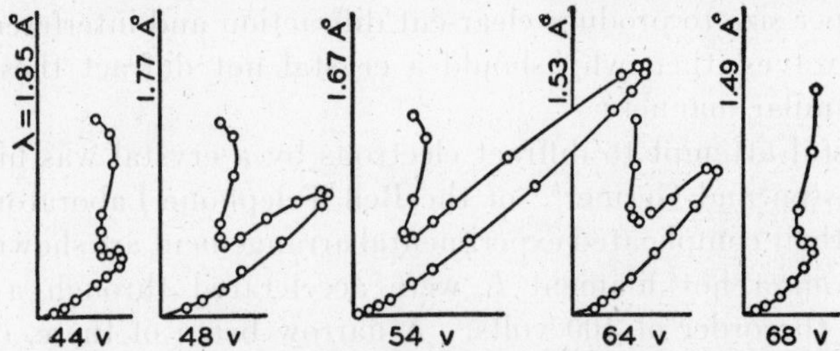


FIG. 2.—Showing how the intensity of the scattered electron beam varies with the angle of scattering and with the energy of the incident electrons.

the angle $\phi$ of Fig. 1. The angle $\psi$ is therefore $\frac{1}{2}\phi$. The Bragg angle $\theta$ occurring in the Bragg expression

$$n\lambda = 2d \sin \theta$$

is of course $(90 - \psi)$ or $(90 - \frac{1}{2}\phi)$. The spacing $d$ is that between planes in the set responsible for the reinforcement. Knowing from X-ray measurements that the spacing $D$ between atoms making up the surface plane of the Ni crystal is 2.15 A°, the spacing $d$ can be calculated from the geometry of the crystal. The spacing of those planes causing a reinforcement peak at $\phi = 50°$ is,

$$d = D \sin \psi = 2.15 \sin 25°$$

Also, from the relationship among angles, the Bragg angle $\theta = 65°$. Hence, the wave length responsible for this supposed first order Bragg reinforcement is

$$\lambda = 2(2.15 \sin 25°) \sin 65° = 1.65 \text{ A°}$$

This is the experimentally determined wave length associated with a 54-volt electron. If one calculates from the de Broglie expression $\lambda = h/mv$ the theoretical wave length of this electron, one finds a value 1.67 A°. Davisson and Germer's work on the reflection of electrons from the atomic planes of a Ni crystal therefore provided excellent evidence that the electron does exhibit wave properties, and that the wave length associated with the electron is at least closely that given by the de Broglie expression.

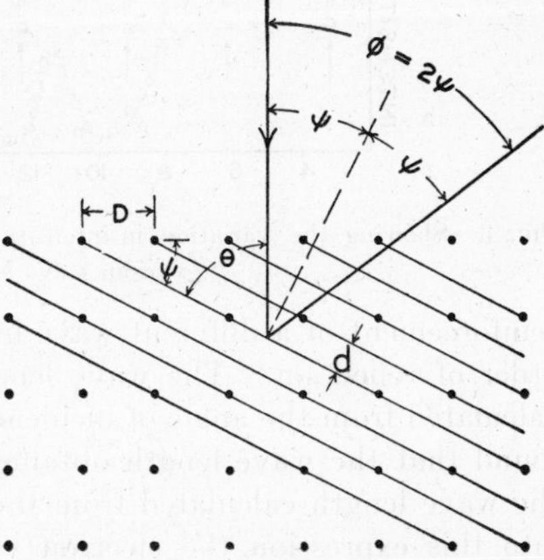

Fig. 3.—Illustrating the reinforcement of electron waves reflected from certain planes of the Ni crystal used by Davisson and Germer.

In the above experiment the electron beam was projected perpendicularly upon the crystal face, and these electron waves were reinforced by that particular set of planes for which the Bragg law was satisfied. These planes were not those parallel to the surface of the crystal, but those inclined at an angle $\psi$ with the face. An attempt was also made by Davisson and Germer to obtain reinforcement from those planes parallel to the surface. In order to do this the electrons were projected obliquely onto the face. As the electrode $E$ connected to a sensitive galvanometer was set to intercept those electrons reflected at various angles, it was found that the reflected beam was most intense in that direction for which the grazing angle of reflection was just equal to the grazing angle of incidence. This is exactly the same finding as that made by the Braggs for X-rays.

Now in the case of X-rays the intensity of reflection was found to vary markedly as the grazing angle of reflection $\theta$ was varied, always keeping it equal, however, to the grazing angle of incidence. A given wave length reinforced at that angle $\theta$ which satisfied the Bragg law $n\lambda = 2d \sin \theta$. Or, for a given setting $\theta$ of the two angles, the reinforcement was much more pronounced for those wave lengths satisfying the Bragg expression. Davisson and Germer attempted a similar experiment with electron waves. Keeping the grazing angles of incidence and reflection each equal to 80°, the de Broglie wave length of the electron was changed by varying the potential difference $V$ through which the electrons were accelerated. Fig. 4 shows the observed[6,8] intensity of reflection for electrons of various energies. Pronounced maxima and minima are obtained. Now it has already been shown that the de Broglie wave length is given by $\lambda = h/\sqrt{2meV}$. The electron wave length is inversely proportional to the square root of the electron energy expressed in volts. Whenever the potential $V$ leads to a wave length which satisfies Bragg's law, with $n$ equal to any integer, there should be an intense reinforcement. The peaks shown in Fig. 4 are due to these reinforcements. Each peak corresponds to

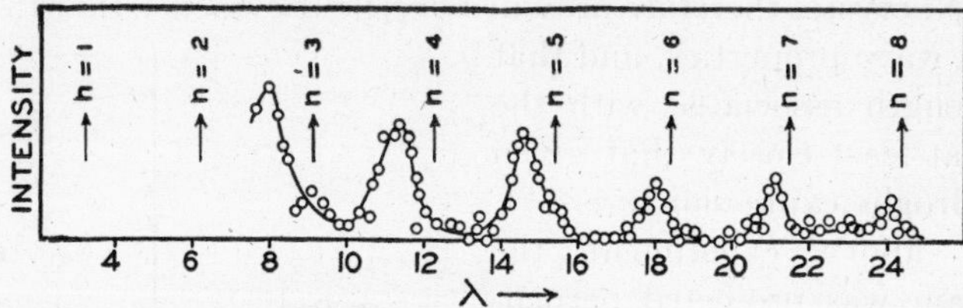


FIG. 4.—Showing the variation in intensity of reflection at a fixed grazing angle of 80°, for various wave lengths of electrons.

reinforcement of a different wave length; and it corresponds to a different order of reflection. The wave length corresponding to any peak can be calculated from the angle of incidence and the spacing of the crystal. It is found that the wave length obtained for a given peak agrees closely with the wave length calculated from the de Broglie expression by substituting into this expression the electron velocity corresponding to the potential required to produce the peak.

It is true that these diffraction peaks do not occur exactly where one would expect from the de Broglie wave length and the Bragg law. The arrows of Fig. 4 indicate the wave lengths for which the crystal should yield a maximum reinforcement according to the Bragg law. It is well to recall here that X-rays of a given wave length were found to reinforce at angles slightly different from those given by the Bragg expression; or, a wave length slightly different from that given by the Bragg law reinforced at a given angle. It was from this finding that investigators first concluded that X-rays are refracted, that crystals have an index of refraction for X-rays slightly different from one. And this conclusion was later borne out com-

[8] S. Kikuchi, *Phys. Zeits.*, **31**, 777 (1930).

pletely by other types of refraction experiments. It was necessary to modify the Bragg law to take account of this refraction.

Then why should one not attempt a similar interpretation in the case of electron waves? It has been found that an index of refraction can be assigned for these waves which makes the positions of reinforcement agree accurately with those expected for a wave length given by the de Broglie expression. This index turns out to be somewhat greater than 1, of the order of 1.1 for a 100-volt electron and a Ni crystal. Furthermore, the index varies with wave length much as it does for any other type of wave. Davisson and Germer's work indicated that the index becomes smaller for the shorter wave lengths. Work of this character left little doubt that electrons do exhibit those properties which can logically be associated only with waves, namely, diffraction and interference. The Nobel Prize was awarded to de Broglie in 1929 and to Davisson and G. P. Thomson in 1937 in recognition of their contributions in this field of physics.

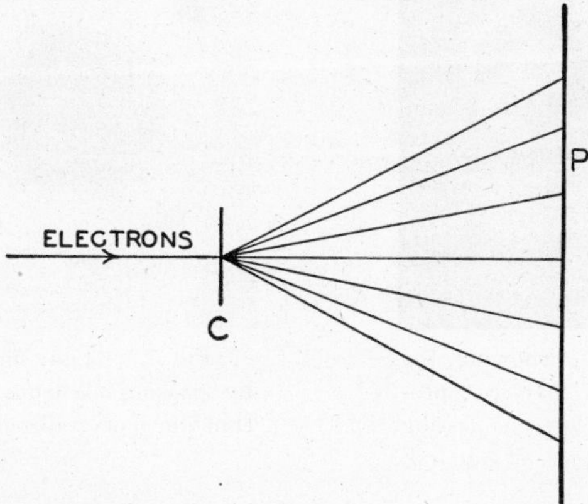


Fig. 5.—Illustrating Thomson's arrangement for studying the diffraction of electrons.

## Transmission through Crystals

Carried out simultaneously with the work described above was another highly important pioneering investigation.[9–11] If electrons are of wave character then they should produce Laue patterns upon passing through crystals. G. P. Thomson,[9] a son of J. J. Thomson, therefore projected a beam of electrons perpendicularly through a thin film of crystalline material. After passing through the film the electrons struck a photographic plate placed as indicated in Fig. 5. If electrons behave as particles one would expect a continuous distribution as they strike the photographic

[9] G. P. Thomson, *Proc. Roy. Soc.*, A, **117**, 600 (1927); **119**, 651 (1928); **125**, 352 (1929).

[10] A. Reid, *Proc. Roy. Soc.*, A, **119**, 663 (1928).

[11] R. Ironside, *Proc. Roy. Soc.*, A, **119**, 668 (1928)

plate. Many passing straight through the crystal would strike at the center, while those deflected at various angles during their passage through the film should strike at various places on the plate. If particles were scattered at all angles, as one would certainly expect them to be, the exposure on the plate should grade off gradually and continuously from the center. But this is not at all what was found. Fig. 6, reproduced from Thomson's early work[9] illustrates what was found. A clear-cut diffraction pattern is obtained, a pattern entirely analogous to that obtained with X-rays passing through a powdered crystal. If powdered crystal diffraction photographs are regarded as convincing evidence of the wave character of X-rays, then

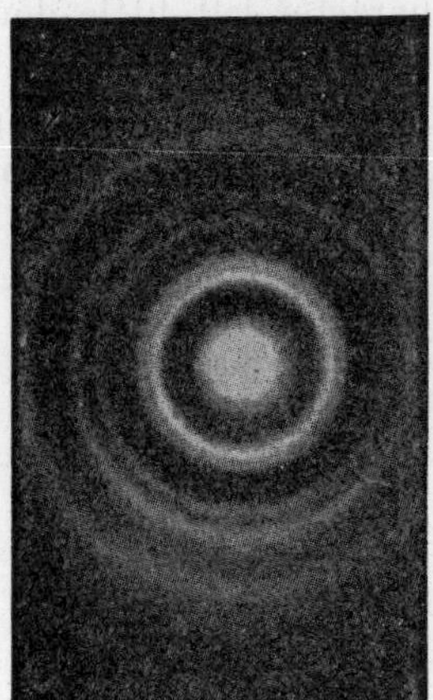

FIG. 6.—Showing the diffraction pattern produced by electrons passing through a piece of gold foil.

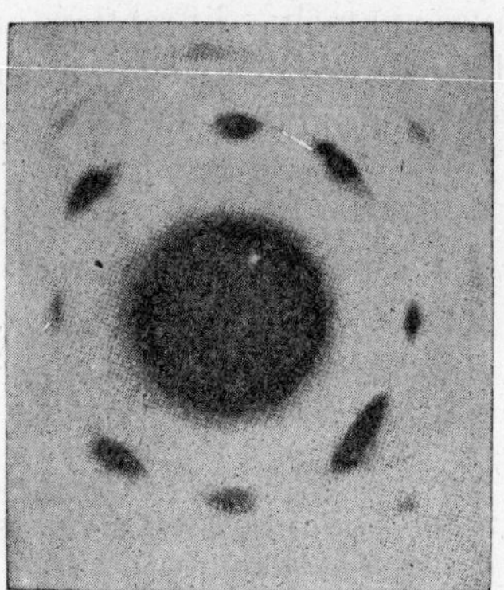

FIG. 7.—"Laue spots" formed by passing electrons through a thin film of crystallized aluminum.

results similar to those illustrated in Fig. 6 must be considered as equally convincing evidence of the wave character of electrons. It was Thomson's pioneer work on electron diffraction by transmission through crystals that won for him the Nobel Prize.

Diffraction patterns similar to Fig. 6 are found for all metallic films which have been rolled or beaten. The uniform rings indicate that these films are of micro-crystalline structure; they are composed of innumerable small crystals oriented at random within the film. It appears that rolling or beating produces the equivalent of a powdered crystal. If one were to send an electron beam through a single crystal of material one would expect the formation of Laue spots rather than concentric rings. This is just what is found.[9,12] Fig. 7, again from the early work of Thomson,[9] shows

[12] G. P. Thomson, *Proc. Roy. Soc.*, A, **133**, 1 (1931).

the spots obtained by passing a beam of electrons through a thin film of crystallized aluminum which had not been subjected to rolling or beating. The similarity between this and the original Laue spots obtained with X-rays is apparent. Just as for X-rays, electron waves passing through single crystals produce spots, whereas they produce concentric ring diffraction patterns when passed through a random mixture of small crystals.

Knowing the spacing of atom planes in a crystal, it is possible to evaluate the wave length of the electrons used from the dimensions of the diffraction pattern and to compare this with the de Broglie wave length. Or, accepting the de Broglie wave length as correct, it is possible to use the observed diffraction pattern to evaluate the crystal spacing and to compare this spacing with that obtained from X-ray studies. Either procedure constitutes a check on the correctness of the wave length assigned to the electron by de Broglie and on the concept of the formation of the diffraction pattern. Choosing the second method of comparison, Table II shows results[9,11] for a number of crystals. The agreement of values obtained from electron

TABLE II

Comparison of the grating space as determined from X-ray and electron diffraction patterns for a number of metals

| Metal | Spacing from X-rays | Spacing from electron waves |
|---|---|---|
| Aluminum | 4.043 | 4.035 |
| Gold | 4.064 | {4.20<br>3.99 |
| Platinum | 3.913 | 3.89 |
| Lead | 4.92 | 4.99 |
| Iron | 2.87 | 2.85 |
| Silver | 4.079 | 4.11 |
| Copper | 3.60 | 3.66 |
| Cuprous oxide | 4.26 | 4.30 |
| Tin (white) | 2.91 | 2.86 |

diffraction studies with those from X-ray studies is entirely satisfactory. Such results, amplified by many later extensive investigations[5,8,12–14] give one complete confidence in electron wave studies. In one recent investigation[14] the de Broglie equation for the wave length of an electron has been found valid over an energy range extending from 24 to 64 electron kilovolts.

## Diffraction by Gases

Although a gas certainly has no crystalline-like structure, no regularity of atomic spacing, it nevertheless possesses certain characteristics which

[13] F. Kirchner. *Phys. Zeits.*, **31**, 1025 (1930); *Zeits. f. Physik*, **76**, 576 (1932).

[14] J. G. Tappert, *Phys. Rev.*, **54**, 1085 (1938).

cause it to produce diffraction patterns. Although attention has not been called to it, certain diffraction phenomena associated with the passage of X-rays through liquids have been known for some time and have been the bases of numerous experimental studies.[15] This X-ray diffraction seems to be brought about by a semblance of regularity in the average spacing between molecules of the liquid and by a more definite regularity associated with the interatomic spacing within the molecules. In a similar way one might hope to obtain electron diffraction patterns produced by gases due

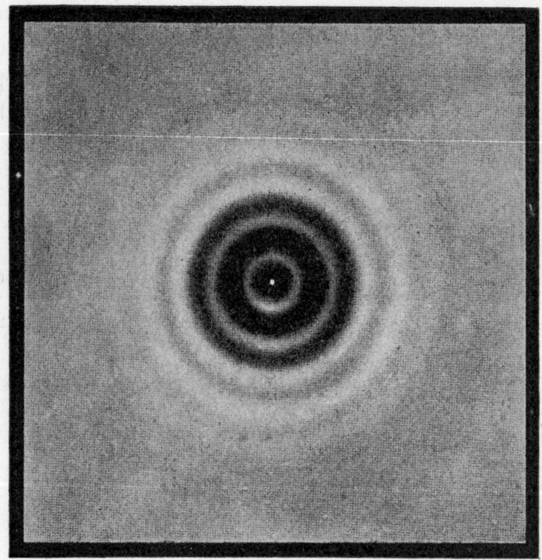

FIG. 8.—Electron diffraction by $As_4$ vapor.

to the regularity of the atomic arrangement and interatomic spacing within the gaseous molecules. Many experimental and theoretical investigations have been carried out on electron diffraction by gases. All except the most recent of these have been well summarized in the literature.[16] Diffraction phenomena are definitely observed, and some of the resulting photographs are surprisingly sharp. One such photograph showing electron diffraction by $As_4$ vapor is reproduced[16] in Fig. 8. Similar diffraction patterns have been obtained[17] for other gases such as $CCl_4$, $CS_2$, $C_2H_2$, and $NH_3$. Considerable information regarding the spacing of atoms within the molecule

[15] G. W. Stewart, *Rev. Mod. Phys.*, **2**, 116 (1930).
[16] L. O. Brockway, *Rev. Mod. Phys.*, **8**, 231 (1936).
[17] P. P. Debye, *Phys. Zeits.*, **40**, 66, 404 (1939).

and regarding the orientation of certain groups of atoms with respect to other groups can be obtained from electron diffraction studies.[18–23]

## 3. CRYSTAL STRUCTURE BY ELECTRON DIFFRACTION

It was soon recognized that an electron beam possesses a distinct advantage over an X-ray beam in the study of the crystal structure of thin films of material and of the surface structure of large crystals. X-rays are relatively penetrating, and only a small fraction of the energy is reflected

FIG. 9.—Electron diffraction pattern from an evaporated gold film 22 A° thick.

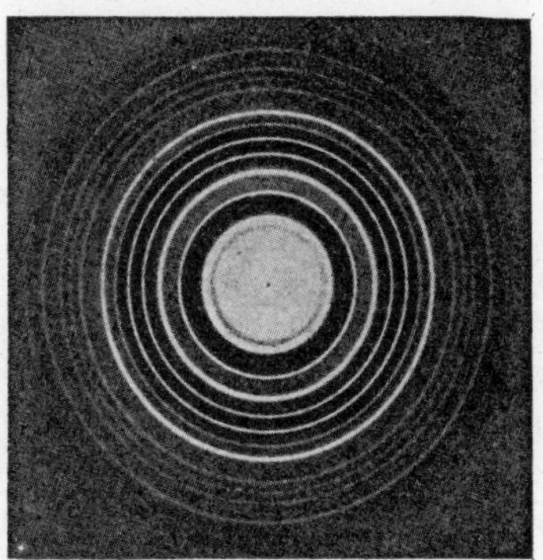

FIG. 10.—Electron diffraction pattern from an evaporated caesium iodide film 30 A° thick.

from any given plane of atoms. In very thin films there does not exist a sufficient number of planes to reflect an appreciable amount of X-ray energy. But electrons of equivalent wave length are far less penetrating, and these thin films will form well defined electron diffraction patterns. Electron diffraction studies are therefore of great importance in investigating the crystalline structure of thin films. In a similar way, since these electrons do not penetrate far into the surface of a large crystal, electron beams can be used to study the surface structures of crystals.

[18] D. P. Stevenson and V. Schomaker, *Jour. Amer. Chem. Soc.*, **61**, 3173 (1939); **62**, 1267, 2423 (1940).

[19] D. P. Stevenson and H. Russell, *Jour. Amer. Chem. Soc.*, **61**, 3264 (1939).

[20] J. E. LuValle and V. Schomaker, *Jour. Am. Chem. Soc.*, **61**, 3520 (1939).

[21] J. Y. Beach and S. H. Bauer, *Jour. Amer. Chem. Soc.*, **62**, 3440 (1940).

[22] H. B. Weiser and W. O. Milligan, *Jour. Phys. Chem.*, **44**, 1081 (1940).

[23] H. A. Skinner and L. E. Sutton, *Trans. Faraday Soc.*, **36**, 1209 (1940).

With such studies in mind there have been devised[24–30] a number of so-called electron diffraction cameras. These are simply convenient designs of apparatus for obtaining the necessary diffraction patterns. The technique of such studies has naturally improved greatly in recent years and it is now possible to obtain exceedingly sharp diffraction rings. Among those studies already mentioned and numerous others referred to in the literature,[31–46] there appear many excellent photographs. Perhaps two of the most remarkable series are an early one by Kirchner[13] and a recent one by Germer.[45] Two photographs of this latter series are reproduced in Figs. 9 and 10. The sharpness of the diffraction rings is truly remarkable. Many similar photographs were obtained by Germer for films of both metals and inorganic compounds deposited by evaporation upon thin supporting films. A great deal has been learned about the structure of thin films from studies of this character.

## 4. DIFFRACTION OF ATOMS AND MOLECULES

It is evident from Table I that the de Broglie wave length associated with a hydrogen molecule participating in the average thermal agitation at a temperature of 200° C is 0.82 A°. This again is of the proper order to show diffraction and interference effects upon reflection from or transmission through a crystal. The penetrating power of such low speed molecules is so small that it is impossible to study any possible diffraction pattern

[24] G. P. Thomson and C. G. Fraser, *Proc. Roy. Soc.*, A, **128**, 641 (1930).
[25] L. H. Germer, *Rev. Sci. Instr.*, **6**, 138 (1935).
[26] R. Morgan and N. Smith, *Rev. Sci. Instr.*, **6**, 316 (1935).
[27] J. A. Darbyshire and E. R. Cooper, *Jour. Sci. Instr.*, **12**, 10, (1935).
[28] H. J. Yearian and J. D. Howe, *Rev. Sci. Instr.*, **7**, 26 (1936).
[29] G. I. Finch, *Rep. on Prog. in Phys.*, **2**, 291 (1935).
[30] R. Jackson and A. G. Quarrell, *Proc. Phys. Soc.*, London, **51**, 237 (1939).
[31] G. P. Thomson, *Phil. Mag.*, **6**, 939 (1928); *Proc. Roy. Soc.*, A, **128**, 649 (1930).
[32] R. C. French, *Proc. Roy. Soc.*, A, **140**, 637 (1933).
[33] S. Kikuchi and S. Nakagawa, *Inst. Phys. Chem. Res.*, Tokyo, *Sci. Papers*, **21**, 80 (1933).
[34] K. H. Storks and L. H. Germer, *Phys. Rev.*, **50**, 676 (1936).
[35] L. H. Germer, *Phys. Rev.*, **44**, 1012 (1933); **49**, 163 (1936); **50**, 659 (1936); **52**, 959 (1937); *Zeits. f. Krist.*, **100**, 277 (1938).
[36] S. C. Curran, *Phil. Mag.*, **24**, 953 (1937).
[37] O. Rüdiger, *Ann. d. Physik*, **30**, 505 (1937).
[38] F. Kirchner, *Ann. d. Physik*, **30**, 683 (1937).
[39] H. Boersch, *Zeits. f. techn. Physik*, **18**, 574 (1937); *Phys. Zeits.*, **38**, 1000 (1937).
[40] L. S. Ornstein, H. Brinkman, A. Hauer and T. Tol, *Physica*, **5**, 693 (1938).
[41] H. Katz, *Ann. d. Physik*, **33**, 160, 169 (1938).
[42] J. T. Burwell, *Jour. Chem. Phys.*, **6**, 749 (1938).
[43] H. Boochs, *Zeits. f. techn. Physik*, **19**, 605 (1938).
[44] J. J. Trillat, *Comptes Rendus*, **209**, 201 (1939).
[45] L. H. Germer, *Phys. Rev.*, **56**, 58 (1939).
[46] H. Dunholter and H. Kersten, *Jour. App. Phys.* **10**, 523 (1939).

produced by transmission through a crystal; the molecules will not go through even the thinnest crystalline film. It is possible, however, to study the reflection of these molecules from the surface planes of a crystal. Experimental studies of this character have been made for several different atoms or molecules reflected from different crystals.

Typical of this work is the pioneering investigation of Estermann and Stern.[47] A stream of He atoms issued from an oven held at a known temperature. A narrow beam of these was allowed to strike the face of a LiF crystal at a known angle of incidence. In order to measure the intensity of the atomic beam scattered in various directions, a sensitive manometer *M* was arranged to catch the atoms scattered in any particular direction. The essential arrangement is shown in Fig. 11. The atomic or molecular beam entering this manometer produces an excess pressure therein. The

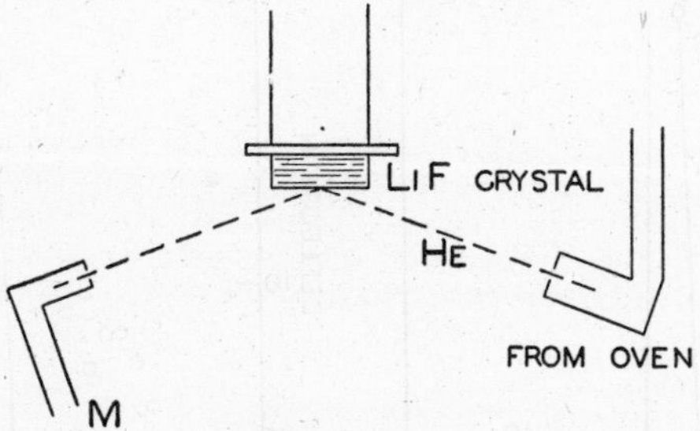


FIG. 11.—Showing the essential arrangement used to study the diffraction of atoms or molecules by crystals.

magnitude of the excess pressure is a measure of the intensity of atomic or molecular rays scattered in any given direction. The sensitive pressure indicating device *M* was arranged so that it could be rotated about an axis perpendicular to the paper in Fig. 11. Keeping the angle of incidence of the molecular beam on the crystal constant, the distribution of molecules scattered at various angles was investigated by setting *M* at various angles. Typical results are reproduced[47] in Figs. 12 and 13.

The abscissae of these curves represent the angular setting of the manometer *M* from that position corresponding to regular reflection. That is, angles are measured with respect to the direction in which a regularly reflected beam should appear. Both figures show an intense scattering of atoms at 0°, corresponding to regular reflection. But each figure shows also quite distinct peaks on either side of this. The existence of these peaks is conclusive evidence of diffraction. The strong central reinforcement accompanied by the weaker reinforcements, one on either side, is entirely

[47] I. Estermann and O. Stern, *Zeits. f. Physik*, **61**, 95 (1930).

analogous to the similar pattern of light intensity reflected from a ruled grating.

Assuming that the two side peaks are first order diffraction peaks produced by the LiF crystal grating, it is possible to calculate the wave length of the atomic beam from the position of the peak and the known spacing of atoms in the surface plane of the crystal. The wave length calculated in this way turns out to be just that which the de Broglie equation

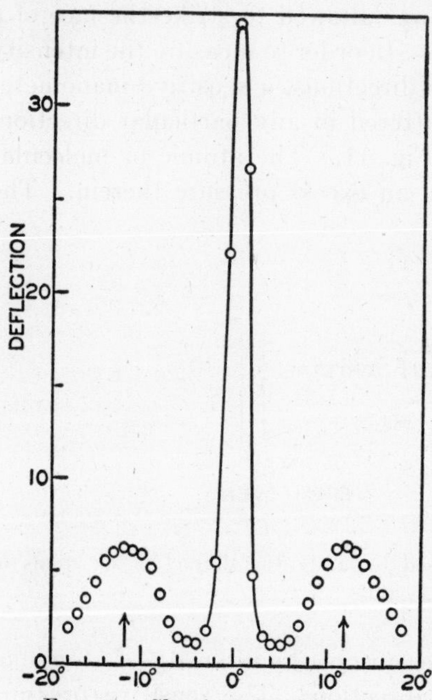


FIG. 12.—Showing the diffraction of He atoms by a LiF crystal. The beam of atoms came from an oven at 295° K and fell upon the crystal face at an angle of incidence of 11½°.

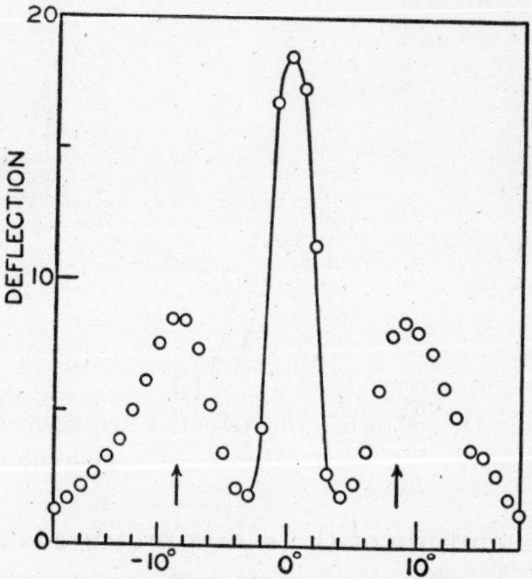


FIG. 13.—The diffraction of He atoms by a LiF crystal. The beam of atoms came from an oven at 580° K and fell upon the crystal face at an angle of incidence of 11½°.

assigns to an atom having the velocity of thermal agitation characteristic of the temperature at which the oven is held. It is important to note that figures 12 and 13 represent identical conditions except for oven temperature. The atoms of Fig. 12 came from an oven held at 295° K, whereas those of Fig. 13 came from an oven at 580° K. In the latter case the thermal velocity of the atoms is greater, and the de Broglie wave length should therefore be smaller. That the actual wave length is smaller is indicated by the fact that the first order diffraction peaks fall closer to the central "image" in Fig. 13 than they do in Fig. 12. Estermann and Stern studied helium beams having velocities corresponding to various temperatures from 100 to 580 K°, and molecular hydrogen beams having velocities corresponding to temperatures from 290 to 580 K°. Furthermore, they reflected these beams from crystals of both NaCl and LiF. In every case diffraction patterns were obtained, and in every case the wave length calculated from the diffraction pattern was essentially that given by the de Broglie equation.

The width of the diffraction peaks in these experiments is due jointly to the width of the slit and to the fact that the beam contains atoms of various velocities. The atoms of different velocities have different wave lengths and therefore reinforce in different directions. The width of the diffraction peak seems to be entirely consistent with the view that the atoms have a Maxwellian distribution of thermal velocities. It is interesting that investigators[48] have used for such experiments "monochromatic beams" of molecules, molecules of one velocity only. Such a beam should have one definite de Broglie wave length instead of a distribution of wave lengths. These monochromatic beams have been obtained in two ways, one by using rotating, toothed wheels to sort out atoms having the one velocity which enables them to pass the wheels at a time when their path is not blocked by a tooth, the other by using those atoms reflected from a crystal which produce one particular part of the diffraction peak. In either case the atoms should be of one velocity and, therefore, of one wave length. Reflection of these monochromatic beams from a LiF crystal has led[48] to relatively sharp diffraction peaks, much sharper than those of Figs. 12 and 13. These measurements with monochromatic atomic beams have shown that the measured wave length agrees with the theoretical de Broglie wave length within approximately one percent.

Similar findings regarding the diffraction of atoms and molecules have since been made by others, and methods of measuring the scattered intensity have been greatly improved. The Pirani gauge, consisting of an electrically heated wire the rate of loss of energy from which depends upon the gaseous pressure, has been refined[49] until it is sensitive to pressure changes of $10^{-8}$ mm. of Hg. Using this pressure indicator Zebal[50] has obtained diffraction patterns by reflecting He, Ne and A atoms from a NaCl crystal. Diffraction has also been obtained[51] with atomic hydrogen reflected from a LiF crystal. An entirely different method of detection was used for this. The scattered hydrogen atoms were allowed to strike a plate coated with molybdenum oxide. The oxide was reduced to metallic molybdenum where struck by

[48] I. Estermann, R. Frisch and O. Stern, *Phys. Zeits.*, **32**, 670 (1931); *Zeits. f. Physik*, **73**, 348 (1931).

[49] A. Ellett and R. M. Zabel, *Phys. Rev.*, **37**, 1112 (1931).

[50] R. M. Zabel, *Phys. Rev.*, **42**, 218 (1932).

[51] T. H. Johnson, *Phys. Rev.*, **35**, 1299 (1930); **37**, 847 (1931).

the diffracted hydrogen beam. The distribution of the diffracted beam was then obtained from the distribution of metallic molybdenum. This method is of course applicable to the study of hydrogen beams only. All of these diffraction patterns are those characteristic of a two-dimensional space lattice made up of the surface layer of atoms. Atomic and molecular beams do not have sufficient penetration to be scattered by the deeper atomic planes.

Several efforts have been made to observe also the diffraction of protons. Dempster[52] obtained quite complex patterns by reflecting from a calcite crystal, protons which had fallen through from 15,000 to 40,000 volts. These patterns have never been interpreted clearly. Sugiura[53] obtained proton diffraction by reflection from thin Pt and W films sputtered on glass. Patterns formed by protons having energies of several hundred electron volts were consistent with the calculated de Broglie wave length. Yearian[54] has obtained evidence for the diffraction of 15 to 20 kilovolt protons as these were passed through $CCl_4$ vapor. Here again the results are not inconsistent with the concept that the proton behaves as a de Broglie wave. In no case, however, have results with protons been as clear-cut as they have with electrons and with thermal atoms and molecules.

Experiments such as those described leave no doubt that atoms and molecules as well as electrons exhibit wave properties, and that the wave length associated with these is just that given by the de Broglie equation. One must admit that physical entities such as electrons, atoms and molecules behave sometimes as particles and sometimes as waves. They possess this dual characteristic just as truly as does radiant energy. No "particle" ever exhibits both the particle and the wave characteristics in the same experiment. It will be recalled that light coming through an opening which is large as compared to the wave length appears to cast a sharp shadow, although close inspection shows the presence of diffraction. When light is sent through an opening whose dimensions are not too many times the wave length, the phenomena of diffraction and interference become quite clear. The only reason one does not observe these as readily for large openings is that the diffraction peaks occur so near the central "image" as to be indistinguishable from it. In order to observe diffraction and intereference phenomena with radio waves, heat waves, light or X-rays, the spacing of diffraction centers must be comparable with the wave length being used.

In a similar way electrons, atoms and molecules passing through large openings appear to proceed in straight lines as particles. Or if they are

[52] A. J. Dempster, *Phys. Rev.*, **34,** 1493 (1929); **35,** 1405 (1930).
[53] Y. Sugiura, *Inst. Phys. Chem. Res.*, Tokyo, *Sci. Papers,* **16,** 29 (1931).
[54] H. J. Yearian, *Jour. Chem. Phys.*, **8,** 24 (1940).

scattered by points many wave lengths apart they appear to be scattered as particles. It is only when they are scattered by points only a few wave lengths apart that diffraction becomes obvious. No doubt the diffraction peaks are always present, but under ordinary circumstances they fall so close to the central "image" that one fails to distinguish them. One therefore interprets the behavior as that of a particle, not realizing that the submerged diffraction effects are actually present. For years before the advent of the wave theory physicists did just this in the case of light. From present knowledge one would certainly expect electrons passing through a sufficiently narrow slit to cause diffraction and interference fringes just as does light. Because of the small slit dimensions required it has been only in relatively recent years that observations of this character have been made for X-rays. A slit comparable with that used for X-rays would be required to observe the effect for electrons. As far as the author knows, no definite experimental observations have been made regarding this point. It is theoretically possible also to observe electron diffraction from ruled gratings, much as has been done for X-rays. Here again no one has yet overcome the experimental difficulties.

One might logically inquire why gross matter such as a rifle bullet, a golf ball, or a baseball does not exhibit wave properties. Certainly no diffraction and interference effects are observed with such bodies of matter. A glance at Table I shows the reason immediately. The de Broglie wave length associated with any one of these bodies traveling at a usual speed is of the order of $10^{-24}$ A°. Clear-cut diffraction phenomena could be observed only when these bodies pass through an opening having dimensions not many multiples of this. There is nothing even remotely approaching this in either an opening or a spacing of diffraction centers. Even if there were, what chance would one have of projecting such bodies through these openings? It appears hopeless that physicists will ever obtain directly diffraction effects with gross bodies of matter. But there is no reason to doubt that even these have a de Broglie wave length associated with them. Perhaps the future will bring some indirect if not some direct way of showing that they do. Lack of knowledge of what the future has in store, along with the firm conviction that it has a great deal once the mysteries of nature are further unraveled, provides the irresistible incentive to carry on research. And past experience has taught that the necessary forerunner of practical application is a thorough understanding of the workings of nature. Power be to those who make a real attempt to understand these workings.

# PROBLEMS

# PROBLEMS

Answers given are frequently only to slide rule accuracy.

For the sake of uniformity it is suggested that the following values be used for constants:

$$e = 4.803 \times 10^{-10} \text{ e.s.u.} = 1.602 \times 10^{-19} \text{ coulombs}$$
$$c = 2.99776 \times 10^{10} \text{ cm/sec.}$$
$$h = 6.614 \times 10^{-27} \text{ erg sec.}$$
$$\frac{h}{e} = 1.377 \times 10^{-17} \text{ erg sec/e.s.u.}$$
$$\frac{e}{m_0} = 1.758 \times 10^{7} \text{ e.m.u./gr.}$$
$$N = 6.023 \times 10^{23} \text{ atoms/gram-atom}$$
$$k = 1.380 \times 10^{-16} \text{ erg/C}^\circ$$
$$g = 980.0 \text{ cm/sec.}^2$$

Again for the sake of uniformity it is suggested that for masses of the light atoms the following be used:

| | | |
|---|---|---|
| $n = 1.00893$ | $Be^8 = 8.00792$ | $C^{14} = 14.00763$ |
| $H^1 = 1.00813$ | $Be^9 = 9.01504$ | $N^{13} = 13.01008$ |
| $H^2 = 2.01473$ | $Be^{10} = 10.01671$ | $N^{14} = 14.00750$ |
| $H^3 = 3.01705$ | $B^{10} = 10.01631$ | $N^{15} = 15.00489$ |
| $He^3 = 3.01707$ | $B^{11} = 11.01292$ | $O^{16} = 16.00000$ |
| $He^4 = 4.00389$ | $C^{11} = 11.01526$ | $O^{17} = 17.00450$ |
| $Li^6 = 6.01686$ | $C^{12} = 12.00398$ | $O^{18} = 18.0065$ |
| $Li^7 = 7.01818$ | $C^{13} = 13.00761$ | |

## Chapter 1

1. An electrometer having a capacity of 30 micromicrofarads has a potential sensitivity of 400 mm. per volt difference of potential applied to the quadrants. In a certain experiment the electrometer drifts through 5 cm. on the scale in 2 minutes. Calculate the current flowing to the electrometer quadrant; express this current in amperes.
*Ans.:* $3.1 \times 10^{-14}$ *amperes.*

2. Calculate the average kinetic energy of thermal agitation of a gaseous atom or molecule at room temperature, 20° C. Calculate the velocity of a hydrogen molecule ($H_2$) having this average energy. Calculate the velocity of an oxygen molecule ($O_2$) having this energy.
*Ans.:* $6.1 \times 10^{-14}$ *ergs;* $1.9 \times 10^5$ *cm/sec.;* $4.8 \times 10^4$ *cm/sec.*

3. A saturation current of $10^{-13}$ amperes is observed from a given ionization chamber of 1000 cc. volume. There is a fixed source which produces uniform ionization throughout the chamber. Calculate the number of pairs of ions formed per second per cc.
*Ans.:* 625 *pairs/cc/sec.*

4. The coefficient of recombination of ions in a given gas at a given pressure is $2 \times 10^{-6}$ per sec. per pair/cc. Suppose that an ionizing agent, say X-rays, falls continuously on this gas and that the intensity of the ionizing radiation is sufficient to produce 5000 pairs of ions per cc. per second. No electric field is applied across the ionized gas. Calculate the number of pairs of ions that exist per cc. after the ionizing agent has been acting for a time sufficiently long that equilibrium conditions exist. *Ans.:* $5 \times 10^4$ *pairs/cc.*

5. Suppose that in the last problem the ionizing agent is shut off abruptly. How long will it be before the ion concentration present will have dropped to ½ of the value existing at the instant the ionizing agent was turned off? How long before it will have dropped to 10% of the initial value? *Ans.:* 10 *sec.;* 90 *sec.*

6. Fig. 14 of the text illustrates the electrical shutter method used by Tyndall and Powell for measuring ion mobilities. Gauze electrodes *AB* represent one electrical shutter, *CD* a second shutter. These shutters are large as compared to the distance between them. Ions come up to *AB* slowly from the left. An alternating potential of variable frequency $f$ is applied between electrodes *A* and *B*; the same alternating potential is applied between *C* and *D*. (*A* is connected to *C*, *B* to *D*.) A d.c. potential of 50 volts is maintained between shutter *AB* and shutter *CD*. The distance between shutters is 1.5 cm. As the frequency of the alternating potential is varied from 100 to 200 cycles/sec., it is found that a maximum current flows to electrode *E* only when the frequency is either 120 or 180. Calculate the mobility of the ion. Is there any frequency below 120 which would lead to a maximum current, and if so what is the lowest one? Would it be possible, and perhaps more convenient, to perform this experiment by applying an alternating potential of fixed frequency and varying the d.c. potential applied between shutters? *Ans.:* 2.7 *cm/sec/volt/cm.; yes,* 60 *cycles/sec.; yes.*

## Chapter 2

1. A small oil drop has a radius of $6 \times 10^{-5}$ cm. and a density of 0.851 gr/cc. It falls freely through air at 76 cm. Hg pressure and 23° C temperature, under which conditions air has a viscosity of $1.832 \times 10^{-4}$ c.g.s. units. Calculate the velocity with which the drop falls: (1) using the uncorrected form of Stokes' law; (2) using the corrected form of the law. *Ans.:* $3.64 \times 10^{-3}$ *cm/sec.;* $4.13 \times 10^{-3}$ *cm/sec.*

2. Suppose the oil drop of the last problem had been much larger, say 0.01 cm. in radius. All other conditions being the same, calculate the velocity with which this drop would fall: (1) using the uncorrected form of Stokes' law; (2) using the corrected form of the law.
*Ans.:* 101 *cm/sec.;* 101 *cm/sec.*

3. In a Millikan oil drop apparatus, with plates shorted so there is no electric field, an oil drop of density 0.891 gr/cc. is observed to fall freely through a distance of 0.140 cm. in 30.0 seconds. Barometric pressure of the air in the apparatus is 74 cm. of Hg; the temperature is 23° C. Under these conditions the viscosity of air is $1.832 \times 10^{-4}$ c.g.s. units. Calculate the radius of the drop, using of course the corrected Stokes' law. (This calculation is readily made by a series of approximations. First calculate the radius ignoring the correction term $\left(1 + \frac{b}{pr}\right)$. The radius so found will be somewhat in error, too high. Now put this slightly incorrect value for $r$ in the correction term and calculate again the radius. This value of $r$ is much nearer the true value, but probably still slightly high. If this last value is used in the correction term a still better value will

result. Continue the approximation in this way until the resulting value of $r$ is the same as that last used in the correction term.) *Ans.:* $6.237 \times 10^{-5}$ *cm.*

4. In the apparatus of the last problem the distance between plates is 0.700 cm. A potential of 550 volts is applied between plates in such a direction as to cause the oil drop of that problem to rise. The time required for the drop to rise through a distance of 0.140 cm. is observed. Various values are found, 71.5, 16.4, 9.2 and 6.4 seconds. Calculate the charge on the drop in each of the four cases. *Ans.: Closely* 1, 2, 3 *and* 4 *electron units.*

5. A certain spherical oil drop $10^{-4}$ cm. in radius has on it at a given time a net charge of 50 electron units. Calculate the energy that would be required to put one additional unit of charge of the same sign onto it. How does this compare with the average kinetic energy of thermal agitation (calculated in problem 2 of Chapter 1) at room temperature? Would another ion of the same sign of charge as the drop be likely to drive itself onto the drop due to its thermal motion? *Ans.:* $11.5 \times 10^{-14}$ *ergs; about twice; no.*

## Chapter 3

1. The cathode fall of potential in a given glow discharge is 600 volts. The Crookes dark space is 5 mm. long. Approximately what is the electric field strength, expressed in volts per centimeter, at the surface of the cathode? *Ans.:* 2400 *volts/cm.*

2. For a given cathode metal and a given gas the cathode fall of potential in the normal glow discharge is independent of the pressure of the gas and independent of the length of the Crookes dark space. Suppose that in the last problem the pressure of the gas were doubled. What change, if any, would you expect in the electric field strength at the surface of the cathode? *Ans.: Would be doubled.*

## Chapter 4

1. Fig. 3 of the text illustrates one method, used by Kirchner, of determining directly the velocity of electrons. $A$, $B$, and $C$ are small openings which define a narrow beam of electrons. An alternating potential of variable frequency is applied between the two plates of the first pair. This same alternating potential is applied between the two plates of the second pair. The lowest frequency of alternating potential for which the two spots on the fluorescent screen merge into one centrally located spot is $3.0 \times 10^7$ cycles/sec. State three other frequencies which would produce a single spot. If the distance between the two pairs of plates is 40 cm., calculate the velocity of the electrons. *Ans.:* 2, 3 *and* 4 *times* $3 \times 10^7$ *cycles/sec.;* $2.4 \times 10^9$ *cm/sec.*

2. A stream of electrons with velocity $2 \times 10^9$ cm/sec. enters a uniform electric field of 100 volts/cm. At the moment of entering the field the electrons are moving perpendicular to the direction of the field. The electrons of course continue to move across the field (in their original direction) and at the same time are deflected laterally by the field. Calculate how far from their original line of flight the electrons would be deflected by the electric field while they are moving 5 cm. measured in the direction of their original line of flight. *Ans.:* 0.549 *cm.*

3 Although the electrons of the last problem really describe a parabolic path while in the electric field, at least the first part of the path can be approximated closely by a circle. Calculate the radius of the approximately equivalent circle. *Ans.:* 22.75 *cm.*

4. Consider two points, $A$ and $B$, on a circle of radius $R$. Let a line be drawn tangent to the circle at $A$. Let $h$ be the perpendicular distance from point $B$ to the tangent; let $d$ be the perpendicular distance from point $B$ to the radius of the circle drawn to point $A$. From the geometry of the circle it can be shown that if $h$ is fairly small as compared to

$d$, then $h$ is given approximately by $h = d^2/2R$. Consider the stream of electrons of problem 2, and let the path be approximated by the circle whose radius was calculated in problem 3. Thence calculate the lateral deflection of the stream while the electrons are moving 5 cm. measured in the direction of their original flight. How does the result of this approximation compare with the true deflection calculated in problem 2? *Ans.: 0.549 cm.*

5. An electron with a velocity of $3 \times 10^9$ cm/sec. moves perpendicular to a uniform magnetic field of 20 oersteds (dynes per unit north pole). Calculate the lateral force exerted on this electron by the magnetic field. *Ans.: $9.6 \times 10^{-10}$ dynes.*
6. Consider the same electron as in the last problem, one moving with a velocity of $3 \times 10^9$ cm/sec. perpendicular to a magnetic field of 20 oersteds. Calculate the radius of the circular path described by the electron while in the field. If this electron had been moving twice as fast in the same magnetic field, what would have been the radius of the circular path? *Ans.: 8.53 cm.; 17.06 cm.*
7. Neglecting any possible change of mass with velocity, calculate the velocity of an electron after it has moved freely (starting from rest) between two electrodes differing in potential by: (1) 500 volts; (2) 1000 volts. *Ans.: $1.33 \times 10^9$ cm/sec.; $1.88 \times 10^9$ cm/sec.*
8. Calculate the average force on the plate of a two electrode tube when bombarded with electrons, if the plate potential is 1000 volts and the plate current 20 milliamperes. *Ans.: 0.21 dynes.*
9. Calculate the number of ergs energy in one electron-volt. (The electron-volt is the energy acquired by an electron in falling through a potential difference of one volt.) Referring to problem 2 of Chapter 1, what is the average kinetic energy of thermal motion of a molecule at about room temperature when this energy is expressed in electron-volts? *Ans.: $1.6 \times 10^{-12}$ ergs; 0.038 electron-volts.*
10. An electron falls freely through a potential difference of 5000 volts. What velocity does it acquire? It then passes through (perpendicular to) an electric field of 200 volts/cm., 2 cm. in length, and falls on a fluorescent screen 30 cm. distant from the center of the electric field. What is the radius of the approximate circular path while in the electric field? What is the lateral displacement of the spot on the screen caused by the electric field? *Ans.: $4.2 \times 10^9$ cm/sec.; 50.0 cm.; 1.20 cm.*
11. Electrons diverge from a beta ray source in a magnetic field which is parallel to the axis of the tube in which the electrons are being studied. The electrons are shot off from the source with a velocity of $10^{10}$ cm/sec., and in a direction making an angle of 10° with the focusing magnetic field. Calculate how strong a magnetic field will be necessary to cause proper focusing (that is to cause the electron to complete one turn of the spiral described in passing the length of the tube) on a screen 25 cm. from the source. *Ans.: 141 oersteds.*
12. Calculate the ratio $m/m_0$ for an electron moving with each of the following velocities: (1) 0.1 that of light; (2) 0.5 that of light; (3) 0.9 that of light; (4) 0.995 that of light. This last velocity is approximately that of the most energetic beta particles (electrons) given off by radioactive materials. *Ans.: 1.004; 1.15; 2.29; 10.0.*
13. An electron moves freely through a potential difference of 50,000 volts. Calculate the velocity it attains: (1) Neglecting any change of mass with velocity; (2) Taking account of the change of mass with velocity. *Ans.: $1.33 \times 10^{10}$ cm/sec.; $1.24 \times 10^{10}$ cm/sec.*
14. Calculate the potential difference, expressed in volts, through which an electron would have to fall to acquire a velocity of 0.995 that of light. *Ans.: $4.6 \times 10^6$ volts.*
15. Calculate the ratio $v/c$ for an electron accelerated through a potential difference of $10^6$ volts. What is the ratio $m/m_0$ for this electron after it has acquired the energy of $10^6$ electron-volts? *Ans.: 0.94; 2.95.*

## CHAPTER 5

1. Hydrogen canal rays proceed through a small hole in the cathode. When viewed in line with the motion a 5000 A° line has a Doppler shift of 7.5 A°. What is the velocity of the canal rays? *Ans.:* $4.5 \times 10^7$ *cm/sec.*

2. In Dempster's study of positive rays, he used a fixed magnetic deflecting field and a variable accelerating potential sufficient to bring the positive particles of the mass desired onto the slit after deflection. If 1000 volts accelerating potential brings $Mg^{24}$ onto the slit, what accelerating potential is required to bring $Mg^{25}$ onto the slit? *Ans.:* 960 *volts.*

3. The most abundant isotope of carbon, $C^{12}$, has an atomic weight 12.00398. Calculate the packing fraction for this atom. *Ans.:* $3.3 \times 10^{-4}$.

4. The physical and the chemical scales of atomic weights are slightly different. On the physical scale the isotope $O^{16}$ is given the weight 16.000000. On the chemical scale the average oxygen mixture which exists in nature is given the weight 16.000000. This average oxygen existing in nature has been found to consist of 99.76% $O^{16}$, 0.04% $O^{17}$, and 0.20% $O^{18}$. Calculate the mean atomic weight of the normal oxygen mixture, expressed on the physical scale. Hence what is the ratio of any atomic weight on the physical scale to the corresponding atomic weight on the chemical scale? *Ans.:* 16.0044; 1.00027.

5. Calculate the energy which would result from the conversion of one gram of mass into energy. Express this energy in ergs, in electron-volts, and in foot pounds. *Ans.:* $9 \times 10^{20}$ *ergs;* $5.6 \times 10^{32}$ *electron-volts;* $6.6 \times 10^{13}$ *ft. lbs.*

6. In the disintegration of one gram atom of a material the total energy released or absorbed (due to the change in mass) is of course divided among the number of atoms in the gram atom disintegrated. Hence, using the result of the last problem, calculate the number of electron-volts energy that should be furnished per atom disintegrating when the disintegration results in the loss of one unit in atomic weight. (No actual disintegration results in the loss of one whole unit in atomic weight. The loss is often of the order of 0.01 unit, however. The energy furnished per atom disintegrating is of course proportional to the loss of mass.) *Ans.:* 931 *MEV.*

7. When $Li^7$ is bombarded with energetic protons it is found that the $Li^7$ nucleus absorbs a proton and then splits into two $He^4$ nuclei. In a given experiment where the protons used had a kinetic energy of 500,000 electron-volts, it was observed that each of the two helium nuclei resulting from the disintegration of a lithium nucleus left the point of disintegration with a kinetic energy of 8.8 MEV. Knowing the masses of $H^1$ and $He^4$, knowing the net gain in kinetic energy accompanying the disintegration, and assuming that this gain in kinetic energy came from the conversion of mass into energy, calculate the atomic weight of $Li^7$. *Ans.:* 7.01802.

8. A proton is accelerated through a potential difference of 50,000 volts. Calculate the velocity it attains: (1) Neglecting any change of mass with velocity; (2) Taking account of the change of mass with velocity. In problem 13 of Chapter 4 you made a similar calculation for an electron accelerated through this same potential difference. How does the error introduced by neglect of the change of mass compare in the two cases? *Ans.:* $3.09 \times 10^8$ *cm/sec.;* $3.09 \times 10^8$ *cm/sec.; much less for the proton.*

9. Calculate the ratio $v/c$ for a proton accelerated through a potential difference of $10^6$ volts. What is the ratio $m/m_0$ for this proton after it has acquired the energy of $10^6$ electron-volts? In problem 15 of Chapter 4 you made a similar calculation for a $10^6$ electron-volt electron. How do the ratios $m/m_0$ compare in the two cases? *Ans.:* 0.0461; 1,001; *much less for the proton.*

## Chapter 6

1. Calculate, according to the Bohr theory, the radius of the circular $K$ orbit in the hydrogen atom. Calculate also the radii of the $L$ and the $M$ orbits.
*Ans.:* $5.27 \times 10^{-9}$ *cm.;* $2.11 \times 10^{-8}$ *cm.;* $4.74 \times 10^{-8}$ *cm.*
2. Calculate for the hydrogen atom, according to the Bohr theory, the ratio of the velocity of the electron in the $K$ orbit to the velocity of light. Make similar calculations for an electron in the $L$ orbit and for one in the $M$ orbit. *Ans.:* 0.0073; 0.0036; 0.0024.
3. Using numerical values for the individual constants involved, calculate the value of the Rydberg constant for hydrogen. Express this in two ways: (1) So that the frequency will come out in the unit "per sec."; (2) So that the frequency will come out as a wave number, in the unit "per cm." *Ans.:* $3.312 \times 10^{15}$ *per sec.;* $1.105 \times 10^{5}$ *per cm.*
4. Calculate the theoretical wavelength of the spectral line that would be emitted by the hydrogen atom as an electron transfers from the $N$ to the $L$ shell. Express this wavelength in A°. Of what series is this line a member? *Ans.:* 4862.8 *A° in vacuum; Balmer.*
5. The ionization potential of Na vapor is 5.13 volts. What is the shortest wavelength radiation Na vapor can emit due to transfers of the outermost electron from one energy level to another? Express this in A°. *Ans.:* 2410 *A°.*
6. Compute the constant relating the resonance potential of an atom in volts and the wavelength, in A°, of the radiation associated with this resonance potential.
*Ans.:* $\lambda = 12367/V$.
7. The photoelectric work function for a Na surface is 2.0 volts. Calculate, and express in A°, the longest wavelength light that will eject photoelectrons from the Na surface.
*Ans.:* 6190 *A°.*
8. The photoelectric work function of a Na surface is 2.0 volts. Calculate the maximum velocity with which photoelectrons are ejected from a Na surface when the surface is illuminated with light of 4000 A° wavelength. *Ans.:* $6.21 \times 10^{7}$ *cm/sec.*
9. The mercury line of wavelength 2536 A° is used to eject photoelectrons from silver. The difference in potential required to bring the ejected electrons to rest is 0.11 volts. Calculate the energy expressed in electron-volts necessary to remove an electron from silver. *Ans.:* 4.77 *electron-volts.*
10. In order to determine the wavelength of a given gamma ray the radiation is allowed to fall upon Pt. The velocities, and thence the energies, of the photoelectrons ejected were determined by bending a beam of the ejected electrons in a magnetic field. Photoelectron groups of several different energies were found. The energies of three of these groups were 121,000, 186,000, and 197,000 electron-volts. Knowing that Pt has energy levels of 2,200, 3,400, 11,500, 13,900, and 78,400 electron-volts, what is the wavelength of the gamma ray, expressed in A°? *Ans.:* 0.062 *A°.*
11. If the gamma ray of the last problem were allowed to fall upon Pb, which has known energy levels of 87,400, 15,800, 13,000 and 3,200 electron-volts, what energies would you expect to find for the various groups of photoelectrons ejected?
*Ans.:* 112, 184, 186 *and* 196 *kilo-electron-volts.*
12. Monochromatic X-rays of 0.7078 A° wavelength are scattered by a small carbon block. The X-rays scattered at an angle of 90° with the direction of the original beam are observed. What is the wavelength, expressed in A°, of the scattered X-rays observed?
*Ans.:* 0.7320 *A°.*

## Chapter 7

1. The spacing between successive planes in a NaCl crystal is 2.820 A°. When a given X-ray is shown upon the surface it is found that the first order Bragg reflection occurs at a

grazing angle of 8° 35′. What is the wavelength of the X-ray? At what angle would the second order Bragg reflection occur? *Ans.:* 0.842 *A*°; 17° 22′.

2. It is found that the critical grazing angle for X-ray reflection of a given wavelength from glass is 20 minutes. What is the index of refraction of glass for X-rays of this wavelength? *Ans.:* 0.9999831.
3. The index of refraction of glass for X-rays of 0.7 A° wavelength is less than unity by $1.64 \times 10^{-6}$. Calculate rather accurately the critical angle at which total reflection sets in. *Ans.:* 0.00181 *radians or* 6.22 *minutes.*
4. A piece of polished metal to be used as a reflection grating for X-rays is ruled with 2000 lines per centimeter. X-rays of 2.5 A° wavelength are shown upon this grating at a grazing angle of exactly 1 degree. At what grazing angles would you expect to find the two first order spectra? Notice how accurately one would have to measure these angles in order to measure precisely by this method the wavelength of an X-ray. *Ans.:* 0.0143 *radians or* 49.1′, *and* 0.0202 *radians or* 1° 9.3′.
5. X-rays of 0.0900 A° wavelength fall on a carbon scatterer. The X-rays scattered in a given direction are found to have a wavelength of 0.1000 A°. At what angle with the original beam was this scattered radiation observed? *Ans.:* 54°.
6. The absorption coefficient of Pb for X-rays of about 0.2 A° wavelength is 1.30 per cm. Calculate what thickness of lead would be necessary to reduce the intensity of these X-rays to 1/20 of its original value. *Ans.:* 2.3 *cm.*
7. A potential difference of 50,000 volts is applied across an X-ray tube. Calculate the wavelength, expressed in A°, of the shortest X-ray emitted. *Ans.:* 0.248 *A*°.
8. If the *K*, *L*, and *M* energy levels of Pt involved in the emission of the *K* X-rays of this element are 78,000, 12,000, and 3,000 electron-volts respectively, calculate the wavelengths of the $K_\alpha$ and $K_\beta$ lines from Pt. Express these in A°. *Ans.:* 0.187 *A*°; 0.165 *A*°.
9. From the energy level values given in the last problem, what is the minimum potential that must be applied across an X-ray tube with a Pt target to cause the emission of the $L_\alpha$ line? *Ans.:* 12,000 *volts.*
10. Taking the molecular weight of NaCl as 58.46 and the density at near room temperature as 2.167 gr/cc., calculate for this crystal the spacing between: (1) 100 planes; (2) 110 planes; (3) 111 planes. Express these in A°. *Ans.:* 2.82 *A*°; 1.99 *A*°; 1.63 *A*°.

### Chapter 8

1. The half life of radon is 3.825 days. What fraction of a given sample of radon will disintegrate in one day? The atomic weight of radon is 222. Starting with one microgram of radon, how many atoms will disintegrate in one day? *Ans.:* 0.166; $4.48 \times 10^{14}$.
2. The half life of ThX is 3.64 days. Calculate the average life of ThX atoms. Calculate the transformation constant of ThX, expressed in units "per sec." *Ans.:* 5.25 *days*; $2.20 \times 10^{-6}$ *per sec.*
3. The half life of $UX_1$ is 24.1 days. How many days after $UX_1$ has been isolated will it take for 90 percent of it to change to $UX_2$? *Ans :* 80 *days.*
4. ThB has a fairly long life as compared to that of ThC. The half life of ThB is 10.6 hours; that of ThC is 60.5 minutes. ThB disintegrates into ThC. Neglecting the fact that a small percentage of the ThB atoms disintegrate during the process, calculate the time required for ThC to build up from 0 to 0.8 of its final equilibrium value. *Ans.:* 140 *minutes.*
5. It is observed that $3.67 \times 10^{10}$ alpha particles are emitted per second per gram of radium. The atomic weight of radium is 226. Calculate the half life of radium in years. *Ans.:* 1595 *years.*

6. The transformation constant of radium is $1.38 \times 10^{-11}$ per second (half life 1590 years). The atomic weight of radium is 226 and that of UI is 238. It is found that 0.331 micrograms of radium are in equilibrium with one gram of UI. Calculate the half life of UI in years. *Ans.: $4.56 \times 10^9$ years.*
7. The three successive products of thoron, that is ThA, ThB and ThC, are in radioactive equilibrium. If there are N atoms of ThA present, calculate the number of ThB atoms present. Calculate also the number of ThC atoms present. *Ans.: $2.7 \times 10^5 N$; $2.6 \times 10^4 N$.*
8. The absorption coefficients in aluminum for beta rays from $UX_1$ and $UX_2$ are 460 and 18 per cm., respectively. What thicknesses of aluminum are needed to reduce these beta rays to $1/100$ of their original intensity? *Ans.: 0.010 cm.; 0.26 cm.*
9. The absorption coefficient of the hard gamma rays from ThC″ in lead is 0.46 per cm. Calculate the thickness of lead required to reduce the intensity of these gamma rays to $1/10$ of its original value. Calculate also the thickness required to reduce the intensity to $1/100$ of its original value. *Ans.: 5.0 cm.; 10.0 cm.*
10. A gamma ray whose wavelength is 0.0124 A° is allowed to fall upon platinum. The energy required to remove a $K$ electron from the Pt atom is 78,000 electron-volts. What is the energy, expressed in MEV, of a photoelectron ejected from the $K$ shell of Pt by this gamma ray? *Ans.: 0.92 MEV.*

### Chapter 9

1. Consider a positively charged particle having an energy of 100 MEV moving perpendicular to a magnetic field of 15,000 oersteds. Calculate the radius of curvature of the path if the particle is a proton. Calculate the radius of curvature if the particle is a positron. *Ans.: 98.7 cm.; 22.3 cm.*
2. Calculate the energy necessary to create an electron-positron pair. Express this energy in MEV. *Ans.: 1.022 MEV.*
3. Calculate the wavelength of the gamma ray which would result if in the annihilation of an electron-positron pair a single gamma ray photon is given out. Assume that the electron and positron were at rest at the time of annihilation. *Ans.: 0.0121 A°.*
4. Electron-positron pairs are produced by gamma rays having a wavelength of 0.0055 A°. What is the total kinetic energy of the pair at the moment of production? Express this energy in MEV. *Ans.: 1.23 MEV.*

### Chapter 10

1. A neutron strikes a nitrogen nucleus and projects it straight forward. The kinetic energy of the nitrogen nucleus, as judged from its range, is 2.5 MEV. By using the laws of conservation of momentum and conservation of energy, calculate the kinetic energy of the neutron. Express this energy in MEV. *Ans.: 10.1 MEV.*
2. Gamma rays from ThC″, which have an energy of 2.62 MEV, are used to disintegrate heavy hydrogen. The heavy hydrogen is thus disintegrated into a proton and a neutron. It is found that the proton leaves the point of disintegration with a kinetic energy of 0.225 MEV. Since the neutron mass is about that of the proton, the neutron possesses essentially the same kinetic energy. Calculate accurately the atomic mass of the neutron. *Ans.: 1.00893.*

### Chapter 11

1. Consider an alpha particle striking a hydrogen nucleus and projecting this nucleus straight forward. Assuming the conservation of kinetic energy and conservation of momentum

at the collision, calculate the ratio of the velocity of the projected hydrogen nucleus to that of the incident alpha particle. *Ans.:* 1.6.

2. The range of alpha particles from RaC′ is approximately 7.0 cm. and the velocity of ejection is approximately $2 \times 10^9$ cm/sec. Using the result of the last problem, knowing that a proton of a given velocity has approximately the same range as an alpha particle of the same velocity, and knowing that the range of a particle is proportional to the cube of its velocity, calculate the range of a proton projected straight forward by impact of a RaC′ alpha particle. *Ans.: 29 cm.*

3. Using the data and results of problems 1 or 2, calculate what fraction of the kinetic energy of an alpha particle is given to a proton which is projected straight forward by the alpha particle. *Ans.:* 0.64.

4. The range of alpha particles from RaC′ is approximately 7.0 cm. and the velocity of ejection is approximately $2 \times 10^9$ cm/sec. When Al is bombarded with alpha particles from RaC′ it is found that the disintegration protons have forward ranges of 90 cm. Knowing that a proton of a given velocity has approximately the same range as an alpha particle of the same velocity, and knowing that the range of a particle is proportional to the cube of its velocity, calculate the ratio of the kinetic energy of the disintegration proton ejected from Al to the kinetic energy of the RaC′ alpha particle which ejects it. *Ans.:* 1.37.

5. Alpha particles are fired through a gas in a cloud chamber. One photograph taken shows a forked track, representing apparently not a disintegration but a collision between the alpha particle and a nucleus of the gas. Measurements from the photograph show that the alpha particle was deviated by an angle of 60° at the collision; the struck nucleus went off at an angle of 30° with the original direction of the alpha particle. Assuming conservation of momentum and conservation of kinetic energy at collision, calculate the atomic mass of the nucleus struck. What was the gas in the cloud chamber? What is the ratio of the velocity of the projected nucleus to the velocity of the incident alpha particle? *Ans.:* 4.0; *helium;* 0.87.

6. Protons in a cyclotron, across which there is a magnetic flux density of 6,500 gauss, describe a circle of radius 32.0 cm. just before emerging from the dees. Neglecting any change of mass with velocity, calculate to two significant figures: (1) The velocity of the protons; (2) The energy of the protons, in MEV; (3) The frequency of the alternating potential applied between dees; (4) The number of complete turns of the spiral described by the protons if the peak value of the alternating potential applied between dees is 20,000 volts. *Ans.:* $2.0 \times 10^9$ *cm/sec.;* 2.1 *MEV;* $10^7$ *cycles/sec.;* 52.

7. Deuterons in a cyclotron describe a circle of radius 32.0 cm. just before emerging from the dees. The alternating potential applied to the dees is the same as that for the protons of the last problem, frequency $10^7$ cycles per second and peak 20,000 volts. Neglecting any change of mass with velocity, calculate to two significant figures: (1) The velocity of the deuterons; (2) The magnetic flux density necessary; (3) The energy of the deuterons in MEV; (4) The number of complete turns of the spiral described by the deuterons. *Ans.:* $2.0 \times 10^9$ *cm/sec.;* 13,000 *gauss;* 4.2 *MEV;* 105.

8. Alpha particles (helium nuclei) in a cyclotron describe a circle of radius 32.0 cm. just before emerging from the dees. The alternating potential applied to the dees is the same as that for the protons and the deuterons of the last two problems, frequency $10^7$ cycles per second and peak 20,000 volts. Neglecting any change of mass with velocity, calculate to two significant figures: (1) The velocity of the alpha particles; (2) The magnetic flux density necessary; (3) The energy of the alpha particles in MEV; (4) The number of complete turns of the spiral described by the alpha particles. *Ans.:* $2.0 \times 10^9$ *cm/sec.;* 13,000 *gauss;* 8.4 *MEV;* 105

9. When $Li^6$ is bombarded with deuterons the disintegration results in the formation of $Li^7$ and a proton. Calculate the energy, in MEV, that is released or absorbed.
*Ans.: 4.92 MEV released.*

10. When $N^{14}$ is bombarded with alpha particles the disintegration results in the formation of $O^{17}$ and a proton. Calculate the energy, in MEV, that is released or absorbed.
*Ans.: 1.15 MEV absorbed.*

11. When $B^{10}$ is bombarded with neutrons the disintegration results in the formation of $Li^7$ and an alpha particle. Calculate the energy, in MEV, that is released or absorbed.
*Ans.: 2.95 MEV released.*

12. When $Li^7$ is bombarded with deuterons the disintegration results in the formation of two alpha particles and one neutron. Calculate the energy, in MEV, that should be released or absorbed. *Ans.: 15.08 MEV released.*

13. In the fission of $U^{235}$ by slow neutrons it appears that the U nucleus absorbs the neutron and then splits into two fragments, one having an atomic weight about 140 and the other an atomic weight about 96. According to Dempster (see curve on page 197 of text) the packing fraction for an atom of atomic weight 236 is $5.5 \times 10^{-4}$, that for an atom of atomic weight 140 is $-3.0 \times 10^{-4}$, and that for an atom of atomic weight 96 is $-6.0 \times 10^{-4}$. Calculate the approximate total energy released in the splitting of uranium. Express this in MEV. *Ans.: 214 MEV.*

## Chapter 12

1. Wilson found that the absorption coefficient of the very penetrating cosmic rays observed in deep mines is 0.0025 per meter of water equivalent. These rays were observed at depths equivalent to 1400 meters of water. Calculate for these penetrating cosmic rays: (1) The fraction of the radiation which gets through 1 meter of water; (2) The fraction that gets through 1400 meters of water. *Ans.: 0.998; 0.030.*

2. Cosmic ray mesotrons travel with approximately the velocity of light. They are radioactive, having a mean life (not half life) of 2 microseconds. Knowing that they disintegrate in accord with the usual law of radioactive decay, and neglecting any relativity considerations, calculate: (1) The fraction of mesotrons that travel 1 kilometer before disintegrating; (2) The fraction that travel 10 kilometers before disintegrating.
*Ans.: 0.19; $5.8 \times 10^{-8}$.*

3. Calculate the minimum energy, in MEV, that must be possessed by a positive or negative cosmic ray electron in order that this electron shall penetrate the Earth's magnetic field and reach the Earth's surface: (1) At the magnetic equator; (2) At a magnetic latitude of 40°. *Ans.: 19,200 MEV; 6,610 MEV.*

4. The path of an energetic cosmic ray charged particle in a magnetic field of 20,000 oersteds has a radius of curvature of 50 cm. The nature of the track indicates that the particle bears a single electronic charge; the mass of the particle is not known. Calculate the momentum of the particle. *Ans.: $1.6 \times 10^{-14}$ gr. cm/sec.*

5. Assuming that the particle of the last problem is an electron, calculate the approximate kinetic energy of the particle. Express this in MEV. *Ans.: 300 MEV.*

## Chapter 13

1. It is found from a cloud chamber photograph that the radius of curvature of the path of a particle in a magnetic field of 4,000 oersteds is 10 cm. The range of the particle, in air at 15° C and 750 mm. of Hg, is 8.0 cm. What is the ratio of the rest mass of this particle to the rest mass of the normal electron? *Ans.: 175.*

2. The path of a charged particle has a radius of curvature of 25 cm. in a magnetic field of 3,000 oersteds. Assuming that this is a mesotron having a rest mass 200 times that of

the normal electron, what range would one expect for the particle in air at 15° C and 750 mm. of Hg? *Ans.: 55 cm.*

3. Taking the average life (not half life) of the mesotron as 2.0 microseconds, what percent of the mesotrons present at a given instant would you expect to disintegrate within the next: (1) one microsecond; (2) five microseconds? *Ans.: 39%; 92%.*

4. The mean life of the mesotron is 2.0 microseconds. What is the radioactive decay constant of mesotrons, expressed as the fraction that decay per second? *Ans.:* $5 \times 10^5$ *per sec.*

## Chapter 14

1. Calculate the DeBroglie wavelength of an electron having a velocity of: (1) $10^8$ cm/sec.; (2) $10^9$ cm/sec. Express these wavelengths in A°. *Ans.: 7.3 A°; 0.73 A°.*

2. Calculate the wavelength of an electron having an energy of 1000 electron-volts. *Ans.: 0.39 A°.*

3. The thermal velocity of a hydrogen molecule at 200° C is approximately $2.4 \times 10^5$ cm/sec. Calculate the DeBroglie wavelength of this molecule. *Ans.: 0.82 A°.*

4. Calculate the DeBroglie wavelength of a 2.0 gram rifle bullet traveling with a velocity of 400 meters/sec. *Ans.:* $8.3 \times 10^{-24}$ *A°.*

5. Calculate, in electron-volts, the energy of a proton which would have a DeBroglie wavelength of 0.5 *A°*. *Ans.: 0.33 electron-volts.*

# AUTHOR INDEX

(Pages are those on which an author or his work is referred to.)


Abelson, P. H., 451, 454, 455
Abraham, M., 116, 134, 139, 141
Adam, H., 382
Aebersold, P. C., 394, 395
Alberti, E., 123, 130
Alfvén, H., 496
Alichanian, A. I., 382
Alichanow, A. I., 382
Allison, S. K., 188, 189, 190, 195
Allison, S. K., & Compton, A. H., *see* Compton, A. H., & Allison, S. K.
Alvarez, L. W., 167, 402, 437, 443, 454, 500
Amaldi, E., 442, 448
Anderson, C. D., 43, 253, 363, 364, 366, 367, 368, 369, 370, 371, 373, 378, 500, 503, 504, 506, 511, 520, 521, 523, 524, 525, 526, 527, 530, 533
Anderson, H. H., 438
Anderson, H. L., 449
Andrade, E. N., da C., 405, 410, 413, 414
Aoki, K., 194, 195
Arakawa, H., 482
Aronberg, L., 199
Asada, T., 174
Astin, A. V., 468
Aston, F. W., 68, 70, 80, 94, 148, 156, 157, 158, 160, 161, 162, 167, 168, 169, 170, 171, 172, 174, 178, 180, 181, 182, 184, 187, 188, 190, 191, 192, 193, 194, 195, 196, 197, 199, 203, 204, 208, 210, 321, 396
Aston, G. H., 354
Aten, A. H. W., 207
Auger, P., 406, 474, 497, 500, 513, 533

Babcock, H. D., 120, 130, 202
Bacher, R. F., 61, 188, 189, 190, 191, 192, 193, 195, 394
Bäcklin, E., 57, 58, 59, 62, 64, 311
Bainbridge, K. T., 173, 174, 175, 176, 180, 181, 184, 187, 188, 189, 190, 191, 192, 193, 194, 195, 208, 438
Baker, C. P., 421
Banerjea, G. B., 60, 64
Barker, E. F., 202
Barkla, C. G., 278, 279, 295, 296, 297, 302
Barnothy, J., 462, 473
Barry, J. G., 494, 495, 496
Barschall, H. H., 449, 450
Bartky, W., 126
Barton, H. A., 431, 432
Bauer, S. H., 549
Beach, J. Y., 549
Beams, J. W., 210, 249
Bearden, J. A., 58, 59, 60, 63, 64, 128, 129, 130, 293, 294, 311, 312
Beardsley, N. F., 482
Beck, G., 513
Becker, H., 386, 388
Becker, J. A., 246, 247
Becquerel, H., 315
Beers, Y., 371
Begeman, L., 48
Bémont, G., 315
Bennet, R. D., 420, 477, 479, 488, 519
Bennett, W. H., 429
Bernet, E. J., 429, 430, 431, 432
Bestelmeyer, A., 130
Bethe, H. A., 184, 187, 188, 189, 190, 191, 192, 193, 194, 195, 197, 381, 387, 398, 399, 427, 433, 434, 436, 440, 444, 445, 453, 507, 513, 524
Bhabha, H. J., 513, 522, 533
Bieler, E. S., 407, 410, 411, 412, 413
Birge, R. T., 52, 54, 58, 59, 63, 64, 118, 119, 120, 121, 122, 128, 129, 130, 208, 218, 223, 224, 234, 245, 282, 293
Birkenbach, L., 205
Blackett, P. M. S., 43, 369, 370, 371, 372, 373, 376, 378, 379, 380, 406, 408, 409, 416, 439, 440, 481, 482, 492, 500, 504, 505, 506, 523, 524
Blake, F. C., 303
Bleakney, W., 92, 167, 174, 177

Bloch, F., 402
Blondlot, R., 262
Boersch, H., 550
Bohr, N., 214, 215, 216, 217, 218, 219, 221, 222, 223, 224, 225, 226, 227, 228, 229, 231, 236, 293, 299, 301, 403, 417, 449, 540
Bollman, V. L., 60, 64, 234, 293
Bond, W. M., 60, 64
Bonner, T. W., 43, 167, 187, 188, 189, 190, 191, 192, 195, 399, 445
Boochs, H., 550
Booth, E. T., 450
Born, M., 228
Bothe, W., 295, 370, 379, 380, 382, 384, 386, 388, 391, 516
Bowden, B. V., 330, 341, 342, 343, 344, 345, 347, 349
Bowen, I. S., 464, 465, 466, 467, 470, 486, 522
Bradbury, N. E., 33, 34, 35, 38, 39
Bragg, W. H., 268, 269, 270, 272, 273, 274, 277, 282, 303, 304, 305, 307, 308, 309, 310, 312, 313, 542, 543, 544, 545
Bragg, W. L., 267, 268, 269, 270, 272, 273, 274, 277, 282, 303, 304, 305, 307, 308, 309, 310, 312, 313, 542, 543, 544, 545
Bramley, A., 167, 323, 458
Brasefield, C. J., 192, 193, 194, 195
Brata, L., 33, 36
Bretscher, E., 399, 455
Brewer, A. K., 91, 94, 95, 96, 97, 167, 323, 458
Brickwedde, F. G., 200, 208
Briggs, G. H., 332, 341, 342
Brinkman, H., 550
Brockway, L. O., 548
Brode, R. B., 523, 529, 530, 532, 533
Brodsky, A. E., 322
Bronson, H. L., 329
Brönsted, J. N., 205
Brooks, H., 329
Brose, E., 75
Broussard, L., 517
Brown, B. W., 468
Brown, G. S., 519
Brubaker, W. M., 43, 187, 188, 189, 190, 191, 192, 195, 399
Brunhes, B., 262
Bucherer, A. H., 113, 115, 116, 123, 130, 134, 135, 138, 139, 140, 142, 144
Buck, J. H., 424
Burton, E. F., 460
Burwell, J. T., 550
Busch, N., 116, 118, 119, 123, 130

Cameron, G. H., 462, 470, 471, 474, 489
Camm, G. L., 490
Campbell, J. S., 120, 127, 130
Campbell, N. R., 316
Cardwell, A. B., 248
Carlson, J. F., 513, 536
Chao, C. Y., 375, 376
Chadwick, J., 372, 373, 378, 379, 380, 389, 390, 391, 393, 395, 396, 397, 399, 404, 405, 407, 410, 411, 412, 413, 414, 426, 441, 443, 444
Chadwick, J., Rutherford, E., and Ellis, C. D., *see* Rutherford, E., Chadwick, J., & Ellis C. D.
Chaffee, E. L., 104, 122, 123, 130
Clark, G. L., 267
Classen, J., 112, 113, 130, 154
Clay, J., 462, 472, 475, 479, 488, 489, 500
Clay, P. H., 472, 489
Clusius, H., 206
Coates, W. M., 421
Cocconi, G., 536
Cochrane, W., 541, 547
Cockroft, J. D., 187, 188, 189, 190, 191, 195, 399, 420, 421, 433, 435
Compton, A. H., 255, 256, 257, 258, 272, 274, 276, 280, 281, 282, 283, 284, 285, 288, 290, 463, 475, 476, 477, 479, 480, 481, 482, 485, 486, 488, 489, 490, 491, 492, 494, 500, 538
Compton, A. H. & Allison, S. K., 253, 257, 259, 261, 272, 274, 275, 279, 282, 283, 287, 288, 289, 293, 294, 299, 303
Compton, K. T., 65, 67, 79, 88, 89, 91, 92, 99, 100, 232, 233, 236, 241, 428
Constable, J. E. R., 441
Cooke, H. L., 460
Cooksey, D., 422, 424
Cooper, E. R., 550
Cork, J. M., 59, 64, 438, 443
Corlin, A., 472
Cornog, R., 167, 437, 443
Corson, D. R., 529, 530, 532, 533
Costa, J. L., 168, 187, 188, 190
Cosyns, M., 482

Coulomb, C. A., 1
Cowie, D. B , 536
Crane, H. R., 356, 357, 374, 385, 399, 529, 533
Crookes, W., 2, 47, 67, 68, 70, 71, 72, 80, 83, 84, 88, 91, 93, 101
Crowther, B. M., 210
Crudup, J., 474
Crussard, J., 500, 504
Curie, I., 332, 336, 372, 373, 378, 386, 387, 388, 389, 399, 452, 453
Curie, P., 315
Curie, Mme. P., 315, 316, 320, 330, 334, 335, 336, 341, 344
Curran, S. C., 550
Curtiss, L. F., 468

D'Agostino, O., 442, 448
Dahl, O., 429, 430, 431, 432
Dallaporta, N., 400
Dancoff, S. M., 394
Darbyshire, J. A., 550
Darrow, K. K., 246, 316, 405, 463, 494, 500, 521, 534, 538
Darwin, C. G., 405, 411
Dasannacharya, B., 279
Das Gupta, N. M., 516
Dauvillier, A., 93
Davidson, W. L., 196
Davies, A. C., 90
Davis, A. P., 91
Davis, B., 232, 233, 273
Davisson, C., 541, 542, 543, 544, 545
Debierne, A., 315
de Broglie, L., 227, 228, 539, 540, 541, 543, 544, 545, 547, 550, 552, 555
Debye, P. P., 312, 548
Dee, P. I., 184, 389, 433, 434, 436
De La Rue, W., 70
Delatisky, B., 491
Dempster, A. J., 126, 148, 154, 155, 156, 157, 162, 172, 173, 174, 176, 177, 196, 197, 199, 316, 321, 323, 554
Dennison, D. M., 202
d'Espine, J., 349
Dessauer, G., 451
DeVault, D. C., 455
Dickel, G., 206
Dixon, E. H., 248
Doan, R. L., 272
Donat, K., 340
Donzova, E. I., 322
Duane, W., 272, 292, 293, 294, 295
DuBridge, L. A., 237, 239, 241, 247, 248, 253
DuMond, J. W. M., 60, 64, 224, 234, 284, 285, 293
Dunholter, H., 550
Dunning, J. R., 402, 450
Dunnington, F. G., 64, 124, 125, 126, 128, 129, 130, 224, 293, 294
du Noüy, P. L., 54
Dushman, S., 246
Dutta, A. K., 517

Edelfson, N. E., 422, 424
Edlén, B., 223
Ehmert, A., 472, 516
Ehrenfest, P., 474, 497, 500, 504, 529, 533
Ehrenhaft, F., 52
Einstein, A., 240, 241, 243, 244, 249, 250, 252, 292, 351
Ellett, A., 553
Ellis, C. D., 354, 355, 359, 361
Ellis, C. D., Rutherford, E., & Chadwick, J., *see* Rutherford, E., Chadwick, J., & Ellis, C. D.
Elster, J., 2, 237, 238
Emeleus, K. G., 91
Epstein, P. S., 493
Ericson, A., 223
Erikson, H. A., 31, 34, 37, 38
Estermann, I., 551, 552, 553
Euler, H., 534
Evans, E. J., 222
Evans, F., 496
Evans, G. R., 455, 534, 537
Evans, R. D., 424
Eve, A. S., 461

Faraday, M., 46, 47, 54, 58, 66, 67, 68, 80, 83, 84, 85, 86, 98, 109, 311, 312
Feather, N., 186, 338, 340, 341, 342, 343, 391, 399, 433, 455
Fedorenko, N., 536
Feldenkrais, M., 431
Fermi, E., 442, 447, 448, 449, 450
Finch, G. I., 550
Flemberg, H., 61, 62, 64
Fletcher, H., 55
Flügge, S., 162, 450, 453
Fonovits-Smereker, H., 336

Forbush, S. E., 480, 489, 491, 492
Forró, M., 462, 473
Fowler, A., 222
Fowler, R. H., 158, 209, 248
Fowler, W. A., 385, 429, 430
Franck, J., 262
Frank, I. M., 382, 384
Fränz, H., 295
Fraser, C. G., 550
Freitag, K., 332
French, R. C., 550
Friedrich, W., 265, 267
Friman, E., 297, 301
Frisch, R., 553
Froman, D. K., 395, 463, 509, 510, 511, 515, 516, 517, 518, 519, 521
Fukushima, I., 61, 62, 64
Fünfer, E., 395

Gamow, G., 346
Gant, D. H. T., 450
Gaskell, J., 491
Gast, P. F., 475, 480, 482
Geiger, H., 49, 64, 329, 331, 333, 335, 336, 404, 405, 406, 511
Geitel, H., 1, 2, 237, 238, 460
Genevese, F., 295
Gerlach, W., 130
Germer, L. H., 541, 542, 543, 544, 545, 550
Gerthsen, C., 295
Getting, I. A., 489, 490
Giauque, W. F., 202
Gibbs, R. C., 120, 128, 130
Gill, P. S., 475, 477, 479, 480, 518
Gingrich, N. S., 257, 283
Glasoe, G. N., 241, 245
Gockel, A., 461
Goldhaber, M., 167, 397, 399, 437, 443, 444
Goldstein, E., 73, 147
Gorodetzky, S., 532, 533
Goucher, F. S., 232, 233
Goudsmit, S., 227
Grace, N. S., 120, 128, 226
Graef, C., 490
Graves, A. C., 196, 517
Graves, E. R., 188, 189, 195
Gray, L. H., 376, 378
Graziadei, H. T., 492, 493
Green, G. K., 424
Grégoire, R., 162, 374, 453
Grindley, G. C., 33
Grosev, L. V., 382, 384
Gross, B., 482
Grosse, A. V., 449, 450
Güntherschulze, A., 67, 68, 71, 81, 83, 84, 85, 89, 91, 94
Gurney, R. W., 352
Guye, C. E., 140, 141, 142

Hafner, E. M., 451
Hafstad, L. R., 429, 430, 431, 432
Haga, H., 263
Hagenow, C. F., 280
Hahn, O., 162, 329, 448, 453, 455
Halford, R. S., 455
Hall, D. B., 534, 535, 536
Hallwachs, W., 237
Halpern, J., 356, 357, 385
Hammer, W., 103
Hardy, J. D., 202
Harkins, W. D., 202, 204, 424
Harmsen, H., 172, 205
Harrington, E. L., 52, 61
Harrington, M. C., 93
Harteck, P., 437
Hatley, C. C., 273
Hauer, A., 550
Haxby, R. O., 189, 195, 429, 430, 431, 432, 451
Hayes, A., 204
Haynes, S. K., 465, 471
Hehl, N., 71
Heisenberg, W., 534
Heitler, W., 381, 507, 509, 513, 522
Helde, M., 399
Hemmendinger, A., 167, 211, 323
Henderson, G. H., 337
Henderson, M. C., 449, 450
Henderson, W. J., 424
Henney, K., 6
Hennings, A. E., 241
Herb, R. G., 429, 430, 431, 432
Hertz, G., 205, 206
Hertz, H., 237
Herzberg, G., 213
Herzog, G., 524, 537
Hess, V. F., 461, 464, 482, 492, 493
Hevesy, G., 203, 205, 316, 320, 321, 322, 340, 352, 353, 433, 458
Heyden, M., 316
Hilberry, N., 487, 534, 535, 536

Hipple, J. A., 174
Hoag, J. B., 5, 79, 316, 320, 330, 333, 334, 335, 336, 534, 535, 536
Hoerlin, H., 475, 480
Hoffmann, G., 475, 509, 519
Hoisington, L. E., 431
Holloway, M. G., 320, 334, 338, 343, 424
Holm, J. M., 75, 80, 82
Holm, R., 68
Holt, J., 458
Hönigschmid, O., 205
Hopfield, J. J., 477
Hopper, V. D., 62, 64
Horton, F., 90
Hosemann, R., 316
Houston, W. V., 60, 64, 119, 120, 127, 128, 129, 130, 226
Howe, C. E., 272
Howe, J. D., 550
Hsiung, D. S., 498
Hudson, C. M., 429, 430, 431
Hughes, A. L., 92, 237, 239, 241, 247, 248, 253
Hughes, D. J., 494
Hull, A. W., 56, 57, 64, 312, 314
Hulme, H. R., 384
Humphreys, R. F., 210
Hunt, F. L., 292, 293, 294, 295
Hupfield, H. H., 375, 376
Hupka, E., 140, 142
Hurst, H. E., 20
Hutchinson, C. A., 207

Ichimiya, T., 529, 533
Illing, W., 491
Immelman, M. N. S., 379, 380
Ironside, R., 545, 547
Ishida, Y., 61, 62, 64
Ising, G., 399

Jackson, R., 550
Jacobsen, I. C., 450
Jaeger, J. C., 384
Jauncey, G. E. M., 284
Jenkins, F. A., 204
Jentschke, W., 337, 338, 399
Jesse, W. P., 481, 485, 496, 518, 523, 536
Johnson, T. H., 463, 475, 480, 482, 484, 486, 487, 493, 494, 495, 496, 500, 534, 553
Johnston, H. L., 202
Joliot, F., 336, 372, 373, 377, 378, 388, 389, 399, 431, 452, 453
Jones, T. J., 92
Jongen, H. F., 484, 489
Jordan, E. B., 174, 175, 176, 180, 184, 187, 188, 189, 190, 191, 192, 193, 195

Kadesch, W. H., 241
Kanner, M. H., 449, 450
Kasiwagi, Y., 85
Katz, H., 550
Kaufmann, W., 110, 111
Keller, F., 68
Kellström, G., 60, 61, 62, 64, 264, 265
Kempton, A., 184, 186, 187, 188, 189, 190, 399, 433, 434, 436
Kennedy, D., 91
Kerst, D. W., 426, 429, 430, 431, 432
Kersten, H., 550
Khurgin, J., 427
Kikuchi, S., 544, 548, 550
Kikuchi, T., 70
King, A., 332, 333
King, L. D. P., 424
Kingdon, K. H., 450
Kinsey, B. B., 421, 433, 435, 436
Kinsler, L. E., 120, 127, 130
Kip, A. F., 26
Kirchner, F., 103, 104, 121, 122, 123, 130, 547, 550
Kirkpatrick, H. A., 285
Kirkpatrick, P., 257, 258, 284, 293
Kirsch, G., 414, 415
Klarmann, H., 379, 380, 382, 384
Klein, E., 92
Knipping, P., 265, 267
Kolhörster, W., 461, 464, 469, 470
Konopinski, E. J., 295
Konstantinowsky, D., 52
Korff, S. A., 468
Kosodaew, M. S., 382
Kovarik, A. F., 252, 316
Kozima, S., 379, 383, 384
Krefft, H., 148
Kretschmar, G. G., 126, 130
Kruger, P. G., 424
Kulenkampff, H., 279
Kunze, P., 370
Kurie, F. N. D., 377, 424
Kuroda, H., 196

Kurz, K., 460
Kusada, S., 490

Laby, T. H., 62, 64
Ladenburg, E., 238
Ladenburg, R., 371
Langer, A., 451
Langevin, P., 36
Langmuir, I., 54, 65, 67, 70, 75, 77, 88
Larsson, A., 264, 273, 275
Lassen, N. O., 450
Laue, M., 265, 266, 267, 269, 303, 304, 305, 312, 313, 545, 546
Lauritsen, C. C., 374, 385, 399, 420, 429, 430
Lauritsen, T., 429, 430
Lavanchy, C., 140, 141, 142
Lawrence, E. O., 249, 421, 422, 424, 425, 436, 438
Lazard, A., 431
Lees, D. S., 440
Lehmann, J. F., 97
Lemaitre, G., 483, 486
Lenard, P., 231, 237, 238
Leprince-Ringuet, L., 474, 500, 504, 532, 533
Lewis, G. N., 209, 436
Lewis, W. B., 187, 188, 189, 190, 191, 195, 330, 341, 342, 343, 344, 345, 347, 349, 399
Libby, W. F., 316, 323, 455
Lichtenecker, K., 249
Linder, E. G., 91
Livingood, J. J., 162, 453, 456
Livingston, M. S., 184, 187, 188, 189, 190, 191, 192, 193, 194, 195, 197, 295, 320, 334, 338, 343, 387, 398, 399, 422, 424, 425, 436, 453, 524
Locher, G. L., 43
Loeb, L. B., 17, 21, 22, 26, 30, 31, 34, 36, 37, 38, 54, 66
Lorentz, H. A., 116, 122, 135, 136, 137, 138, 139, 140, 141, 142, 144, 145
Loughridge, D. H., 475, 480, 482
Lukanow, H., 172
Lukirsky, P., 241, 245, 293
LuValle, J. E., 549

MacDonald, R. T., 209
MacPherson, H. G., 523
Madgwick, E., 352
Majumdar, V. D., 60
Malassez, J., 130
Mann, W. B., 424
Mano, G., 187, 188, 189, 190, 191, 195, 399
Marsden, E., 404, 405, 406, 410, 411
Marx, E., 249, 262
Masuda, T., 462, 473
Mattauch, J., 56, 64, 162, 174, 191, 192, 196, 453
McCurdy, W. H., 71, 77, 79, 88, 99, 100
McKeehan, L. W., 252, 316
McKibben, J. L., 429, 430, 431, 432
McLennan, J. C., 460
McMillan, E., 377, 451
Meek, J. M., 66
Meitner, L., 329, 332, 354, 372, 373, 375, 376, 378
Menzel, D. H., 208
Mercier, M. P., 332
Merrill, F. H., 429
Merton, T. R., 199
Middleton, W., 443
Miller, P. H., 60, 64
Miller, R. R., 94
Milligan, W. O., 549
Millikan, R. A., 46, 48, 49, 50, 51, 52, 53, 54, 55, 56, 57, 58, 59, 61, 62, 63, 64, 101, 241, 244, 245, 311, 312, 363, 370, 462, 463, 464, 465, 466, 467, 470, 471, 474, 475, 479, 480, 483, 486, 488, 489, 522
Miwa, M., 379, 383, 384
Miyazaki, Y., 462, 473
Mohler, F. L., 232, 233
Montgomery, C. G., 513, 519, 536
Montgomery, D. D., 536
Morgan, J. E., 516, 517
Morgan, K. Z., 474, 514, 516, 517, 534, 535, 536
Morgan, R., 550
Morris, L. W., 248
Morse, P. M., 89, 91
Moseley, H. G. J., 296, 297, 298, 299, 301, 302, 303, 408
Mott-Smith, H., 77
Müller, H. W., 70
Murphey, B. F., 183
Murphy, G. M., 200, 208

Nageotte, E., 532, 533
Nakagawa, S., 550

Neddermeyer, S. H., 378, 500, 503, 504, 506, 511, 520, 521, 523, 524, 525, 526, 527, 530, 533
Neher, H. V., 465, 466, 467, 471, 475, 479, 480, 486, 518, 522, 533, 534, 535, 536
Neumann, G., 123, 130, 139, 140, 142, 144
Nielsen, R. A., 33, 34
Nielsen, W. M., 474, 514, 516, 517, 534, 535, 536
Nier, A. O., 177, 178, 206, 317, 321, 322, 323, 450
Nimmo, R. R., 338, 340, 341, 342, 343
Nishina, Y., 462, 473, 482, 529, 533
Nordheim, L. W., 534, 535, 536
Northrup, D. L., 429, 430
Nuttall, J. M., 333, 335, 336

Occhialini, G. P. S., 43, 369, 370, 371, 372, 373, 376, 378, 379, 380, 518
O'Conor, J. S., 352
Ogata, K., 174, 194, 195, 196
Okuda, T., 174, 194, 195, 196
Oliphant, M. L. E., 23, 90, 93, 184, 186, 187, 188, 189, 190, 191, 192, 195, 197, 210, 399, 433, 434, 435, 436, 437
Olmstead, P. S., 236
Olpin, A. R., 241, 245, 293
O'Neal, R. D., 167, 437, 443
Oppenheimer, J. R., 513
Ornstein, L. S., 550
Orthmann, W., 354
Osgood, T. H., 425
Otis, R. M., 464

Pahl, M., 316
Paneth, F. A., 316, 320, 321, 322, 340, 352, 353, 433
Paschen, F., 119, 130, 222
Patterson, R. A., 272
Pauthenier, M., 424
Pecher, C., 458, 459
Peierls, R., 536
Perkinson, D. B., 429, 430, 431, 432
Perlow, G. J., 445
Perrin, F., 101, 406
Perry, C. T., 104, 122, 123, 130
Petterson, H., 414, 415
Philipp, K., 340, 372, 373, 378
Pickering, W. H., 518
Pickup, E., 533
Pike, E. W., 84, 85
Plattanaik, B., 60, 64
Plesset, M. S., 513
Pohl, R., 262, 263
Polanyi, M., 314
Pollard, E., 187, 190, 191, 192, 193, 194, 195, 196, 197
Pollock, H. C., 450
Pomerantz, M. A., 534
Pontecorvo, B., 442, 448
Potter, R. D., 458
Powell, C. F., 33, 35, 36
Powers, P. N., 402
Prilezaev, S., 241, 245, 293

Quarrell, A. G., 550

Rabi, I. I., 400
Rabinov, I. I., 263
Rahmel, H. A., 519
Ramsey, W. E., 536
Rasetti, F., 316, 335, 342, 345, 433, 442, 448, 534, 536, 537
Rayleigh, Lord, 249
Rayton, W. M., 332, 333
Read, D. N., 475
Regener, E., 49, 64, 329, 471
Reid, A., 545
Reimann, A. L., 248
Reusse, W., 295
Richard-Foy, R., 532, 533
Richardson, J. R., 377
Richardson, O. W., 241, 246
Richtmyer, F. K., 225, 294, 304
Rigden, P. J., 60, 64
Ringo, R., 341, 342
Risser, J. R., 424
Roberts, G. E., 534
Robinson, H. R., 63, 64, 251
Rodine, M. T., 431
Roentgen, W. C., 260, 262, 271, 272, 315
Rose, M. E., 427
Rosenblum, S., 330, 341, 344
Ross, P. A., 257, 258, 284, 290, 293
Rossi, B., 463, 494, 495, 498, 500, 515, 534, 535, 536
Royds, T., 329
Royt, L. E., 431
Rüdiger, O., 550
Ruhlig, A. J., 529, 533

Rumbaugh, L. H., 210
Russell, H., 549
Rutherford, E., 29, 49, 64, 183, 184, 186, 187, 188, 189, 190, 214, 302, 315, 320, 324, 325, 329, 330, 339, 340, 341, 344, 349, 393, 399, 403, 404, 405, 406, 410, 411, 412, 413, 414, 415, 416, 433, 434, 435, 436, 437, 438, 439, 460
Rutherford, E., Chadwick, J., & Ellis, C. D., 316, 330, 336, 337, 339, 340, 349, 352, 353, 355, 356, 358, 359, 361
Ryde, J. W., 89
Ryerson, C. M., 534, 535, 536

Sabine, P. E., 241
Sadler, C. A., 296, 297
Safford, F. J., 429
Saha, M. N., 219, 220, 222, 232, 235
Saha, N. K., 219, 220, 222, 232, 235
Sanders, F. H., 16, 17
Sargent, B. W., 320
Scarre, O. C., 322
Schaefer, G., 123, 130
Schaitberger, G., 293
Schein, M., 481, 485, 496, 523, 536
Scherrer, P., 312
Schiebold, E., 314
Schmeiser, K., 516
Schmerwitz, G., 80
Schmidt, G. C., 315
Schomaker, V., 549
Schonland, B. F. J., 491
Schopper, E., 60, 64, 329
Schrödinger, E., 228, 259, 285, 539
Schultz, H. L., 206
Schulze, H., 338
Schütze, W., 172, 205
Schwarz, G., 293, 294
Seaborg, G. T., 162, 453, 455, 456
Seeliger, R., 98
Seemann, H., 314
Segrè, E., 442, 448, 450, 455
Seidl, F. G. P., 494, 495
Sekido, Y., 462, 473, 482
Semat, H., 273, 314, 541
Serber, R., 426
Shane, C. D., 120, 128, 130, 226
Shankland, R. S., 285
Shaw, A. E., 125, 126, 127, 129, 130
Shaw, C. H., 59
Shepherd, W. G., 189, 195
Sherr, R., 167, 438, 441
Shiba, K., 59, 60, 64
Shima, S., 196
Shindo, S., 196
Shire, E. S., 210
Shoupp, W. E., 429, 430, 431, 432, 451
Shrader, J. E., 329
Shrum, G. M., 226
Shutt, R. P., 496
Siegbahn, M., 272, 275, 297, 301, 311
Simamura, H., 482
Simon, A. W., 258, 285
Simon, S., 110
Simons, L., 379, 380, 381, 382, 384
Sittkus, A., 474
Skaggs, L. S., 188, 189, 195
Skinner, H. A., 549
Skobelzyn, D., 365, 370
Sloan, D. H., 421
Sluckaia, M. M., 322
Smith, D. O., 480
Smith, L. G., 167
Smith, N., 550
Smith, N. M., 188, 189, 195, 434, 436, 445
Smith, P. T., 92
Smyth, H. D., 232, 233
Smythe, W. R., 167, 206, 211, 323
Soddy, F., 199, 315, 320, 324, 455, 460
Södermann, M., 59, 64
Sommerfeld, A., 224, 225, 226, 227, 228, 263
Spedding, F. H., 120, 128, 130, 226
Spees, A. H., 139, 144, 371, 385, 456
Spottiswoode, W., 70
Starr, M. A., 523, 533
Stearns, J. C., 395, 463, 509, 510, 511, 515, 516, 517, 518, 519, 521
Steinmaurer, R., 463
Stenström, W., 272
Stephens, W. E., 429, 430, 431, 432, 451
Stern, O., 400, 551, 552, 553
Stetter, G., 337, 338, 399
Stevenson, E. C., 43, 497, 526, 527, 533, 537
Stevenson, D. P., 549
Stever, H. G., 533, 534, 535, 536
Stewart, D. W., 207, 548
Stewart, R. L., 125
Stockmann, L. L., 468
Storks, K. H., 550

Störmer, C., 483
Strassmann, F., 448
Street, J. C., 43, 488, 497, 526, 527, 533, 537
Suetsugu, T., 61, 62, 64
Sugawara, Y., 194, 195
Sugita, T., 379, 383
Sugiura, Y., 554
Sutherland, G. B. B. M., 202
Sutton, L. E., 549
Swann, W. F. G., 173, 472, 496
Swanson, D. C., 394

Takeuchi, T., 379, 383, 529, 533
Tappart, J. G., 547
Tarrant, G. T. P., 375, 376, 378
Tate, J. T., 92
Teal, G. K., 209
Thibaud, J., 371, 377
Thomas, L. H., 427
Thompson, F. C., 458
Thompson, J. L., 491, 492, 493
Thomson, G. P., 66, 541, 545, 546, 547, 550
Thomson, J. J., 70, 72, 76, 89, 93, 95, 99, 101, 108, 109, 110, 148, 149, 150, 151, 153, 154, 160, 162, 177, 199, 214, 237, 316, 403
Thomson, J. J., & Thomson, G. P., 1, 2, 8, 21, 22, 23, 26, 29, 30, 31, 47, 48, 66, 68, 71, 82, 83, 84, 85, 92, 93, 95, 110, 237, 241
Thornton, R. L., 421
Tol, T., 550
Townsend, J. S., 11, 14, 16, 18, 20, 21, 22, 23, 24, 26, 29, 91
Tricker, R. A. R., 142, 143
Trillat, J. J., 550
Trump, J. G., 429
Turner, C. M., 429, 430, 431
Turner, L. A., 79, 88, 99, 100, 448, 449
Turner, R. N., 475, 476, 479, 480, 481, 486, 491, 492
Tuve, M. A., 429, 430, 431, 432
Tyndall, A. M., 33, 35

Uhlenbeck, G. E., 227
Ulrey, C. T., 291
Urey, H. C., 200, 203, 205, 206, 207, 208, 209
Uyterhoeven, W., 93

Vajifdar, M. B., 60
Vallart, M. S., 483, 486, 490, 492
Van Atta, C. M., 429, 430
Van Atta, L. C., 428, 429, 430, 431, 432
Van de Graaff, R. J., 33, 428, 429, 430, 431 432, 433
van der Pol, B., 87, 88
Van Gemert, A., 472, 473
Van Voorhis, C. C., 92
Varney, R. N., 33
von Friesen, S., 64
von Nordroff, R., 273

Wadlund, A. P. R., 58, 64
Walcher, W., 203, 204, 205
Walke, H. J., 444, 455, 456, 458
Waller, T., 275
Walter, B., 263
Walton, E. T. S., 184, 420, 421, 433, 434, 435, 436
Ward, F. A. B., 341
Warren, R. E., 429, 430, 431
Washburn, E. W., 209
Watson, W. W., 206
Webster, H. C., 386, 387
Wefelmeier, W., 316
Wehnelt, A., 71, 80
Weiser, H. B., 549
Wells, W. H., 424, 429, 430, 431, 432, 451
Wensel, H. T., 293
Wentzel, G., 253
Westhaver, J. W., 91, 95, 96, 97
Wheeler, J. A., 449
White, H. E., 225, 228
Wiechert, E., 102
Wien, W., 73, 147, 148
Wilkins, T. R., 316, 323, 332
Williams, E. J., 455, 533, 534, 537
Williams, J. H., 189, 195
Williams, N. H., 56, 57, 64
Williams, R. C., 120, 128, 130
Wilson, C. T. R., 1, 41, 42, 43, 45, 47, 460
Wilson, H. A., 48, 71, 75, 80, 86, 87, 89, 90
Wilson, J. G., 500, 503, 504, 505, 506
Wilson, R. R., 427
Wilson, V. C., 2, 426, 472, 473
Winch, R. P., 248
Wind, C. H., 263

Wolf, F., 118, 119, 120, 122, 130
Wollan, E. O., 477, 479, 481, 485, 488, 496, 523, 536
Wolz, K., 116, 123, 130
Woo, Y. H., 283
Wood, A., 316
Wood, A. B., 339
Woodward, R. H., 488, 497, 516
Wooldridge, D. E., 206
Wooster, W. A., 354, 359
Wulf, T., 461
Wüllner, A., 70
Wynn-Williams, C. E., 330, 341, 344
Yearian, H. J., 550, 554
Yoshimoto, S., 174
Yovanovitch, D. K., 349
Yukawa, H., 533, 534

Zabel, R. M., 553
Zahn, C. T., 139, 144, 371, 385, 456
Zanstra, H., 485
Zeiller, O., 511
Zeleny, J., 70, 98
Zermer, F., 52
Zimmermann, G., 81
Zinn, W. H., 290
Zuber, K., 379, 380, 381, 382, 384

# SUBJECT INDEX


Absorption, limits, X-ray, 288
of cosmic rays by matter, 462, 468, 500, 503
of X-rays, 286
Accelerating tubes, 431
Actinium, radioactive series, 318
Alpha particles, collision with nuclei, 408
disintegration by, 393, 396, 412, 438
fine structure, 330, 341, 344, 346
ionization by, 43, 336, 350
long range, 339, 346
nature of, 317, 329
range and velocity, 330
ranges, table, 318, 323
scattering by thin films, 403
straggling, 331
Altitude variation of cosmic ray intensity, 461, 463, 518
Annihilation radiation, 375
Artificial disintegration, by alpha particle bombardment, 393, 396, 412, 438
by deuteron bombardment, 184, 436
by neutron bombardment, 441
by photon bombardment, 393, 443
by proton bombardment, 184, 433
first successful experiments, 412
radioactivity, 373, 437, 439, 442, 445, 452
Atomic character of electricity, 46, 49
structure, general concept of, 40, 417
weights, accurate determination of, 168, 183, 187
physical versus chemical scale, 182
tables of, 169, 182, 187, 447
Atoms and molecules, diffraction of, 550
Atoms, the general structure of, 40, 417
Avogadro's number, methods of evaluating, 54, 57
table of experimental values, 64

Balmer series, 214, 220, 221
Barytron, *see* Mesotron
Beta rays, continuous velocity spectrum, 352
ionization by, 44, 350
line velocity spectra, 354, 359
Beta rays, nature of, 317, 349
origin of, 353, 355
tables of materials emitting, 318, 323
Bohr's theory of radiation, 216, 221
Brackett series, 221, 222
Bragg's law, 270
Bursts, cosmic ray, 478, 509, 519

Carnegie Model C cosmic ray meter, 477
Cathode dark space, 67, 71, 80, 89, 91
drop of potential, 83, 84
rays, nature of, 72, 101
Characteristic beta ray velocity spectra, 354, 359
line gamma ray spectra, 355
X-ray spectra, 295, 358, 454
Collision, ionization by negative ions, 11
by positive ions, 18
theory of ionization by, 11, 18, 21
Compton effect, 255, 281
Contact potential, 245
Continuous beta ray velocity spectrum, 352
X-ray spectrum, 291
Cosmic rays, absorption in matter, 462, 468, 500, 503
altitude variation, 461, 463, 518
bursts, 478, 509, 519
coincidence studies, 497
dissipation of energy, 507
diurnal variation, 489, 491, 492
early history, 460
east-west effect, 494, 518
energy distribution, 486
galactic rotation effect, 490
ionization at sea level, 488
latitude variation, 466, 475, 479, 481, 482, 484, 518
nature of, 462, 463, 483, 496, 504, 517
number per second, 487
penetration to great depths, 2, 462, 472
seasonal variation, 480, 489, 491
showers, 509

Creation and annihilation of electron-positron pairs, 366, 373, 374, 378, 507, 513
Critical potentials, *see* Ionization and resonance potentials
Crookes dark space, 67, 71, 80, 89, 91
Crystal structure from, electron diffraction, 547, 549
  x-ray diffraction, 303
Current density at cathode, 71
Currents, small, methods of measuring, 5
Cyclotron, 422

DeBroglie, equation, 227, 539
  wave lengths, table, 540
  waves, 227, 538
Decay of a radioactive material, 325
Deflection of charged particles in electric fields, 104
  in magnetic fields, 106
Deuteron, magnetic moment of, 401
Deuterons, disintegration by, 184, 436
Diffraction of, atoms and molecules, 550
  electrons by gases, 547
    by crystals, 541, 545
  protons, 554
  X-rays, 262, 265, 271, 303
Disintegration by, alpha particles, 393, 396, 412, 438
  deuterons, 184, 436
  neutrons, 441
  photons, 397, 443
  protons, 184, 433
Diurnal variation of cosmic rays, 489, 491, 492
Duane-Hunt law, 292

$e$, early methods of measuring, 47
  experimental values, table, 62, 64
  Millikan's determination of, 49
  typical student data to determine, 52
  X-ray method of determining, 57
East-west effect, cosmic ray, 494, 518
Einstein's photoelectric equation, 240, 250
Electric field distribution in glow discharge, experimental results, 79
  methods of measuring, 74
Electrical conductivity of a gas, dependence on field strength, 2, 4
  on gas pressure, 2
Electrical conductivity of a gas, dependence on ionizing agent, 3
  on shielding, 2
  ionization theory of, 7
  normal air, 1, 3
  discharge, types of, 65
Electron-positron pair creation and annihilation, 366, 373, 374, 378, 507, 513
Electrons, deflection in electric fields, 104
  in magnetic fields, 106
  diffraction by crystals, 541, 545
    by gases, 547
    crystal structure by, 547, 549
  discovery, 46, 49
  early methods of measuring $e$, 47
  ejection of positive ions by, 22, 90
  experimental values of $e$, table, 62, 64
  ionization by, 44, 92
  mean free path of, in discharge, 96
  Millikan's determination of $e$, 49
  mobility of, 39
  reflection from crystals, 541
  refraction of De Broglie waves, 544
  typical student data to determine $e$, 52
  velocity, direct measurement of, 102
  X-ray method of determining $e$, 57
Electrostatic generator, Van de Graaff, 427
$e/m$ for electrons, by deflection methods, 108, 120, 121, 130
  by spectroscopic methods, 119, 120, 127, 130
  methods of measuring, 108, 119, 121, 127
  summary of experimental values, 128, 130
  variation with velocity, 111, 113, 116, 129, 134, 138
Energies of disintegration, table, 446
Energy and mass, interchangeability of, 185, 374, 387, 396, 445, 449
  distribution of cosmic rays, 486

Faraday dark space, 67, 97
Fine structure of alpha rays, 330, 341, 344, 346
  of spectral lines, 224
Fission, 447

Galactic rotation, effect on cosmic rays, 49
Gamma rays, ionization by, 351

Gamma rays, line spectra, 355
methods of determining wave lengths, 351
nature of, 317, 350
origin of, 355
wave length range, 350
Gases, conductivity of, 1
Geiger-Nuttall law, 335
Glow discharge, cathode dark space, 67, 71, 80, 89, 91
fall of potential, 83, 84
Crookes dark space, 67, 71, 80, 89, 91
distribution of ions in, 86
electric field distribution in, 74, 79
elementary theory of, 89
Faraday dark space, 67, 97
general appearance, 66
negative glow, 67, 97
normal versus the abnormal, 71
positive column, 67, 68, 80, 98
potential distribution in, 82
required to maintain, 73
striations in, 66, 68, 98
typical photographs of, 67, 69
Growth of a radioactive product, 326

*h*, value of, 244, 245, 294
Half life period, 316, 326
table, 318
Heavy electron, *see* Mesotron
water, properties of, 210
*h/e*, value of, from, Duane-Hunt law, 293
photoelectric effect, 243
Rydberg constant, 257, 293
High energy particles, production of, 420

Induction accelerator, 426
Inverse square law, failure of, 410
Ionization and resonance potentials, calculated from spectral lines, 234, 235
general existence of, 229
methods of measuring, 231
tables of, 234, 235
by, alpha rays, 43, 336, 350
collision, Townsend's theory, 11
cosmic rays at sea level, 488
electrons, 44, 92, 350
mesotrons, 524, 527, 531
negative ion collision, 11
Ionization by, positive ion collision, 18
X-rays or gamma rays, 44, 351
current, dependence on field strength, 4
methods of measuring, 5
saturation, 2, 4, 10
theory of conduction, 7
Ions, distribution in glow discharge, 86
manner of formation, 39, 43
Isomers, nuclear, 455
Isotopes, existence of, 153, 155, 160, 162, 177
masses from mass spectrograph studies, 168, 178, 187
from nuclear studies, 183, 187
tables, 169, 182, 187, 447
methods of detecting existence, 198
of studying, 148, 154, 156, 198
separation of, 203
table of stable, 163

Kinetic energy, exact expression for, 145

Latitude variation of cosmic ray intensity, 466, 475, 479, 481, 482, 484, 518
Laue, X-ray photographs, 266
Lead, variation in atomic weight of, 322
Life, mean, of mesotrons, table, 536
Line beta ray velocity spectra, 354, 359
Lives, half, of radioactive materials, tables, 318, 323
Long range alpha particles, 339, 346
Lyman series, 221, 222

Magnetic moment of, deuteron, 401
neutron, 400
proton, 401
Mass and energy, interchangeability of, 185, 374, 387, 396, 445, 449
Mass of the mesotron, methods of evaluating, 529
table of experimental values, 533
of the neutron, 390, 395, 399
spectrographs, 148, 154, 156, 173
variation with velocity, 111, 113, 116, 129, 134, 138
Meson, *see* Mesotron
Mesotron, discovery, 520, 524
evidence from cloud chamber photographs, 523
from cosmic ray studies, 521
ionizing power, 524, 527, 531

Mesotron, mass, 522, 529, 533
mean life, table, 536
methods of evaluating mass, 529
observation of disintegration particle, 536
radioactive decay, 481, 534
Millikan's oil drop experiment, 49
Mobilities of ions, aging effect, 34, 37
effect of impurities on, 34, 38
methods of measuring, 31
simple theory of, 9, 36
typical values, 34, 35
variation with pressure, 35
with temperature, 35
Moseley's law, 296, 302

Negative glow, 67, 97
Neutrino, 354, 356
Neutron, collimation of beam, 394
discovery, 386
disintegration by, 441
magnetic moment, 400
mass, 390, 395
table of experimental values, 399
projection of nuclei by, 388, 390
sources, 393
Normal versus the abnormal discharge, 71
Nuclear charge equal to atomic number, 408
isomers, 455
Nucleus, size of, 407

Packing fraction curve, 170, 196, 197, 198
Parabolas, positive ion, 151, 172, 173
Paschen series, 221, 222
Pfund series, 222
Photoelectric effect, early history, 236
Einstein's theory of, 240, 250
Millikan's study of, 241
possible time lag, 248
with X-rays or $\gamma$-rays, 249
Photons, disintegration by, 397, 443
ejection of photoelectrons by, 240, 249
production of electron-positron pairs by, 374, 378
radiation and absorption of, 213, 216
scattering of X-ray, 254
Pickering series, 222
Polarization of X-rays, 278

Positive column, 67, 68, 98
ions, ejection by electron bombardment, 22, 90
rays, existence of isotopes, 153, 155, 160, 162, 177
methods of studying, 148, 154, 156
nature of, 147
Positron, abundance in nature, 371
charge, 370
creation and annihilation of electron-positron pairs, 366, 373, 374, 375, 378
discovery, 362
ejected from artificial radioactive materials, 453
$e/m$, 371
mass, 370
sources, 372
Potassium, radioactivity of, 167, 211, 316, 323
Potential distribution in glow discharge, 82
required to maintain discharge, 73
Production of high energy particles, 420
Proton, magnetic moment of, 401
Proton-neutron model of the nucleus, 419
Protons, diffraction of, 554
disintegration by, 184, 433

Radiant energy, emission and absorption, 213, 216
Radioactive constants, relationships among, 325
decay of mesotrons, 481, 534
equilibrium, 327, 329
materials, table, 318, 323
transformation series, 317, 319
theory of, 324
Radioactivity, artificial, 373, 437, 439, 442, 452
natural, 315
Range of alpha particles, 318, 323, 330
Recombination of ions, coefficient of, 8, 27
disappearance of ions due to, 28
measurement of coefficient of, 29
rate of, 8, 27
variation with pressure, 30
with temperature, 30
Reflection of electrons from crystals, 541
of X-rays, 269, 271, 277
Refraction of electron waves, 544
of X-rays, 272

Refractive indices, X-ray, table, 275
Resonance potentials, *see* Ionization and resonance potentials
Richardson's equation, 246
Rossi curve for cosmic ray showers, 516
Rydberg constant, 219, 223, 302

Scattering of alpha particles by thin films, 403
of X-rays, classical theory, 280
Compton theory, 255, 281
Seasonal variation of cosmic rays, 480, 489, 491
Separation of isotopes, 203
Showers, and bursts, cosmic ray, 478, 509, 519
Size of the nucleus, 407
Sommerfeld's theory of fine structure, 224
Sparking potentials, available tables of, 26
experimental test of theory, 25
theory of, 23, 25, 26
Spectrometer, Bragg crystal X-ray, 267
Spinning electron, 227
Stokes' law, 47, 50
Striations in positive column, 66, 68, 80, 98
Structure of atoms, general, 40, 417

Thorium, radioactive series, 318
Townsend, first and second coefficients, 23
theory of ionization by collision, 11, 18, 21
of sparking potential, 23, 25
Tracers, radioactive and stable isotopes as, 458
Transformation series, radioactive, 317, 319
theory, radioactive, 324

Uranium, fission of, 447
radioactive series, 318

Van de Graaff generator, 427
Variation of mass with velocity, experimental evidence, 138
theories of, 111, 129, 134
Velocity of electrons, direct measurement of, 102
Viscosity of air, elimination of small error in, 60
table, 61

Water, heavy, properties of, 210
Wave lengths, De Broglie, of particles, table, 540
obtained from photoelectric data, 251
mechanics, 228, 253, 259, 285
Wilson cloud expansion chamber, 41
Work function, 84, 240, 244, 245, 247

X-rays, absorption, 286
Bragg crystal spectrometer, 267
characteristic spectra, 295, 358, 454
continuous spectrum, 291
crystal structure by, 303
diffraction and interference, 262, 265, 271, 303
discovery, 260
indices of refraction, table, 275
ionization by, 44
Laue photographs, 266
polarization, 278
production, 261
reflection by crystals, 269
by ruled gratings, 271
refraction, 272
scattering, 154, 280
velocity, 262